Test Item File and Resource Guide
for

COLLEGE ALGEBRA:
A GRAPHING APPROACH
AND
PRECALCULUS:
A GRAPHING APPROACH

Larson/Hostetler/Edwards

David C. Falvo

The Pennsylvania State University
The Behrend College

D. C. Heath and Company

Lexington, Massachusetts   Toronto

Address editorial correspondence to:

D. C. Heath and Company
125 Spring Street
Lexington, MA 02173

Published simultaneously in Canada.

Printed in the United States of America.

International Standard Book Number: 0–669–34016–2

10 9 8 7 6 5 4 3 2 1

PREFACE

The *Test Item File and Resource Guide* for *College Algebra: A Graphing Approach* and *Precalculus: A Graphing Approach* is a supplement to the text by Roland E. Larson, Robert P. Hostetler and Bruce H. Edwards.

We begin with a Survey of Assessment Techniques written by Karen S. Norwood-Hernandez of North Carolina State University. This discusses a broad range of standard and alternative assessment strategies, including many examples and suggestions for grading the latter type.

Part one of the test item file is a bank of questions arranged by text section. To assist you in selecting questions and administering examinations, each question is followed by a three-item code line. The first item of the code indicates the level of difficulty of the question: routine (1) or challenging (2). (Challenging questions require three or more steps to obtain the solution.) The second item of the code indicates the type of question: multiple-choice (M) or open-ended (O). The last item in the code is the answer (Ans).

Part two of the test item file includes a bank of chapter tests. The first three exams for each chapter are multiple choice. The last two exams for each chapter are completion style. The tests are geared to 50-minute class periods and the exams are primarily intended as samples to given instructors ideas for questions.

Finally, the last part of this test item file includes the answers to the sample chapter tests. I have made every effort to see that the answers are correct. However, I would appreciate very much hearing about any errors or other suggestions for improvement.

Computerized versions of this test item file with a User Manuals are available for the IBM-PC, IBM-compatible computers, and the Macintosh. The program has these advantages:

 • Multiple choice test questions can be converted to an open-ended format at the touch of a button.

 • Each multiple-choice test question offers a choice of five possible responses, one of which is correct.

 • The distracters, or incorrect answers, are designed to be common errors or to look like reasonable answers.

 • Questions can be selected from the computerized version in a variety of ways to accommodate differing class needs, including previewing questions on screen, entering the question number after consulting this test item file, and selecting randomly by section, question type, or level of difficulty. In addition, common math notation symbols are available for editing or adding questions.

For more information, please contact your local D. C. Heath representative, or call the D. C. Heath Marketing Department at 800-235-3565.

This test item file and resource guide is the result of the efforts of Richard Bambauer, Lisa Bickel, Linda Bollinger, Patti Jo Campbell, Linda Donico, Darin Johnson, Linda Kifer, Deanna Larson, Jill Larson, Timothy Larson, Amy Marshall, John Musser, Steven Nichols, Scott O'Neil, Jessica Pflueger, Louis Rieger, Laurie Sontheimer, Evelyn Wedzikowski, and Nancy Zawadzki.

I would like to thank my family for their patience and support during the several months I worked on this project.

David C. Falvo
The Pennsylvania State University,
The Behrend College

CONTENTS

Part 1 – Test Items

In computerized version, Chapter P is renamed Chapter 0.

C H A P T E R P
Prerequisites: Review of Basic Algebra

P.1 The Real Number System

1. Determine how many natural numbers there are in the set:

$$\{ -3, -\tfrac{1}{2}, 2, 0.3535\ldots\}$$

(a) 1   (b) 2   (c) 3

(d) 4   (e) None of the numbers are natural numbers.

1—M—Answer: a

2. Determine how many integers there are in the set:

$$\{ -3, -\tfrac{1}{2}, 2, 0.3535\ldots\}$$

(a) 1   (b) 2   (c) 3

(d) 4   (e) None of the numbers are integers.

1—M—Answer: b

3. Determine how many integers there are in the set:

$$\{ 5, -16, \tfrac{2}{3}, 0\}$$

(a) 4   (b) 3   (c) 2

(d) 1   (e) None of the numbers are integers.

1—M—Answer: b

4. Determine how many rational numbers there are in the set:

$$\{ -3, -\tfrac{1}{2}, 2, 0.3535\ldots\}$$

(a) 4   (b) 3   (c) 2

(d) 1   (e) None of the numbers are rational.

1—M—Answer: a

5. Determine how many irrational numbers there are in the set:

$$\{ -3, -\tfrac{1}{2}, 2, 0.3535\ldots\}$$

(a) 4   (b) 3   (c) 2

(d) 1   (e) None of the numbers are irrational.

1—M—Answer: e

6. Which of the following is a true statement?

   (a) $|-3| + |6-5| \leq -(-4)$ (b) $|14 + -2| - |-16| = 28$ (c) $|16 - -4| - |3 - 5| \geq 12$

   (d) Both a and b are true.   (e) Both a and c are true.

   1—M—Answer: e

7. Which of the following is a true statement?

   (a) $|-3| - |4-6| = 1$ (b) $|-5| + |-13| = -|-18|$ (c) $|-6 - -3| \geq |-4|$

   (d) Both a and b are true.   (e) Both b and c are true.

   1—M—Answer: a

8. Which of the following is a true statement?

   (a) $\dfrac{-5}{|-5|} = 1$ (b) $-|-5| + |-3-2| \geq -1$ (c) $|-6+4| < |-3-8|$

   (d) Both a and c are true.   (e) Both b and c are true.

   1—M—Answer: e

9. Which of the following is a true statement?

   (a) $-3|-3| < |-3(-3)|$ (b) $\dfrac{4}{|-12|} \leq \dfrac{|-12|}{-4}$ (c) $|16| - |12| \geq |16-12|$

   (d) Both a and c are true.   (e) Both b and c are true.

   1—M—Answer: d

10. Which of the following is a true statement?

    (a) $4|-3| - 6 = -18$ (b) $\dfrac{|-3|}{-3} \leq 0$ (c) $|-5 - -7| = |-5| - |-7|$

    (d) Both a and b are true.   (e) Both b and c are true.

    1—M—Answer: b

11. Evaluate: $|-3+2|$

    (a) 1   (b) −1   (c) 5   (d) −5   (e) None of these

    1—M—Answer: a

12. Evaluate: $|-4| - |-2|$

    (a) −2   (b) 2   (c) −8   (d) 6   (e) None of these

    1—M—Answer: b

13. Evaluate: $-3|-6| + |-1|$

    (a) −19   (b) 19   (c) 17   (d) −17   (e) None of these

    1—M—Answer: d

14. Evaluate: $-|-5| - 5$

   (a) 0   (b) -10 (c) 10   (d) 25   (e) None of these

   1—M—Answer: b

15. Use inequality notation to describe: b is at least 5.

   (a) $b > 5$ (b) $b \geq 5$ (c) $b < 5$ (d) $b \leq 5$ (e) None of these

   1—M—Answer: b

16. Use inequality notation to describe: x is positive.

   1—O—Answer: $x > 0$

17. Use inequality notation to describe: x is nonnegative.

   (a) $x > 0$ (b) $x < 0$ (c) $x \geq 0$ (d) $x \leq 0$ (e) None of these

   1—M—Answer: c

18. Use inequality notation to describe: y is no larger than 10

   (a) $y \leq 10$ (b) $y < 10$ (c) $y \geq 10$ (d) $y > 10$ (e) None of these

   1—M—Answer: a

19. Use inequality notation to describe: y is at least 5.

   (a) $y \leq 5$ (b) $y < 5$ (c) $y \geq 5$ (d) $y > 5$ (e) None of these

   1—M—Answer: c

20. Use absolute value notation to describe: The distance between x and 5 is at least 6.

   (a) $|x + 5| > 6$ (b) $|x - 5| > 6$ (c) $|x - 5| \geq 6$

   (d) $|6 - x| \geq 5$ (e) None of these

   2—M—Answer: c

21. Use absolute value notation to describe: 6 is at most 3 units from x.

   (a) $|x - 3| < 6$ (b) $|x - 6| \leq 3$ (c) $|x - 6| \geq 3$

   (d) $|x - 3| \geq 6$ (e) None of these

   2—M—Answer: b

22. Use absolute value notation to describe: The distance between x and 7 is greater than 2.

   (a) $|x - 7| \geq 2$ (b) $|x - 2| < 7$ (c) $|x - 7| > 2$

   (d) $|x - 2| > 7$ (e) None of these

   2—M—Answer: c

23. Use absolute value notation to describe: y is closer to 5 than y is to -6.

2—O—Answer: $|y - 5| < |y + 6|$

24. Use absolute value notation to describe: The distance between x and 16 is no more than 5.

(a) $|x - 5| \leq 16$ (b) $|x - 5| > 16$ (c) $|x - 16| \leq 5$

(d) $|x - 16| > 5$ (e) None of these

2—M—Answer: c

25. Find the distance between -43 and 16.

(a) 27   (b) -27 (c) -59 (d) 59   (e) None of these

1—M—Answer: d

26. Find the distance between x and -42.

(a) $x - 42$ (b) $x + 42$ (c) $|x - 42|$ (d) $|x + 42|$ (e) None of these

1—M—Answer: d

27. Find the distance between $-\frac{2}{3}$ and $-\frac{1}{2}$.

(a) $-\frac{1}{3}$ (b) $\frac{1}{6}$ (c) $\frac{1}{2}$ (d) $\frac{7}{6}$ (e) None of these

1—M—Answer: b

28. Find the distance between x and -3.

(a) $|x - 3|$ (b) $|x + 3|$ (c) $x - 3$ (d) $x + 3$ (e) None of these

1—M—Answer: b

29. Determine the distance between a and b given $a > b$.

(a) $a - b$ (b) $b - a$ (c) $a + b$ (d) ab (e) None of these

1—M—Answer: a

30. The sales at a local store were projected to be \$13,750 per week. The accuracy of this projection is considered good if the actual sales differ from the projected sales by no more than \$1375.00. Determine from weekly sales listed below any weeks where the projection was not considered good.

(a) \$12,370   (b) \$14,980   (c) \$15,025

(d) \$12,475   (e) The projection was good in each of these cases.

2—M—Answer: a

31. The sales at a local store were projected to be $13,750 per week. The accuracy of this projection is considered good if the actual sales differ from the projected sales by no more than $1375. Determine from weekly sales listed below any weeks when the projection was not considered good.

(a) $13,150   (b) $14,120   (c) $12,350

(d) $12,750   (e) The projection was good in each of these cases

2—M—Answer: c

32. The sales at a local store were projected to be $15,970 per week. The accuracy of this projection is considered good if the actual sales differ from the projected sales by no more than $1597. Determine from the weekly sales listed below any weeks when the projection was not considered good.

(a) $17,470   (b) $14,520   (c) $15,370

(d) $16,570   (e) The projection was considered good in each of these cases.

2—M—Answer: e

33. While traveling you enter the interstate near the 234 mile marker, then exit near the 130 mile marker. Determine the number of miles traveled on the interstate.

(a) 364   (b) 104   (c) 234   (d) 130   (e) None of these

1—M—Answer: b

34. While traveling you enter the interstate near the 125 mile marker, then exit near the 81 mile marker. Determine the number of miles traveled on the interstate.

(a) 125   (b) 81   (c) 44   (d) 206   (e) None of these

1—M—Answer: c

35. While traveling you enter the interstate near the 26 mile marker, then exit near the 180 mile marker. Determine the number of miles traveled on the interstate.

(a) 154   (b) 206   (c) 180   (d) 26   (e) None of these

1—M—Answer: a

P.2 | Properties of Real Numbers and the Basic Rules of Algebra

1. Identify the property illustrated by $5\left(\frac{1}{5} + x\right) = 5\left(\frac{1}{5}\right) + 5(x)$.

(a) Commutative   (b) Distributive   (c) Associative

(d) Inverse   (e) None of these

1—M—Answer: b

2. Identify the property illustrated by $\left(\frac{\sqrt{7}}{2} - y\right) + \left(-\frac{\sqrt{7}}{2} + y\right) = 0$.

   (a) Inverse   (b) Identity   (c) Associative

   (d) Commutative   (e) None of these

   1—M—Answer: a

3. Identify the property illustrated by $3[x + (-1)] = 3x + 3(-1)$.

   (a) Commutative   (b) Associative   (c) Distributive

   (d) Identity   (e) Inverse

   1—M—Answer: c

4. Identify the property illustrated by $3 + (2 + 7) = (3 + 2) + 7$.

   1—O—Answer: Associative

5. Identify the property illustrated by $7\left(\frac{1}{7}\right) = 1$.

   1—O—Answer: Inverse

6. Evaluate: $-\frac{1}{8} + \frac{4}{3}$

   (a) $-\frac{3}{5}$ (b) $-\frac{1}{24}$ (c) $1\frac{5}{24}$ (d) $\frac{3}{24}$ (e) None of these

   1—M—Answer: c

7. Evaluate: $4 + 2(-3) - (2 \div 2)$

   (a) -3 (b) 8   (c) -2 (d) 0   (e) None of these

   1—M—Answer: a

8. Evaluate (if possible): $5 \div 0$

   (a) 0   (b) 5   (c) 1   (d) 25   (e) Undefined

   1—M—Answer: e

9. Evaluate: $7 \cdot \frac{0}{3}$

   1—O—Answer: 0

10. Multiply, then reduce to lowest terms: $(-3)\left(\frac{2}{5}\right)\left(-\frac{1}{2}\right)$

    1—O—Answer: $\frac{3}{5}$

11. Divide, then reduce to lowest terms: $\frac{6}{5} \div \frac{4}{3}$

    1—O—Answer: $\frac{9}{10}$

12. Perform the indicated operations and reduce to lowest terms: $\frac{2}{5} - \frac{9}{20} + \frac{1}{15}$

1—O—Answer: $\frac{1}{60}$

13. Evaluate: $(2^3 \cdot 3^2)^{-1}$

(a) -72 (b) $\frac{1}{46656}$ (c) $-\frac{1}{36}$ (d) $\frac{1}{72}$ (e) None of these

1—M—Answer: d

14. Evaluate: $(6^{-2})(3^0)(2^3)$

(a) $\frac{2}{9}$ (b) -288 (c) -216 (d) $\frac{1}{6}$ (e) None of these

1—M—Answer: a

15. Evaluate: $(4)^{-2}(3)^0(-1)^2$

(a) 0 (b) -8 (c) -16 (d) $\frac{1}{16}$ (e) None of these

1—M—Answer: d

16. Evaluate: $(2)^3(2)^{-3}$

(a) 1 (b) 0 (c) -36 (d) -64 (e) None of these

1—M—Answer: a

17. Evaluate: $\dfrac{4(2)^{-1}}{(3)^{-2}(2)}$

(a) $\frac{2}{3}$ (b) 0 (c) 9 (d) $\frac{4}{9}$ (e) None of these

1—M—Answer: c

18. Write $(3x)(3x)(3x)(3x)(3x)$ in exponential form.

1—O—Answer: $(3x)^5$

19. Simplify: $\left(\dfrac{x^{-3}y^2}{z} \right)^{-4}$

(a) $\dfrac{z^4}{x^7y^6}$ (b) $\dfrac{y^2z^4}{x^7}$ (c) $\dfrac{x^{12}z^4}{y^8}$

(d) $\dfrac{z^4}{x^{12}y^8}$ (e) None of these

1—M—Answer: c

20. Simplify: $\left(\dfrac{3x^2y^3}{xw^{-2}}\right)^3$

(a) $9w^6x^3y^9$ (b) $9w^{-8}x^8y^{27}$ (c) $27w^6x^3y^9$

(d) $3w^6x^3y^9$ (e) None of these

1—M—Answer: c

21. Simplify: $3x^2(2x)^3(5x^{-1})$

(a) $30x^{-6}$ (b) $\frac{6}{5}x^6$ (c) $\frac{24}{5}x^4$

(d) $120x^4$ (e) None of these

1—M—Answer: d

22. Simplify: $(3x^2y^3z)^{-2}(xy^4)$

1—O—Answer: $\dfrac{1}{9x^3y^2z^2}$

23. Simplify: $(-2x^2)^5(5x^3)^{-2}$

1—O—Answer: $-\dfrac{32x^4}{25}$

24. Simplify: $\left(\dfrac{x^{-5}y^2}{z^2}\right)^{-3}$

(a) $\dfrac{x^{-8}y^{-1}}{z^{-1}}$ (b) $\dfrac{x^{15}z^6}{y^6}$ (c) $\dfrac{z^5}{x^{-2}y^{-1}}$

(d) $\dfrac{x^{-15}y^6}{z^6}$ (e) None of these

1—M—Answer: b

25. Evaluate $3x^2y^{-4}$ when $x = -1$ and $y = -2$.

1—O—Answer: $\frac{3}{16}$

26. Evaluate $2x^4 + 3x$ when $x = -3$.

(a) 1287   (b) 153   (c) -15 (d) 1215   (e) None of these

1—M—Answer: b

27. Evaluate $7(-x)^3$ for $x = 2$.

(a) -1 (b) -42 (c) -56 (d) 2744   (e) None of these

1—M—Answer: c

28. Evaluate $4x^{-2}$ for $x = 3$.

(a) 36   (b) -24 (c) $\frac{1}{144}$ (d) $\frac{4}{9}$ (e) None of these

1—M—Answer: d

29. Evaluate $3x^0 - x^{-2}$ for $x = 4$.

  (a) -16 (b) $\frac{47}{16}$ (c) $\frac{15}{16}$ (d) -5 (e) None of these

  1—M—Answer: b

30. Rewrite in scientific notation: 0.000004792

  (a) 0.4792×10^5 (b) 4.792×10^{-6} (c) 4.792×10^{-5}
  (d) 4.792×10^6 (e) None of these

  1—M—Answer: b

31. Rewrite in decimal form: 3.75×10^{-7}

  1—O—Answer: 0.000000375

32. Multiply: $(0.00000526)(72,000,000,000)^2$

  (a) 3.7872×10^4 (b) 2.726784×10^{-20} (c) 2.726784×10^{16}
  (d) 2.726784×10^{-14} (e) None of these

  2—M—Answer: c

33. Simplify and write in decimal form:

$$\frac{(5.1 \times 10^{-5})(3 \times 10^6)}{1.7 \times 10^{-2}}$$

  2—O—Answer: 9000

34. Simplify and write in scientific notation:

$$\frac{(32,700,000,000,000)(72,000,000,000)^2}{0.0000000041}$$

  2—O—Answer: 4.13×10^{43}

35. Represent the number 0.0021367 in scientific notation.

  (a) 0.21367×10^{-2} (b) 21367×10^{-7} (c) 2.1367×10^{-2}
  (d) 2.1367×10^{-3} (e) None of these

  1—M—Answer: d

36. The highest peak in the Western hemisphere, located in Argentina, has an elevation of 22,831 feet. Represent this in scientific notation.

  (a) 22.831×10^4 (b) 2.2831×10^4 (c) 0.22831×10^5
  (d) 2.2831×10^3 (e) None of these

  1—M—Answer: b

37. The total area of Chile is approximately 2.9×10^5 square miles. Write this in decimal form.

(a) 2900   (b) 29,000   (c) 290,000

(d) 2,900,000   (e) None of these

1—M—Answer: c

P.3 Radicals and Rational Exponents

1. Evaluate: $\dfrac{1}{81^{-1/2}}$

(a) $\dfrac{1}{9}$ (b) 9   (c) $-\dfrac{1}{9}$ (d) -9 (e) None of these

1—M—Answer: b

2. Evaluate: $\left(\dfrac{8}{27}\right)^{-2/3}$

1—O—Answer: $\dfrac{9}{4}$

3. Evaluate: $\left(\dfrac{1}{64}\right)^{-2/3}$

(a) -16 (b) $\dfrac{1}{16}$ (c) $\dfrac{1}{512}$ (d) -512 (e) None of these

1—M—Answer: e

4. Evaluate: $\left(\dfrac{1}{64}\right)^{3/2}$

(a) $\dfrac{1}{512}$ (b) -512 (c) $\dfrac{1}{16}$ (d) -16 (e) None of these

1—M—Answer: a

5. Evaluate: $\dfrac{1}{27^{-1/3}}$

(a) $\dfrac{1}{3}$ (b) 3   (c) $-\dfrac{1}{3}$ (d) $-\dfrac{1}{9}$ (e) None of these

1—M—Answer: b

6. Simplify: $\sqrt[3]{-625x^7y^5}$

(a) $5xy\sqrt[3]{-5x^4y^2}$ (b) $-5xy\sqrt[3]{5x^4y^2}$ (c) $-125x^2y\sqrt[3]{5xy^2}$

(d) $-5x^2y\sqrt[3]{5xy^2}$ (e) Does not simplify

1—M—Answer: d

7. Simplify: $\sqrt{75x^2y^{-4}}$

    (a) $\dfrac{5\sqrt{3}x}{y^2}$

    (b) $\dfrac{3\sqrt{5}|x|}{y^2}$

    (c) $5\sqrt{3}|x|y^2$

    (d) $\dfrac{5\sqrt{3}|x|}{y^2}$

    (e) None of these

    1—M—Answer: d

8. Simplify: $\sqrt{x^2y^2}$

    (a) $\pm|xy|$

    (b) $|xy|$

    (c) xy

    (d) $-xy$

    (e) None of these

    1—M—Answer: b

9. Simplify $\sqrt{a^4b^2}$ if a and b are both negative.

    (a) a^2

    (b) $\pm|a^2b|$

    (c) $-a^2b$

    (d) $\pm a^2b$

    (e) None of these

    2—M—Answer: c

10. Simplify: $\sqrt[3]{24x^4y^5}$

    (a) $3x^2y^2\sqrt[3]{6x^2y^3}$

    (b) $8xy\sqrt[3]{3xy}$

    (c) $2xy\sqrt[3]{6xy^2}$

    (d) $2xy\sqrt[3]{3xy^2}$

    (e) None of these

    1—M—Answer: d

11. Rationalize the denominator: $\dfrac{3}{\sqrt{7}+2}$

    (a) $\sqrt{7}-2$

    (b) $\dfrac{3\sqrt{7}-6}{5}$

    (c) $\dfrac{3\sqrt{7}-2}{3}$

    (d) $\dfrac{3\sqrt{7}-2}{5}$

    (e) None of these

    1—M—Answer: a

12. Rationalize the denominator: $\dfrac{5}{7-\sqrt{2}}$

    (a) $\dfrac{35+5\sqrt{2}}{47}$

    (b) $\dfrac{35+\sqrt{2}}{47}$

    (c) $7+\sqrt{2}$

    (d) $\dfrac{35+\sqrt{2}}{3}$

    (e) None of these

    1—M—Answer: a

13. Rationalize the denominator: $\dfrac{2}{\sqrt[3]{2x}}$

(a) $\dfrac{\sqrt[3]{2x}}{x}$

(b) $\dfrac{\sqrt[3]{4x^2}}{x}$

(c) $\dfrac{2\sqrt[3]{2x}}{2x}$

(d) $\sqrt[3]{4x}$

(e) None of these

2—M—Answer: b

14. Simplify by rationalizing the denominator: $\dfrac{6x}{5-\sqrt{2}}$

(a) $\dfrac{6x(5+\sqrt{2})}{23}$

(b) $2x(5+\sqrt{2})$

(c) $\dfrac{30x-\sqrt{2}}{23}$

(d) $\dfrac{6x(5-\sqrt{2})}{21}$

(e) None of these

1—M—Answer: a

15. Simplify by rationalizing the denominator: $\dfrac{4}{\sqrt[3]{x}}$

(a) $\dfrac{4\sqrt[3]{x}}{x}$

(b) $\dfrac{4\sqrt[3]{x^2}}{x}$

(c) 4

(d) $4\sqrt[3]{x}$

(e) None of these

1—M—Answer: b

16. Simplify by rationalizing the numerator: $\dfrac{6-\sqrt{2}}{5}$

(a) $\dfrac{34}{5(6+\sqrt{2})}$

(b) $\dfrac{4}{30+\sqrt{2}}$

(c) $\dfrac{34}{5(6-\sqrt{2})}$

(d) $\dfrac{32}{5(6-\sqrt{2})}$

(e) None of these

1—M—Answer: a

17. Simplify by rationalizing the numerator: $\dfrac{\sqrt[3]{3}}{12}$

(a) $\dfrac{1}{\sqrt[3]{4}}$

(b) $\dfrac{3}{4\sqrt[3]{3}}$

(c) $\dfrac{1}{4\sqrt[3]{3}}$

(d) $\dfrac{1}{4\sqrt[3]{9}}$

(e) None of these

1—M—Answer: d

18. Simplify by rationalizing the numerator: $\dfrac{\sqrt{2}-\sqrt{5}}{12}$

(a) $\dfrac{1}{4(\sqrt{2}-\sqrt{5})}$ 　　　　(b) $\dfrac{-1}{4(\sqrt{2}+\sqrt{5})}$ 　　　　(c) $\dfrac{-7}{4(\sqrt{2}+\sqrt{5})}$

(d) $\dfrac{1}{4\sqrt{2}+\sqrt{5}}$ 　　　　(e) None of these

1—M—Answer: b

19. Simplify by rationalizing the numerator: $\dfrac{5+2\sqrt{5}}{15}$

(a) $\dfrac{-4}{5(1-\sqrt{5})}$ 　　　　(b) $\dfrac{2}{3(5+2\sqrt{5})}$ 　　　　(c) $\dfrac{1}{5-2\sqrt{5}}$

(d) $\dfrac{1}{3(5-2\sqrt{5})}$ 　　　　(e) None of these

1—M—Answer: d

20. Simplify by rationalizing the numerator: $\dfrac{\sqrt[3]{16}}{7}$

(a) $\dfrac{16}{7\sqrt[3]{16}}$ 　　　　(b) $\dfrac{1}{7\sqrt[3]{256}}$ 　　　　(c) $\dfrac{4}{7\sqrt[3]{4}}$

(d) $\dfrac{2}{7\sqrt[3]{16}}$ 　　　　(e) None of these

1—M—Answer: c

21. Rationalize the numerator: $\dfrac{3-\sqrt{2}}{5}$

1—O—Answer: $\dfrac{7}{5(3+\sqrt{2})}$

22. Write as a single radical: $\sqrt[3]{\sqrt{2x}}$

(a) $\sqrt[6]{2x}$ 　　(b) $\sqrt[5]{2x}$ 　　(c) $\sqrt[3]{2x}$ 　　(d) $\sqrt[3]{4x^2}$ 　　(e) None of these

1—M—Answer: a

23. Simplify: $\sqrt[3]{\sqrt{3x+1}}$

1—O—Answer: $\sqrt[6]{3x+1}$

24. Simplify: $3\sqrt{2}\sqrt[3]{4}$

(a) $6\sqrt[6]{2}$ 　　(b) $3\sqrt[6]{8}$ 　　(c) $6\sqrt{2}$ 　　(d) $3\sqrt[6]{32}$ 　　(e) None of these

2—M—Answer: a

25. Simplify: $(\sqrt[3]{81x^4y^9})(\sqrt[3]{2xy^2})$

    2—O—Answer: $3xy^3\sqrt{6x^2y^2}$

26. Simplify: $\sqrt{3x^2}\sqrt[3]{3x^2}$

    2—O—Answer: $\sqrt[6]{(3x^2)^5}$

27. Simplify: $\sqrt[6]{8x^3y^3}$

    (a) $\sqrt{8xy}$ (b) $\sqrt[3]{2xy}$ (c) $\sqrt{2xy}$ (d) $\sqrt[3]{8xy}$ (e) None of these

    1—M—Answer: c

28. Simplify: $\sqrt[6]{9x^2y^2}$

    (a) $\sqrt{3xy}$ (b) $\sqrt[3]{3xy}$ (c) $\sqrt{9xy}$ (d) $\sqrt[3]{9xy}$ (e) None of these

    1—M—Answer: b

29. Simplify: $3\sqrt[3]{4x^5y^3} + 7x\sqrt[3]{32x^2y^6}$

    2—O—Answer: $(3 + 14y)xy\sqrt[3]{4x^2}$

30. Simplify: $4\sqrt{9x} - 2\sqrt{4x} + 7$

    (a) $8x + 7$ (b) $8\sqrt{x} + 7$ (c) $2\sqrt{5x} + 7$

    (d) Does not simplify   (e) None of these

    1—M—Answer: b

31. Simplify: $7\sqrt{25xy^2} - 4\sqrt{75xy^2} + 2\sqrt{12xy^2}$

    (a) $35|y|\sqrt{x} - 16|y|\sqrt{3x}$ (b) $19|y|\sqrt{2x}$ (c) $35|y|\sqrt{x} - 6|y|\sqrt{2x}$

    (d) $5|y|\sqrt{38x}$ (e) None of these

    1—M—Answer: a

32. Simplify: $2x^2y\sqrt[3]{2x} + 7x^2\sqrt[3]{2xy^3} - 4\sqrt[3]{16x^7y^3}$

    (a) $x^6y^3\sqrt[3]{2x}$ (b) $x^2y\sqrt[3]{2x}$ (c) $9x^2y\sqrt[3]{2x} - 8y\sqrt[3]{2x^7y}$

    (d) $2x^3y$ (e) None of these

    2—M—Answer: b

33. Write $\sqrt[3]{2x^2}$ in exponential form.

    (a) $2x^{3/2}$ (b) $2x^{2/3}$ (c) $(2x)^{2/3}$

    (d) $(2x^2)^{1/3}$ (e) None of these

    1—M—Answer: d

34. The period T, in seconds, of a pendulum is $T = 2\pi\sqrt{\dfrac{L}{32}}$ where L is the length of the pendulum in feet. Find the period of a pendulum whose length is $\frac{1}{2}$ foot.

    (a) π (b) $\dfrac{\pi}{2}$ (c) $\dfrac{\pi}{4}$ (d) $\dfrac{\pi}{8}$ (e) None of these

    2—M—Answer: c

35. The period T, in seconds, of a pendulum is $T = 2\pi\sqrt{\dfrac{L}{32}}$ where L is the length of the pendulum in feet. Find the period of a pendulum whose length is 8 feet.

    (a) π (b) $\dfrac{\pi}{2}$ (c) $\dfrac{\pi}{4}$ (d) $\dfrac{\pi}{8}$ (e) None of these

    2—M—Answer: a

P.4 Polynomials and Special Products

1. Find the degree of the polynomial: $5x^4 - 2x^3 - 7x + 1$

   (a) 4 (b) 5 (c) 8 (d) 12 (e) None of these

   1—M—Answer: a

2. Find the degree of the polynomial: $5x^4 - 2x^2 + x$

   (a) 7 (b) 6 (c) 5 (d) 4 (e) None of these

   1—M—Answer: d

3. Find the degree of the polynomial: $4x^3 - 2x + 1$

   (a) 2 (b) 3 (c) 4 (d) 5 (e) This is not a polynomial.

   1—M—Answer: b

4. Find the degree of the polynomial: $5x^2 - 3x + 1$

   (a) 2 (b) 3 (c) 4 (d) 5 (e) This is not a polynomial.

   1—M—Answer: a

5. Identify any polynomials.

   (a) $4x^3 - 7\sqrt{x} + 3$ (b) $\dfrac{x^2 + 2x + 1}{x - 3}$ (c) $x^{-3} + 2x^{-2} + x$

   (d) None of these are polynomials. (e) All of these are polynomials.

   1—M—Answer: d

6. Identify any polynomials.

   (a) $3x^2 - 2x + 1$ (b) $\dfrac{x+1}{x-1}$ (c) $x + \dfrac{1}{x}$

   (d) None of these are polynomials. (e) All of these are polynomials.

   1—M—Answer: a

7. Identify any polynomials.

   (a) $\dfrac{3x+1}{2x-2}$ (b) $x + 2x^{-1} + 1$ (c) $\dfrac{1}{4}x^3 - \dfrac{2}{3}x - 2$

   (d) None of these are polynomials. (e) All of these are polynomials.

   1—M—Answer: c

8. Identify any polynomial.

   (a) $\frac{1}{2}x^3 + x - \frac{1}{3}$ (b) $7 + 4x^3 - 6x^7$ (c) $x + 1$

   (d) None of these are polynomials. (e) All of these are polynomials.

   1—M—Answer: e

9. Simplify: $(6x^3 + 2x - 7) + (4x^2 + x + 1) - (x^3 + 3x^2 - 2)$

   (a) $5x^3 + 7x^2 + 3x - 8$ (b) $5x^3 + x^2 + 3x - 4$ (c) $5x^6 - x^4 + x - 8$

   (d) $7x^6 - 8$ (e) None of these

   1—M—Answer: b

10. Simplify: $(7x^4 - 2x^3 + 5x^2) + (7x^3 - 2x^2 + 5) - (6x^3 + 2x^2 - 12x)$

    (a) $7x^4 - x^3 + x^2 + 12x + 5$ (b) $7x^4 - x^3 + 5x^2 - 12x + 5$ (c) $-x^{10} + 5$

    (d) $-x^9 + x^6 + 7x^4 - 12x + 5$ (e) None of these

    1—M—Answer: a

11. Simplify: $(-4x^2 + 2x) - (5x^3 + 2x^2 - 1) + (x^2 + 1)$

    (a) $-9x^3 + 5x^2$ (b) $5x^3 - x^2 + 2x + 1$ (c) $6x^6$

    (d) $-5x^3 - 5x^2 + 2x + 2$ (e) None of these

    1—M—Answer: d

12. Simplify: $(2x^2 + 3x - 1) + (x^3 + x^2 + 5) - (2x^2 - 5x + 7)$

    (a) $x^3 - 2x + x^2 + 4$ (b) $x^3 + x^2 + 8x - 3$ (c) $8x^5 + 4$

    (d) $63x^3 + 5x^6$ (e) None of these

    1—M—Answer: b

13. Simplify: $(3x^2 - 2x) + (7x^3 - 2x^2 + 1) - (16x^2 - 7)$

    (a) $7x^3 - 15x^2 - 2x + 8$ (b) $7x^3 + 15x^2 - 6$ (c) $7x^3 - 15x^2 - 2x - 6$

    (d) $15x^5 + 7x^3 - 2x - 6$ (e) None of these

    1—M—Answer: a

14. Simplify: $(-2x^2 + 3x - 9) - (4x^2 - x + 2) + (x^3 - 2x^2 + 1)$

    (a) $x^3 - 8x^2 + 3x - 6$ (b) $x^3 - 8x^2 + 4x - 10$ (c) $x^3 - 2x^2 + 2x - 6$

    (d) $x^3 - 4x^2 + 2x - 6$ (e) None of these

    1—M—Answer: b

15. Simplify: $3x(5x + 2) - 14(2x^2 - x + 1)$

    (a) $28x^2 - 3x - 14$ (b) $13x^2 - 8x + 14$ (c) $-13x^2 + 20x - 14$

    (d) $13x^2 - 20x + 14$ (e) None of these

    1—M—Answer: c

16. Simplify: $3x(7x - 6) - 4x(x - 2)$

    (a) $17x^2 - 10x$ (b) $-84x^4 + 240x^3 - 144x^2$ (c) $21x^2 - 14x$

    (d) $72x^3 - 96x^2$ (e) None of these

    1—M—Answer: a

17. Simplify: $(3x^4 - 7x^2) + 2x(x^2 - 1)(3x)$

    (a) $9x^4 - 13x^2$ (b) $9x^4 - 19x^3 - 2x$ (c) $3x^4 + 2x^3 - 7x^2 - 3x$

    (d) $15x^7 - 50x^5 + 35x^3$ (e) None of these

    1—M—Answer: a

18. Simplify: $(5 - 2x)(3) - (3x + 2)(-2)$

    (a) $-6x^2 + 11x + 10$ (b) $-9x + 1$ (c) $-10x + 20$

    (d) 19 (e) None of these

    1—M—Answer: d

19. Write the following polynomial in standard form: $(3x^2 + 2x) + x(1 - 7x) + (2x + 5)$

    1—O—Answer: $-4x^2 + 5x + 5$

20. Write in standard form: $3x^2 - 2x(1 + 3x - x^2)$

    1—O—Answer: $2x^3 - 3x^2 - 2x$

21. Multiply: $(2x^2 - 5)^2$

    (a) $4x^2 - 25$ (b) $4x^4 - 25$ (c) $4x^4 - 20x^2 + 25$

    (d) $4x^4 - 10x^2 - 25$ (e) None of these

    1—M—Answer: c

22. Multiply: $(x - 2)(x^2 + 2x + 4)$

    (a) $x^3 - 8$ (b) $x^3 - 6x^2 + 12x - 8$ (c) $x^3 + 4x^2 - 8$

    (d) $x^3 + 4x^2 + 8x - 8$ (e) None of these

    1—M—Answer: a

23. Multiply: $(x + 4y)^2$

    (a) $x^2 + 4xy + y^2$ (b) $x^2 + 16y^2$ (c) $x^2 + 8xy + 16y^2$

    (d) $x^2 + 4y^2$ (e) None of these

    1—M—Answer: c

24. Multiply: $(x - 2\sqrt{3})(x + 2\sqrt{3})$

    (a) $x^2 - 12$ (b) $x^2 - 36$ (c) $x^2 - 6$

    (d) $x^2 - 4\sqrt{3}$ (e) None of these

    1—M—Answer: a

25. Multiply: $(3x - 7)(2x + 9)$

    (a) $6x^2 + 13x - 63$ (b) $6x^2 - 63$ (c) $6x^2 - 13x - 63$

    (d) $6x^2 + 63$ (e) None of these

    1—M—Answer: a

26. Expand: $(2x - 1)^3$

    2—O—Answer: $8x^3 - 12x^2 + 6x - 1$

27. Expand: $[(x - 1) + y]^2$

    2—O—Answer: $x^2 - 2x + 1 + 2xy - 2y + y^2$

28. Multiply: $(x - 2)(x + 2)(x^2 + 4)$

    2—O—Answer: $x^4 - 16$

29. Multiply: $(2x - y)(x + y)$

    (a) $2x^2 - y^2$ (b) $2x^2 + xy - y^2$ (c) $-2x^2y^2$

    (d) $x^2y^2 - xy$ (e) None of these

    1—M—Answer: b

30. Multiply: $[(x+1) - y][(x+1) + y]$

(a) $x^2 + 2x + 1 - y^2$ (b) $x^2 + 1 - y^2$ (c) $x^2 y^2 + y^2$

(d) $-x^2 y^2 + 2xy^2 + y^2$ (e) None of these

1—M—Answer: a

31. Expand: $(3 + 2y)^3$

(a) $9 + 6y^3$ (b) $27 + 8y^3$ (c) $27 + 54y + 36y^2 + 8y^3$

(d) $27 + 18y + 12y^2 + 8y^3$ (e) None of these

2—M—Answer: d

32. Represent the area of the region as a polynomial in standard form.

(a) $-x^2 - 8x + 96$ (b) $-3x^2 + 72$

(c) 40 (d) $3x^2 - 24x + 96$

(e) None of these

2—M—Answer: d

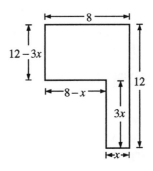

33. Represent the area of the region as a polynomial in standard form.

(a) $84x$ (b) $-10x^2 + 18x + 90$

(c) $-6x^2 + 90x$ (d) $10x + 36$

(e) None of these

2—M—Answer: c

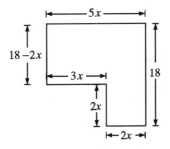

34. Represent the area of the shaded region as a polynomial in standard form.

(a) $6x^2 + 72x$ (b) $48x - 18$

(c) $90x - 6x^2$ (d) $90x$

(e) None of these

2—M—Answer: a

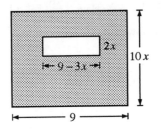

35. Represent the area of the shaded region as a polynomial in standard form.

(a) $140x$ (b) $144x - 4x^2$

(c) $55x$ (d) $120x^2$

(e) None of these

2—M—Answer: b

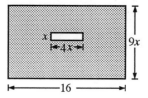

36. Represent the area of the shaded region as a polynomial in standard form.

(a) $-2x + 18$ (b) $12x + 14$

(c) 14 (d) $11x + 14$

(e) None of these

2—M—Answer: d

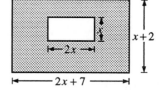

P.5 Factoring

1. Factor: $3x^2 - 15x$

(a) $45x^3$ (b) $3(x^2 - 5)$ (c) $3x(x - 5)$

(d) $3x(x - 5x)$ (e) None of these

1—M—Answer: c

2. Factor: $(2x - 1)(x + 3) + (2x - 1)(2x + 1)$

2—O—Answer: $(2x - 1)(3x + 4)$

3. Factor completely: $(3x + 2)(x - 7) + (4x - 1)(x - 7)$

2—O—Answer: $(x - 7)(7x + 1)$

4. Factor: $8x^3 - 27$

(a) $(2x - 3)^3$ (b) $(2x - 3)(4x^2 - 12x + 9)$ (c) $(2x - 3)(4x^2 + 6x + 9)$

(d) $(2x + 3)(4x^2 - 6x + 9)$ (e) None of these

1—M—Answer: c

5. Factor: $x^3 + 216$

(a) $(x + 6)^3$ (b) $(x + 6)(x^2 - 6x + 36)$ (c) $(x - 6)(x^2 + 6x - 36)$

(d) $(x + 6)(x^2 + 36)$ (e) None of these

1—M—Answer: b

6. Factor: $y^3 - (x+1)^3$

    (a) $(y - x - 1)(y^2 + xy + y + x^2 + 2x + 1)$ (b) $(y - x + 1)(y^2 + xy + y + x^2 + 1)$

    (c) $(y + x - 1)(y^2 - xy - y + x^2 - 2x - 1)$ (d) $(y - x - 1)^3$

    (e) None of these

    2—M—Answer: a

7. Factor: $(a - b)^2 - x^2$

    (a) $(a - b - x)^2$ (b) $(a - b - x)(a + b + x)$ (c) $(a - b - x)(a - b + x)$

    (d) $a^2 - 2ab + b^2 - x^2$ (e) None of these

    1—M—Answer: c

8. Factor: $81 - 4x^2$

    (a) $(9 - 2x)^2$ (b) $(9 - 2x)(9 + 2x)$ (c) $(81 - 4x)^2$

    (d) $(3 - 2x)^2(3 + 2x)^2$ (e) None of these

    1—M—Answer: b

9. Factor completely: $(x + 3)^2 - a^2$

    2—O—Answer: $(x + 3 - a)(x + 3 + a)$

10. Factor completely: $9x^2 + 24xy + 16y^2$

    (a) $(9x + 4y)(x + 4y)$ (b) $(9x + 16y)(x + y)$ (c) $(3x - 4y)^2$

    (d) $(3x + 4y)^2$ (e) None of these

    1—M—Answer: d

11. Factor completely: $9x^2 - 24x + 16$

    1—O—Answer: $(3x - 4)^2$

12. Factor: $9x^2 - 42x + 49$

    (a) $(3x - 7)^2$ (b) $(9x - 7)^2$ (c) $(3x + 7)^2$

    (d) $x(9x - 42 + 49)$ (e) None of these

    1—M—Answer: a

13. Factor: $x^2 + 13x - 14$

    (a) $(x - 7)(x + 2)$ (b) $(x + 7)(x - 2)$ (c) $(x - 14)(x - 1)$

    (d) $(x - 14)(x + 1)$ (e) None of these

    1—M—Answer: e

14. Factor: $x^2 + x - 12$

(a) $(x-4)(x-3)$ (b) $(x+4)(x-3)$ (c) $(x+6)(x-2)$

(d) $(x-12)(x-1)$ (e) None of these

1—M—Answer: b

15. Factor: $x^2 - 2x - 15$

(a) $(x-3)(x+5)$ (b) $(x-15)(x+1)$ (c) $(x+3)(x-5)$

(d) $(x+3)(x+5)$ (e) None of these

1—M—Answer: c

16. Factor: $3x^2 - 13x - 16$

(a) $(3x-16)(x-1)$ (b) $(3x+16)(x-1)$ (c) $(x+16)(3x-1)$

(d) $(x-16)(3x+1)$ (e) None of these

1—M—Answer: e

17. Factor completely: $3x^2 - 19x - 14$

(a) $(3x+2)(x-7)$ (b) $(3x-7)(x+2)$ (c) $(3x-2)(x+7)$

(d) $(3x+7)(x-2)$ (e) None of these

1—M—Answer: a

18. Factor completely: $14x^2 - 19x - 3$ **19.** Factor completely: $35x^2 + 9x - 2$

1—O—Answer: $(2x-3)(7x+1)$ **1—O—Answer:** $(5x+2)(7x-1)$

20. Factor completely: $2rs + 3rst - 8r - 12rt$

(a) $r(2s+3st-8-12t)$ (b) $(rs-4r)(2+3t)$ (c) $r(s-4)(2-3t)$

(d) $r(s-4)(2+3t)$ (e) None of these

2—M—Answer: d

21. Factor completely: $3rv - 2vt - 6rs + 4st$

2—O—Answer: $(v-2s)(3r-2t)$

22. Factor: $3xz + 2yz - 6xw - 4yw$

(a) $(3x+2y)(z+2w)$ (b) $(3x+2y)(z-2w)$ (c) $(3x-2y)(z-2w)$

(d) $(3xz+2yz)(6xw+4yw)$ (e) None of these

2—M—Answer: b

23. Factor: $4x^3 + 6x^2 - 10x$

1—O—Answer: $2x(2x+5)(x-1)$

24. Factor into linear factors: $6x^3 + 33x^2y - 63xy^2$

(a) $3x(2x - 3y)(x + 7y)$ (b) $(6x^2 - 9xy)(x + 7y)$ (c) $3x(2x + 3y)(x + 7y)$

(d) $(6x^2 + 9xy)(x + 7y)$ (e) None of these

1—M—Answer: a

25. Factor completely: $3x^4 - 48$

(a) $3(x - 2)^2(x + 2)^2$ (b) $3(x - 2)^4$ (c) $3x^2(x - 4)^2$

(d) $3(x^2 + 4)(x + 2)(x - 2)$ (e) None of these

2—M—Answer: d

26. Factor: $3x - 24x^4$

2—O—Answer: $3x(1 - 2x)(1 + 2x + 4x^2)$

27. Factor completely: $x^2(2x + 1)^3 - 4(2x + 1)^2$

(a) $(2x + 1)^2(2x^3 - 3)$ (b) $(2x + 1)^2(2x^3 + x^2 - 4)$ (c) $(2x + 1)^3(x^2 - 4)$

(d) $(2x + 1)^3(x^2 - 8x - 4)$ (e) None of these

2—M—Answer: b

28. Factor: $4(x + 2)^2 - 3x(x + 2)^3$

(a) $-(x + 2)^2(3x - 2)(x + 2)$ (b) $-(x + 2)^2(3x^2 + 6x - 4)$ (c) $(x + 2)^2(-3x^2 + 6)$

(d) $(x + 2)^2(-3x^2 + 6x + 4)$ (e) None of these

1—M—Answer: b

29. Factor: $9x(3x - 5)^2 + (3x - 5)^3$

(a) $(3x - 5)^3(9x + 1)$ (b) $(3x - 5)^2(6x - 5)$ (c) $(3x - 5)^2(12x - 5)$

(d) $(3x - 5)(30x^2 - 70)$ (e) None of these

1—M—Answer: c

30. Factor: $6x(2x + 3)^{-4} - 24x^2(2x + 3)^{-5}$

(a) $-6x(2x - 3)(2x + 3)^{-5}$ (b) $-6x(8x^2 + 12x - 1)(2x + 3)^{-4}$

(c) $6x(2x + 3)^{-5}[(2x + 3)^{-1} + 4x]$ (d) $6x(2x + 3)^{-4}(-8x^2 - 12x)$

(e) None of these

2—M—Answer: a

31. Factor: $(3x+2)^{-3} - 9x(3x+2)^{-4}$

(a) $(3x+2)^{-4}[(3x+2)^{-1} - 9x]$ (b) $(-27x^2 - 18x)(3x+2)^{-3}$

(c) $-2(3x-1)(3x+2)^{-4}$ (d) $-(27x^2 + 18x - 1)(3x+2)^{-3}$

(e) None of these

2—M—Answer: c

32. Factor: $2x(4x-1)^{-2} + (4x-1)^{-1}$

(a) $(8x^2 - 1)(4x-1)^{-1}$ (b) $(4x-1)^{-1}(8x^2 - 2x + 1)$ (c) $(2x+1)(4x-1)^{-2}$

(d) $(6x-1)(4x-1)^{-2}$ (e) None of these

1—M—Answer: d

33. The trinomial $x^2 - 4x + c$ will factor for which of the following values of c?

(a) 3   (b) -5 (c) -12

(d) All of these   (e) None of these

2—M—Answer: d

34. The trinomial $4x^2 + 3x + c$ will factor for which of the following values of c?

(a) 6   (b) 0   (c) -1

(d) Both a and b   (e) Both b and c

1—M—Answer: e

35. The total surface area of a right circular cylinder is found by using the formula $S = 2\pi r^2 + 2\pi rh$. Write the formula in factored form.

1—O—Answer: $S = 2\pi r(r + h)$

36. The volume of the frustum of a cone can be found by using the formula $V = \frac{1}{3}(a^2\pi h + ab\pi h + b^2\pi h)$. Write the formula is factored form.

1—O—Answer: $V = \frac{1}{3}\pi h(a^2 + ab + b^2)$

P.6 Factional Expressions

1. Find the domain: $\frac{1}{2}x^2 + 2x + 1$

(a) $(-\infty, \infty)$ (b) $[0, \infty)$ (c) $(-\infty, \frac{1}{2})(\frac{1}{2}, \infty)$

(d) $[\frac{1}{2}, \infty)$ (e) None of these

1—M—Answer: a

2. Find the domain: $\frac{3x + 1}{x^2 - 2x}$

(a) $(-\infty, 0)(0, \infty)$ (b) $(-\infty, -2)(0, \infty)$ (c) $(-\infty, 0)(0, 2)(2, \infty)$

(d) $(-\infty, -\frac{1}{3})(-\frac{1}{3}, 0)(0, 2)(2, \infty)$ (e) None of these

1—M—Answer: c

3. Find the domain: $\frac{x + 1}{4 - x^2}$

(a) $(-\infty, \infty)$ (b) $(-\infty, -1)(-1, 2)(2, \infty)$ (c) $(-\infty, -2)(2, \infty)$

(d) $(-\infty, -2)(-2, -1)(-1, 2)(2, \infty)$ (e) None of these

1—M—Answer: e

4. Find the domain: $\sqrt{x + 2}$

(a) $(-\infty, \infty)$ (b) $[0, \infty)$ (c) $[-2, \infty)$

(d) $(-\infty, -2)$ (e) None of these

1—M—Answer: c

5. Find the domain: $\sqrt{3 - x}$

(a) $(-\infty, 3]$ (b) $[3, \infty)$ (c) $(-\infty, 0]$

(d) $(-3, 3)$ (e) None of these

1—M—Answer: a

6. Reduce: $\frac{x^2 - 8x + 12}{5x - 30}$

(a) $\frac{x - 2}{5}$ (b) $\frac{2 + x}{-5}$ (c) $\frac{x + 2}{5}$

(d) $\frac{-x - 2}{5}$ (e) None of these

1—M—Answer: a

7. Reduce to lowest terms: $\frac{2x^2 + 5x - 3}{6x - 3}$

1—O—Answer: $\frac{x + 3}{3}$

8. Reduce to lowest terms: $\frac{4x - 2x^2}{x^2 + x - 6}$

1—O—Answer: $\frac{-2x}{x + 3}$

9. Reduce: $\dfrac{x^2 - 7x + 10}{x^2 - 8x + 15}$

   (a) $\dfrac{x + 2}{x + 3}$ (b) $\dfrac{x - 2}{x - 3}$ (c) $\dfrac{x + 3}{x + 2}$

   (d) $\dfrac{x - 2}{x + 3}$ (e) None of these

   1—M—Answer: b

10. Reduce: $\dfrac{x^2 + 3x - 10}{x^2 + 2x - 15}$

   (a) $\dfrac{x - 2}{x - 3}$ (b) $\dfrac{x - 3}{x - 2}$ (c) $\dfrac{x + 2}{x - 3}$

   (d) $\dfrac{x + 2}{x + 3}$ (e) None of these

   1—M—Answer: a

11. Multiply: $\dfrac{1}{x + y}\left(\dfrac{x}{y} + \dfrac{y}{x}\right)$

   (a) $\dfrac{1}{y} + \dfrac{1}{x}$ (b) 1   (c) $\dfrac{x + y}{xy}$

   (d) $\dfrac{x^2 + y^2}{xy(x + y)}$ (e) None of these

   1—M—Answer: d

12. Multiply, then simplify: $\dfrac{2 - x}{x^2 + 4} \cdot \dfrac{x + 2}{x^2 + 5x - 14}$

   (a) $-\dfrac{x + 2}{(x^2 + 4)(x + 7)}$ (b) $\dfrac{1}{(x + 2)(x + 7)}$ (c) $\dfrac{x + 2}{(x^2 + 4)(x + 7)}$

   (d) $\dfrac{-1}{(x + 2)(x + 7)}$ (e) None of these

   1—M—Answer: a

13. Multiply, then simplify: $\dfrac{x^2 - 5x + 4}{x^2 + 4} \cdot \dfrac{x + 2}{x^2 + 3x - 4}$

   1—O—Answer: $\dfrac{x^2 - 2x - 8}{(x^2 + 4)(x + 4)}$

14. Multiply, then simplify: $\dfrac{x^2 + 4x + 4}{x - 2} \cdot \dfrac{2 - x}{3x + 6}$

   (a) $\dfrac{x - 2}{3}$ (b) $\dfrac{x + 2}{3}$ (c) $-\dfrac{x - 2}{3}$

   (d) $-\dfrac{x + 2}{3}$ (e) None of these

   1—M—Answer: d

15. Divide, then simplify: $\dfrac{x+1}{x^2-1} \div \dfrac{x^2+1}{x-1}$

1—O—Answer: $\dfrac{1}{x^2+1}$

16. Divide: $\dfrac{x+y}{x^3-x^2} \div \dfrac{x^2+y^2}{x^2-x}$

(a) $\dfrac{1}{x(x+y)}$ (b) $\dfrac{x+y}{x(x^2+y^2)}$ (c) $\dfrac{x(x^2+y^2)}{x+y}$

(d) $-x$ (e) None of these

1—M—Answer: b

17. Divide: $\dfrac{4x-16}{5x+15} \div \dfrac{4-x}{2x+6}$

(a) 0   (b) $-\dfrac{4(x-4)}{5(x+3)^2}$ (c) $-\dfrac{8}{5}$

(d) $-\dfrac{3}{10}$ (e) None of these

1—M—Answer: c

18. Divide: $\dfrac{x^2-2x-63}{x+1} \div \dfrac{9-x}{x^2+x}$

(a) 585   (b) $-x(x+7)$ (c) x^2+7x

(d) $\dfrac{x^2-2x-63}{9-x}$ (e) None of these

1—M—Answer: b

19. Subtract, then simplify: $\dfrac{1}{x} - \dfrac{x}{2y}$

(a) $\dfrac{2y-x}{2xy}$ (b) $\dfrac{1-x}{2xy}$ (c) $\dfrac{1-x}{x-2y}$

(d) $\dfrac{2y-x^2}{2xy}$ (e) None of these

1—M—Answer: d

20. Subtract, then simplify: $\dfrac{2}{x-3} - \dfrac{1}{x+2}$

(a) $\dfrac{1}{(x-3)(x+2)}$ (b) $\dfrac{x-1}{(x-3)(x+2)}$ (c) $\dfrac{x+7}{(x-3)(x+2)}$

(d) $\dfrac{x+1}{(x-3)(x+2)}$ (e) None of these

1—M—Answer: c

21. Subtract, then simplify: $\dfrac{3}{x} - \dfrac{9}{x+1}$

1—O—Answer: $\dfrac{3(1-2x)}{x(x+1)}$

22. Add, then simplify: $\dfrac{4}{x+2} + \dfrac{7}{x-3}$

(a) $\dfrac{11}{x-1}$ (b) $\dfrac{11}{2x-1}$ (c) $\dfrac{11x+2}{(x+2)(x-3)}$

(d) $\dfrac{11x+2}{x^2-6}$ (e) None of these

1—M—Answer: c

23. Add, then simplify: $\dfrac{2}{x^2-9} + \dfrac{5}{x^2-x-12}$

(a) $\dfrac{7}{(x^2-9)(x^2-x-12)}$ (b) $\dfrac{7x^2-x-21}{(x^2-9)(x^2-x-12)}$ (c) $\dfrac{7x-7}{(x-3)(x-4)(x+3)}$

(d) $\dfrac{7x-23}{(x-3)(x+3)(x-4)}$ (e) None of these

2—M—Answer: d

24. Subtract, then simplify: $\dfrac{3}{x^2+2x+1} - \dfrac{1}{x+1}$

(a) $\dfrac{4-x}{x^2+2x+1}$ (b) $\dfrac{-x^2+5x+2}{(x+1)(x^2+2x+1)}$ (c) $\dfrac{-x^2+x+2}{(x^2+2x+1)(x+1)}$

(d) $\dfrac{2-x}{x^2+2x+1}$ (e) None of these

2—M—Answer: d

25. Add, then simplify: $\dfrac{3}{x^2+x-2} + \dfrac{x}{x^2-x-6}$

(a) $\dfrac{x^2+2x-9}{(x-3)(x+2)(x-1)}$ (b) $\dfrac{x^3+3x^2-5x-6}{(x^2+x-2)(x^2-x-6)}$ (c) $\dfrac{4x-10}{(x-3)(x+2)(x-1)}$

(d) $\dfrac{3+x}{2x^2-8}$ (e) None of these

2—M—Answer: a

26. Add, then simplify: $\dfrac{x+1}{x^2+x-2} + \dfrac{x+3}{x^2-4x+3}$

(a) $\dfrac{2x^2+3}{(x-1)(x-3)(x+2)}$ (b) $\dfrac{2x^3+x^2-3}{(x^2+x-2)(x^2-4x+3)}$ (c) $\dfrac{2x+4}{-3x+1}$

(d) $\dfrac{2x^2+3x+3}{(x-1)(x-3)(x+2)}$ (e) None of these

2—M—Answer: d

27. Simplify: $\dfrac{\dfrac{2}{x+1} - \dfrac{x}{x+2}}{\dfrac{1}{x+1}}$

(a) $\dfrac{-x^2 + 3x + 4}{x+2}$ (b) $\dfrac{-x^2 + x + 4}{x+2}$ (c) $\dfrac{2-x}{x+2}$

(d) $\dfrac{-x^2 + 3x + 3}{(x+1)(x+2)}$ (e) None of these

1—M—Answer: b

28. Simplify: $\dfrac{\dfrac{1}{x} - \dfrac{1}{x+1}}{\dfrac{1}{x^2 + 2x + 1}}$

(a) $x + 1$ (b) $\dfrac{x}{x+1}$ (c) $\dfrac{x+1}{x}$

(d) $\dfrac{1}{x(x+1)(x^2 + 2x + 1)}$ (e) None of these

2—M—Answer: c

29. Simplify: $\dfrac{\dfrac{1}{x} + \dfrac{7}{x+1}}{\dfrac{1}{x^2 - 1}}$

(a) $\dfrac{8x^2 - 7x - 1}{x}$ (b) $\dfrac{8x^2 - 1}{x}$ (c) $\dfrac{7x^2 - 6x + 1}{x}$

(d) $\dfrac{8x + 1}{x(x+1)(x^2 - 1)}$ (e) None of these

2—M—Answer: a

30. Simplify: $\dfrac{\dfrac{1}{x} - \dfrac{1}{y}}{xy}$

(a) $\dfrac{1}{x^2 y^2}$ (b) $\dfrac{y-x}{x^2 y^2}$ (c) $\dfrac{x-y}{x^2 y^2}$

(d) $y - x$ (e) None of these

1—M—Answer: b

31. Simplify: $\dfrac{(3x+5)^{1/3} - \dfrac{x}{(3x+5)^{2/3}}}{(3x+5)^{2/3}}$

    (a) $\dfrac{x-1}{(3x+5)^{4/3}}$
    (b) $\dfrac{9x^2 + 29x + 25}{(3x+5)^{2/3}}$
    (c) $\dfrac{2x+5}{(3x+5)^{2/3}}$

    (d) $\dfrac{2x+5}{(3x+5)^{4/3}}$
    (e) None of these

    2—M—Answer: d

32. Simplify: $\dfrac{(7x+2)^{1/3} - \dfrac{x}{(7x+2)^{2/3}}}{(7x+2)^{2/3}}$

    (a) $\dfrac{6x+2}{(7x+2)^{4/3}}$
    (b) $\dfrac{6x+2}{(7x+2)^{2/3}}$
    (c) $\dfrac{49x^2 + 13x + 4}{(7x+2)^{4/3}}$

    (d) $\dfrac{x+4}{(7x+2)^{4/3}}$
    (e) None of these

    2—M—Answer: a

33. Simplify: $\dfrac{(x+2)^{1/2}}{(x+2)^{1/2} - 4(x+2)^{3/2}}$

    2—O—Answer: $-\dfrac{1}{4x+7}$

34. Simplify: $\dfrac{\sqrt{x} + (6/\sqrt{x})}{\sqrt{x}}$

    (a) $\dfrac{6}{x}$
    (b) $1 + 6\sqrt{x}$
    (c) $\dfrac{x + 6\sqrt{x}}{x}$

    (d) $\dfrac{x+6}{x}$
    (e) None of these

    2—M—Answer: d

35. Simplify: $\dfrac{\sqrt{1+x} - (x/\sqrt{1+x})}{1+x}$

    (a) $\dfrac{1 + 2\sqrt{1+x}}{1+x}$
    (b) $\dfrac{-x + \sqrt{1+x}}{(1+x)\sqrt{1+x}}$
    (c) $\dfrac{1}{1+x}$

    (d) $\dfrac{\sqrt{1+x}}{(1+x)^2}$
    (e) None of these

    2—M—Answer: d

36. Simplify: $\dfrac{(3/\sqrt{x+2}) - \sqrt{x+2}}{5\sqrt{x+2}}$

   2—O—Answer: $\dfrac{1-x}{5(x+2)}$

37. Rationalize the denominator: $\dfrac{x}{3 - \sqrt{x+9}}$

   2—O—Answer: $-(3 + \sqrt{x+9})$

38. The efficiency of a Carnot engine can be determined by using the formula $\mathrm{Eff} = 1 - \dfrac{T_2}{T_1}$.
   Write this as a single fraction.

   (a) $\dfrac{T_1}{1 - T_2}$ (b) $\dfrac{1 - T_2}{T_1}$ (c) $\dfrac{T_1 - T_2}{T_1}$

   (d) $\dfrac{T_1 - T_2}{T_1 T_2}$ (e) None of these

   1—M—Answer: c

P.7   The Cartesian Plane

1. The triangle shown in the figure has vertices at the points
$(-1, -1)$, $(-1, 2)$, and $(1, 1)$. Shift the triangle 3 units to
the right and 2 units down and find the vertices of the shifted
triangle.

   (a) $(2, 1)$, $(2, 4)$, $(4, 3)$
   (b) $(-4, 1)$, $(-4, 4)$, $(-2, 3)$
   (c) $(-4, -3)$, $(-4, 0)$, $(-2, -1)$
   (d) $(2, -3)$, $(2, 0)$, $(4, -1)$
   (e) None of these

   1—M—Answer: d

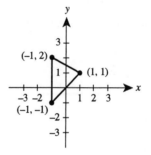

2. The triangle shown in the figure has vertices at the points
$(-1, 2)$, $(1, 2)$ and $(0, 0)$. Shift the triangle 2 units up and
find the vertices of the shifted triangle.

   (a) $(1, 2)$, $(3, 2)$, $(2, 0)$
   (b) $(-1, 4)$, $(1, 4)$, $(0, 2)$
   (c) $(-1, 0)$, $(1, 0)$, $(0, -2)$
   (d) $(-3, 2)$, $(-1, 2)$, $(-2, 2)$
   (e) None of these

   1—M—Answer: b

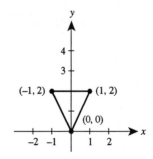

3. The triangle shown in the figure has vertices at the points $(-1, 2)$, $(1, 2)$ and $(0, 0)$. Shift the triangle 3 units to the left and find the vertices of the shifted triangle.

   (a) $(-1, -1)$, $(1, -1)$, $(0, -3)$
   (b) $(-4, 2)$, $(-2, 2)$, $(-3, 0)$
   (c) $(-1, -1)$, $(-1, 1)$, $(-3, 0)$
   (d) $(2, 2)$, $(-2, 2)$, $(-3, 0)$
   (e) None of these

   1—M—Answer: b

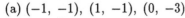

4. Find the distance between the points $(3, 17)$ and $(-2, 5)$.

   (a) 13   (b) $\sqrt{145}$ (c) $\sqrt{485}$
   (d) $3\sqrt{51}$ (e) None of these

   1—M—Answer: a

5. Find the distance between the points $(-6, 10)$ and $(12, 2)$.

   (a) $2\sqrt{7}$ (b) $2\sqrt{97}$ (c) 10
   (d) $2\sqrt{65}$ (e) None of these

   1—M—Answer: b

6. Find the distance between the points $(3, -1)$ and $(7, 2)$.

   1—O—Answer: 5

7. Find the distance between the points $(3, 5)$ and $(-2, -1)$.

   1—O—Answer: $\sqrt{61}$

8. Find the midpoint of the line segment joining $(3, 7)$ and $(-6, 1)$.

   (a) $\left(-\frac{3}{2}, 4\right)$ (b) $\left(\frac{9}{2}, 3\right)$ (c) $(-3, 6)$
   (d) $(-3, 4)$ (e) None of these

   1—M—Answer: a

9. Find the midpoint of the line segment joining $(-3, 1)$ and $(5, -7)$.

   (a) $(-4, 4)$ (b) $(1, -3)$ (c) $(-4, -3)$
   (d) $(1, 4)$ (e) None of these

   1—M—Answer: b

10. Find the midpoint of the line segment joining $(-2, 1)$ and $(16, 3)$.

    (a) $(7, 2)$ (b) $(9, 1)$ (c) $(14, 4)$
    (d) $(-9, -1)$ (e) None of these

    1—M—Answer: a

11. Find the midpoint of the line segment joining $(6, 9)$ and $(-3, 1)$.

    1—O—Answer: $\left(\frac{3}{2}, 5\right)$

12. Find the midpoint of the line segment joining $(-6, -2)$ and $(5, -1)$.

    1—O—Answer: $\left(-\frac{1}{2}, -\frac{3}{2}\right)$

13. The point $(3, 2)$ is the midpoint of (x, y) and $(5, 1)$. Find the point (x, y).

    (a) $(3, 1)$ (b) $(1, 3)$ (c) $(10, 2)$
    (d) $\left(4, \frac{3}{2}\right)$ (e) None of these

    1—M—Answer: b

14. Find the distance between the origin and the midpoint of the two points $(3, 3)$ and $(3, 5)$.

    (a) $3\sqrt{2}$ (b) 7   (c) $\sqrt{34}$ (d) 5   (e) None of these

    2—M—Answer: d

15. Find the distance between the origin and the midpoint of the two points $(2, 7)$ and $(6, 5)$.

    (a) 10   (b) $2\sqrt{13}$ (c) $4\sqrt{13}$ (d) $2\sqrt{5}$ (e) None of these

    2—M—Answer: b

16. Find the distance between the origin and the midpoint of the two points $(5, 7)$, $(-3, 1)$.

    (a) $\sqrt{17}$ (b) 5   (c) $\sqrt{10}$ (d) 4   (e) None of these

    2—M—Answer: a

17. Find x so that the distance between the points $(6, -1)$ and $(x, 9)$ is 12.

    (a) $2\sqrt{31}$ (b) $6 + 2\sqrt{11}$ (c) $6 + 4\sqrt{10}$
    (d) $-6 + 4\sqrt{5}$ (e) None of these

    2—M—Answer: b

18. Find x so that the distance from the origin to the point $(x, 9)$ is 15.

    (a) $\pm 3\sqrt{34}$ (b) $\pm 2\sqrt{11}$ (c) ± 9
    (d) ± 12 (e) None of these

    2—M—Answer: d

19. Find the point $(x, 0)$ that is equidistant from $(6, 1)$ and $(-2, 5)$.

    2—O—Answer: $\left(\frac{1}{2}, 0\right)$

20. Find the point $(0, y)$ that is equidistant from $(6, 1)$ and $(-1, -2)$.

    2—O—Answer: $\left(0, \frac{16}{3}\right)$

21. Identify the type of triangle that has $(-5, -1)$, $(2, 2)$, and $(0, -3)$ as vertices.

(a) Scalene   (b) Right isosceles   (c) Equilateral

(d) Isosceles   (e) None of these

2—M—Answer: b

22. Identify the type of triangle that has $(1, 10)$, $(-3, -2)$, and $(3, 16)$ as vertices.

(a) Isosceles   (b) Right   (c) Scalene

(d) Equilateral   (e) These points do not form a triangle.

2—M—Answer: e

23. Identify the type of triangle that has $(0, 0)$, $(4, 0)$ and $(2, 2\sqrt{3})$ as vertices.

(a) Scalene   (b) Right   (c) Isosceles

(d) Equilateral   (e) These points do not form a triangle.

2—M—Answer: d

24. Identify the type of triangle that has $(0, 0)$, $(4, 0)$ and $(2, 4\sqrt{2})$ as vertices.

(a) Scalene   (b) Right   (c) Isosceles

(d) Equilateral   (e) These points do not form a triangle.

2—M—Answer: c

25. Determine the quadrant in which the point (x, y) must be located if $x > 0$ and $y < 0$.
(a) I   (b) II   (c) III   (d) IV   (e) None of these

1—M—Answer: d

26. Determine the quadrant in which the point (x, y) must be located if $x < 0$ and $y > 0$.

(a) I   (b) II   (c) III   (d) IV   (e) None of these

1—M—Answer: b

27. Determine the quadrant(s) in which the point (x, y) must be located if $xy < 0$.

(a) II   (b) II and III   (c) II and IV

(d) I and III   (e) None of these

1—M—Answer: c

28. Find the length of the hypotenuse of the right triangle determined by the points $(1, 1), (-2, 1)$ and $(-2, 4)$.

(a) 6   (b) $3\sqrt{2}$ (c) $2\sqrt{3}$ (d) 9   (e) None of these

2—M—Answer: b

29. Find the length of the hypotenuse of the right triangle determined by the points $(-1, 1)$, $(3, 1)$ and $(3, -3)$.

(a) $4\sqrt{2}$ (b) $2\sqrt{2}$ (c) $16\sqrt{2}$ (d) 6   (e) None of these

2—M—Answer: a

30. Find a relationship between x and y so that (x, y) is equidistant from the two points $(4, -1)$ and $(6, 3)$.

(a) $x - 4y + 3 = 0$ (b) $2x + 4y - 31 = 0$ (c) $x + 2y - 7 = 0$
(d) $2x - 8y - 45 = 0$ (e) None of these

2—M—Answer: c

31. Find a relationship between x and y so that (x, y) is equidistant from the two points $(3, -1)$ and $(2, 5)$.

(a) $x - 6y + 18 = 0$ (b) $3x - 12y + 26 = 0$ (c) $2x + 8y + 29 = 0$
(d) $2x - 12y + 19 = 0$ (e) None of these

2—M—Answer: d

32. In a football game, the quarterback throws a pass from the 8-yard line, 15 yards from the sideline. The pass is caught on the 43-yard line, 3 yards from the same sideline. How long was the pass? (Assume the pass and the reception are on the same side of midfield.)

(a) 40 yards   (b) 36.1 yards   (c) 39.4 yards
(d) 37 yards   (e) None of these

2—M—Answer: d

33. In a football game, the quarterback throws a pass from the 3-yard line, 10 yards from the sideline. The pass is caught on the 43-yard line, 40 yards from the same sideline. How long was the pass? (Assume the pass and the reception are on the same side of midfield.)

(a) 60 yards   (b) 55 yards   (c) 50 yards
(d) 45 yards   (e) None of these

2—M—Answer: c

34. A homeowner needs to determine the distance y from the peak to the lower edge of the roof on the garage. He knows the distance from the ground to the peak is $14\frac{1}{2}$ feet and the distance from the lower edge of the roof to the ground is 11 feet. Find y if the garage is 20 feet wide.

2—O—Answer: 10.6 feet

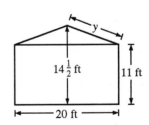

35. A homeowner wants to determine the distance y from the peak to the lower edge of the roof on his garage. He knows the distance from the ground to the peak is 13 feet and the distance from the lower edge of the roof to the ground is 10 feet. Find y if the garage is 18 feet wide. (Round to 1 decimal place.)

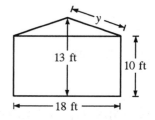

(a) 10.1 feet   (b) 9.8 feet   (c) 9.5 feet

(d) 9.3 feet   (e) None of these

2—M—Answer: c

C H A P T E R   O N E
Functions and Graphs

1.1 Graphs and Graphing Utilities

1. Determine which of the following points does *not* lie on the graph of $y = \dfrac{2}{x^2 + 4}$.

    (a) $\left(0, \dfrac{1}{2}\right)$ (b) $\left(1, \dfrac{2}{5}\right)$ (c) $\left(-2, \dfrac{1}{4}\right)$

    (d) $\left(-1, \dfrac{2}{3}\right)$ (e) None of these

    1—M—Answer: d

2. Determine which of the following points does *not* lie on the graph of $y = x^3 + 4x - 1$.

    (a) $(0, -1)$ (b) $(1, 4)$ (c) $(-1, -4)$

    (d) $(3, 38)$ (e) None of these

    1—M—Answer: c

3. Complete the solutions table for $y = 4x^2 + 2$.

x	-2	0	2
y			

    1—O—Answer:

x	-2	0	2
y	18	2	18

4. Complete the solutions table for $y = 25x\left(\dfrac{4x}{x^2 + 5} + 2\right)$.

x	-2	0	2	4
y				

    1—O—Answer:

x	-2	0	2	4
y	$-\dfrac{500}{9}$	0	$\dfrac{1300}{9}$	$\dfrac{5800}{21}$

5. Which of the following range settings was used to obtain the graph at the right?

(a)
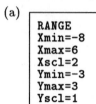
```
RANGE
Xmin=-8
Xmax=6
Xscl=2
Ymin=-3
Ymax=3
Yscl=1
```

(b)
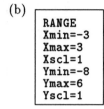
```
RANGE
Xmin=-3
Xmax=3
Xscl=1
Ymin=-8
Ymax=6
Yscl=1
```

(c)
```
RANGE
Xmin=-3
Xmax=3
Xscl=1
Ymin=-8
Ymax=6
Yscl=2
```

(d)
```
RANGE
Xmin=-8
Xmax=6
Xscl=1
Ymin=-3
Ymax=3
Yscl=1
```

(e) None of these

1—M—Answer: c

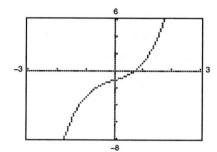

6. Which of the following range settings was used to obtain the graph at the right?

(a)
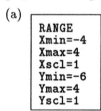
```
RANGE
Xmin=-4
Xmax=4
Xscl=1
Ymin=-6
Ymax=4
Yscl=1
```

(b)
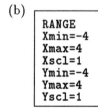
```
RANGE
Xmin=-4
Xmax=4
Xscl=1
Ymin=-4
Ymax=4
Yscl=1
```

(c)
```
RANGE
Xmin=-4
Xmax=4
Xscl=1
Ymin=-6
Ymax=4
Yscl=2
```

(d)
```
RANGE
Xmin=-6
Xmax=4
Xscl=1
Ymin=-4
Ymax=4
Yscl=1
```

(e) None of these

1—M—Answer: a

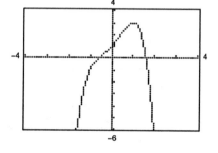

7. Match the equation with the graph.

(a) $y = \sqrt{9 - x^2}$

(b) $y = |x^2 - 9|$

(c) $y = \sqrt{x^2 - 9}$

(d) $y = (9 - x)^2$

(e) None of these

1—M—Answer: a

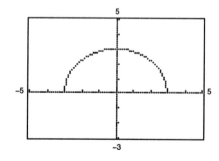

8. Match the equation with the graph.

    (a) $y = \sqrt{x - 3}$ (b) $y = |x - 3|$

    (c) $y = (x - 3)^2$ (d) $y = x - 3$

    (e) None of these

    1—M—Answer: b

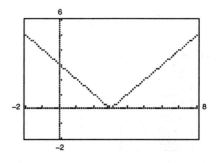

9. Use a graphing utility to graph $y = \dfrac{24}{x^2 + 4}$. Use the standard viewing rectangle.

    (a)

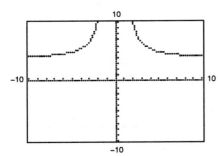

    (b)

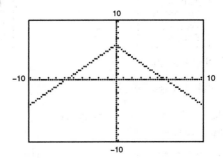

    (c)

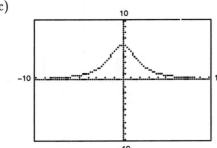

    (d)

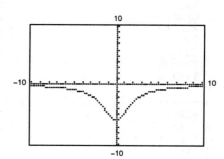

    (e) None of these

    1—M—Answer: c

10. Use a graphing utility to graph $y = 6 + 3x - 2x^2$. Use the standard viewing rectangle.

(a)

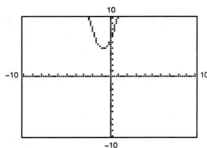

(b)

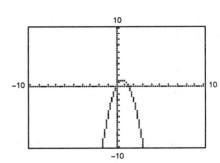

(c)

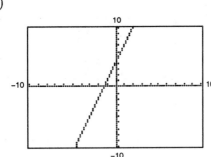

(d)

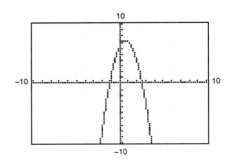

(e) None of these

1—M—Answer: d

11. Use a graphing utility to graph $y = x\sqrt{5 - x}$. Use the standard viewing rectangle.

(a)

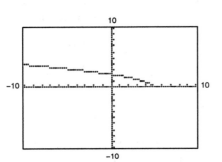

(b)

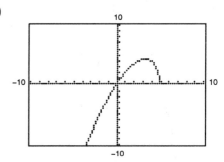

(c)

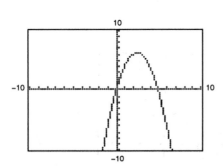

(d)

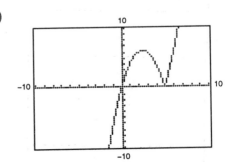

(e) None of these

1—M—Answer: b

12. Use a graphing utility to graph $y = x^3 + 4x$. Use the standard viewing rectangle.

(a)

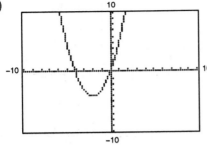

(b)

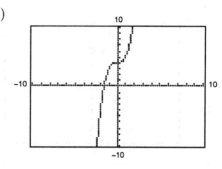

(c)

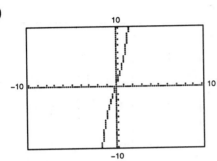

(d)

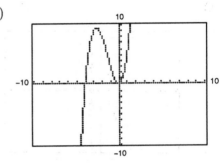

(e) None of these

1—M—Answer: c

13. Use a graphing utility and the specified viewing rectangle to graph
$y = x^4 + 3x^3 - x + 4$.

```
RANGE
Xmin=-5
Xmax=3
Xscl=1
Ymin=-4
Ymax=12
Yscl=2
```

(a)

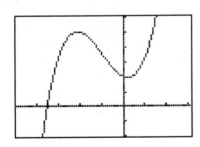

(b)

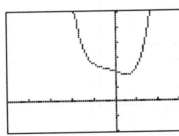

(c)

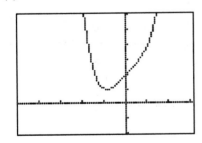

(d)

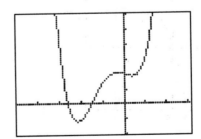

(e) None of these

1—M—Answer: d

14. Use a graphing utility and the specified viewing rectangle to graph $y = -30\sqrt{9-x}$.

```
RANGE
Xmin=-50
Xmax=30
Xscl=10
Ymin=-350
Ymax=50
Yscl=50
```

(a)

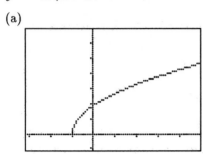

(b)

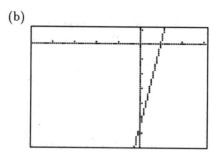

(c)

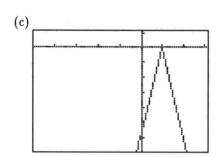

(d)

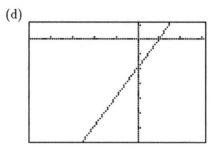

(e) None of these

1—M—Answer: a

15. Use a graphing utility and the specified viewing rectangle to graph $y = \frac{1}{4}(-x^2 - 5x + 3)$.

```
RANGE
Xmin=-12
Xmax=8
Xscl=2
Ymin=-12
Ymax=8
Yscl=2
```

(a)

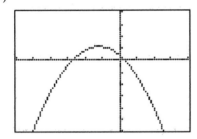

(b)

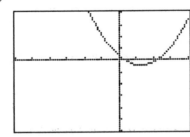

(c)

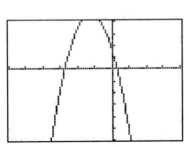

(d)

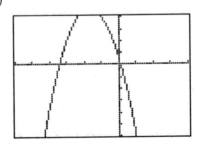

(e) None of these

1—M—Answer: a

16. Use a graphing utility and the specified viewing rectangle to graph
$y = 7 - x + 2x^3$.

1—O—Answer: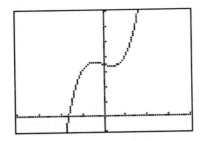

```
RANGE
Xmin=-4
Xmax=4
Xscl=1
Ymin=-2
Ymax=14
Yscl=2
```

17. Use a graphing utility to graph of $y = |2x + 1| - 3$.

(a)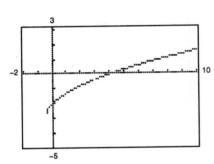

(b)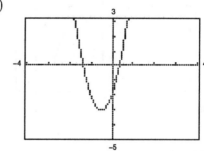

(c)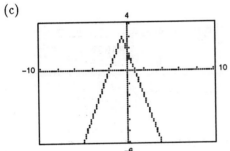

(d)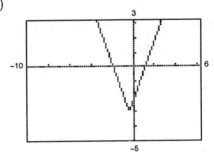

(e) None of these

1—M—Answer: d

18. Use a graphing utility to graph $y = 2x^3 + x^2 + x - 1$.

(a)
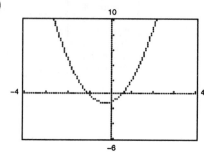

(b)
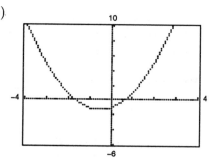

(c)
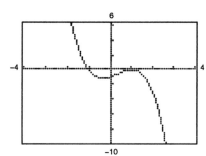

(d)
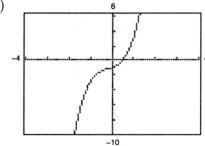

(e) None of these

1—M—Answer: d

19. Which equation(s) must be entered in a graphing utility to obtain the graph of $x^2 + y^2 = 25$?

(a) $y^2 = 25 - x^2$
                    (b) $y = \sqrt{25 - x^2}$
                    (c) $y = \sqrt{25 - x^2}$
$$y = -\sqrt{25 - x^2}$$

(d) $y = \sqrt{x^2 - 25}$
                    (e) None of these
$$y = -\sqrt{x^2 - 25}$$

1—M—Answer: c

20. Which equation(s) must be entered in a graphing utility to obtain the graph of $x^2 + 7y^2 = 49$?

(a) $y^2 = \frac{1}{7}(49 - x^2)$
          (b) $y = \frac{1}{7}\sqrt{49 - x^2}$
          (c) $y = \frac{1}{7}\sqrt{49 - x^2}$
$$y = -\frac{1}{7}\sqrt{49 - x^2}$$

(d) $y = \sqrt{7 - x^2/7}$
                (e) None of these
$$y = -\sqrt{7 - x^2/7}$$

1—M—Answer: d

21. What equation(s) must be entered in a graphing utility to obtain the graph of $2x^2 + 5y^2 = 20$?

1—O—Answer: $y = \sqrt{4 - 2x^2/5}$
$$y = -\sqrt{4 - 2x^2/5}$$

22. Use a graphing utility to graph $x^2 + y^2 = 81$. (Use a square setting.)

(a)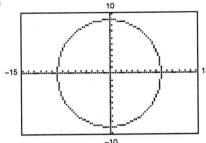

(b)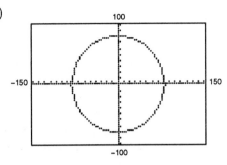

(c)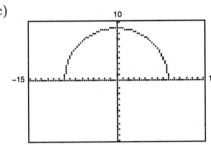

(d)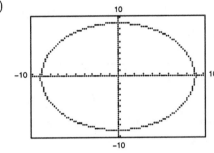

(e) None of these

2—M—Answer: a

23. Use a graphing utility to graph $3x^2 + y^2 = 40$. (Use a square setting.)

(a)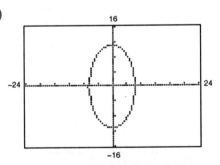

(b)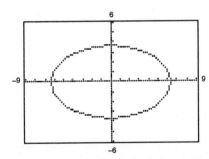

(c)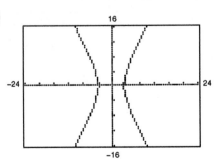

(d)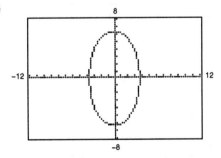

(e) None of these

2—M—Answer: d

24. Use a graphing utility to graph $x^2 + 2y^2 = 16$. (Use a square setting.)

2—O—Answer:

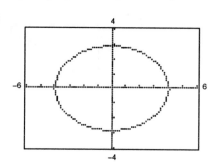

25. Use a graphing utility to approximate the value of y to two decimal places when $x = 0$ for $y = \sqrt{x + 6}$.

(a) 2.48   (b) 2.45   (c) 2.65

(d) −1.10   (e) None of these

2—M—Answer: b

26. Use a graphing utility to approximate the value of y to two decimal places when $x = 0$ for $y = -\sqrt{11 - x^2}$.

(a) 3.32   (b) −2.24   (c) 1.91

(d) −4.12   (e) None of these

2—M—Answer: e

27. The depreciated value y of a certain machine after t years is determined using the model

$y = 35,000 - 5000t, \ 0 \le t \le 5.$

Use a graphing utility to graph this equation over the given interval.

(a)

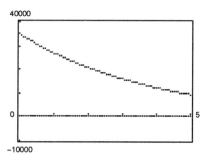

(b)

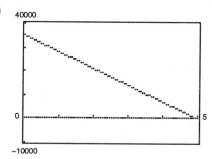

27. —CONTINUED—

(c)

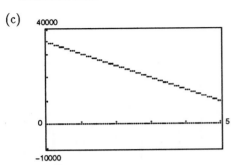

(d)

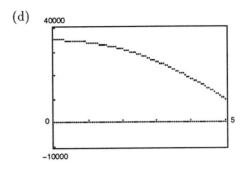

(e) None of these

2—M—Answer: c

28. The table gives the average attendance per professional basketball game in the United States.

Year	1983	1984	1985	1986	1987	1988	1989
Attendance per game	10,220	10,620	11,141	11,893	12,765	13,419	15,088

(Source: *National Basketball Association*)

A model for the average attendance per game between 1983 and 1989 is

$$y = 11x^4 - 252.6x^3 + 2143.1x^2 - 7279.5x + 18716.7,$$

where y is the average attendance per game and x is the year with $x = 3$ corresponding to 1983. Use a graphing utility to estimate the average attendance per game in 1986 according to the model.

(a) 14,902   (b) 12,091   (c) 11,885

(d) 11,463   (e) None of these

2—M—Answer: c

29. The total sales of food contractors in the United States between 1980 and 1990 can be approximated by the model

$$y = \tfrac{1}{2}(87x^2 + 604x + 13,634), \quad 0 \le x \le 10$$

where y is the sales, in millions of dollars, and x is the year with $x = 0$ corresponding to 1980. Graph this equation. (Source: *National Restaurant Association*)

2—O—Answer:

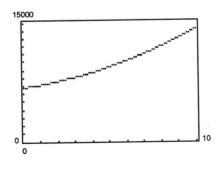

1.2 | Lines in the Plane

1. Determine the slope of the line shown at the right.

    (a) $\frac{2}{3}$ (b) $-\frac{2}{3}$ (c) $\frac{3}{2}$

    (d) $-\frac{3}{2}$ (e) None of these

    1—M—Answer: c

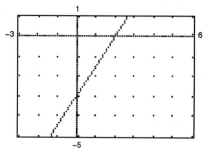

2. Determine the slope of the line shown at the right.

    (a) $-\frac{1}{2}$ (b) $\frac{1}{2}$ (c) 2

    (d) -2 (e) None of these

    1—M—Answer: a

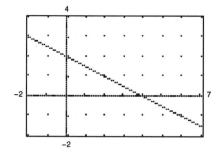

3. Determine the slope of the line that passes through the points $(1, 3)$ and $(-2, -2)$.

    (a) $\frac{3}{5}$ (b) $\frac{1}{3}$ (c) $\frac{5}{3}$

    (d) 1   (e) None of these

    1—M—Answer: c

4. Determine the slope of the line that passes through the points $(-1, 6)$ and $(11, -6)$.

    (a) 1   (b) -1 (c) 0

    (d) $\frac{6}{5}$ (e) None of these

    1—M—Answer: b

5. Determine the slope of the line that passes through the points $(1, 4)$ and $(-1, -2)$.

    1—O—Answer: 3

6. Use the slope to describe the behavior of the line that passes through $(3, 0)$ and $(9, -2)$.

    (a) Rises from left to right   (b) Falls from left to right   (c) Horizontal

    (d) Vertical   (e) None of these

    2—M—Answer: b

7. Use the slope to describe the behavior of the line that passes through $(5, 6)$ and $(-1, 6)$.

   (a) Rises from left to right   (b) Falls from left to right   (c) Horizontal

   (d) Vertical   (e) None of these

   2—M—Answer: c

8. Find an equation of the line that passes through the point $(4, -1)$ and has a slope of $\frac{1}{2}$.

   (a) $y = \frac{1}{2}x - 1$ (b) $y = \frac{1}{2}x + 1$ (c) $y = \frac{1}{2}x + 3$

   (d) $y = \frac{1}{2}x - 3$ (e) None of these

   1—M—Answer: d

9. Find an equation of the line that passes through the point $(1, -1)$ and has a slope of -3.

   (a) $y = -3x - 2$ (b) $y = -3x + 2$ (c) $y = -3x - 1$

   (d) $y = -3x + 4$ (e) None of these

   1—M—Answer: b

10. Find an equation of the line that passes through the points $(1, -3)$ and $(4, 3)$.

    (a) $y = 2x - 5$ (b) $y = -2x - 1$ (c) $y = \frac{3}{2}x + \frac{3}{2}$

    (d) $y = 2x + 5$ (e) None of these

    1—M—Answer: a

11. Find an equation of the line that passes through the points $(4, 2)$ and $(-8, 5)$.

    (a) $y = 4x - 18$ (b) $y = 4x + 4$ (c) $y = -\frac{1}{4}x - 1$

    (d) $y = -\frac{1}{4}x + 6$ (e) None of these

    1—M—Answer: e

12. Which of the following points does **not** lie on the line that contains the point $(7, 7)$ and has a slope $\frac{2}{7}$.

    (a) $\left(4, \frac{43}{7}\right)$ (b) $(0, 5)$ (c) $(-7, 2)$

    (d) $(-14, 1)$ (e) All of these lie on the line.

    2—M—Answer: c

13. Determine which points lie on the line that contains the point $(5, 7)$ with a slope of 0.

    (a) $(5, 0)$ (b) $(0, 7)$ (c) $(7, 5)$

    (d) All of these lie on the line.   (e) None of these lie on the line.

    1—M—Answer: b

14. Determine which points lie on the vertical line that contains the point (5, 1).

  (a) (5, 0) (b) (0, 1) (c) (1, 5)

  (d) All of these points lie on the line. (e) None of these points lie on the line.

  1—M—Answer: a

15. Determine which points lie on the line that contains the point (2, −3) and has a slope of $-\frac{7}{4}$.

  (a) $\left(4, -\frac{13}{2}\right)$ (b) (−2, 4) (c) $\left(0, \frac{1}{2}\right)$

  (d) All of these points lie on the line. (e) None of these points lie on the line.

  2—M—Answer: d

16. Find an equation of the line shown at the right.

  (a) $y = \frac{2}{3}x - \frac{11}{3}$ (b) $y = \frac{4}{5}x + 4$

  (c) $y = -\frac{2}{3}x - 4$ (d) $y = -\frac{4}{5}x - \frac{7}{2}$

  (e) None of these

  2—M—Answer: a

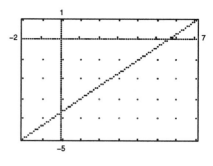

17. Find an equation of the line shown at the right.

  (a) $y = \frac{3}{4}x + 2$ (b) $y = -\frac{1}{3}x + \frac{5}{4}$

  (c) $y = -\frac{1}{2}x + \frac{2}{3}$ (d) $y = -\frac{3}{5}x + \frac{7}{5}$

  (e) None of these

  2—M—Answer: d

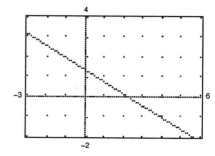

18. Rewrite the equation of the line $2x - 5y = 20$ in slope-intercept form.

  (a) $y = -\frac{5}{2}x + 4$ (b) $y = \frac{5}{2}x - 4$ (c) $y = \frac{2}{5}x - 4$

  (d) $y = -\frac{2}{5}x + 4$ (e) None of these

  1—M—Answer: c

19. Rewrite the equation of the line $x + 7y = 35$ in slope-intercept form.

  (a) $y = \frac{1}{7}x - 5$ (b) $y = -\frac{1}{7}x + 5$ (c) $y = 7x + 5$

  (d) $y = -7x + 5$ (e) None of these

  1—M—Answer: b

20. Describe the graph of $6x - y = 12$.

    (a) Rises from left to right   (b) Falls from left to right   (c) Horizontal

    (d) Vertical   (e) None of these

    2—M—Answer: a

21. Rewrite the equation $y = \frac{1}{4}x + 3$ in general form.

    (a) $4x - y = 12$ (b) $x - 4y = 12$ (c) $x - 4y = -12$

    (d) $x + 4y = 12$ (e) None of these

    1—M—Answer: c

22. Rewrite the equation $y = -\frac{2}{3}x + \frac{1}{6}$ in general form.

    (a) $2x + 3y = 1$ (b) $4x - 3y = 1$ (c) $4x - 6y = 1$

    (d) $2x + 6y = 1$ (e) None of these

    1—M—Answer: e

23. Use a graphing utility to graph the equations $y = x + 1$, $y = 2x + 1$, and $y = \frac{1}{2}x + 1$ on the same viewing rectangle. Adjust the view so that the slopes appear visually correct.

(a)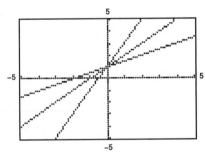

(b)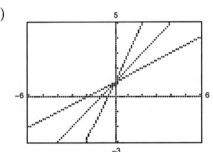

(c)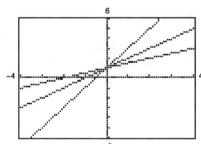

(d)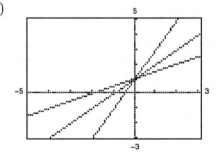

(e) None of these

    1—M—Answer: b

24. Use a graphing utility to graph the equations $y = 2x - 2$ and $y = -\frac{1}{2}x + 1$ on the same viewing rectangle. Adjust the view so that the slopes appear visually correct.

(a)

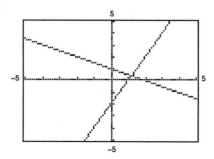

(b)

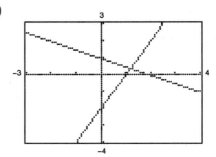

(c)

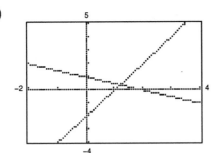

(d)

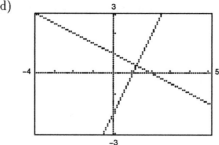

(e) None of these

1—M—Answer: d

25. What is the slope of the line parallel to the line $4x - 2y = 9$?

(a) $\frac{9}{2}$　　　　　　　　(b) $\frac{9}{4}$　　　　　　　　(c) $-\frac{2}{4}$

(d) 2　　　　　　　　(e) None of these

1—M—Answer: d

26. What is the slope of the line parallel to the line $7x - 2y = 12$?

(a) $\frac{7}{2}$　　　　　　　　(b) $-\frac{2}{7}$　　　　　　　　(c) $\frac{12}{7}$

(d) -6　　　　　　　　(e) None of these

1—M—Answer: a

27. What is the slope of the line perpendicular to the line $y = 7$?

(a) 0　　　　　　　　(b) Undefined　　　　　　　　(c) $\frac{1}{7}$

(d) $-\frac{1}{7}$　　　　　　　　(e) None of these

1—M—Answer: b

28. What is the slope of the line perpendicular to the line $3x - 4y = 12$?

(a) Undefined   (b) 0   (c) $\frac{4}{3}$

(d) $-\frac{3}{4}$ (e) None of these

1—M—Answer: e

29. Find an equation of the line that passes through $(3, 10)$ parallel to the line $x - 3y = 1$.

(a) $y = \frac{1}{3}x + 9$ (b) $y = 3x + 1$ (c) $y = -3x + 19$

(d) $y = -\frac{1}{3}x + 11$ (e) None of these

2—M—Answer: a

30. Find an equation of the line that passes through $(-1, -3)$ parallel to the line $2x + y = 19$.

(a) $y = -2x - 3$ (b) $y = -2x - 5$ (c) $y = 2x - 1$

(d) $y = -\frac{1}{2}x - \frac{7}{2}$ (e) None of these

2—M—Answer: b

31. Find an equation of the line that passes through $(6, 2)$ perpendicular to the line $3x + 2y = 2$.

(a) $y = -\frac{3}{2}x + 11$ (b) $y = -\frac{2}{3}x + 6$ (c) $y = \frac{3}{2}x - 7$

(d) $y = \frac{2}{3}x - 2$ (e) None of these

2—M—Answer: d

32. Find an equation of the line that passes through $(8, 17)$ perpendicular to the line $x + 2y = 2$.

2—O—Answer: $y = 2x + 1$

33. Which viewing rectangle should be used to graph $y = \frac{1}{3}x + 2$ and $y = -3x - 1$ so that the lines appear perpendicular?

(a)
```
RANGE
Xmin=-7
Xmax=2
Xscl=1
Ymin=-2
Ymax=4
Yscl=1
```

(b)
```
RANGE
Xmin=-9
Xmax=3
Xscl=1
Ymin=-3
Ymax=5
Yscl=1
```

(c)
```
RANGE
Xmin=-9
Xmax=6
Xscl=1
Ymin=-5
Ymax=5
Yscl=1
```

(d) All of these   (e) None of these

2—M—Answer: d

34. Which viewing rectangle should be used to graph $3x - 4y = -4$ and $4x + 3y = -3$ so that the lines appear perpendicular?

(a)
```
RANGE
Xmin=-4
Xmax=4
Xscl=1
Ymin=-3
Ymax=3
Yscl=1
```

(b)
```
RANGE
Xmin=-4
Xmax=4
Xscl=1
Ymin=-4
Ymax=4
Yscl=1
```

(c)
```
RANGE
Xmin=-5
Xmax=4
Xscl=1
Ymin=-3
Ymax=3
Yscl=1
```

(d) All of these

(e) None of these

2—M—Answer: c

35. Graph the description. An employee is paid \$14.00 per hour plus \$1.50 for each unit produced per hour.

(a) 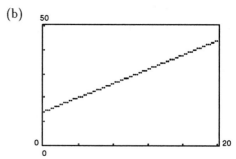   (b)

(c)   (d)

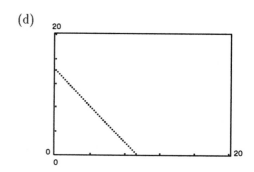

(e) None of these

2—M—Answer: b

36. Graph the description. You buy a car for \$16,000. Each year the car depreciates \$1200.

2—O—Answer:

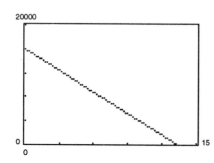

37. In 1990, a company had a profit of $1.3 million. In 1992, the company had a profit of $1.2 million. Write a linear equation giving the profit P, in millions of dollars, in terms of the year, t. Let $t = 0$ represent 1990.

(a) $P = -0.1t + 1.3$ (b) $P = -0.01t + 1.3$ (c) $P = -0.05t + 1.3$

(d) $P = -0.2t + 1.3$ (e) None of these

1—M—Answer: c

38. The cost of parts on your automobile repair bill was $148. The cost for labor was $25 per hour. Write a linear equation giving the total cost C, in terms of t, the number of hours.

1—O—Answer: $C = 148 + 25t$

39. The radio advertising expenditures in the United States was about $3700 million in 1980 and $7800 million in 1988. Predict the expenditures in 1996, assuming the expenditures follow a linear growth pattern. (Source: *McCann-Erickson, Inc.*)

(a) $15,600 million   (b) $11,900 million   (c) $11,500 million

(d) $10,400 million   (e) None of these

2—M—Answer: b

40. Your salary was $18,000 in 1983 and $27,900 in 1992. If your salary follows a linear growth pattern, what will it be in 1995?

(a) $29,300   (b) $29,900   (c) $31,200

(d) $37,200   (e) None of these

2—M—Answer: c

1.3 Functions

1. Given A $= \{-2, -1, 0, 1\}$ and B $= \{1, 2, 3\}$, determine which of the sets of ordered pairs represents a function from A to B.

(a) $\{(-2, 1), (-1, 1), (0, 1), (1, 1)\}$ (b) $\{(-2, 1), (-2, 2), (-2, 3)\}$

(c) $\{(-2, 1), (-1, 2), (-1, 3)\}$ (d) All of these

(e) None of these

1—M—Answer: a

2. Given A $= \{-1, 0, 1, 2\}$ and B $= \{1, 2, 3\}$, determine which of the sets of ordered pairs represents a function from A to B.

(a) $\{(-1, 1), (0, 2), (1, 2), (2, 3)\}$ (b) $\{(-1, 2), (0, 1), (2, 3)\}$

(c) $\{(-1, 2), (0, 2), (1, 3), (2, 3)\}$ (d) All of these

(e) None of these

1—M—Answer: d

3. Given A = {1, 2, 3} and B = {−2, −1, 0, 1}, determine which of the sets of ordered pairs represents a function from A to B.

    (a) {(1, −2), (2, −2), (3, −1), (2, 0), (2, 1)}   (b) {(1, −2), (2, −1), (2, 0), (3, 1)}

    (c) {(1, −2), (2, −1), (3, 0), (1, 1)}   (d) All of these

    (e) None of these

    1—M—Answer: e

4. Which of the following does not represent y as a function of x?

    (a) $3x^2 + y = 9$ (b) $x + 4y = 22$ (c) $x + 2y^2 = 6$

    (d) $y + 5x^2 = 2$ (e) $9x + 3 = 2y$

    1—M—Answer: c

5. Which of the following does not represent y as a function of x?

    (a) $x^2 + y^2 = 16$ (b) $x^2 - 10y = 1$ (c) $x + y = 4$

    (d) $y + 7x = 4$ (e) $8y - 4x^2 = 3$

    1—M—Answer: a

6. Which of the following does not represent y as a function of x?

    (a)

    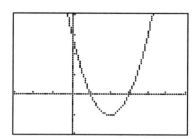

    (b)

    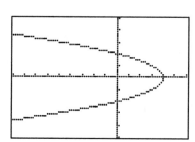

    (c)

    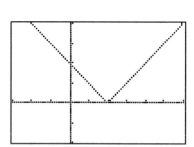

    (d)

    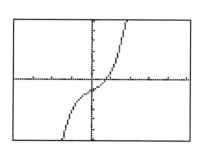

    (e) None of these

    1—M—Answer: b

7. Which of the following does not represent y as a function of x?

(a)

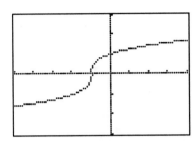

(b)

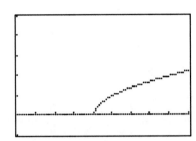

(c)

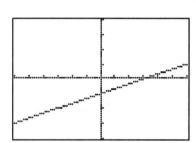

(d)

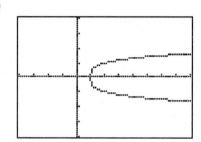

(e) None of these

1—M—Answer: d

8. Given $f(x) = 9x^2 + 1$, find $f(2)$.

(a) 19   (b) 37   (c) 12

(d) 18   (e) None of these

1—M—Answer: b

9. Given $f(x) = 6 - 2x^2$, find $f(-3)$.

(a) 12   (b) 24   (c) −12

(d) −24   (e) None of these

1—M—Answer: c

10. Given $f(x) = \dfrac{2}{x-3}$, find $f(-1)$.

(a) $\dfrac{1}{2}$ (b) −1   (c) 1

(d) $-\dfrac{2}{3}$ (e) None of these

1—M—Answer: e

11. Given $f(x) = \sqrt{x^2 + 2}$, find $f(-4)$.

1—O—Answer: $\sqrt{18}$

12. Given $f(x) = \begin{cases} x^2 + 1, & x < 4 \\ 6x - 7, & x \geq 4 \end{cases}$, find $f(-2)$.

    (a) -19 (b) 5   (c) 4

    (d) -5 (e) None of these

    1—M—Answer: b

13. Given $f(x) = \begin{cases} \sqrt{-x}, & x \leq 0 \\ 6x, & x > 0 \end{cases}$, find $f(4)$.

    (a) 2   (b) -2 (c) 10

    (d) 24   (e) None of these

    1—M—Answer: d

14. Given $f(x) = \begin{cases} x - 19, & x < -5 \\ |x + 3|, & x \geq -5 \end{cases}$, find $f(-4)$.

    (a) -15 (b) 1   (c) -1

    (d) -23 (e) None of these

    1—M—Answer: b

15. Given $f(x) = \begin{cases} |x - 2|, & x \leq 1 \\ |2x - 5|, & x > 1 \end{cases}$, find $f(1)$.

    (a) 1   (b) -1 (c) 3

    (d) -3 (e) None of these

    1—M—Answer: a

16. Find the domain of the function $\{ (-2, 1), (-1, 0), (0, -3), (1, -8) \}$.

    (a) $[-2, 1]$ (b) $(-\infty, \infty)$ (c) $\{-2, -1, 0, 1\}$

    (d) $\{1, 0, -3, -8\}$ (e) $\{-8, -3, -2, -1, 0, 1\}$

    1—M—Answer: c

17. Find the domain of the function $\{ (1, 1), (2, 4), (3, 9)\}$.

    (a) $[1, 9]$ (b) $\{1, 2, 3, 4, 9\}$ (c) $\{1, 4, 9\}$

    (d) $\{1, 2, 3\}$ (e) None of these

    1—M—Answer: d

18. Find the domain of the function: $f(x) = \dfrac{9}{x}$

    (a) $(9, \infty)$ (b) $(-\infty, \infty)$ (c) All real numbers $x \neq 0$

    (d) All real numbers $x \neq 9$ (e) None of these

    1—M—Answer: c

19. Find the domain of the function: $f(x) = \sqrt{5-x}$

    (a) $(-\infty, 5]$ (b) $(-\infty, 5)$ (c) $[-5, \infty)$

    (d) $(-5, \infty)$ (e) None of these

1—M—Answer: a

20. Find the domain of the function: $f(x) = \dfrac{1}{\sqrt{x^2+1}}$

    (a) $(-\infty, -1), (-1, 1), (1, \infty)$ (b) $(-\infty, 0), (0, \infty)$ (c) $(-\infty, \infty)$

    (d) $(-\infty, -1), (-1, \infty)$ (e) None of these

1—M—Answer: c

21. Find the domain of the function: $f(x) = \dfrac{1}{x^2-3x+2}$

    (a) $(-\infty, -2), (-2, 1), (1, \infty)$ (b) $(-\infty, 1), (1, 2), (2, \infty)$ (c) $(-\infty, \infty)$

    (d) $\left(-\infty, \dfrac{1}{2}\right), \left(\dfrac{1}{2}, \infty\right)$ (e) None of these

2—M—Answer: b

22. Use a function key on a calculator to evaluate 1.9^3.

    (a) 6.859   (b) 5.7   (c) 3.61

    (d) 7.999   (e) None of these

1—M—Answer: a

23. Use a function key on a calculator to evaluate $\sqrt[3]{36}$.

    (a) 6   (b) 12   (c) 2.94

    (d) 3.30   (e) 3.98

1—M—Answer: d

24. Use a function key on a calculator to evaluate $\dfrac{1}{4.91}$.

    (a) 0.228   (b) 0.332   (c) 0.324

    (d) 2.216   (e) 0.204

1—M—Answer: e

25. If $f(x) = \dfrac{1}{2}x$, find $\dfrac{f(x+h) - f(x)}{h}$.

    (a) 2   (b) $\dfrac{1}{2}$ (c) $\dfrac{x + \frac{1}{2}h}{h}$

    (d) 1   (e) None of these

2—M—Answer: b

26. If $f(x) = x^2$, find $\dfrac{-f(3) + f(x - 3)}{x}$.

(a) $\dfrac{9}{x}$

(b) $x^2 + 6x + 9$

(c) $x - 6$

(d) $\dfrac{18 + x}{x}$

(e) None of these

2—M—Answer: c

27. If $f(x) = \dfrac{1}{x}$, find $\dfrac{f(x) - f\left(\frac{1}{h}\right)}{h}$.

(a) $\dfrac{1}{h}\left(\dfrac{1}{x} - \dfrac{1}{h}\right)$

(b) $\dfrac{x - h}{h}$

(c) $\dfrac{h}{x - h}$

(d) $\dfrac{1}{hx} - 1$

(e) None of these

2—M—Answer: d

28. Which of the functions fits the data?

x	-4	-2	0	2	4	6
y	8	4	0	4	8	12

(a) $f(x) = 2|x|$

(b) $f(x) = 2x^2$

(c) $f(x) = 2x$

(d) $f(x) = 2\sqrt{x}$

(e) None of these

1—M—Answer: a

29. Which of the functions fits the data?

x	-2	0	1	3	5	10
y	-6	0	3	9	15	30

(a) $f(x) = x^3$

(b) $f(x) = \sqrt[3]{x}$

(c) $f(x) = |x|^3$

(d) $f(x) = 3x$

(e) None of these

1—M—Answer: d

30. Which of the functions fits the data?

x	-4	-2	0	2	8
y	16	4	0	4	64

(a) $f(x) = 4x$

(b) $f(x) = x^2$

(c) $f(x) = \frac{1}{2}x^2$

(d) $f(x) = 2|x|$

(e) None of these

1—M—Answer: b

31. An open box is made from a rectangular piece of material by cutting equal squares from each corner and turning up the sides. Write the volume of the box as a function of x if the material is 24 inches by 16 inches.

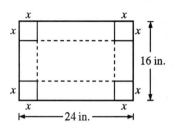

(a) $V = (24 - x)(16 - x)$ (b) $V = x(24 - x)(16 - x)$

(c) $V = x(24 - 2x)(16 - 2x)$ (d) $V = (24 - 2x)(16 - 2x)$

(e) None of these

1—M—Answer: c

32. An open box is made from a rectangular piece of material by cutting equal squares from each corner and turning up the sides. Write the volume of the box as a function of x if the material is 18 inches by 12 inches.

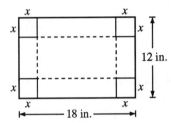

1—O—Answer: $V = x(12 - 2x)(18 - 2x)$

33. The expenditures for personal flowers, seeds, and potted plants, in billions of dollars, in the United States from 1980 to 1990 can be modeled by

$$f(x) = \begin{cases} \frac{1}{10}(3x + 40), & 0 \le t \le 6 \\ \frac{1}{20}(11x + 63), & 7 \le t \le 10 \end{cases}$$

where t is the year with $t = 0$ corresponding to 1980. Use this model to find the expenditures in 1985. (Source: *U.S. Bureau of Economic Analysis*)

1—O—Answer: $5.5 billion

34. You invest $12,000 to start a business. Each unit costs $3.40 and is sold for $5.60. Let x be the number of units produced and sold. Write the profit P as a function of x. ($P = $ Revenue $-$ Cost)

(a) $P = 9.00x + 12,000$ (b) $P = 9.00x - 12,000$ (c) $P = 2.20x + 12,000$

(d) $P = 2.20x - 12,000$ (e) None of these

2—M—Answer: d

1.4 Graphs of Functions

1. Use a graphing utility to graph the function $f(x) = 9 - x^2$ using the specified viewing rectangle.

```
RANGE
Xmin=-6
Xmax=6
Xscl=1
Ymin=-4
Ymax=12
Yscl=2
```

(a)

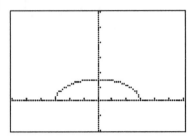

(b)

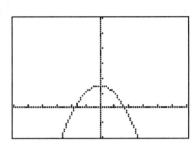

(c)

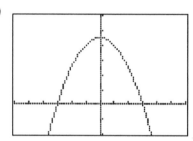

(d)

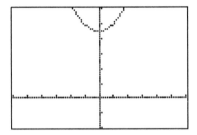

(e) None of these

1—M—Answer: c

2. Use a graphing utility to graph the function $f(x) = \dfrac{1}{x + 2}$ using the specified viewing rectangle.

```
RANGE
Xmin=-8
Xmax=4
Xscl=1
Ymin=-4
Ymax=4
Yscl=1
```

(a)

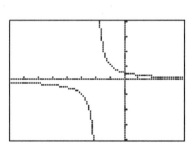

(b)

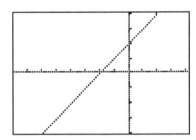

2. —CONTINUED—

(c)

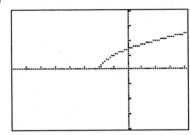

(d)

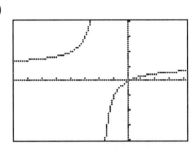

(e) None of these

1—M—Answer: a

3. Find the domain of the function shown at the right.

(a) $(-\infty, \infty)$ (b) $(-\infty, 3]$ (c) $(3, \infty)$

(d) $[3, \infty)$ (e) None of these

1—M—Answer: d

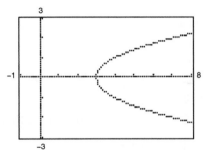

4. Find the domain of the function shown at the right.

(a) $(-3, 3)$ (b) $(-\infty, \infty)$ (c) $(-2, \infty)$

(d) $(-3, 5)$ (e) None of these

1—M—Answer: b

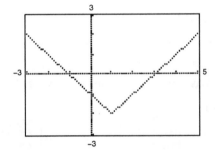

5. Find the range of the function shown at the right.

(a) $(-\infty, \infty)$ (b) $(-8, 1)$ (c) $[-3, \infty)$

(d) $[-1, 5]$ (e) None of these

1—M—Answer: e

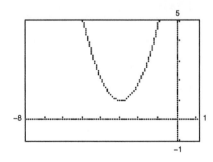

6. Find the range of the function shown at the right.

 1—O—Answer: $[0, \infty)$

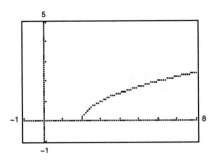

7. Use the graph shown at the right to find $f(-2)$.

 (a) 2   (b) −2   (c) 3

 (d) −6   (e) None of these

 1—M—Answer: a

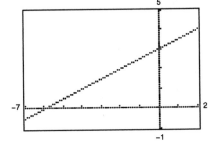

8. Use the graph shown at the right to find $f(3)$.

 (a) 3   (b) −3   (c) −3 and 3

 (d) 0   (e) None of these

 1—M—Answer: d

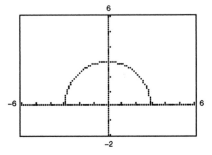

9. Which viewing rectangle shows the most complete graph of the function $f(x) = x^2 + x - 3$.

(a)
```
RANGE
Xmin=-6
Xmax=6
Xscl=1
Ymin=-1
Ymax=7
Yscl=1
```

(b)
```
RANGE
Xmin=0
Xmax=6
Xscl=1
Ymin=-4
Ymax=4
Yscl=1
```

(c)
```
RANGE
Xmin=-6
Xmax=6
Xscl=1
Ymin=-4
Ymax=4
Yscl=1
```

(d)
```
RANGE
Xmin=-9
Xmax=0
Xscl=1
Ymin=-3
Ymax=3
Yscl=1
```

(e) None of these

1—M—Answer: c

10. Which viewing rectangle shows the most complete graph of the function $f(x) = 5x\sqrt{100 - x^2}$.

(a)
```
RANGE
Xmin=-20
Xmax=20
Xscl=4
Ymin=-100
Ymax=100
Yscl=10
```

(b)
```
RANGE
Xmin=-100
Xmax=100
Xscl=10
Ymin=-100
Ymax=100
Yscl=100
```

(c)
```
RANGE
Xmin=-100
Xmax=100
Xscl=10
Ymin=-20
Ymax=20
Yscl=4
```

(d)
```
RANGE
Xmin=-20
Xmax=20
Xscl=4
Ymin=-300
Ymax=300
Yscl=50
```

(e) None of these

1—M—Answer: d

11. Use the vertical line test to determine which of the following represents y as a function of x.

(a)
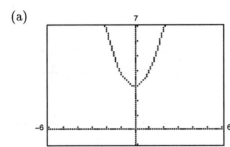

(b)
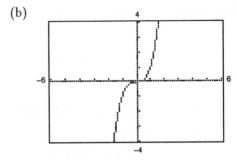

(c)
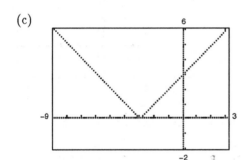

(d) All of these are functions of x.

(e) None of these are functions of x.

1—M—Answer: d

12. Use the vertical line test to determine which of the following represents y as a function of x.

(a)

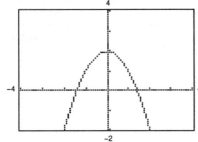

(b)

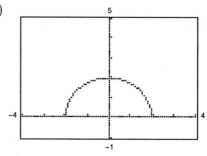

(c)

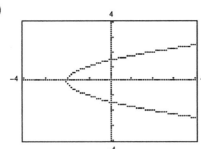

(d) Both a and c

(e) Both a and b

1—M—Answer: e

13. Determine the open intervals in which the function is increasing, decreasing, or constant.

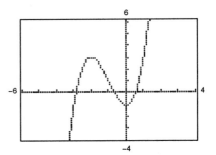

(a) Increasing on $(-\infty,\ \infty)$

(b) Increasing on $(-\infty,\ 0)$
Decreasing on $(0,\ \infty)$

(c) Increasing on $(-\infty,\ -2)$, $(0,\ \infty)$
Decreasing on $(-2,\ 0)$

(d) Increasing on $(-\infty,\ 3)$
Decreasing on $(3,\ \infty)$

(e) None of these

1—M—Answer: c

14. Determine the open intervals in which the function is increasing, decreasing, or constant.

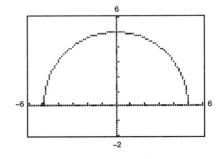

(a) Increasing on $(-5,\ 5)$

(b) Increasing on $(-\infty,\ 0)$
Decreasing on $(0,\ \infty)$

(c) Increasing on $(0,\ 6)$

(d) Increasing on $(-\infty,\ 6)$
Decreasing on $(6,\ \infty)$

(e) None of these

1—M—Answer: e

15. Determine the open interval in which the function is increasing, decreasing, or constant.

1—O—Answer: Increasing on $\left(-\infty,\ -\frac{1}{2}\right)$

Decreasing on $\left(-\frac{1}{2},\ \infty\right)$

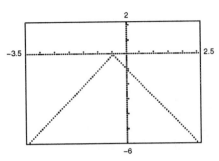

16. Use a graphing utility to approximate any relative minimum or relative maximum of $f(x) = -2x^2 + x - 3$.

    (a) Relative maximum at $(0.24, -2.88)$

    (b) Relative minimum at $(-0.22, -3.12)$

    (c) Relative maximum at $(0, -3)$

    (d) Relative minimum at $(0, -3)$

    (e) None of these

    2—M—Answer: a

17. Use a graphing utility to approximate any relative minimum or relative maximum of $f(x) = x^3 - x$.

    (a) Relative maximum at $(-0.58, -0.38)$

    (b) Relative maximum at $(-0.58, 0.38)$
        Relative minimum at $(0.58, -0.38)$

    (c) Relative maximum at $(0.58, -0.38)$
        Relative minimum at $(-0.58, 0.38)$

    (d) No relative minimum or relative maximum

    (e) None of these

    2—M—Answer: b

18. Use a graphing utility to approximate any relative minimum or relative maximum of $f(x) = x^5 + x + 1$.

    2—O—Answer: No relative minimum or relative maximum

19. The perimeter of a rectangle is 12 meters. Use a graphing utility to approximate the maximum area of the rectangle.

    (a) 3 square meters   (b) 6 square meters   (c) 9 square meters

    (d) 12 square meters   (e) None of these

    2—M—Answer: c

20. The perimeter of a rectangle is 36 feet. Use a graphing utility to approximate the dimensions of the rectangle that yields a maximum area.

    (a) 6 ft × 6 ft   (b) 9 ft × 9 ft   (c) 18 ft × 3 ft

    (d) 18 ft × 9 ft   (e) None of these

    2—M—Answer: b

21. Use a graphing utility to graph: $f(x) = \begin{cases} 2x + 1, & x \leq 1 \\ x^2, & x > 1 \end{cases}$

(a)

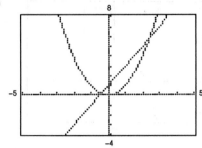

(b)

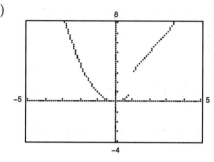

(c)

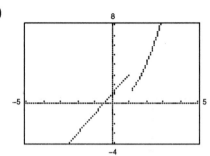

(d)

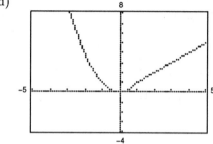

(e) None of these

1—M—Answer: c

22. Use a graphing utility to graph: $f(x) = \begin{cases} -x^2 + 2, & x \leq 0 \\ x + 2, & x > 0 \end{cases}$

(a)

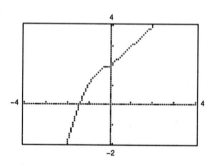

(b)

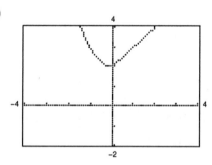

22. —CONTINUED

(c)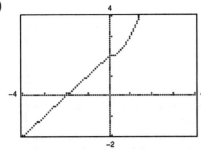

(d)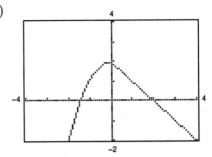

(e) None of these

1—M—Answer: a

23. Match the function with the graph.

(a) $f(x) = \begin{cases} x - 1, & x \le 2 \\ -2x + 4, & x > 2 \end{cases}$

(b) $f(x) = \begin{cases} x - 1, & x \le 2 \\ -\frac{1}{2}x + 2, & x > 2 \end{cases}$

(c) $f(x) = \begin{cases} -x + 1, & x \le 2 \\ x + 4, & x > 2 \end{cases}$

(d) $f(x) = \begin{cases} -x - 1, & x \le 2 \\ -2x + 8, & x > 2 \end{cases}$

(e) None of these

1—M—Answer: b

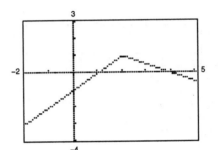

24. Find the compound function graphed at the right.

1—O—Answer: $f(x) = \begin{cases} x^2, & x \le 1 \\ 1, & x > 1 \end{cases}$

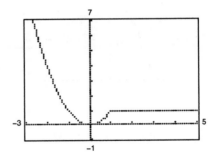

25. Use a graphing utility to graph the function $f(x) = [[x + 2]]$.

(a)

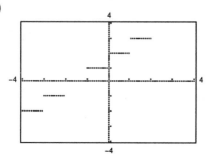

(b)

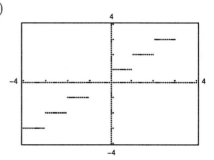

(c)

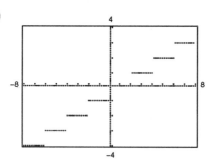

(d)

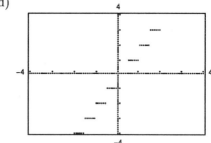

(e) None of these

1—M—Answer: a

26. Use a graphing utility to graph the function $f(x) = 4 + [[x]]$.

1—O—Answer:

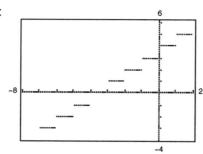

27. Find the domain of $f(x) = [[x - 5]]$.

(a) All real numbers   (b) All integers   (c) All positive integers

(d) All real numbers greater than 5   (e) None of these

1—M—Answer: a

28. Find the range of $f(x) = [[x - 5]]$.

(a) All real numbers   (b) All integers   (c) All positive integers

(d) All real numbers greater than 5   (e) None of these

1—M—Answer: b

29. Determine which of the following are graphs of odd functions.

(a)

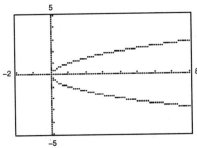

(b)

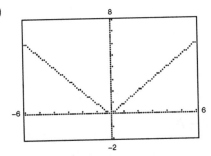

(c)

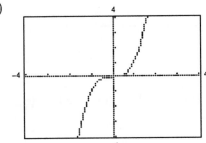

(d) All of these

(e) None of these

1—M—Answer: c

30. Determine which of the following are graphs of even functions.

(a)

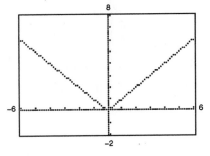

(b)

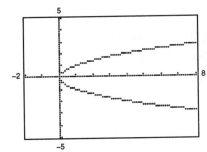

(c)

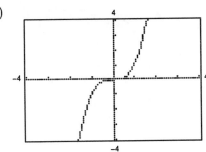

(d) All of these

(e) None of these

1—M—Answer: a

31. Is the following function even or odd? $f(x) = 2x^3 + 3x^2$

    (a) Even   (b) Odd   (c) Both   (d) Neither

    1—M—Answer: d

32. Is the following function even or odd? $f(x) = 4x^3 + 3x$

    (a) Even   (b) Odd   (c) Both   (d) Neither

    1—M—Answer: b

33. Use a graphing utility to determine the interval(s) on the real axis for which $f(x) \geq 0$ for $f(x) = 9 - x^2$.

    (a) $(-\infty, \infty)$ (b) $[-3, 3]$ (c) $[0, 3]$

    (d) $(-\infty, -3), (3, \infty)$ (e) None of these

    1—M—Answer: b

34. Use a graphing utility to determine the interval(s) on the real axis for which $f(x) \geq 0$ for $f(x) = \sqrt{x - 9}$.

    (a) $(-\infty, \infty)$ (b) $[-9, 9]$ (c) $[-3, 3]$

    (d) $[9, \infty)$ (e) None of these

    1—M—Answer: d

35. Write the height h of the rectangle as a function of x.

    (a) $h(x) = 2x + 3 - x^2$ (b) $h(x) = x^2 - 2x + 3$

    (c) $h(x) = x^2 - 2x - 3$ (d) $h(x) = 2x + 3 + x^2$

    (e) None of these

    2—M—Answer: a

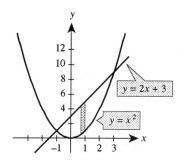

36. Write the height h of the rectangle as a function of x.

    (a) $h(x) = -x^2 + 4x + 1 - \frac{2}{3}x - \frac{2}{3}$

        $= -x^2 + \frac{10}{3}x + \frac{1}{3}$

    (b) $h(x) = -x^2 + 4x + 1 + \frac{2}{3}x + \frac{2}{3}$

        $= -x^2 + \frac{14}{3}x + \frac{5}{3}$

    (c) $h(x) = \frac{2}{3}x + \frac{2}{3} - x^2 - 4x - 1$

        $= -x^2 - \frac{10}{3}x - \frac{1}{2}$

    (d) $h(x) = \frac{2}{3}x + \frac{2}{3} + x^2 - 4x + 1$

        $= x^2 - \frac{10}{3} + \frac{5}{3}$

    (e) None of these

    2—M—Answer: a

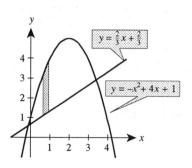

1.5 | Shifting, Reflecting, and Stretching Graphs

1. Describe the transformation of the graph of $f(x) = x^2$ for the graph of $g(x) = (x + 9)^2$.

   (a) Vertical shift 9 units up   (b) Vertical shift 9 units down

   (c) Horizontal shift 9 units to the right   (d) Horizontal shift 9 units to the left

   (e) None of these

   1—M—Answer: d

2. Describe the transformation of the graph of $f(x) = |x|$ for the graph of $g(x) = |x| - 20$.

   (a) Vertical shift 20 units up   (b) Vertical shift 20 units down

   (c) Horizontal shift 20 units to the right   (d) Horizontal shift 20 units to the left

   (e) None of these

   1—M—Answer: b

3. Describe the transformation of the graph of $f(x) = \sqrt{x}$ for the graph of $g(x) = \sqrt{x - 5}$.

   (a) Vertical shift 5 units up   (b) Vertical shift 5 units down

   (c) Horizontal shift 5 units to the right   (d) Horizontal shift 5 units to the left

   (e) None of these

   1—M—Answer: c

4. Describe the transformation of the graph of $f(x) = x^3$ for the graph of $g(x) = 7 + x^3$.

   (a) Vertical shift 7 units up   (b) Vertical shift 7 units down

   (c) Horizontal shift 7 units to the right   (d) Horizontal shift 7 units to the left

   (e) None of these

   1—M—Answer: a

5. The graph at the right is a transformation of the graph of $f(x) = x^2$. Find an equation for the function.

   (a) $g(x) = (x - 3)^2$ (b) $g(x) = x^2 + 3$

   (c) $g(x) = (x + 3)^2$ (d) $g(x) = x^2 - 3$

   (e) None of these

   1—M—Answer: c

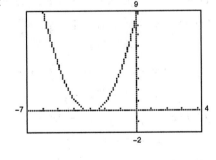

6. The graph at the right is a transformation of the graph of $f(x) = \sqrt{x}$. Find an equation for the function.

   (a) $g(x) = \sqrt{x} - 1$ (b) $g(x) = \sqrt{x} + 1$

   (c) $g(x) = \sqrt{x - 1}$ (d) $g(x) = \sqrt{x + 1}$

   (e) None of these

   1—M—Answer: a

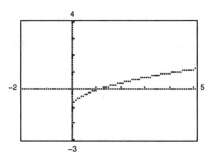

7. The graph at the right is a transformation of the graph of $f(x) = x^3$. Find an equation for the function.

   (a) $g(x) = x^3 + 3$ (b) $g(x) = (x + 3)^3$

   (c) $g(x) = x^3 - 3$ (d) $g(x) = (x - 3)^3$

   (e) None of these

   1—M—Answer: d

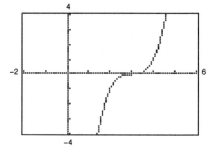

8. The graph at the right is a transformation of the graph of $f(x) = |x|$. Find an equation for the function.

   (a) $g(x) = |x + 4|$ (b) $g(x) = |x| + 4$

   (c) $g(x) = |x| - 4$ (d) $g(x) = |x - 4|$

   (e) None of these

   1—M—Answer: b

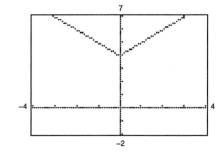

9. Graph $g(x) = |x + 2|$ using a transformation of the graph of $f(x) = |x|$.

(a)
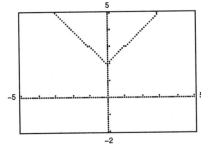

(b)
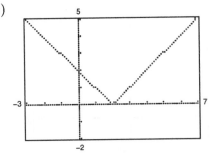

(c)
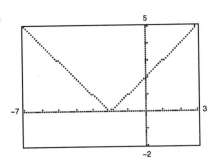

(d)
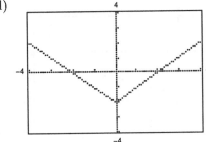

(e) None of these

1—M—Answer: c

10. Graph $g(x) = (x - 1)^2$ using a transformation of the graph of $f(x) = x^2$.

(a)
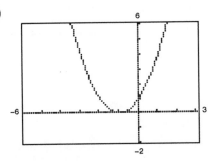

(b)
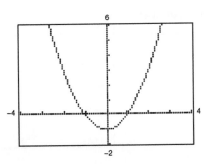

(c)
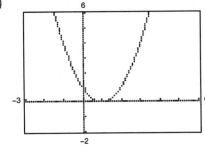

(d)
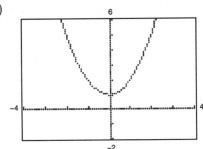

(e) None of these

1—M—Answer: c

11. Graph $g(x) = 3 + \sqrt{x}$ using a transformation of the graph of $f(x) = \sqrt{x}$.

(a)

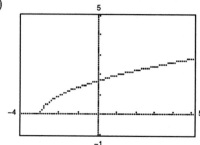

(b)

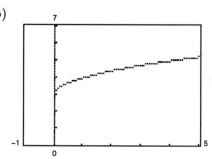

(c)

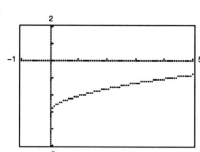

(d)

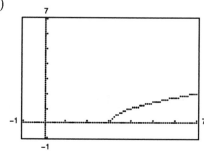

(e) None of these

1—M—Answer: b

12. Graph $g(x) = \sqrt[3]{x+4}$ using a transformation of the graph of $f(x) = \sqrt[3]{x}$.

1—O—Answer:

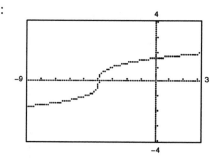

13. Describe the transformation of the graph of $f(x) = |x|$ for the graph of $g(x) = -|x|$.

(a) Reflection in the x-axis   (b) Reflection in the y-axis

(c) Horizontal shift 1 unit to the right   (d) Vertical shift 1 unit down

(e) None of these

1—M—Answer: a

14. Describe the transformation of the graph of $f(x) = x^6$ for the graph of $g(x) = (-x)^6$.

    (a) Reflection in the x-axis   (b) Reflection in the y-axis

    (c) Horizontal shift 1 unit to the right   (d) Vertical shift 1 unit down

    (e) None of these

    1—M—Answer: b

15. The graph at the right is a transformation of the graph of $f(x) = x^3$. Find the equation for the function.

    1—O—Answer: $g(x) = -x^3$

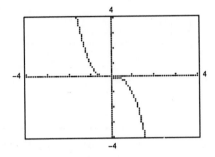

16. The graph at the right is a transformation of the graph of $f(x) = x^4$. Find the equation for the function.

    1—O—Answer: $g(x) = (-x)^4$

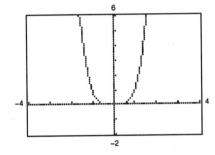

17. Graph $g(x) = (-x)^2$ using a transformation of the graph of $f(x) = x^2$.

    (a)

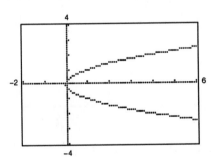

    (b)

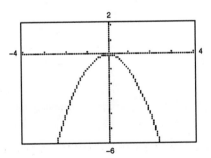

17. —CONTINUED—

(c)

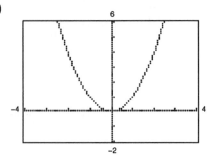

(d)

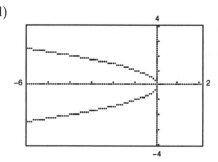

(e) None of these

1—M—Answer: c

18. Graph $g(x) = -\sqrt{x}$ using a transformation of the graph of $f(x) = \sqrt{x}$.

(a)

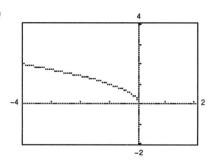

(b)

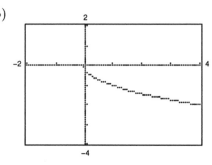

(c)

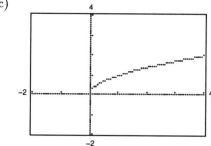

(d)

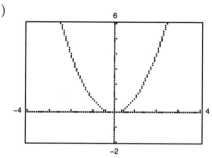

(e) None of these

1—M—Answer: b

19. Which sequence of transformations will yield the graph of $g(x) = (x + 1)^2 + 10$ from the graph of $f(x) = x^2$?

(a) Horizontal shift 10 units to the right
Vertical shift 1 unit up

(b) Horizontal shift 1 unit to the left
Vertical shift 10 units up

(c) Horizontal shift 1 unit to the right
Vertical shift 10 units up

(d) Horizontal shift 10 units to the left
Vertical shift 1 units up

1—M—Answer: b

20. Which sequence of transformations will yield the graph of $g(x) = -|x + 9|$ from the graph of $f(x) = |x|$?

(a) Reflection in the x axis
   Horizontal shift 9 units to the left

(b) Reflection in the y-axis
   Horizontal shift 9 units to the left

(c) Reflection in the x-axis
   Horizontal shift 9 units to the right

(d) Reflection in the y-axis
   Horizontal shift 9 units to the right

1—M—Answer: a

21. What sequence of transformations will yield the graph of $g(x) = \sqrt[4]{x - 3} + 2$ from the graph of $f(x) = \sqrt[4]{x}$?

1—O—Answer: Horizontal shift 3 units to the right
   Vertical shift 2 units up

22. A function is a reflection in the y-axis and a vertical shift 5 units up of the graph of $f(x) = |x|$. Write an equation for the function.

(a) $g(x) = |x| + 5$

(b) $g(x) = -|x| + 5$

(c) $g(x) = |-x| + 5$

(d) $g(x) = -|x| - 5$

(e) None of these

1—M—Answer: c

23. The graph at the right is a transformation of the graph of $f(x) = x^2$. Find an equation for the function.

(a) $g(x) = (x + 3)^2 + 1$

(b) $g(x) = (x + 1)^2 - 3$

(c) $g(x) = (x - 3)^2 + 1$

(d) $g(x) = (x + 1)^2 + 3$

(e) None of these

1—M—Answer: e

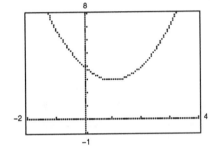

24. The graph at the right is a transformation of the graph of $f(x) = \sqrt{x}$. Find an equation for the function.

(a) $g(x) = \sqrt{-x} + 2$

(b) $g(x) = \sqrt{-x + 2}$

(c) $g(x) = -\sqrt{x} + 2$

(d) $g(x) = -\sqrt{x - 2}$

(e) None of these

1—M—Answer: c

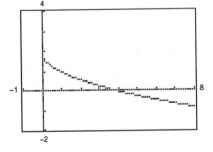

25. The graph at the right is a transformation of the graph of $f(x) = |x|$. Find an equation for the function.

(a) $g(x) = |x - 1| - 4$

(b) $g(x) = |x - 4| - 1$

(c) $g(x) = |x - 1| + 4$

(d) $g(x) = |x + 4| - 1$

(e) None of these

1—M—Answer: d

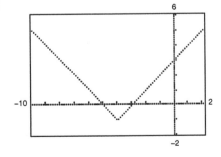

26. The graph at the right is a transformation of the graph of $f(x) = x^3$. Find an equation for the function.

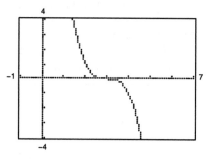

(a) $g(x) = -x^3 + 3$ (b) $g(x) = -(x - 3)^3$

(c) $g(x) = -(x + 3)^3$ (d) $g(x) = -x^3 - 3$

(e) None of these

1—M—Answer: b

27. Graph $g(x) = |x + 2| - 3$ using a transformation of the graph of $f(x) = |x|$.

(a)

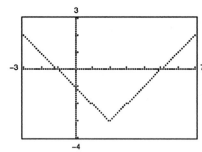

(b)

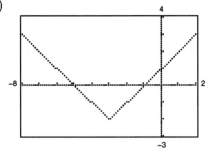

(c)

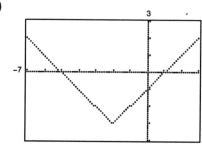

(d)

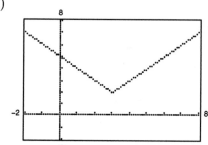

(e) None of these

1—M—Answer: c

28. Graph $g(x) = -x^2 + 2$ using a transformation of the graph of $f(x) = x^2$.

(a)

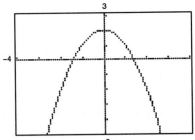

(b)

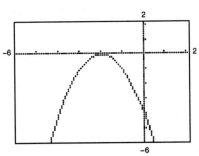

(c)

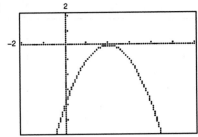

(d)

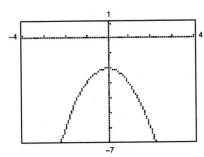

(e) None of these

1—M—Answer: a

29. Graph $g(x) = (x - 1)^3 + 1$ using a transformation of the graph of $f(x) = x^3$.

(a)

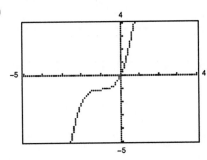

(b)

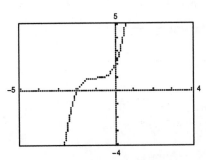

(c)

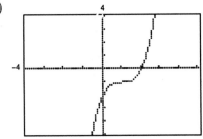

(d)

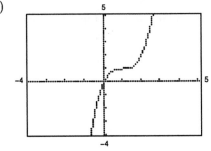

(e) None of these

1—M—Answer: d

30. Graph $g(x) = \sqrt{x-4} - 3$ using a transformation of the graph of $f(x) = \sqrt{x}$.

1—O—Answer:

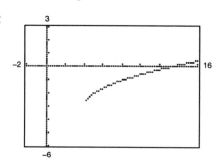

31. Describe the nonrigid transformation of the graph of $f(x) = x^2$ for the graph of $g(x) = 2x^2 + 1$.

(a) Vertical shift 1 unit down
   Vertical stretch

(b) Vertical shift 1 unit up
   Vertical shrink

(c) Horizontal shift 2 units to the left
   Vertical shrink

(d) Vertical shift 1 unit up
   Vertical stretch

(e) None of these

2—M—Answer: d

32. Describe the nonrigid transformation of the graph of $f(x) = \sqrt{x}$ for the graph of $g(x) = \frac{1}{3}\sqrt{x+4}$.

(a) Horizontal shift 4 units to the left
   Vertical shrink

(b) Horizontal shift 4 units to the left
   Vertical stretch

(c) Horizontal shift 4 units to the right
   Vertical stretch

(d) Horizontal shift 4 units to the right
   Vertical shrink

(e) None of these

2—M—Answer: a

33. Find an equation of the function whose graph is a horizontal shift 9 units to the right and a vertical stretch (by 4) of the graph of $f(x) = \sqrt[3]{x}$.

(a) $g(x) = \frac{1}{4}\sqrt[3]{x+9}$

(b) $g(x) = \frac{1}{4}\sqrt[3]{x-9}$

(c) $g(x) = 4\sqrt[3]{x-9}$

(d) $g(x) = 4\sqrt[3]{x+9}$

(e) None of these

2—M—Answer: c

34. Find an equation of the function whose graph is a vertical shift 5 units down and a vertical shrink (by 6) of the graph of $f(x) = |x|$.

(a) $g(x) = \frac{1}{6}|x+5|$

(b) $g(x) = \frac{1}{6}|x| - 5$

(c) $g(x) = 6|x| - 5$

(d) $g(x) = 6|x-5|$

(e) None of these

2—M—Answer: b

1.6 | Combinations of Functions

1. Given $f(x) = 2x - 4$ and $g(x) = 1 + 3x$, find $(f + g)(x)$.

   (a) $5x - 3$ (b) $x - 3$ (c) $-(x + 3)$

   (d) 0 (e) None of these

   1—M—Answer: a

2. Given $f(x) = 6$ and $g(x) = 2x^2 - 1$, find $(f - g)(x)$.

   (a) $2x^2 + 5$ (b) $2x^2 - 7$ (c) $-2x^2 + 7$

   (d) $-2x^2 + 5$ (e) None of these

   1—M—Answer: c

3. Given $f(x) = 2x$ and $g(x) = x - 1$, find $(fg)(x)$.

   (a) $x + 1$ (b) $2x^2 - 2x$ (c) $3x - 1$

   (d) $2x^2 - 1$ (e) None of these

   1—M—Answer: b

4. Given $f(x) = \dfrac{1}{x}$ and $g(x) = x^2 - 5$, find $(fg)x$.

   (a) $\dfrac{x}{x^2 - 5}$ (b) $x(x^2 - 5)$ (c) $\dfrac{x^2 - 5}{x}$

   (d) $x - 5$ (e) None of these

   1—M—Answer: c

5. Given $f(x) = x$ and $g(x) = 3x - 1$, find $(f/g)(x)$.

   (a) $3x^2 - x$ (b) $\dfrac{3x - 1}{x}$ (c) $\dfrac{x}{3x - 1}$

   (d) $4x - 1$ (e) None of these

   1—M—Answer: c

6. Given $f(x) = \dfrac{1}{x}$ and $g(x) = \dfrac{x}{4}$, find $(f/g)(x)$.

   (a) $\dfrac{x^2}{4}$ (b) 4 (c) $\dfrac{x + 4}{4x}$

   (d) $\dfrac{4}{x^2}$ (e) None of these

   1—M—Answer: d

7. Given $f(x) = x - 2$ and $g(x) = 6 - 2x$, find $(f + g)(-2)$.

   (a) 6   (b) 2   (c) -2

   (d) -14 (e) None of these

   1—M—Answer: a

8. Given $f(x) = x$ and $g(x) = x^2 - 7$, find $(fg)(3)$.

   (a) -13 (b) 29   (c) 5

   (d) 6   (e) None of these

   1—M—Answer: d

9. Given $f(x) = 9x + 1$ and $g(x) = 4 - x$, find $(f - g)(5)$.

   (a) 37   (b) 47   (c) 55

   (d) -46 (e) None of these

   1—M—Answer: b

10. Given $f(x) = x^2 + 3$ and $g(x) = x - 1$, find $(f/g)(-1)$.

    (a) 2   (b) 0   (c) -2

    (d) Undefined   (e) None of these

    1—M—Answer: c

11. Use a graphing utility to graph $(f + g)(x)$ if $f(x) = 2x - 3$ and $g(x) = x + 5$.

    (a)

    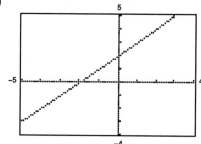

    (b)

    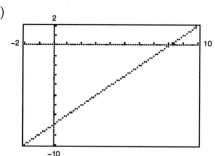

11. —CONTINUED—

(c)

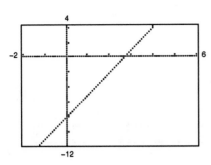

(d)

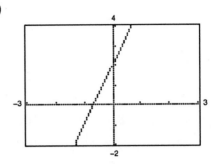

(e) None of these

1—M—Answer: d

12. Use a graphing utility to graph $(f - g)(x)$ if $f(x) = x^2$ and $g(x) = -x$.

(a)

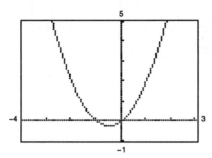

(b)

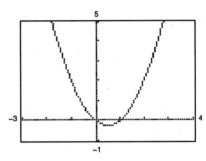

(c)

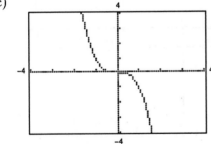

(d)

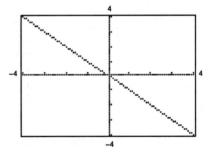

(e) None of these

1—M—Answer: a

13. Use a graphing utility to graph $(f/g)(x)$ if $f(x) = 2x^2 - x$ and $g(x) = x$.

(a)

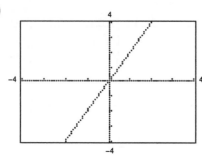

(b)

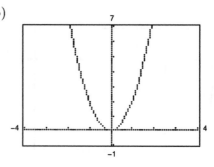

(c)

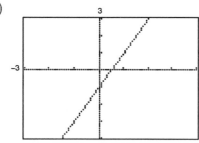

(d)

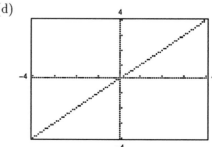

(e) None of these

1—M—Answer: c

14. Use a graphing utility to graph $(fg)(x)$ if $f(x) = \dfrac{1}{x}$ and $g(x) = x + 2$.

1—O—Answer:

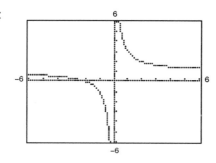

15. Given $f(x) = x - 7$ and $g(x) = 4x$, find $(f \circ g)(x)$.

(a) $3x - 7$ (b) $4x^2 - 7x$ (c) $4x - 7$

(d) $4(x - 7)$ (e) None of these

1—M—Answer: c

16. Given $f(x) = x^2$ and $g(x) = x + 5$, find $(g \circ f)(x)$.

(a) $(x + 5)^2$ (b) $x^2 + 5$ (c) $x^2 + 25$

(d) $x^2 + 5x^2$ (e) None of these

1—M—Answer: b

17. Given $f(x) = x^2 + 5$ and $g(x) = 6 - x$, find $(f \circ f)(x)$.

(a) $x^4 + 10$ (b) $x^4 + 25$ (c) $(x^2 + 5)^2 + 5$

(d) $x^2 + 10$ (e) None of these

1—M—Answer: c

18. Given $f(x) = x^2 - 2x$ and $g(x) = 3x + 2x$, find $(f \circ g)(x)$.

(a) $4x^2 + 8x + 3$ (b) $2x^2 - 4x + 3$ (c) $2x^3 - x^2 - 6x$

(d) $3x^2 + x$ (e) None of these

1—M—Answer: a

19. Given $f(x) = 4 - 2x^2$ and $g(x) = 2 - x$, find $(f \circ g)(x)$.

(a) $4x^2 - 16x + 20$ (b) $2x^2 - 4$ (c) $2x^2 - 2$

(d) $-2x^3 - 4x^2 - 4x + 8$ (e) None of these

1—M—Answer: e

20. Given $f(x) = \dfrac{1}{x^2}$ and $g(x) = \sqrt{x^2 + 4}$, find $(f \circ g)(x)$.

(a) $\dfrac{1}{x^2 + 4}$ (b) $\dfrac{1}{\sqrt{x^2 + 4}}$ (c) $x^2 + 4$

(d) $\dfrac{1}{x^2\sqrt{x^2 + 4}}$ (e) None of these

1—M—Answer: a

21. Given $f(x) = x + 4$ and $g(x) = 3x$, find $(f \circ g)(2)$.

(a) 36   (b) 10   (c) 32

(d) 16   (e) None of these

1—M—Answer: b

22. Given $f(x) = x^2$ and $g(x) = \sqrt{x - 6}$, find $(f \circ g)(-1)$.

(a) -7 (b) 7   (c) $\sqrt{7}$

(d) Undefined   (e) None of these

1—M—Answer: a

23. Given $f(x) = \dfrac{1}{x}$ and $g(x) = \dfrac{1}{x}$, find $(f \circ g)(9)$.

(a) 0   (b) $\dfrac{1}{9}$ (c) 9

(d) Undefined   (e) None of these

1—M—Answer: c

24. Given $f(x) = x^3 + 4$ and $g(x) = \sqrt[3]{x}$, find $(f \circ g)(-3)$.

(a) 29   (b) $\sqrt{27}$ (c) -1

(d) 1   (e) None of these

1—M—Answer: d

25. Use a graphing utility to graph $(f \circ g)(x)$ if $f(x) = x - 1$ and $g(x) = x + 9$.

(a)

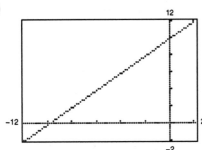

(b)

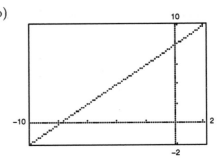

(c)

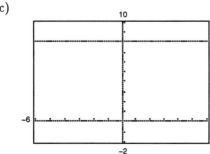

(d)

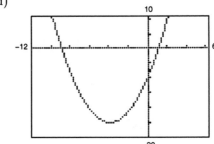

(e) None of these

1—M—Answer: b

26. Use a graphing utility to graph $(f \circ g)(x)$ if $f(x) = x^2 - 2$ and $g(x) = \sqrt{x + 6}$.

(a)

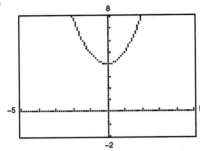

(b)

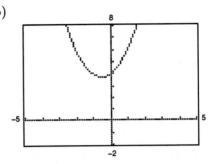

(c)

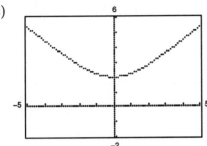

(d)

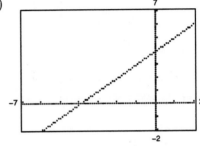

(e) None of these

1—M—Answer: d

27. Find functions f and g such that $(f \circ g)(x) = h(x)$: $h(x) = \sqrt{(x + 1)^2 - 3}$

(a) $f(x) = x + 1$, $g(x) = \sqrt{x - 3}$ (b) $f(x) = \sqrt{(x + 1)^2}$, $g(x) = \sqrt{3}$

(c) $f(x) = (x + 1)^2$, $g(x) = -3$ (d) $f(x) = \sqrt{x^2 - 3}$, $g(x) = x + 1$

(e) None of these

2—M—Answer: d

28. Find functions f and g such that $(f \circ g)(x) = h(x)$: $h(x) = (x + 2)^4 - x - 2$

(a) $f(x) = x^4 - x - 2$, $g(x) = x + 2$ (b) $f(x) = x^4 - x$, $g(x) = x + 2$

(c) $f(x) = x + 2$, $g(x) = x^4 - x - 2$ (d) $f(x) = x^4$, $g(x) = x - 2$

(e) None of these

2—M—Answer: b

29. Find functions f and g such that $(f \circ g)(x) = h(x)$: $h(x) = \dfrac{1}{x^2 - 2}$

    (a) $f(x) = \dfrac{1}{x - 2}$, $g(x) = x^2 - 2$ (b) $f(x) = x^2 - 2$, $g(x) = \dfrac{1}{x^2 - 2}$

    (c) $f(x) = \dfrac{1}{x^2 - 2}$, $g(x) = \sqrt{x - 2}$ (d) $f(x) = \dfrac{1}{x^2}$, $g(x) = \sqrt{x^2 - 2}$

    (e) None of these

    2—M—Answer: d

30. Given $f(x) = \sqrt{x}$ and $g(x) = x^2 + 4$, find the domain of $(f \circ g)(x)$.

    (a) $(-\infty, 0]$ (b) $[0, \infty)$ (c) $(-\infty, \infty)$

    (d) $(-\infty, -2), (-2, 2)$ (e) None of these

    2—M—Answer: c

31. Given $f(x) = \dfrac{1}{x^2 - 1}$ and $g(x) = x + 3$, find the domain of $(f \circ g)(x)$.

    (a) $(-\infty, \infty)$ (b) $(-\infty, -1), (-1, 1), (1, \infty)$

    (c) $(-\infty, -4), (-4, -2), (-2, \infty)$ (d) $[-3, \infty)$

    (e) None of these

    2—M—Answer: c

32. Given $f(x) = \dfrac{1}{\sqrt{x}}$ and $g(x) = x + 3$, find the domain of $(f \circ g)(x)$.

    (a) $(0, \infty)$ (b) $(-3, \infty)$ (c) $(-\infty, -3), (-3, \infty)$

    (d) $(-\infty, 0), (0, \infty)$ (e) None of these

    2—M—Answer: b

33. Given $f(x) = \dfrac{1}{x^2 - 1}$ and $g(x) = 1 - x$, find the domain of $(f \circ g)(x)$.

    (a) $(-\infty, 0), (0, 2), (2, \infty)$ (b) $(-\infty, -1), (-1, 1), (1, \infty)$

    (c) $(1, \infty)$ (d) $(-1, 1)$ (e) None of these

    2—M—Answer: a

34. The weekly cost of producing x units in a manufacturing process is given by the function $C(x) = 30x + 400$. The number of units produced in t hours is given by $x(t) = 75t$, find $(C \circ x)(t)$.

    2—O—Answer: $2250t + 400$

35. The cost of producing x units in a manufacturing process is given by the function $C(x) = 1.25x + 65$. The revenue obtained from selling x units is given by $R(x) = 2.75x - 0.0025x^2$. Determine the profit as a function of the number of units sold if $P = R - C$.

    2—O—Answer: $P = -0.0025x^2 + 1.50x - 65$

1.7 | Inverse Functions

1. Which of the following is the inverse of $f(x) = x + 1$?

   (a) $f^{-1}(x) = x + 1$ (b) $f^{-1}(x) = x - 1$ (c) $f^{-1}(x) = -(x + 1)$

   (d) $f^{-1}(x) = \dfrac{1}{x + 1}$ (e) None of these

   1—M—Answer: b

2. Which of the following is the inverse of $f(x) = 6x$?

   (a) $f^{-1}(x) = \dfrac{x}{6}$ (b) $f^{-1}(x) = 6x$ (c) $f^{-1}(x) = -6x$

   (d) $f^{-1}(x) = \dfrac{1}{6x}$ (e) None of these

   1—M—Answer: a

3. Which of the following is the inverse of $f(x) = 5 - x$?

   (a) $f^{-1}(x) = x + 5$ (b) $f^{-1}(x) = x - 5$ (c) $f^{-1}(x) = \dfrac{1}{5 - x}$

   (d) $f^{-1}(x) = 5 - x$ (e) None of these

   1—M—Answer: d

4. Algebraically, determine which sets of functions are not inverses of each other.

   (a) $f(x) = x^2 + 1$ (b) $f(x) = x^2 - 1$ (c) $f(x) = 1 - x^2$

   $\quad g(x) = \sqrt{x - 1}$ $\quad g(x) = \sqrt{x + 1}$ $\quad g(x) = \sqrt{1 + x^2}$

   (d) All of these are inverses of each other. (e) None of these are inverses of each other.

   1—M—Answer: c

5. Algebraically, determine which sets of functions are not inverses of each other.

   (a) $f(x) = x^3 + 2$ (b) $f(x) = 2 - x^3$ (c) $f(x) = x^3 - 2$

   $\quad g(x) = \sqrt[3]{x - 2}$ $\quad g(x) = \sqrt[3]{2 - x}$ $\quad g(x) = \sqrt[3]{x + 2}$

   (d) All of these are inverses of each other. (e) None of these are inverses of each other.

   1—M—Answer: d

6. Algebraically, determine which sets of functions are not inverses of each other.

   (a) $f(x) = \dfrac{2}{x - 3}$ (b) $f(x) = \dfrac{5}{x}$ (c) $f(x) = \dfrac{x}{2}$

   $\quad g(x) = \dfrac{x - 3}{2}$ $\quad g(x) = \dfrac{5}{x}$ $\quad g(x) = 2x$

   (d) All of these are inverses of each other. (e) None of these are inverses of each other.

   1—M—Answer: a

7. If f is a one-to-one function on its domain, the graph of $f^{-1}(x)$ is a reflection of the graph of $f(x)$ with respect to:

(a) x-axis   (b) y-axis   (c) line $y = x$

(d) line $y = -x$ (e) origin

1—M—Answer: c

8. Graphically, determine which sets of functions are not inverses of each other.

(a) $f(x) = 9 + x$ (b) $f(x) = x^2$ (c) $f(x) = \dfrac{x+3}{3}$

       $g(x) = 9 - x$ $g(x) = -x^2$ $g(x) = \dfrac{3}{x+3}$

(d) All of these are inverses of each other.   (e) None of these are inverses of each other.

1—M—Answer: e

9. Graphically, determine whether the functions $f(x) = (x+1)^3$ and $g(x) = \sqrt[3]{x} - 1$ are inverses of each other.

1—O—Answer: Yes, they are inverses of each other.

10. Graphically, determine whether the functions $f(x) = \sqrt{x^2 - 5}$ and $g(x) = x^2 + 5$ are inverses of each other.

1—O—Answer: No, they are not inverses of each other.

11. In which graph does y not represent a one-to-one function of x?

(a)

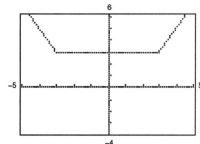

(b)

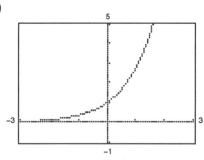

(c)

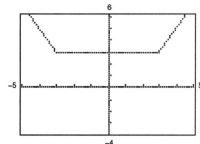

(d) All of these are one-to-one functions of x.

(e) None of these are one-to-one functions of x.

2—M—Answer: a

12. In which graph does y not represent a one-to-one function of x?

(a)

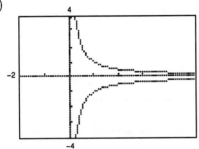

(b)

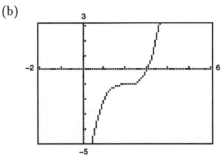

(c)

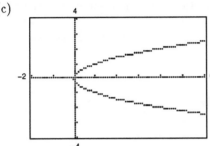

(d) All of these are one-to-one functions of x.

(e) None of these are one-to-one functions of x.

2—M—Answer: b

13. In which graph does y not represent a one-to-one function of x?

(a)

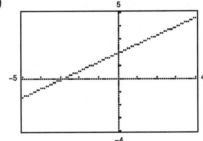

(b)

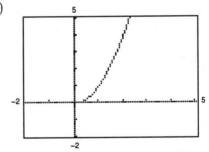

(c)

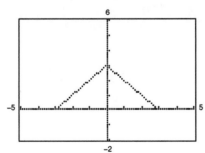

(d) All of these are one-to-one functions of x.

(e) None of these are one-to-one functions of x.

2—M—Answer: c

14. In which graph does y not represent a one-to-one function of x?

(a)

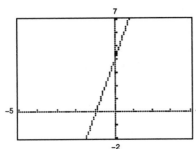

(b)

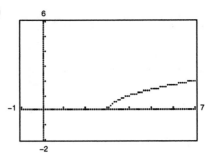

(c)

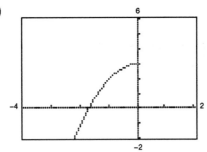

(d) All of these are one-to-one functions of x.

(e) None of these are one-to-one functions of x.

2—M—Answer: d

15. Determine which function is *not* one-to-one.

(a) $y = \sqrt[3]{x^2 + 1}$ (b) $y = \dfrac{2}{x}$ (c) $y = 7x - 2$

(d) $y = \sqrt{2 - x}$ (e) None of these

2—M—Answer: a

16. Determine which function is one-to-one.

(a) $y = |2 - x|$ (b) $y = x^2 + 2$ (c) $y = \sqrt{2 - x^2}$

(d) $y = \dfrac{1}{x + 2}$ (e) None of these

2—M—Answer: d

17. Determine which function is one-to-one.

(a) $y = |x + 1|$ (b) $y = \sqrt{5 + x}$ (c) $y = \sqrt{x^2 + 1}$

(d) $y = x^2 + 1$ (e) None of these

1—M—Answer: b

18. Determine which function is one-to-one.

(a) $y = \dfrac{9}{x}$ (b) $y = 3 + x^2$ (c) $y = |-4x|$

(d) $y = x^4$ (e) None of these

1—M—Answer: a

19. Determine whether the function $f(x) = \dfrac{6}{x}$ is one-to-one. If it is, find its inverse.

1—O—Answer: f is one-to-one, $f^{-1}(x) = \dfrac{6}{x}$

20. Determine whether the function $f(x) = \dfrac{7}{x+2}$ is one-to-one. If it is, find its inverse.

(a) Not one-to-one

(b) $f^{-1}(x) = \dfrac{x+2}{7}$

(c) $f^{-1}(x) = \dfrac{7-2x}{x}$

(d) $f^{-1}(x) = -\dfrac{7}{x+2}$

(e) None of these

2—M—Answer: c

21. Determine whether the function $f(x) = \dfrac{1}{x}$ is one-to-one. If it is, find its inverse.

1—O—Answer: $f^{-1}(x) = \dfrac{1}{x}$

22. Given $f(x) = 7x + 2$, find $f^{-1}(x)$.

(a) $7x + 2$

(b) $\dfrac{1}{7x+2}$

(c) $\dfrac{x-2}{7}$

(d) $\dfrac{x}{7} - 2$

(e) None of these

1—M—Answer: c

23. Given $f(x) = \sqrt{2x - 1}$, find $f^{-1}(x)$.

(a) $\sqrt{2y - 1},\ y \geq \dfrac{1}{2}$

(b) $x^2 + 1,\ x \geq 0$

(c) $\dfrac{1}{2}(x^2 + 1),\ x \geq 0$

(d) $\dfrac{1}{\sqrt{2x-1}},\ x \geq \dfrac{1}{2}$

(e) None of these

2—M—Answer: c

24. Given $f(x) = 3x^3 - 1$, find $f^{-1}(x)$.

(a) $\dfrac{1}{3x^3 - 1}$

(b) $3x^{-1} - 1$

(c) $3(x + 1)$

(d) $\sqrt[3]{\dfrac{x+1}{3}}$

(e) None of these

1—M—Answer: d

25. Given $f(x) = x - 1$, identify the graph of $f^{-1}(x)$.

(a)
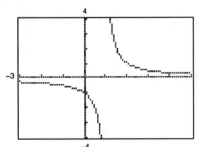

(b)
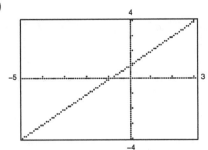

(c)
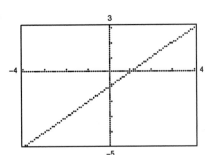

(d)
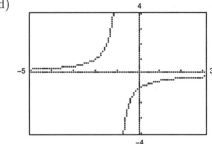

(e) None of these

1—M—Answer: b

26. Given $f(x) = \dfrac{x}{3}$, identify the graph of $f^{-1}(x)$.

(a)
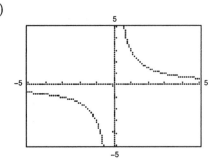

(b)
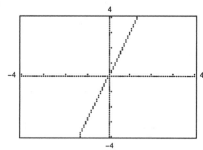

26. —CONTINUED—

(c)

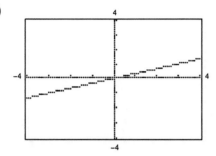

(d)

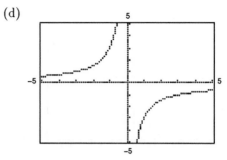

(e) None of these

1—M—Answer: b

27. Given $f(x) = 3 + x$, identify the graph of $f^{-1}(x)$.

(a)

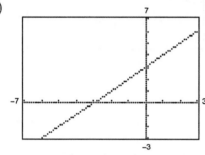

(b)

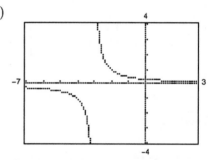

(c)

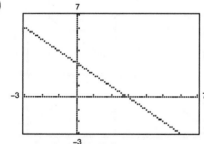

(d)

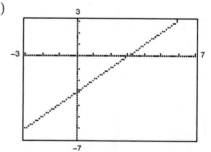

(e) None of these

1—M—Answer: d

28. Given $f(x) = 4x$, identify the graph of $f^{-1}(x)$.

(a)

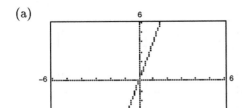

(b)

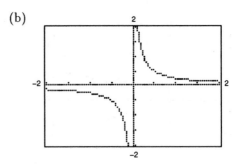

(c)

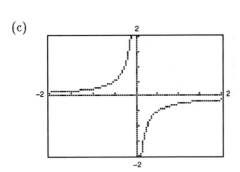

(d)

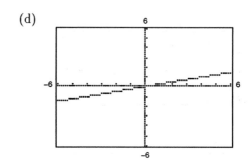

(e) None of these

1—M—Answer: d

29. Use a graphing utility to graph $f(x) = x + 1$ and its inverse on the same viewing rectangle.

(a)

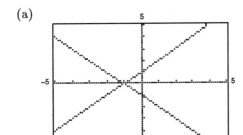

(b)

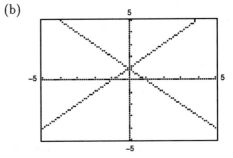

(c)

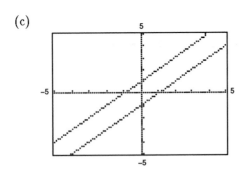

(d)

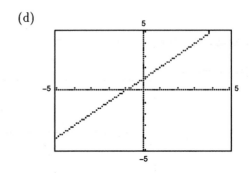

(e) None of these

2—M—Answer: c

30. Use a graphing utility to graph $f(x) = x^2 + 2$, $x \geq 0$ and its inverse on the same viewing rectangle.

(a)
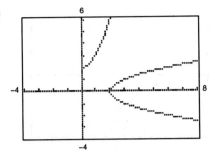

(b)
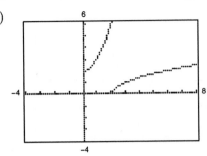

(c)
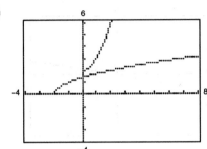

(d)
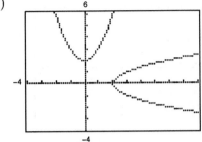

(e) None of these

2—M—Answer: b

31. Use a graphing utility to graph $f(x) = x^3 - 3$ and its inverse on the same viewing rectangle.

2—O—Answer:

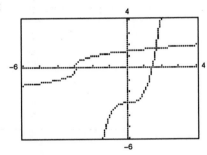

32. Use a graphing utility to graph $f(x) = \dfrac{x + 2}{3}$ and its inverse on the same viewing rectangle.

2—O—Answer:

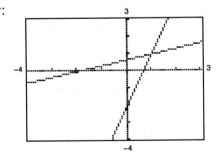

33. Given $f(x) = 1 - 3x$ and $g(x) = x + 2$, find $(f^{-1} \circ g^{-1})(1)$.

    (a) $\frac{2}{3}$ (b) -6 (c) -11

    (d) $-\frac{1}{3}$ (e) None of these

    2—M—Answer: a

34. Given $f(x) = x^2$ and $g(x) = 2x - 3$, find $(g^{-1} \circ f^{-1})(9)$.

    (a) 66   (b) -6 (c) -3

    (d) 3   (e) None of these

    2—M—Answer: d

35. Given $f(x) = x - 4$ and $g(x) = 3 - x$, find $(f^{-1} \circ g^{-1})(-1)$.

    (a) 6   (b) 8   (c) -6

    (d) -1 (e) None of these

    2—M—Answer: b

36. Given $f(x) = \sqrt[3]{x}$ and $g(x) = x - 5$, find $(f^{-1} \circ g^{-1})(-3)$.

    (a) -6 (b) -4 (c) 2

    (d) -8 (e) None of these

    2—M—Answer: e

C H A P T E R   T W O
Solving Equations and Inequalities

2.1 | Linear Equations

1. Is $3x + 4(x - 2) = 10x$ a conditional equation or an identity?

(a) Conditional   (b) Identity   (c) Neither   (d) Both

1—M—Answer: a

2. Is $3(x^2 + 2) = 5x - 9$ a conditional equation or an identity?

(a) Conditional   (b) Identity   (c) Neither   (d) Both

1—M—Answer: a

3. Is $3x + 2 = 9x^2 - 1$ a conditional equation or an identity?

1—O—Answer: Conditional

4. Is $3(x^2 + 2x) = 7 + 3x^2$ a conditional equation or an identity?

(a) Conditional   (b) Identity   (c) Neither   (d) Both

1—M—Answer: a

5. Is $2x + (3 - x)(3 + x) + 1 = 2 - (x - 4)(x + 2)$ a conditional equation or an identity?

(a) Conditional   (b) Identity   (c) Neither   (d) Both

1—M—Answer: b

6. Is $3 + \dfrac{3}{x - 1} = \dfrac{3x}{x - 1}$ a conditional equation or an identity?

(a) Conditional   (b) Identity   (c) Neither   (d) Both

1—M—Answer: b

7. Solve for x: $8x - 2 = 13 - 2x$

(a) $\frac{2}{3}$ (b) $\frac{3}{2}$ (c) $\frac{11}{6}$ (d) $-\frac{2}{3}$ (e) None of these

1—M—Answer: b

8. Solve for x: $13x - 9 = 3x + 10$

(a) $\frac{19}{10}$ (b) $\frac{10}{19}$ (c) $\frac{1}{10}$ (d) $\frac{19}{16}$ (e) None of these

1—M—Answer: a

9. Solve for x: $7 - 3x + 2 = 4x - 1$

   (a) 5   (b) 10   (c) $\frac{7}{10}$ (d) $\frac{10}{7}$ (e) None of these

   1—M—Answer: d

10. Solve for x: $4 + 7x - 3x + 2 = 8x + 6$

    (a) No solution   (b) 0   (c) 1
    (d) 2   (e) None of these

    1—M—Answer: b

11. Solve for x: $3x - 6 = 9$

    (a) $\frac{17}{3}$ (b) -18 (c) 1   (d) 5   (e) None of these

    1—M—Answer: d

12. Solve for x: $0.3x - 4 = 2$

    (a) 2   (b) $\frac{9}{5}$ (c) 20   (d) $-\frac{20}{3}$ (e) None of these

    1—M—Answer: c

13. Solve for x: $4x - 7(3x + 6) = 4x - 9$

    (a) $\frac{7}{11}$ (b) $-\frac{11}{7}$ (c) $-\frac{33}{13}$ (d) $-\frac{17}{7}$ (e) None of these

    1—M—Answer: b

14. Solve for x: $5(3x - 2) + 5x - 7 = 16 + 2x$

    1—O—Answer: $\frac{11}{6}$

15. Solve for x: $2[x - (3x + 1)] = 4 - 2x$

    (a) -1 (b) -3 (c) 1   (d) $-\frac{1}{3}$ (e) None of these

    2—M—Answer: b

16. Determine which of the following is a solution of the equation $2(1 - x) - (4x + 3) = 11$.

    (a) 2   (b) -2 (c) 1   (d) -3 (e) None of these

    1—M—Answer: b

17. Determine which of the following is a solution of the equation $2(3x - 6) - 3(5 - x) = 9$.

    (a) -2 (b) 5   (c) 2   (d) 4   (e) None of these

    1—M—Answer: d

18. Determine which of the following is a solution of the equation $\sqrt{2x} = 4$.

(a) 16   (b) 8   (c) −8, 8   (d) 2   (e) None of these

1—M—Answer: b

19. Determine which of the following is a solution of the equation $(x-2)(x-1) = 6$.

(a) 3   (b) 2   (c) 4   (d) 6   (e) None of these

1—M—Answer: c

20. Solve for x: $0.15x + 0.10(30 - x) = 20$

(a) −56   (b) 340   (c) 1695   (d) $\frac{850}{7}$ (e) None of these

2—M—Answer: b

21. Solve for r: $6390 = 6000(1 + r)$

(a) 0.07   (b) 0.065   (c) 0.06   (d) 0.09   (e) None of these

1—M—Answer: b

22. Solve for x: $3[2x - (7x - 1)] = 5x + 13$

(a) $\frac{4}{5}$ (b) −2   (c) $\frac{7}{13}$ (d) $-\frac{1}{2}$ (e) None of these

2—M—Answer: d

23. Solve for x: $\dfrac{3x}{5} + x = \dfrac{2}{3}$

2—O—Answer: $\dfrac{5}{12}$

24. Solve for x: $\dfrac{4x + 1}{4} - \dfrac{2x + 3}{3} = \dfrac{7}{12}$

(a) 4   (b) $\dfrac{9}{2}$ (c) −2   (d) $\dfrac{3}{2}$ (e) None of these

2—M—Answer: a

25. Solve for x: $\dfrac{3x}{2} - \dfrac{x + 1}{4} = 6$

(a) 5   (b) $\dfrac{23}{5}$ (c) $\dfrac{35}{8}$ (d) $\dfrac{1}{2}$ (e) None of these

1—M—Answer: a

26. Solve for x: $\frac{3}{4}x - \frac{1}{2}(x + 5) = 2$

(a) −2   (b) 18   (c) 26   (d) 28   (e) None of these

1—M—Answer: b

27. Solve for x: $\dfrac{3x+2}{5} - \dfrac{6x+4}{3} = \dfrac{14}{3}$

(a) $-\dfrac{44}{21}$　　　(b) 5　　　(c) $\dfrac{37}{12}$　　　(d) -4　　　(e) None of these

1—M—Answer: d

28. Solve for x: $\dfrac{2x-5}{x-3} = \dfrac{4x+1}{2x}$

2—O—Answer: -3

29. Solve for x: $3 - \dfrac{4x+5}{x-2} = \dfrac{7x-9}{x-2}$

(a) $-\dfrac{1}{4}$　　　　　　　(b) -1　　　　　　　(c) 1

(d) No solution　　　　　(e) None of these

2—M—Answer: a

30. Solve for x: $\dfrac{7x}{x-2} + \dfrac{2x}{x+2} = 9$

(a) $-\dfrac{18}{5}$　　　(b) $\dfrac{2}{3}$　　　(c) $-\dfrac{2}{5}$　　　(d) $\dfrac{5}{18}$　　　(e) None of these

2—M—Answer: a

31. Solve for x: $\dfrac{4}{x} = \dfrac{7}{3}$

(a) $\dfrac{7}{12}$　　　(b) $\dfrac{3}{28}$　　　(c) $\dfrac{28}{3}$　　　(d) $\dfrac{12}{7}$　　　(e) None of these

1—M—Answer: d

32. Solve for x: $8 = 3 + \dfrac{2}{x}$

(a) $\dfrac{2}{5}$　　　(b) $\dfrac{5}{2}$　　　(c) $\dfrac{8}{5}$　　　(d) $\dfrac{4}{3}$　　　(e) None of these

1—M—Answer: a

33. Solve for x: $\dfrac{1}{x-2} + \dfrac{3}{x+3} = \dfrac{4}{x^2+x-6}$

(a) $\dfrac{4}{7}$　　　(b) 3　　　(c) $\dfrac{7}{4}$　　　(d) 1　　　(e) None of these

1—M—Answer: c

34. Solve for x: $\dfrac{1}{x-3} - \dfrac{2}{x+3} = \dfrac{2x}{x^2-9}$

(a) $-\dfrac{1}{2}$ (b) 3   (c) -3

(d) -3 and 3   (e) None of these

1—M—Answer: e

35. Solve $0.134x + 0.12(250 - x) = 50$ for x. Round your result to two decimal places.

(a) 1428.57   (b) 5624.30   (c) 3562.86

(d) -23.09 (e) None of these

1—M—Answer: a

36. Solve $1.93(x - 1) + 0.911x = 65.3$ for x. Round your results to two decimal places.

(a) 23.34   (b) 0.04   (c) 22.31

(d) 23.66   (e) None of these

1—M—Answer: d

37. Solve $0.55 + 13.9(2.1 - x) = 14$ for x. Round your results to two decimal places.

1—O—Answer: 1.13

38. The handicap, H, for the bowler with an average score, A, of less than 200 is determined using the formula $H = 0.8(200 - A)$. Find a bowler's average score if his handicap is 64.

(a) 110   (b) 120   (c) 130   (d) 140   (e) None of these

1—M—Answer: b

39. The handicap, H, for the bowler with an average score, A, of less than 200 is determined using the formula $H = 0.8(200 - A)$. Find a bowler's average score if his handicap is 8.

(a) 160   (b) 170   (c) 180   (d) 190   (e) None of these

1—M—Answer: d

40. The handicap, H, for the bowler with an average score, A, of less than 200 is determined using the formula $H = 0.8(200 - A)$. Find a bowler's average score if his handicap is 32.

(a) 160   (b) 170   (c) 180   (d) 190   (e) None of these

1—M—Answer: a

2.2 | Linear Equations and Modeling

1. A telephone call costs $0.31 for the first minute plus $0.24 for each additional minute. Write an algebraic expression for the cost of a call lasting x minutes.

   (a) $0.31 + 0.24x$ (b) $0.24x$ (c) $0.31 + 0.24(x - 1)$

   (d) $0.31 + 0.24(x + 1)$ (e) None of these

   1—M—Answer: c

2. The cost of mailing a package is $0.29 for the first ounce plus $0.25 for each additional ounce. Write an algebraic expression for the cost of a package weighing x ounces.

   (a) $0.29 + 0.25x$ (b) $0.25x$ (c) $0.29 + 0.25(x + 1)$

   (d) $0.29 + 0.25(x - 1)$ (e) None of these

   1—M—Answer: d

3. The length of a rectangular room is 5 feet longer than the width. Write an algebraic expression for the perimeter of a room with width x feet.

   (a) $x(x + 5)$ (b) $2x + 2(x + 5)$ (c) $2x + 2(5x)$

   (d) $2x + 2x + 5$ (e) None of these

   1—M—Answer: b

4. The length of a rectangular room is 2 feet longer than the width. Write an algebraic expression for the perimeter of a room with width x feet.

   (a) $x(x + 2)$ (b) $4x + 2$ (c) $2x + 2(x + 2)$

   (d) $x + (x + 2)$ (e) None of these

   1—M—Answer: c

5. A jacket is discounted by 20%. Write an algebraic expression for the sale price of a jacket that originally sells for x dollars.

   (a) $x - 0.20x$ (b) $x - 0.20$ (c) $x + 0.20x$

   (d) $0.20x - x$ (e) None of these

   1—M—Answer: a

6. A stereo is discounted 40%. Write an algebraic expression for the sale price of a stereo that originally sells for x dollars.

   (a) $x - 0.40$ (b) $x - 0.40x$ (c) $x + 0.40$

   (d) $0.40x$ (e) None of these

   1—M—Answer: b

7. Use an algebraic expression to represent the sum of the squares of two consecutive odd numbers.

   (a) $x^2 + (x+1)^2$ (b) $x^2 + x^2 + 1$ (c) $x^2 + (x+2)^2$

   (d) $(x^2 + 1) + (x^2 + 3)$ (e) None of these

   1—M—Answer: c

8. Use an algebraic expression to represent the sum of the squares of three consecutive numbers.

   1—O—Answer: $x^2 + (x+1)^2 + (x+2)^2$

9. Use an algebraic expression to represent the distance a person travels at 55 miles per hour in $(4-t)$ hours.

   (a) $\dfrac{4-t}{55}$ (b) $55(4-t)$ (c) $\dfrac{55}{4-t}$

   (d) $(55)4 - t$ (e) None of these

   1—M—Answer: b

10. 460 is what percent of 340?

    (a) 74%   (b) 0.74%   (c) 1.35%   (d) 135.3%   (e) None of these

    1—M—Answer: d

11. What is 0.17% of 432?

    1—O—Answer: 0.7344

12. 35 is what percent of 748?

    1—O—Answer: 4.68%

13. 29 is what percent of 37?

    (a) 7.8%   (b) 78.4%   (c) 12.76%   (d) 127.6%   (e) None of these

    1—M—Answer: b

14. Eleanor invests $18,000 in two funds paying $9\frac{1}{4}\%$ and $10\frac{1}{2}\%$ simple interest. How much is invested at $9\frac{1}{4}\%$ if the total yearly interest is $1827.50?

    (a) $1300.00   (b) $5000.00   (c) $8000.00

    (d) $10,000.00   (e) None of these

    2—M—Answer: b

15. Maria inherited $15,000. She decided to invest it in two funds, one paying $9\frac{1}{4}\%$ simple interest, the other paying $11\frac{1}{2}\%$ simple interest. Her annual income from these investments will total $1623.75. How much did she invest in the fund that pays $9\frac{1}{4}\%$ simple interest?

    (a) $4500   (b) $10,500   (c) $488   (d) $14,512   (e) None of these

    2—M—Answer: a

16. Ann invested $8000 in a fund that pays $2\frac{1}{2}$% more simple interest per year than a similar fund in which her husband had invested $10,000. At the end of a year their interest totaled $1690.00. What rate of interest did Ann receive?

    2—O—Answer: $10\frac{7}{9}$%

17. Two trains traveling the same speed leave the city. The southbound train reaches its destination in 45 minutes. The eastbound train reaches its destination in 1 hour. How fast were the trains traveling if their destinations are 88 miles apart?

    (a) 70.4 mph   (b) 1.2 mph   (c) 2 mph   (d) 49.6 mph   (e) None of these

    2—M—Answer: a

18. Two brothers, Bob and Bill, live 450 miles apart. Starting at the same time they plan to drive until they meet. Bill averages 10 miles per hour faster than Bob who averages 50 mph. How long will it take them to meet?

    (a) $3\frac{2}{15}$ hours   (b) $3\frac{9}{11}$ hours   (c) $4\frac{1}{11}$ hours
    (d) $4\frac{1}{2}$ hours   (e) None of these.

    2—M—Answer: c

19. Two friends living 216 miles apart in bordering states are planning to meet at the state line. The speed limit in one state is 55 mph and 65 mph in the other. Assuming each will drive the speed limit and each will travel the same length of time, determine how far from the state line the person who is traveling at 65 mph lives.

    (a) 99 miles   (b) 117 miles   (c) 108 miles   (d) 180 miles   (e) None of these

    2—M—Answer: b

20. Find the original price of a television set that was reduced 40% and is now priced at $285.50.

    1—O—Answer: $475.83

21. Your weekly gross income after a 2.3% cost of living raise is $593.34. What was your income before the raise?

    (a) $575   (b) $590   (c) $580   (d) $585   (e) None of these

    1—M—Answer: c

22. The price of a new car including a 6% sales tax is $17,362.80. What was the price of the car before the sales tax was added?

    (a) $16,380   (b) $17,040   (c) $16,321   (d) $16,870   (e) None of these

    1—M—Answer: a

23. Jan has $2.80 in quarters and nickels. If there are 20 coins in all, how many quarters does Jan have?

    (a) 12   (b) 11   (c) 10   (d) 9   (e) None of these

    2—M—Answer: d

24. A 15-quart radiator contains a 40% concentration of antifreeze. How much of the solution must be drained and replaced by 100% antifreeze to bring the solution up to 70%.

    (a) 4.5 quarts   (b) 5 quarts   (c) 10.5 quarts

    (d) 7.5 quarts   (e) None of these

    2—M—Answer: d

25. Determine the number of milliliters of a 70% sulfuric acid solution that must be added to 160 milliliters of a 25% solution to make a 30% solution.

    (a) 40   (b) 35   (c) 25   (d) 20   (e) None of these

    2—M—Answer: d

26. You want to measure the height of a steeple. To do this, you measure the steeple's shadow and find it is $8\frac{3}{4}$ feet long. You also measure the shadow of a 4 foot stake and find that its shadow is $2\frac{1}{3}$ feet long. Determine the height of the steeple.

    (a) 12 ft   (b) 15 ft   (c) 19 ft   (d) 22 ft   (e) None of these

    1—M—Answer: b

27. You want to make a scale model of a rectangular room that is 10 feet wide and 15 feet long. If the width of the model is 9 inches, what will be the length?

    (a) $10\frac{1}{4}$ in.   (b) 12 in.   (c) 13 in.   (d) $13\frac{1}{2}$ in.   (e) None of these

    2—M—Answer: d

28. You want to measure the height of a tree. To do this, you measure the tree's shadow and find that it is 52.5 feet long. You also measure the shadow of a 4 foot stake and find that its shadow is 6 feet long. How tall is the tree?

    (a) 35 ft   (b) $78\frac{3}{4}$ ft   (c) 42 ft   (d) $60\frac{1}{3}$ ft   (e) None of these

    1—M—Answer: a

29. A company has fixed costs of $10,000 per month and variable costs of $9.75 per unit manufactured. The company has $96,190 available to cover the monthly costs. How many units can the company manufacture?

    (a) 9866   (b) 8840   (c) 10,891   (d) 9463   (e) None of these

    2—M—Answer: b

30. A company has fixed cost of $8000 per month and variable costs of $8.65 per unit manufactured. The company has $64,000 available to cover the monthly costs. How many units can the company manufacture?

    (a) 6473   (b) 7399   (c) 8324   (d) 6920   (e) None of these

    2—M—Answer: a

31. A homeowner wants to fence in a section of his backyard. The fenced-in area will be rectangular with the length $1\frac{1}{3}$ times the width. How many feet of fencing will he need to buy if the width is 27 feet long?

(a) 36 ft   (b) 63 ft   (c) 126 ft   (d) 972 ft   (e) None of these

2—M—Answer: c

32. Find a number such that seven subtracted from twice this number is 75.

(a) 41   (b) 69   (c) 90   (d) 62   (e) None of these

1—M—Answer: a

33. The sum of three consecutive odd integers is 75. Find the smallest of these integers.

(a) 23   (b) 27   (c) 24   (d) 25   (e) None of these

1—M—Answer: a

34. Find the original price of a television set that was reduced 40% and is now priced at $285.51.

(a) $399.70   (b) $475.85   (c) $114.20   (d) $713.75   (e) None of these

1—M—Answer: b

35. Solve for P: $A = P + PRT$

(a) $A - PRT$

(b) $A - RT$

(c) $\dfrac{A}{RT}$

(d) $\dfrac{A}{1 + RT}$

(e) None of these

1—M—Answer: d

36. Solve for h: $V = \dfrac{\pi}{3}r^2 h$

(a) $\dfrac{V}{3\pi r^2}$

(b) $\dfrac{\pi r^2 V}{3}$

(c) $\dfrac{\pi r^2}{3V}$

(d) $\dfrac{3V}{\pi r^2}$

(e) None of these

1—M—Answer: d

37. Solve for h: $A = \dfrac{1}{2}(a + b)h$

(a) $\dfrac{A}{2(a + b)}$

(b) $\dfrac{2A}{a + b}$

(c) $2A(a + b)$

(d) $A - \dfrac{1}{2}(a + b)$

(e) None of these

1—M—Answer: b

38. Solve for p: $g = \dfrac{4\pi^2 p}{r^2}$

1—O—Answer: $\dfrac{gr^2}{4\pi^2}$

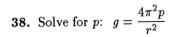

2.3 Solving Equations Graphically

1. Which of the following is an intercept of the graph of $3x + 2y = 9$?

(a) $(1, 3)$ (b) $(0, 3)$ (c) $(3, 0)$ (d) $(3, 1)$ (e) None of these

1—M—Answer: c

2. Which of the following is not an intercept of the graph of $x^2 - y = 4$?

(a) $(0, -4)$ (b) $(0, 4)$ (c) $(-2, 0)$ (d) $(2, 0)$ (e) None of these

1—M—Answer: b

3. Find the intercepts of the graph of $2x - y = -2$.

(a) x-intercept: $(-1, 0)$ (b) x-intercept: $(2, 0)$ (c) x-intercept: $(0, -1)$
      y-intercept: $(0, 2)$ y-intercept: $(0, -1)$ y-intercept: $(2, 0)$

(d) x-intercept: $(1, 0)$ (e) None of these
      y-intercept: $(0, -2)$

1—M—Answer: a

4. Find the intercepts of the graph of $3x + 7y = 21$.

(a) x-intercept: $(0, 7)$ (b) x-intercept: $(0, 3)$ (c) x-intercept: $(3, 0)$
      y-intercept: $(3, 0)$ y-intercept: $(7, 0)$ y-intercept: $(0, 7)$

(d) x-intercept: $(7, 0)$ (e) None of these
      y-intercept: $(0, 3)$

1—M—Answer: d

5. Find the intercepts: $y = -4x^2 + 4x - 1$

1—O—Answer: $\left(\frac{1}{2}, 0\right)$, $(0, -1)$

6. Find the intercepts: $y = x^2 - 2x - 3$

1—O—Answer: $(-1, 0), (3, 0), (0, -3)$

7. Find the x-intercept(s): $3x^2 + 2y^2 + 4xy - 12 = 0$

(a) $(\pm\sqrt{6}, 0)$ (b) $(\pm 2, 0)$ (c) $(4, 0)$ (d) $(6, 0)$ (e) None of these

1—M—Answer: b

8. Find the x-intercept(s): $y = x^3(x + 2)(3x - 1)$

(a) $(0, 0), (-2, 0), \left(\frac{1}{3}, 0\right)$ (b) $(0, 0)$ (c) $(0, 0), (2, 0), (-1, 0)$

(d) $(-2, 0), \left(\frac{1}{3}, 0\right)$ (e) None of these

1—M—Answer: a

9. Determine which of the following are zeros of the function $f(x) = 2x^3 + x^2 - 3x$.

    (a) $x = 0$ (b) $x = 1$ (c) $x = -\frac{3}{2}$

    (d) All of these are zeros.   (e) None of these are zeros.

    1—M—Answer: d

10. Determine which of the following are zeros of the function $f(x) = 2x^3 + 5x^2 - x + 4$.

    (a) $x = 1$ (b) $x = 0$ (c) $x = -3$

    (d) All of these are zeros.   (e) None of these are zeros.

    1—M—Answer: e

11. Rewrite the equation $5(x + 3) = 6(x - 1) + 8$ in standard form.

    (a) $x - 13 = 0$ (b) $x = 13$ (c) $-x - 13 = 0$

    (d) $x = -13$ (e) None of these

    1—M—Answer: a

12. Rewrite the equation $\dfrac{2}{x} + 6 = \dfrac{x}{4}$ in standard form.

    (a) $8 + 24x = x^2$ (b) $x^2 + 24x - 8 = 0$ (c) $x^2 - 24x - 8 = 0$

    (d) $x^2 - 24x - 2 = 0$ (e) None of these

    1—M—Answer: c

13. Use the graph of $y = 2x^3 - x^2 - 7x + 6$ shown at the right to approximate the solution of $2x^3 - x^2 - 7x + 6 = 0$.

    1—O—Answer: -2, 1, 1.5

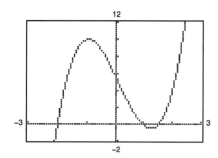

14. Use the graph of $y = \dfrac{1}{\sqrt{x}}$ shown at the right to approximate the solution of $\sqrt{x}\,y = 1$.

    1—O—Answer: No solution

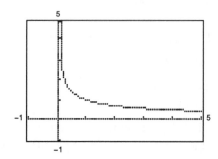

15. Which of the following range settings should be used to graph $y = x^2 - 17x + 47$ in order to approximate the solutions of $x^2 - 17x + 47 = 0$?

    (a)
    ```
    RANGE
    Xmin=-10
    Xmax=10
    Xscl=1
    Ymin=-10
    Ymax=10
    Yscl=1
    ```
    (b)
    ```
    RANGE
    Xmin=10
    Xmax=30
    Xscl=10
    Ymin=10
    Ymax=30
    Yscl=10
    ```
    (c)
    ```
    RANGE
    Xmin=-20
    Xmax=5
    Xscl=5
    Ymin=-20
    Ymax=5
    Yscl=5
    ```
    (d)
    ```
    RANGE
    Xmin=-5
    Xmax=20
    Xscl=5
    Ymin=-30
    Ymax=20
    Yscl=10
    ```

    (e) None of these

    1—M—Answer: d

16. Which of the following range settings should be used to graph $y = x^3 + 2x^2 - 5x + 10$?

    (a)
    ```
    RANGE
    Xmin=-8
    Xmax=6
    Xscl=2
    Ymin=-5
    Ymax=30
    Yscl=5
    ```
    (b)
    ```
    RANGE
    Xmin=0
    Xmax=8
    Xscl=1
    Ymin=0
    Ymax=30
    Yscl=5
    ```
    (c)
    ```
    RANGE
    Xmin=-2
    Xmax=8
    Xscl=1
    Ymin=-2
    Ymax=8
    Yscl=1
    ```
    (d)
    ```
    RANGE
    Xmin=-1
    Xmax=9
    Xscl=1
    Ymin=-4
    Ymax=28
    Yscl=4
    ```

    (e) None of these

    1—M—Answer: a

17. Use a graphing utility to approximate the solution(s) of $x^3 - x + 9 = 0$.

    (a) -2.25 (b) -1.75 (c) 9.00 (d) -4.25 (e) None of these

    1—M—Answer: a

18. Use a graphing utility to approximate the solution(s) of $\frac{1}{2}(x^2 - 9x + 19) = 0$.

    (a) $2.95, \ 6.21$ (b) $3.38, \ 5.62$ (c) $3.00, \ 5.50$

    (d) $-5.65, \ -3.33$ (e) None of these

    1—M—Answer: b

19. Use a graphing utility to approximate the solution(s) of $x^3 + 5x^2 - x + 16 = 0$.

    (a) 6.32 (b) 2.91 (c) 0.13 (d) -5.67 (e) None of these

    1—M—Answer: d

20. Use a graphing utility to approximate the solution(s) of $\dfrac{1}{x-3} = 9$.

    (a) 3.00 (b) 3.11 (c) 2.90 (d) No solution   (e) None of these

    1—M—Answer: b

21. Use a graphing utility to approximate the solution(s) of $x^5 = x^2 - 2$.

    (a) -2 (b) 2 (c) -1 (d) No solution   (e) None of these

    1—M—Answer: c

22. Use a graphing utility to approximate the solution(s) of $x^4 + 2x^3 + 5x - 1 = 0$.

(a) -2.72, 0.20 (b) -1, 0 (c) -2.72, -0.11

(d) No solution   (e) None of these

1—M—Answer: a

23. Algebraically, find the point(s) of intersection of the graphs of $y = -\frac{1}{6}x + 2$ and $y = 2x + \frac{17}{2}$.

(a) $\left(\frac{13}{2}, 6\right)$ (b) $(6, -3)$ (c) $\left(-3, \frac{5}{2}\right)$

(d) $(-6, 3)$ (e) None of these

1—M—Answer: c

24. Algebraically, find the point(s) of intersection of the graphs of $y = 5x - 14$ and $y = -3x - 6$.

(a) $(1, -9)$ (b) $(2, -4)$ (c) $(3, -15)$

(d) No solution   (e) None of these

1—M—Answer: a

25. Algebraically, find the point(s) of intersection of the graphs of $y = \frac{1}{4}x^2 - \frac{17}{4}$ and $y = \frac{1}{2}x - \frac{1}{2}$.

(a) $(5, -3)$ (b) $(5, 2)$, $(-3, -2)$ (c) $\left(2, -\frac{1}{2}\right)$, $\left(-2, -\frac{3}{2}\right)$

(d) No solution   (e) None of these

2—M—Answer: b

26. Algebraically, find the point(s) of intersection of the graphs of $y = x - 3$ and $y = -\frac{1}{2}x^2 - 3$.

(a) $(-2, -5)$ (b) $(0, -3)$ (c) $(-2, -5)$, $(0, -3)$

(d) No solution   (e) None of these

2—M—Answer: c

27. Use a graphing utility to approximate any points of intersection of the graphs of $y = x - 7$ and $y = 3x + 1$.

(a) $(-4, -11)$ (b) $(3, -4)$ (c) $(-1, -4)$

(d) $(6, -1)$ (e) None of these

1—M—Answer: a

28. Use a graphing utility to approximate any points of intersection of the graphs of $y = -x + 4$ and $y = \frac{1}{2}x - 3$.

(a) $(-3.33, 6.67)$ (b) $(0.67, 3.33)$ (c) $(3.33, 0.33)$

(d) $(4.67, -0.67)$ (e) None of these

1—M—Answer: d

29. Use a graphing utility to approximate any points of intersection of the graphs of $y = -x + 6$ and $y = 2x^2 + x - 1$.

    (a) $(-2.44, 8.44)$, $(1.44, 4.56)$ (b) $(1.44, 4.56)$ (c) $(-1.87, 7.87)$, $(1.87, 4.13)$

    (d) No solution   (e) None of these

    2—M—Answer: a

30. Use a graphing utility to approximate any points of intersection of the graphs of $y = 3x^2 + 2x + 4$ and $y = -3x - 2$.

    2—O—Answer: No solution

31. The perimeter of a rectangular region with length x is 95 feet. Approximate the dimensions of the region if the area of the region is 524 square feet.

    2—O—Answer: 30.08 ft by 17.42 ft

32. The perimeter of a rectangular region with length x is 132 feet. Approximate the dimensions of the region is the area of the region is 1044 square feet.

    2—O—Answer: 39.71 ft by 26.29 ft

33. Between 1970 and 1990, the number of cattle and sheep, y (in 1000's), that grazed on national forest land can be modeled by the following equations. (Let $t = 0$ represent 1970.)

    $y = 1600 - 11t$ Cattle
    $y = 1650 - 30t$ Sheep

    Approximate when more cattle than sheep were grazing in national forests.

    2—O—Answer: Between 1972 and 1973

2.4 Quadratic Equations

1. Write the quadratic equation in standard form: $x^2 - 4x = x + 2$

    (a) $x^2 - 3x = 2$ (b) $x^2 - 5x = 2$ (c) $x^2 - 5x - 2 = 0$

    (d) $x^2 = 3x - 2$ (e) None of these

    1—M—Answer: c

2. Write the quadratic equation in standard form: $\dfrac{3}{x+7} - \dfrac{4}{x+2} = 6$

    (a) $6x^2 + 55x + 106 = 0$ (b) $6x^2 + 55x + 72 = 0$ (c) $6x^2 - x + 106 = 0$

    (d) $6x^2 - x = 72$ (e) None of these

    2—M—Answer: a

3. Write the quadratic equation in standard form: $x^2 = 64x$

   (a) $x^2 = 64x$ (b) $x^2 - 64x = 0$ (c) $x - 64 = 0$

   (d) $64 - x^2 = 0$ (e) None of these

   1—M—Answer: b

4. Write the quadratic equation in standard form: $\dfrac{1}{x+1} - \dfrac{3}{x-2} = 5$

   (a) $x = -5$ (b) $2x - 6 = 0$ (c) $5x^2 + 2x - 5 = 0$

   (d) $5x^2 - 3x - 5 = 0$ (e) None of these

   1—M—Answer: d

5. Write the quadratic equation in standard form: $x^2 + 1 = \dfrac{3x - 2}{5}$

   (a) $x^2 - \dfrac{3}{5}x + 3 = 0$ (b) $5x^2 - 3x + 15 = 0$ (c) $5x^2 - 3x + 7 = 0$

   (d) $5x^2 - 3x + 3 = 0$ (e) None of these

   1—M—Answer: c

6. Solve by factoring: $5x^2 - 2 = 3x$

   (a) $\frac{2}{5}, -1$ (b) $-\frac{1}{5}, 2$ (c) $-\frac{2}{5}, 1$ (d) $\frac{1}{5}, -2$ (e) None of these

   1—M—Answer: c

7. Solve by factoring: $2x^2 + 4x = 9x + 18$

   (a) $-2, \frac{9}{2}$ (b) $2, -\frac{9}{2}$ (c) $\frac{9}{2}$ (d) $-\frac{9}{2}$ (e) None of these

   1—M—Answer: a

8. Solve by factoring: $4x^2 + 12x + 9 = 0$

   1—O—Answer: $-\frac{3}{2}$

9. Solve by factoring: $3x^2 + 19x - 14 = 0$

   1—O—Answer: $-7, \frac{2}{3}$

10. Solve by factoring: $2x^2 + x = 3$

    1—O—Answer: $-\frac{3}{2}, 1$

11. Solve by extracting square roots: $2x^2 = 162$

    (a) 9   (b) -9 (c) $-9, 9$

    (d) 81   (e) None of these

    1—M—Answer: c

12. Solve by extracting square roots: $7(x+2)^2 = 12$

    1—O—Answer: $\frac{1}{7}(-14 \pm 2\sqrt{21})$

13. Solve by extracting square roots: $(x + 7)^2 = 5$

    1—O—Answer: $-7 \pm \sqrt{5}$

14. Solve by extracting square roots: $3x^2 = 192$

(a) ± 8 (b) 8   (c) -1

(d) 64   (e) None of these

1—M—Answer: a

15. Solve by extracting square roots: $(2x+3)^2 = 4$

(a) $\frac{1}{2}, \frac{5}{2}$ (b) $-\frac{1}{2}$ (c) $-\frac{5}{2}, -\frac{1}{2}$

(d) ± 2 (e) None of these

1—M—Answer: c

16. Solve by completing the square: $x^2 - 8x + 2 = 0$

1—O—Answer: $4 \pm \sqrt{14}$

17. Solve by completing the square: $x^2 + 4x - 2 = 0$

(a) $2 \pm \sqrt{6}$ (b) $2 \pm \sqrt{2}$ (c) $-2 \pm \sqrt{2}$

(d) $-2 \pm \sqrt{6}$ (e) None of these

1—M—Answer: d

18. Solve by completing the square: $x^2 - 6x + 1 = 0$

(a) $3 \pm \sqrt{26}$ (b) $3 \pm \sqrt{10}$ (c) $3 \pm \sqrt{17}$

(d) $3 \pm 2\sqrt{2}$ (e) None of these

1—M—Answer: d

19. Solve by completing the square: $1 - x = x(x+3)$

(a) $x = -\frac{3}{2} \pm \frac{\sqrt{13}}{2}$ (b) $-2 \pm \sqrt{5}$ (c) $-1 \pm \sqrt{2}$

(d) $\frac{3}{2} \pm \frac{\sqrt{11}}{2}$ (e) None of these

1—M—Answer: b

20. Solve by completing the square: $6x - x^2 = 3$

(a) $-3 \pm 2\sqrt{3}$ (b) $3 \pm \sqrt{6}$ (c) $3 \pm 2\sqrt{3}$

(d) 3, 9   (e) None of these

1—M—Answer: b

21. Solve by completing the square: $2x^2 - 8x + 5 = 0$

(a) $2 \pm \frac{\sqrt{6}}{2}$ (b) $-2 \pm \frac{\sqrt{3}}{2}$ (c) $4 \pm \frac{\sqrt{19}}{2}$

(d) $8 \pm \frac{\sqrt{5}}{2}$ (e) None of these

2—M—Answer: a

22. Use a graphing utility to solve the equation: $3x^2 + 18x - 22 = 0$

    (a) $-19.56, -16.44$ (b) $-4.29, -1.71$ (c) $-4.89, -1.11$

    (d) $4.96, 7.04$ (e) None of these

    2—M—Answer: e

23. Use a graphing utility to solve the equation: $7x^2 - 14x + 6 = 0$

    (a) $13.65, 14.35$ (b) $-0.01, 2.01$ (c) $0.62, 1.38$

    (d) No solution   (e) None of these

    2—M—Answer: c

24. Use a graphing utility to solve the equation: $4x^2 - 16x - 13 = 0$

    (a) $-0.06, 4.06$ (b) $2.97, 5.03$ (c) $1.13, 2.87$

    (d) No solution   (e) None of these

    2—M—Answer: e

25. Use a graphing utility to solve the equation: $2x^2 + 12x + 13 = 0$

    (a) $-7.80, -4.20$ (b) $-4.58, -1.42$ (c) $0.38, 2.62$

    (d) $-2.40, 2.40$ (e) None of these

    2—M—Answer: b

26. Use a graphing utility to solve the equation: $2x^2 - 7x - 12 = 0$

    2—O—Answer: $-1.26, 4.76$

27. Solve for x : $\dfrac{3x + 25}{x + 7} - 5 = \dfrac{3}{x}$

    (a) $\dfrac{3}{2}, 7$ (b) $\dfrac{7}{2}, 3$ (c) $-\dfrac{3}{2}, -7$

    (d) $-\dfrac{7}{2}, -3$ (e) None of these

    1—M—Answer: d

28. Solve for x: $\dfrac{2x - 1}{x} + 1 = \dfrac{4}{x + 1}$

    (a) 1 (b) -1 (c) $-\dfrac{1}{3}, 1$ (d) $-1, \dfrac{1}{3}$ (e) None of these

    1—M—Answer: c

29. Complete the square: $2x^2 + 9x - 4$

(a) $2\left(x + \dfrac{9}{4}\right)^2 - \dfrac{113}{8}$

(b) $2\left(x + \dfrac{9}{4}\right)^2 - \dfrac{145}{16}$

(c) $2\left(x + \dfrac{9}{4}\right)^2 + \dfrac{49}{8}$

(d) $2\left(x + \dfrac{9}{4}\right)^2 + \dfrac{17}{16}$

(e) None of these

2—M—Answer: a

30. Complete the square: $3x^2 - 2x + 1$

(a) $(3x - 1)^2$

(b) $3(x - 1)^2 + 1$

(c) $3\left(x - \dfrac{1}{3}\right)^2 + \dfrac{1}{9}$

(d) $3\left(x - \dfrac{1}{3}\right)^2 + \dfrac{2}{3}$

(e) None of these

2—M—Answer: d

31. Complete the square: $2x^2 - 6x + 9$

2—O—Answer: $2\left(x - \dfrac{3}{2}\right)^2 + \dfrac{9}{2}$

32. Complete the square in the denominator: $\dfrac{3}{4x^2 + 10x - 7}$

(a) $\dfrac{3}{4(x + \frac{5}{4})^2 - \frac{53}{4}}$

(b) $\dfrac{3}{4(x + \frac{5}{2})^2 - 32}$

(c) $\dfrac{3}{4(x + \frac{5}{4})^2 - \frac{3}{4}}$

(d) $\dfrac{3}{4(x + \frac{5}{2})^2 + 18}$

(e) None of these

2—M—Answer: a

33. Complete the square in the denominator: $\dfrac{5}{2x^2 - 3x + 1}$

(a) $\dfrac{5}{2\left(x - \frac{3}{2}\right)^2 + \frac{13}{4}}$

(b) $\dfrac{5}{2\left(x - \frac{3}{2}\right)^2 + 1}$

(c) $\dfrac{5}{2\left(x - \frac{3}{4}\right)^2 + \frac{11}{2}}$

(d) $\dfrac{5}{2\left(x - \frac{3}{2}\right) - \frac{5}{4}}$

(e) None of these

2—M—Answer: e

34. The daily cost in dollars, C, of producing x chairs is given by the quadratic equation $C = x^2 - 120x + 4200$. How many chairs are produced each day if the daily cost is \$600?

(a) 60   (b) 600   (c) 90   (d) 40   (e) None of these

2—M—Answer: a

35. You plan to stabilize a T.V. antenna with two guy wires. The guy wires are attached to the antenna 30 feet from the base. How much wire will you need if each of the wires is secured 20 feet from the base of the antenna?

(a) $10\sqrt{13}$ ft   (b) $20\sqrt{5}$ ft   (c) $20\sqrt{13}$ ft   (d) $10\sqrt{5}$ ft   (e) None of these

2—M—Answer: c

36. Find the smaller of two consecutive positive integers such that the one number times twice the other equals 612.

(a) -18 (b) 12   (c) 18   (d) 17   (e) None of these

2—M—Answer: d

2.5 The Quadratic Formula

1. Identify the Quadratic Formula.

(a) $x = -b \pm \dfrac{\sqrt{b^2 - 4ac}}{2a}$ (b) $x = \dfrac{-b \pm \sqrt{b^2 - 4a}}{2c}$ (c) $x = \dfrac{-b \pm \sqrt{b^2 - 4ac}}{2a}$

(d) $x = \dfrac{-b \pm \sqrt{b^2 - 4ac}}{2}$ (e) None of these

1—M—Answer: c

2. Use the discriminant to determine the number of real solutions: $4x^2 - 2x - 7 = 0$

(a) 0   (b) 1   (c) 2   (d) 3   (e) None of these

1—M—Answer: c

3. Use the discriminant to determine the number of real solutions: $7x^2 - 3x + 15 = 0$

(a) 0   (b) 1   (c) 2   (d) 3   (e) None of these

1—M—Answer: a

4. Use the discriminant to determine the number of real solutions: $\frac{1}{3}x^2 - 2x + 3 = 0$

(a) 0   (b) 1   (c) 2   (d) 3   (e) None of these

1—M—Answer: b

5. Use the discriminant to determine the number of real solutions: $10x = x^2 - 14x + 50$

1—O—Answer: 2

6. Use the discriminant to determine the number of real solutions: $5x^2 - 7x + 16 = 0$

   1—O—Answer: 0

7. Use the discriminant to determine which quadratic equation has one (repeated) real number solution.

   (a) $3x^2 + 4x + 2 = 0$ (b) $x^2 - 5x - 4 = 0$ (c) $9x^2 - 6x + 1 = 0$

   (d) $7x^2 + 2x - 1 = 0$ (e) None of these

   1—M—Answer: c

8. Use the discriminant to determine which quadratic equation has no real solutions.

   (a) $x^2 + 4x + 2 = 0$ (b) $9x^2 - 6x + 1 = 0$ (c) $x^2 - 5x + 4 = 0$

   (d) $7x^2 + 2x - 1 = 0$ (e) None of these

   1—M—Answer: e

9. Solve for x: $x^2 - 3x + \dfrac{3}{2} = 0$

   1—O—Answer: $\dfrac{3 \pm \sqrt{3}}{2}$

10. Solve for x: $-3x^2 + 4x + 6 = 0$

   1—O—Answer: $\dfrac{2 \pm \sqrt{22}}{3}$

11. Solve for x: $(x + 2)^2 = -16x$

   (a) $-8 \pm 2\sqrt{15}$ (b) $-10 \pm 4\sqrt{6}$ (c) $-10 \pm 2\sqrt{26}$

   (d) $-8 \pm 4\sqrt{15}$ (e) None of these

   1—M—Answer: b

12. Solve for x: $\dfrac{1}{x - 1} + \dfrac{x}{x + 2} = 2$

   1—O—Answer: $-1 \pm \sqrt{7}$

13. Solve: $3x^2 - 6x + 2 = 0$

   (a) $\dfrac{3 \pm \sqrt{3}}{3}$ (b) $1 \pm \sqrt{3}$ (c) $\dfrac{3 \pm \sqrt{15}}{3}$

   (d) $\dfrac{1}{3}, 2$ (e) None of these

   1—M—Answer: a

14. Solve: $(x - 1)^2 = 3x + 5$

   (a) $1, 4$ (b) $\dfrac{5 \pm \sqrt{39}}{2}$ (c) $\dfrac{5 \pm \sqrt{41}}{2}$

   (d) $-1, 6$ (e) None of these

   2—M—Answer: c

15. Solve: $4x^2 + 12x = 135$

    (a) $-\dfrac{9}{2}, \dfrac{15}{2}$ (b) $-\dfrac{5}{2}, \dfrac{3}{2}$ (c) $-\dfrac{15}{2}, \dfrac{9}{2}$

    (d) $\dfrac{-3 \pm \sqrt{6}}{2}$ (e) None of these

    2—M—Answer: c

16. Use your calculator to solve: $2.5x^2 + 3.267x - 8.97 = 0$ Round your answers to three decimal places.

    (a) $-6.643, 3.376$ (b) $-5.271, -1.263$ (c) $-8.276, 1.742$

    (d) $-2.657, 1.350$ (e) None of these

    2—M—Answer: d

17. Use your calculator to solve: $1.37x^2 - 2.4x - 5.41 = 0$ Round your answers to three decimal places.

    (a) $0.228, 4.572$ (b) $-1.296, 3.048$ (c) $-1.775, 4.175$

    (d) $-5.720, 2.432$ (e) None of these

    2—M—Answer: b

18. Use a calculator to solve: $3x^2 - 0.24x - 0.57 = 0$

    (a) $0.478, -0.398$ (b) $0.474, -0.394$ (c) $1.434, -1.194$

    (d) $1.422, -1.182$ (e) None of these

    1—M—Answer: a

19. Use a calculator to solve: $27x^2 - 3.2x - 71 = 0$

    (a) $1.680, -1.561$ (b) $1.682, -1.563$ (c) $-1.678, 1.623$

    (d) $-1.680, 1.569$ (e) None of these

    2—M—Answer: b

20. Use a calculator to solve: $3x^2 - 0.482x - 1.2 = 0$

    (a) $-0.557, 0.718$ (b) $-0.718, 0.557$ (c) $-1.671, 2.154$

    (d) $-0.547, 0.708$ (e) None of these

    2—M—Answer: a

21. Use a calculator to solve: $62x^2 - 78.2x + 5.1 = 0$

    (a) $-0.062, 1.323$ (b) $-3.244, 1.983$ (c) $0.069, 1.192$

    (d) $4.277, 73.903$ (e) None of these

    2—M—Answer: c

22. Use a calculator to solve: $3.2x^2 + 0.61x - 7.4 = 0$

(a) -1.619, 1.428 (b) -0.842, 2.748 (c) -5.181, 4.570

(d) -0.617, 1.529 (e) None of these

2—M—Answer: a

23. Solve for x: $2x^2 - 5(x - 1) = 3(x + 5)$

(a) $\dfrac{1 \pm \sqrt{39}}{2}$ (b) $\pm \dfrac{\sqrt{15}}{3}$ (c) 0, 1, -5

(d) -1, 5 (e) None of these

2—M—Answer: d

24. Solve for x: $(2x + 5)^2 = 9$

(a) -4, -1 (b) -1 (c) 38 (d) 14, 8 (e) None of these

1—M—Answer: a

25. Solve for x: $(3x - 1)^2 = 25$

(a) $-\frac{4}{3}$, 2 (b) -2, 2 (c) 2 (d) -2, $\frac{4}{3}$ (e) None of these

1—M—Answer: a

26. Solve for x: $\dfrac{2}{5}x^2 - \dfrac{1}{2} = 0$

(a) $\pm \dfrac{\sqrt{2}}{5}$ (b) $\pm \dfrac{\sqrt{5}}{5}$ (c) $\pm \dfrac{5\sqrt{2}}{4}$

(d) $\pm \dfrac{1}{2}\sqrt{5}$ (e) None of these

1—M—Answer: d

27. Solve for x: $4x + 3(x^2 - 1) = 2 + 3x^2$

(a) $\pm \dfrac{\sqrt{5}}{2}$ (b) $\dfrac{5}{4}$ (c) $\dfrac{2 \pm \sqrt{34}}{12}$

(d) $\dfrac{-2 \pm \sqrt{10}}{6}$ (e) None of these

1—M—Answer: b

28. Solve for x: $(x - 2)(x + 1) = (x - 3)^2$

(a) $\frac{11}{5}$ (b) 2, 9 (c) 11 (d) 7, -2 (e) None of these

1—M—Answer: a

29. Solve for x: $2x^2 - 5x = x^2 + 1$

    (a) 0, 5   (b) $\dfrac{4}{11}$ (c) $\dfrac{5 \pm \sqrt{29}}{2}$

    (d) $\dfrac{-5 \pm \sqrt{21}}{2}$ (e) None of these

1—M—Answer: c

30. Solve for x: $(x + 1)^2 + x^2 = 9$

    (a) 8   (b) ± 2 (c) $\dfrac{1 \pm \sqrt{15}}{2}$

    (d) $\dfrac{-1 \pm \sqrt{17}}{2}$ (e) None of these

1—M—Answer: d

31. Solve for x: $(x - 1)^2 + (x + 1)^2 = 100$

    (a) $\pm 5\sqrt{2}$ (b) $\pm 2\sqrt{5}$ (c) ± 7

    (d) -4, 6   (e) None of these

1—M—Answer: c

32. Two airplanes leave simultaneously from the same airport, one flying due east, and the other flying due north. The eastbound plane is flying 50 miles per hour slower than the northbound one. If after 4 hours they are 1000 miles apart, how fast is the northbound plane traveling?

    (a) 150 mph   (b) 200 mph   (c) 100 mph   (d) 300 mph   (e) None of these

2—M—Answer: b

33. An open box is to be constructed from a square piece of material by cutting a 3-inch square from each corner. Find the dimensions of the square piece of material if the box is to have a volume of 363 cubic inches.

    (a) 14″ by 14″   (b) 17″ by 17″   (c) 20″ by 20″   (d) 23″ by 23″   (e) None of these

2—M—Answer: b

34. Find two consecutive positive integers m and n such that $n^2 - m^2 = 27$.

    2—O—Answer: 13, 14

35. The Curriers have decided to fence in part of their back yard to form a rectangular region with an area of 1248 square feet. The fence will extend 2 feet on each side of their 48-foot-wide house. How many feet of fencing will they need to enclose the play area? (There is no fence along the house wall.)

2—O—Answer: 104 feet

36. Use the cost equation, $C = 0.5x^2 + 15x + 6000$, to find the number of units, x, that a manufacturer can produce with a total cost, C, of \$13,700.

(a) 140   (b) 110   (c) 94,056,500   (d) 47,134,000   (e) None of these

2—M—Answer: b

2.6 | Other Types of Equations

1. Solve for x: $3x^3 = 27x$

(a) 3   (b) -3, 3   (c) -3, 0, 3

(d) 0, 3   (e) None of these

1—M—Answer: c

2. Solve for x: $3x^3 - 24x^2 + 21x = 0$

(a) 7, 1   (b) -7, -1 (c) 0, 1, 7

(d) 0, -1, -7 (e) None of these

1—M—Answer: c

3. Solve for x: $20x^3 - 500x = 0$ **4.** Solve for x: $7x^3 = 252x$

1—O—Answer: $0, \pm 5$ **1—O—Answer:** $\pm 6, 0$

5. Solve: $x^3 + x^2 - 2x = 2$

(a) -1, $\pm\sqrt{2}$ (b) $1 \pm \sqrt{3}$ (c) 0, $1 \pm \sqrt{3}$

(d) -2, 1   (e) None of these

2—M—Answer: a

6. Solve: $x^3 - 5x - 2x^2 + 10 = 0$

(a) -2, $\pm\sqrt{5}$ (b) $\pm\sqrt{5}$ (c) 2, $\sqrt{5}$

(d) 2, $\pm\sqrt{5}$ (e) None of these

2—M—Answer: d

7. Solve for x: $3x - 2\sqrt{x} - 5 = 0$

(a) $\frac{5}{3}$ (b) -1, $\frac{5}{3}$ (c) 1, $\frac{25}{9}$ (d) $\frac{25}{9}$ (e) None of these

1—M—Answer: d

8. Solve for x: $x^{2/3} - 6x^{1/3} = 7$

   2—O—Answer: $343, -1$

9. Solve for x: $\sqrt{2 - 5x} = 5x$

   (a) $\frac{1}{5}$ (b) $-\frac{2}{5}$ (c) $\frac{1}{5}, -\frac{2}{5}$ (d) $\frac{1}{10}$ (e) None of these

   1—M—Answer: a

10. Solve for x: $\sqrt[3]{4x - 1} = 3$

    1—O—Answer: 7

11. Solve for x: $\sqrt{15x + 4} = 4 - \sqrt{2x + 3}$

    (a) 3   (b) $\frac{11}{169}$ (c) $3, \frac{11}{169}$ (d) $-3, -\frac{11}{169}$ (e) None of these

    2—M—Answer: b

12. Solve for x: $\sqrt{x + 1} = 9 - \sqrt{x}$

    2—O—Answer: $\frac{1600}{81}$

13. Solve for x: $(x^2 + 4)^{2/3} = 25$

    (a) $-5.8, 5.8$ (b) $-4.6, 4.6$ (c) 21
    (d) $-11, 11$ (e) None of these

    1—M—Answer: d

14. Solve: $(x^2 - 2x + 5)^{2/3} = 4$

    (a) $-3, 1$ (b) $-1 \pm \sqrt{13}$ (c) $-1, 3$
    (d) 1   (e) None of these

    2—M—Answer: c

15. Solve: $\dfrac{1}{x - 1} + \dfrac{x}{x + 2} = 2$

    (a) $-2, 1$ (b) $-2, 0, 1$ (c) $-1 \pm \sqrt{7}$
    (d) $-1 \pm \sqrt{3}$ (e) None of these

    2—M—Answer: c

16. Solve for x: $\dfrac{2}{x^2 - 1} + \dfrac{1}{x + 1} = 5$

(a) $\dfrac{6}{5}$

(b) -1, $\dfrac{6}{5}$

(c) $\dfrac{1 \pm \sqrt{41}}{10}$

(d) $\pm \dfrac{\sqrt{2}}{2}$

(e) None of these

1—M—Answer: a

17. Solve for x: $\dfrac{4}{x} - \dfrac{3}{x + 1} = 7$

(a) -1, 5

(b) 3

(c) $\dfrac{-3 \pm \sqrt{37}}{7}$

(d) $\dfrac{-7 \pm \sqrt{77}}{14}$

(e) None of these

1—M—Answer: c

18. Solve for x: $|2 - 4x| = 12$

(a) $-\frac{5}{2}$, $\frac{7}{2}$ (b) $-\frac{5}{2}$, $-\frac{7}{2}$ (c) $\frac{5}{2}$, $-\frac{5}{2}$ (d) $-\frac{5}{2}$ (e) None of these

1—M—Answer: a

19. Solve: $|x^2 - 2x| = x$

(a) 0 (b) 0, ± 1 (c) 0, ± 3 (d) 0, 1, 3 (e) None of these

1—M—Answer: d

20. Solve: $|x^2 - 2x| = 3x - 6$

(a) 2 (b) 2, ± 3 (c) 2, 3 (d) ± 3 (e) None of these

2—M—Answer: c

21. Use a graphing utility to approximate the solutions of $2x^4 - 7x^2 + 5 = 0$.

1—O—Answer: ± 1, ± 1.58

22. Use a graphing utility to approximate the solutions of $x^3 + 3x^2 = 5x$.

(a) -4.19, 1.19

(b) 0, ± 4.19

(c) 0, ± 1.19

(d) 0, -4.19, 1.19

(e) None of these

1—M—Answer: d

23. Use a graphing utility to approximate the solutions of $9x^4 - 24x^2 + 16 = 0$.

(a) ± 1.15 (b) 1.15 (c) 0, ± 1.15 (d) 1.33 (e) None of these

1—M—Answer: a

24. Use a graphing utility to approximate the solutions of $3x + 5 = \sqrt{2 - 2x}$.

1—O—Answer: -1

25. Use a graphing utility to approximate the solutions of $\sqrt{x + 16} = 3 + \sqrt{x - 2}$.

(a) 3   (b) 4.25   (c) 0.5   (d) No solution   (e) None of these

2—M—Answer: b

26. Use a graphing utility to approximate the solution of $(x^2 - 9x + 2)^{3/2} = 216$.

(a) -0.5, 9   (b) ± 3, 4.5   (c) -2.87, 11.87

(d) 1.63, 16.37   (e) None of these

2—M—Answer: c

27. Use a graphing utility to approximate the solution of $\dfrac{1}{x} - \dfrac{1}{x + 1} = 1$.

(a) -1, 0   (b) -1.62, 0.62   (c) -2.12, 0.12

(d) -1, 1   (e) None of these

2—M—Answer: b

28. Use a graphing utility to approximate the solutions of $\dfrac{x}{x^2 - 9} + \dfrac{2}{x + 3} = 3$.

(a) -0.20, 0.43   (b) -2.56, 1.56   (c) -3, 7

(d) -0.62, 1.62   (e) None of these

2—M—Answer: e

29. Use a graphing utility to approximate the solutions of $|3x + 10| = 13$.

(a) 1   (b) -1, 1   (c) -7.67, 1

(d) 1, 7.67   (e) None of these

2—M—Answer: c

30. Use a graphing utility to approximate the solutions of $|x^2 - 2x| = 2x - 3$.

(a) 1, 3, ± 1.73 (b) 1.73, 3   (c) 1, 3

(d) 3   (e) None of these

2—M—Answer: b

31. A church youth group decides to go bowling. They can rent three lanes for two hours for a total of $60. The cost per person will drop by $.60 if they can get 5 visitors to attend also. How many people are in the youth group?

(a) 18   (b) 20   (c) 22   (d) 24   (e) None of these

2—M—Answer: b

32. During a one week leave, three military personnel decide to rent a car and share equally in the cost. By adding a fourth person to the group, each person could save $12.25. How much is the weekly rental for the car?

(a) $49   (b) $163   (c) $189   (d) $147   (e) None of these

2—M—Answer: d

33. The demand equation for a certain product is $p = 25(20 - \sqrt{x})$ where x is the number of units demanded per day and p is the price per unit. Find the demand if the price is set at $250.

(a) 100   (b) 10   (c) 19   (d) 14   (e) None of these

2—M—Answer: a

34. The demand equation for a certain product is $p = 40 - \sqrt{0.0001x + 1}$ where x is the number of units demanded per day and p is the price per unit. Find the demand if the price is set at $10.50.

(a) 92,316,410   (b) 4,765,180   (c) 8,692,500

(d) 576,910   (e) None of these

2—M—Answer: c

35. Find the height of the rectangular solid if the volume is $80x$ cubic units.

(a) 5   (b) 10   (c) 3

(d) 6   (e) None of these

1—M—Answer: c

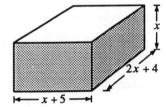

2.7 Linear Inequalities and Graphing Utilities

1. Match the inequality with the graph.

(a) $|x - 7| < 4$ (b) $|x - 1| < 3$
(c) $|x + 3| < 7$ (d) $|x + 3| < 4$
(e) None of these

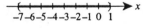

1—M—Answer: d

2. Match the inequality with the graph.

(a) $|x + 4| < -2$ (b) $|x - 2| > 4$
(c) $|x - 2| < 4$ (d) $|x - 6| > 2$
(e) None of these

1—M—Answer: b

3. Match the inequality with the graph.

   (a) $|x + 2| > 5$ (b) $|x + 3| \geq 2$

   (c) $|x - 1| \leq 5$ (d) $|x - 5| \geq 2$

   (e) None of these

   1—M—Answer: b

4. Use absolute value to define the interval: $x < -3$ or $x > 3$

   1—O—Answer: $|x| > 3$

5. Use absolute value to define the interval: $-7 < x < 3$

   2—O—Answer: $|x + 2| < 5$

6. Graph the solution: $3 - 2x < 15$

   (a)

   (b)

   (c)

   (d)

   (e) None of these

   1—M—Answer: a

7. Solve the inequality algebraically: $14 - 2x \leq 5$

   (a) $\left(-\infty, \frac{9}{2}\right)$ (b) $\left(-\infty, \frac{9}{2}\right]$ (c) $\left(\frac{9}{2}, \infty\right)$ (d) $\left[\frac{9}{2}, \infty\right)$ (e) None of these

   1—M—Answer: d

8. Solve the inequality algebraically: $3 - 2x \leq 9$

   (a) $(-\infty, -3]$ (b) $(-\infty, 3]$ (c) $[-3, \infty)$ (d) $[3, \infty)$ (e) None of these

   1—M—Answer: c

9. Solve the inequality algebraically: $5x + 6 > 7x + 9$

   (a) $\left(-\frac{3}{2}, \infty\right)$ (b) $\left(\frac{6}{5}, \frac{9}{7}\right)$ (c) $\left(-\infty, -\frac{3}{2}\right)$ (d) $\left(\frac{3}{2}, \infty\right)$ (e) None of these

   1—M—Answer: c

10. Solve the inequality algebraically: $4 - 3x \geq 5x + 12$

    (a) $(-\infty, -1]$ (b) $(-\infty, 8]$ (c) $[-1, \infty)$ (d) $(-\infty, -2)$ (e) None of these

    1—M—Answer: a

11. Use a graphing utility to solve the inequality: $6 - 5x \le x - 6$

    (a) $[0, \infty)$ (b) $[2, \infty)$ (c) $(-\infty, 2]$ (d) $(-\infty, 0)$ (e) None of these

    1—M—Answer: b

12. Use a graphing utility to solve the inequality: $5 + 2x > 4x + 7$

    (a) $x < 1$ (b) $x > 1$ (c) $x > -1$ (d) $x < -1$ (e) None of these

    1—M—Answer: d

13. Graph the solution: $-6 < 7x + 2 \le 5$

    (a) 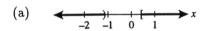   (b)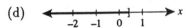

    (c)    (d)

    (e) None of these

    1—M—Answer: b

14. Graph the solution: $\frac{1}{2} < 3 - x < 5$

    1—O—Answer: 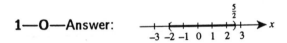

15. Graph the solution: $-16 \le 7 - 2x < 5$

    1—O—Answer: 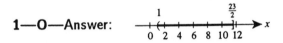

16. Solve the inequality algebraically: $-16 \le 7 - 2x \le 5$

    (a) $x \le 1$ or $x \ge \frac{23}{2}$ (b) $-1 \le x \le \frac{23}{2}$ (c) $1 \le x \le \frac{23}{2}$

    (d) $-\frac{23}{2} \le x \le 1$ (e) None of these

    1—M—Answer: c

17. Solve the inequality algebraically: $-2 < 3x + 1 < 7$

    (a) $-1 \le x \le 2$ (b) $-\frac{1}{3} < x < \frac{8}{3}$ (c) $x > 2$

    (d) $-1 < x < 2$ (e) None of these

    1—M—Answer: d

18. Use a graphing utility to solve the inequality: $-6 < 7x + 2 \leq 5$
    (a) $x < -\frac{8}{7}$ or $x > \frac{3}{7}$ (b) $-\frac{8}{7} < x \leq \frac{3}{7}$ (c) $x > -\frac{8}{7}$
    (d) $x < \frac{3}{7}$ (e) None of these
    1—M—Answer: b

19. Graph the solution: $|3x - 1| \geq 5$

    (a)   (b)

    (c)   (d)

    (e) None of these
    1—M—Answer: b

20. Graph the solution: $|x + 2| < 9$

    (a)   (b)

    (c)   (d)

    (e) None of these
    1—M—Answer: a

21. Solve the inequality algebraically: $|3x - 1| > 2$
    (a) $\left(-\frac{1}{3},\ 1\right)$ (b) $\left[-\frac{1}{3},\ 1\right]$ (c) $\left(-\infty,\ -\frac{1}{3}\right),\ (1, \infty)$
    (d) $\left(-\infty,\ -\frac{1}{3}\right],\ [1, \infty)$ (e) None of these
    1—M—Answer: c

22. Solve the inequality algebraically: $|x + 5| \leq 2$
    1—O—Answer: $-7 \leq x \leq -3$

23. Use a graphing utility to solve the inequality: $|2x + 5| > 3$
    (a) $x < -4$ or $x > -1$ (b) $-4 < x < -1$ (c) $x < 1$ or $x > 4$
    (d) $x < -1$ or $x > 4$ (e) None of these
    1—M—Answer: a

24. Graph the solution: $|3x - 1| > 9$

1—O—Answer:

25. Find the interval for which the radicand is nonnegative: $\sqrt{5 - 4x}$

(a) $\left(-\infty, -\frac{4}{5}\right]$ (b) $\left[\frac{5}{4}, \infty\right)$ (c) $\left(-\infty, \frac{4}{5}\right]$ (d) $\left(-\infty, \frac{5}{4}\right]$ (e) None of these

1—M—Answer: d

26. Find the interval for which the radicand is nonnegative: $\sqrt{2 - 3x}$

(a) $\left[-\infty, -\frac{3}{2}\right]$ (b) $\left(-\infty, \frac{2}{3}\right]$ (c) $\left[\frac{2}{3}, \infty\right)$ (d) $\left[\frac{3}{2}, \infty\right)$ (e) None of these

1—M—Answer: b

27. Find the intervals for which the radicand is nonnegative: $\sqrt{7 + 5x}$

(a) $\left(-\infty, \frac{5}{7}\right]$ (b) $\left(-\infty, -\frac{7}{5}\right]$ (c) $\left[-\frac{5}{7}, \infty\right)$ (d) $\left[\frac{7}{5}, \infty\right)$ (e) None of these

1—M—Answer: e

28. Find the interval for which the radicand is positive: $\dfrac{1}{\sqrt{2 + 5x}}$

(a) $\left(-\infty, -\dfrac{2}{5}\right)$ (b) $\left(-\infty, -\dfrac{5}{2}\right)$ (c) $\left(-\dfrac{5}{2}, \infty\right)$ (d) $\left(-\dfrac{2}{5}, \infty\right)$ (e) None-of these

1—M—Answer: d

29. Find the interval for which the radicand is positive: $\dfrac{1}{\sqrt[4]{3 - 4x}}$

(a) $\left(\dfrac{4}{3}, \infty\right)$ (b) $\left(-\dfrac{3}{4}, \infty\right)$ (c) $\left(-\infty, \dfrac{3}{4}\right)$ (d) $\left(-\infty, -\dfrac{4}{3}\right)$ (e) None of these

1—M—Answer: c

30. Use absolute value notation to define the interval on the real number line.

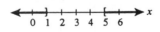

(a) $x \leq 1$ or $x \geq 5$ (b) $|x - 3| \leq 2$ (c) $|x - 3| \geq 2$

(d) $|x + 3| \geq 2$ (e) None of these

1—M—Answer: c

31. Use absolute value notation to define the interval on the real number line.

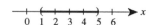

1—O—Answer: $|x - 3| < 2$

32. Use absolute value notation to define all real numbers on the real number line within 6 units of 10.

(a) $|x - 6| \geq 10$ (b) $|x - 10| \geq 6$ (c) $|x - 6| \geq 10$

(d) $|x - 10| \leq 6$ (e) None of these

1—M—Answer: d

33. The revenue for selling x units of a product is $R = 35.95x$. The cost of producing x units is $14.75x + 848$. In order to obtain a profit, the revenue must be greater than the cost. For what values of x will this product return a profit?

(a) $x > 123$ (b) $x > 117$ (c) $x > 52$ (d) $x > 40$ (e) None of these

2—M—Answer: d

34. The revenue for selling x units of a product is $R = 257x$. The cost of producing x units is $193x + 5248$. In order to obtain a profit, the revenue must be greater than the cost. For what values of x will this product return a profit?

(a) $x > 103$ (b) $x > 82$ (c) $x > 77$ (d) $x > 12$ (e) None of these

2—M—Answer: b

35. The revenue for selling x units of a product is $R = 4.50x$. The cost of producing x units is $3x + 3717$. In order to obtain a profit, the revenue must be greater than the cost. For what values of x will this product return a profit?

(a) $x > 1893$ (b) $x > 1239$ (c) $x > 2478$ (d) $x > 496$ (e) None of these

2—M—Answer: c

36. You buy a bag of candy that costs \$2.90 per pound. The weight that is listed on the bag is 1.10 pounds. If the scale that weighed the candy is only accurate to within 0.125 of a pound, how much money might you have been overcharged or undercharged?

(a) $22\frac{1}{8}¢$ (b) $17\frac{3}{4}¢$ (c) $36\frac{1}{4}¢$ (d) $31\frac{1}{2}¢$ (e) None of these

2—M—Answer: c

37. You buy a bag of candy that costs \$3.15 per pound. The weight that is listed on the bag is 0.90 pounds. If the scale that weighed the candy is only accurate to within 0.125 of a pound, how much money might you have been overcharged or undercharged?

(a) $39\frac{3}{8}¢$ (b) $29\frac{1}{4}¢$ (c) $16\frac{2}{3}¢$ (d) $51\frac{1}{2}¢$ (e) None of these

2—M—Answer: a

2.8 Other Types of Inequalities and Graphing Utilities

1. Solve the inequality: $(x-2)^2 \le 9$

   1—O—Answer: $[-1, 5]$

2. Solve the inequality: $(x+3)^2 \ge 4$

   (a) $[1, 5]$ (b) $(-\infty, 5]$ (c) $(-\infty, -5] \cup [-1, \infty)$

   (d) $[-5, -1]$ (e) None of these

   1—M—Answer: c

3. Solve the inequality: $(x-1)^2 \le 25$

   (a) $[-4, 6]$ (b) $(-\infty, -4] \cup [6, \infty)$ (c) $(-\infty, -6] \cup [4, \infty)$

   (d) $[-6, 4]$ (e) None of these

   1—M—Answer: a

4. Use a graphing utility to solve $(x+1)^2 \ge 9$.

   (a) $-4, 2$ (b) $(-\infty, -4] \cup [2, \infty)$ (c) $[-2, 4]$

   (d) $(-\infty, -2) \cup (4, \infty)$ (e) None of these

   1—M—Answer: b

5. Solve the inequality: $x^2 - x > 6$

   1—O—Answer: $(-\infty, -2) \cup (3, \infty)$

6. Solve the inequality: $3x^3 - 6x^2 > 0$

   (a) $(-\infty, 0) \cup (2, \infty)$ (b) $(0, 2)$ (c) $(-\infty, 0)$

   (d) $(2, \infty)$ (e) None of these

   1—M—Answer: d

7. Use a graphing utility to solve $2x^2 + 3x \ge 5$.

   (a) $[-2.5, 1]$ (b) $[-2.5, \infty)$ (c) $(-\infty, -2.5] \cup [1, \infty)$

   (d) $(-\infty, -1.5) \cup [5, \infty)$ (e) None of these

   1—M—Answer: c

8. Solve: $2x^2 + 3x < 9$

   (a) $\left(-3, \frac{3}{2}\right)$ (b) $(-\infty, -3) \cup \left(\frac{3}{2}, \infty\right)$ (c) $\left[-3, \frac{3}{2}\right]$

   (d) $(-\infty, 3) \cup (9, \infty)$ (e) None of these

   1—M—Answer: a

9. Solve: $2x^2 - 5x > 3$

    (a) $\left(-\frac{1}{2},\ 3\right)$ 　　　　(b) $\left(-\infty, -\frac{1}{2}\right) \cup (3,\ \infty)$ 　　　　(c) $(-\infty, -3) \cup \left(\frac{1}{2},\ \infty\right)$

    (d) $\left(-\frac{1}{2},\ \infty\right)$ 　　　　(e) None of these

    1—M—Answer: b

10. Use a graphing utility to solve $2x^3 \leq 4x^4$.

    (a) $(-\infty,\ \infty)$ 　　　　(b) $\left[0,\ \frac{1}{2}\right]$ 　　　　(c) $(-\infty,\ 0] \cup \left[\frac{1}{2},\ \infty\right)$

    (d) $\left[\frac{1}{2},\ \infty\right)$ 　　　　(e) None of these

    1—M—Answer: c

11. Solve: $x^2 + 1 \geq 0$

    (a) $(-\infty,\ \infty)$ 　　　　(b) $[-1,\ 1]$ 　　　　(c) $(-\infty,\ -1] \cup [1,\ \infty)$

    (d) $(-1,\ 1)$ 　　　　(e) None of these

    2—M—Answer: a

12. Use a graphing utility to solve $x^2 + 4x + 2 \leq 0$.

    (a) $[-3.41,\ \infty)$ 　　　　(b) $[-3.41,\ -0.59]$ 　　　　(c) $(-\infty,\ -3.41] \cup [-0.59,\ \infty)$

    (d) $[-2,\ 2]$ 　　　　(e) None of these

    2—M—Answer: b

13. Solve: $x^2 + 6x + 1 \geq 0$

    (a) $(-\infty,\ -3 - 2\sqrt{2}] \cup [-3 + 2\sqrt{2},\ \infty)$ 　　　　(b) $[-3 - 2\sqrt{2},\ -3 + 2\sqrt{2}]$

    (c) $(-\infty,\ -3 - \sqrt{10}] \cup [-3 + \sqrt{10},\ \infty)$ 　　　　(d) $[-3 - \sqrt{10},\ -3 + \sqrt{10}]$

    (e) None of these

    2—M—Answer: a

14. Use a graphing utility to solve $x^2 + x - 3 < 0$.

    (a) $(-\infty,\ -3) \cup (1,\ \infty)$ 　　　　(b) $(-\infty,\ -2.30) \cup (1.30,\ \infty)$ 　　　　(c) $(-2.30,\ 1.30)$

    (d) $(-3,\ 1)$ 　　　　(e) None of these

    2—M—Answer: c

15. Use a graphing utility to solve $x^2 - 4x + 2 < 0$.

    (a) $(-3.41,\ -0.59)$ 　　　　(b) $(0.59,\ 3.41)$ 　　　　(c) $(-\infty,\ -3.41) \cup (-0.59,\ \infty)$

    (d) $(-\infty,\ 0.59) \cup (3.41,\ \infty)$ 　　　　(e) None of these

    2—M—Answer: b

16. Solve: $x^2 + 3x + 4 > 0$

    (a) $(-\infty, \infty)$ (b) $(-\infty, 0) \cup (0, \infty)$ (c) Empty set

    (d) $\left(\dfrac{-3 - \sqrt{7}}{2}, \dfrac{-3 + \sqrt{7}}{2} \right)$ (e) None of these

    2—M—Answer: a

17. Solve: $x^2 - 3x + 4 < 0$

    (a) $(-\infty, \infty)$ (b) $(-\infty, 0) \cup (0, \infty)$ (c) Empty set

    (d) $\left(\dfrac{3 - \sqrt{7}}{2}, \dfrac{3 + \sqrt{7}}{2} \right)$ (e) None of these

    2—M—Answer: c

18. Solve: $x^2 + 6x + 9 \le 0$

    (a) $(-\infty, -3]$ or $[-3, \infty)$ (b) -3 (c) $(-\infty, \infty)$

    (d) Empty set   (e) None of these

    2—M—Answer: b

19. Use a graphing utility to solve $x^2 + 3x + 9 \ge 0$.

    (a) $(-\infty, -3] \cup [3, \infty)$ (b) $[-3, 3]$ (c) $(-\infty, \infty)$

    (d) Empty set   (e) None of these

    2—M—Answer: c

20. Solve: $x^2 + 4 < 2x$

    (a) $(-\infty, \infty)$ (b) $(-\infty, -2) \cup (2, \infty)$ (c) $(-2, 2)$

    (d) Empty set   (e) None of these

    2—M—Answer: d

21. Solve the inequality: $\dfrac{x + 16}{3x + 2} \le 5$

    (a) $\left(-\infty, -\frac{2}{3}\right] \cup \left[\frac{3}{7}, \infty\right)$ (b) $\left[-\frac{2}{3}, \frac{3}{7}\right]$ (c) $\left(-\infty, -\frac{2}{3}\right) \cup \left[\frac{3}{7}, \infty\right)$

    (d) $\left(-\frac{2}{3}, \frac{3}{7}\right]$ (e) None of these

    2—M—Answer: c

22. Use a graphing utility to solve $\dfrac{x + 7}{3x - 1} < 1$.

    (a) $(0.33, 4)$ (b) $[0.33, 4]$ (c) $(-\infty, 0.33) \cup (4, \infty)$

    (d) $(-\infty, 0.33] \cup [4, \infty)$ (e) None of these

    2—M—Answer: c

23. Solve the inequality: $\dfrac{3x-7}{x+2} < 1$

2—O—Answer: $\left(-2, \dfrac{9}{2}\right)$

24. Solve the inequality: $\dfrac{2}{x-1} < 5$

(a) $(-\infty, 1)$ 　　　　(b) $\left(\dfrac{7}{5}, \infty\right)$ 　　　　(c) $\left(-\infty, -\dfrac{3}{5}\right) \cup \left(\dfrac{7}{5}, \infty\right)$

(d) $(-\infty, 1) \cup \left(\dfrac{7}{5}, \infty\right)$ 　　　　(e) None of these

2—M—Answer: d

25. Use a graphing utility to solve $\dfrac{2}{x+1} \geq 5$.

(a) $(-\infty, -1) \cup \left(-\dfrac{3}{5}, \infty\right)$ 　　　(b) $\left(-\infty, -\dfrac{3}{5}\right]$ 　　　(c) $\left(-1, -\dfrac{3}{5}\right]$

(d) $\left(-\infty, \dfrac{1}{5}\right]$ 　　　(e) None of these

2—M—Answer: c

26. Solve the inequality: $\dfrac{4}{x+1} \leq \dfrac{3}{x+2}$

(a) $(-\infty, -5] \cup (-2, -1)$ 　　　(b) $(-5, -2) \cup [-1, \infty)$ 　　　(c) $(-\infty, -5) \cup (-2, -1)$

(d) $(-5, -2] \cup [-1, \infty)$ 　　　(e) None of these

2—M—Answer: a

27. Solve the inequality: $\dfrac{3}{x-2} \leq \dfrac{5}{x+2}$

(a) $(-\infty, -2) \cup (2, 6)$ 　　　(b) $(-2, 2) \cup [6, \infty)$ 　　　(c) $[8, \infty)$

(d) $(-2, 2) \cup [8, \infty)$ 　　　(e) None of these

2—M—Answer: d

28. Solve the inequality: $\dfrac{2}{x-1} \leq \dfrac{3}{x+1}$

(a) $(-1, 1) \cup [5, \infty)$ 　　　(b) $(-\infty, -1) \cup (1, 5]$ 　　　(c) $[5, \infty)$

(d) Empty set 　　　(e) None of these

2—M—Answer: a

29. Use a graphing utility to solve $\dfrac{3}{x-1} \leq \dfrac{2}{x+1}$.

(a) $(-\infty, -5]$ 　　　(b) $(-\infty, -5] \cup (-1, 1)$ 　　　(c) $[-5, -1) \cup (1, \infty)$

(d) $(-\infty, -2] \cup (1, \infty)$ 　　　(e) None of these

2—M—Answer: b

30. Solve the inequality: $\dfrac{2}{x+2} \geq \dfrac{3}{x-1}$

    (a) $[-8, \infty)$ (b) $[-8, -2) \cup (1, \infty)$ (c) $(-\infty, -8] \cup (-2, 1)$

    (d) $(-\infty, -8]$ (e) None of these

    2—M—Answer: c

31. Find the domain of $\sqrt{x^2 - 7x - 8}$.

    (a) $(-\infty, -1] \cup [8, \infty)$ (b) $(-\infty, -1) \cup (8, \infty)$ (c) $[-1, 8]$

    (d) $(-1, 8)$ (e) None of these

    1—M—Answer: a

32. Find the domain of $\sqrt{169 - 9x^2}$.

    (a) $\left(-\frac{13}{3}, \frac{13}{3}\right)$ (b) $\left[-\frac{13}{3}, \frac{13}{3}\right]$ (c) $\left(-\infty, -\frac{13}{3}\right] \cup \left(\frac{13}{3}, \infty\right)$

    (d) $\left(-\infty, -\frac{13}{3}\right) \cup \left(\frac{13}{3}, \infty\right)$ (e) None of these

    1—M—Answer: b

33. Find the domain of $\sqrt{36 - x^2}$.   34. Find the domain of $\sqrt{16 - 4x^2}$.

    1—O—Answer: $[-6, 6]$ **1—O—Answer:** $[-2, 2]$

35. Find the domain of $\dfrac{1}{\sqrt{x^2 - 7x - 8}}$.

    (a) $[-1, 8]$ (b) $(-\infty, -1] \cup [8, \infty)$ (c) $(-\infty, -1) \cup (8, \infty)$

    (d) $(-1, 8)$ (e) None of these

    1—M—Answer: c

36. P dollars, invested at interest rate, r, compounded annually, increases to an amount $A = P(1 + r)^2$ in two years. If an investment of \$750 is to increase to an amount greater than \$883 in two years, then the interest rate must be greater than what percentage?

    (a) 8.86%   (b) 8.5%   (c) 17.7%   (d) 5.6%   (e) None of these

    2—M—Answer: b

37. P dollars, invested at interest rate, r, compounded annually, increases to an amount $A = P(1 + r)^2$ in two years. If an investment of \$970 is to increase to an amount greater than \$1100 in two years, then the interest rate must be greater than what percentage?

    (a) 5.5%   (b) 6.0%   (c) 6.5%   (d) 7.0%   (e) None of these

    2—M—Answer: c

CHAPTER THREE
Polynomial Functions: Graphs and Zeros

3.1 Quadratic Functions

1. Match the correct graph with the function: $f(x) = 2(x-3)^2 - 1$

(a)

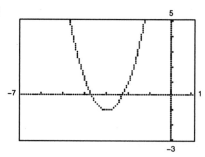

(b)

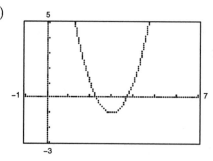

(c)

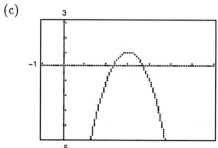

(d)

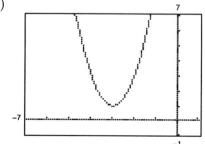

(e) None of these

1—M—Answer: b

2. Match the correct graph with the function: $f(x) = -\frac{1}{2}(x-2)^2 + 1$

(a)

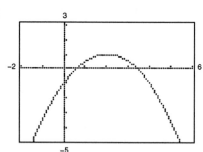

(b)

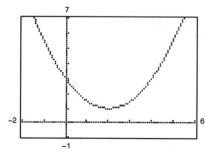

2. —CONTINUED—

(c)

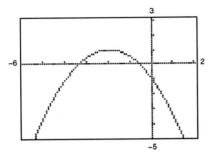

(d)

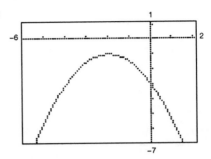

(e) None of these

1—M—Answer: a

3. Match the correct graph with the function: $f(x) = 3(x + 2)^2 - 1$

(a)

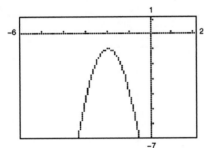

(b)

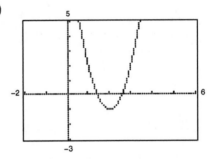

(c)

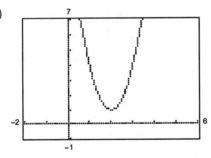

(d)

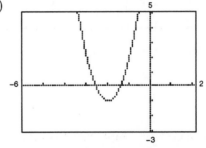

(e) None of these

1—M—Answer: d

4. Match the correct graph with the function: $f(x) = \frac{1}{3}(x+3)^2 + 1$

(a)
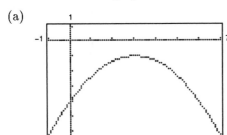

(b)
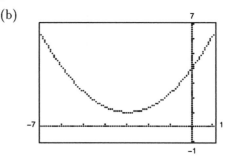

(c)
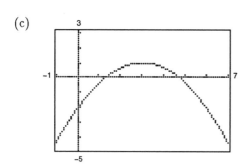

(d)
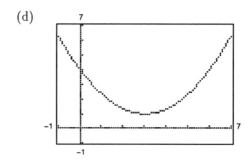

(e) None of these

1—M—Answer: b

5. Write the standard form of the equation of the parabola.

(a) $y = (x-2)^2 + 3$ (b) $y = (x+2)^2 - 3$

(c) $y = (x-2)^2 - 3$ (d) $y = (x+2)^2 + 3$

(e) None of these

1—M—Answer: c

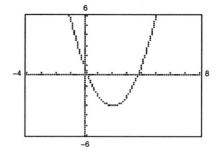

6. Write the standard form of the equation of the parabola.

(a) $y = (x-3)^2 - 1$ (b) $y = -(x+3)^2 - 1$

(c) $y = -(x+1)^2 + 3$ (d) $y = -(x-1)^2 - 3$

(e) None of these

1—M—Answer: c

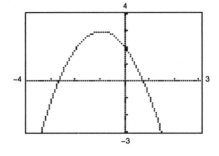

7. Write the standard form of the equation of the parabola.

1—O—Answer: $y = -(x-3)^2 - 1$

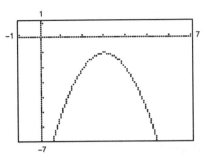

8. Match the correct equation with the parabola.

(a) $y = 5(x-1)^2 - 2$ (b) $y = (x+2)^2 - 1$

(c) $y = (x-2)^2 - 1$ (d) $y = (x-1)^2 + 2$

(e) None of these

1—M—Answer: c

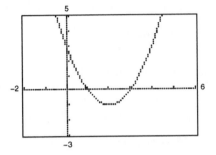

9. Match the correct equation with the parabola.

(a) $y = -\frac{1}{4}(x-4)^2 - 1$ (b) $y = -\frac{1}{4}(x+4) - 1$

(c) $y = -(x-1)^2 + 4$ (d) $y = -1(x-1)^2 - 4$

(e) None of these

1—M—Answer: a

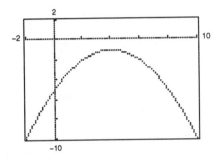

10. Write in the form $y = a(x-h)^2 + k$: $y = 2x^2 + 16x + 9$

(a) $y = 2(x+4)^2 - 7$ (b) $y = 2(x+2)^2 + 5$ (c) $y = 2(x+4)^2 - 23$

(d) $y = 2(x+8)^2 + 73$ (e) None of these

1—M—Answer: c

11. Write in the form $y = a(x-h)^2 + k$: $y = x^2 - 8x + 2$

(a) $y = (x-4)^2 - 18$ (b) $y = (x-4)^2 - 14$ (c) $y = (x-8)^2 + 66$

(d) $y = (x-4)^2 + 18$ (e) None of these

1—M—Answer: b

12. Write in the form $y = a(x-h)^2 + k$: $y = -x^2 + 3x - 2$

1—O—Answer: $y = -\left(x - \dfrac{3}{2}\right)^2 + \dfrac{1}{4}$

13. Write in the form $y = a(x - h)^2 + k$: $y = -2x^2 - 4x - 5$

    (a) $y = -2(x - 1)^2 - 2$ (b) $y = (2x - 2)^2 - 1$ (c) $y = -2(x + 2)^2 - 1$

    (d) $y = -2(x + 1)^2 - 3$ (e) None of these

    2—M—Answer: d

14. Write in the form $y = a(x - h)^2 + k$: $y = 3x^2 + 12x + 17$

    (a) $y = (x + 2)^2 + \frac{13}{3}$ (b) $y = 3(x + 2)^2 + 21$ (c) $y = 3(x + 2)^2 + 5$

    (d) $y = (x + 2)^2 + \frac{29}{3}$ (e) None of these

    2—M—Answer: c

15. Use a graphing utility to compare the graph of $f(x) = \frac{1}{2}x^2$ with the graph of $g(x) = x^2$.

    (a) f is broader than g.   (b) f is more narrow than g.   (c) f is a reflection of g.

    (d) f is a vertical shift of g 1 unit up.   (e) None of these

    1—M—Answer: a

16. Use a graphing utility to compare the graph of $f(x) = (x - 2)^2 + 6$ with the graph of $g(x) = x^2$.

    (a) Horizontal shift 2 units left   (b) Horizontal shift 2 units right
        Vertical shift 6 units up   Vertical shift 6 units up

    (c) Horizontal shift 6 units left   (d) Horizontal shift 6 units right
        Vertical shift 2 units down   Vertical shift 2 units up

    (e) None of these

    1—M—Answer: b

17. Find the vertex of the parabola: $y = 4x^2 + 8x + 1$

    (a) $(-2, 1)$ (b) $(1, 13)$ (c) $(0, 1)$ (d) $(-1, -3)$ (e) None of these

    2—M—Answer: d

18. Find the vertex of the parabola: $y = x^2 - 4x + 10$

    (a) $(-2, 22)$ (b) $(4, 10)$ (c) $(2, 6)$ (d) $(-2, 6)$ (e) None of these

    1—M—Answer: c

19. Find the x and y-intercepts: $y = x^2 - 5x + 4$

    (a) $(0, -4), (0, 1), (4, 0)$ (b) $(0, 4), (4, 0), (1, 0)$ (c) $(0, -4), (-4, 0), (-1, 0)$

    (d) $(0, 4), (-4, 0), (-1, 0)$ (e) None of these

    1—M—Answer: b

20. Find the x and y intercepts: $y = x^2 + 3x - 4$

(a) $(0, -4)$, $(-4, 0)$, $(1, 0)$

(b) $(0, -4)$, $(4, 0)$, $(-1, 0)$

(c) $(0, 4)$, $(-4, 0)$, $(0, 1)$

(d) $(4, 0)$, $(0, 4)$, $(-1, 0)$

(e) None of these

1—M—Answer: a

21. Sketch the graph of
$$f(x) = (x + 5)^2 - 4.$$
1—O—Answer:

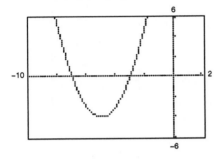

22. Sketch the graph of
$$f(x) = -x^2 - 4x.$$
2—O—Answer:

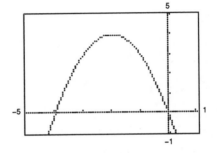

23. Sketch the graph of $f(x) = x^2 + 4x + 3$.

(a)

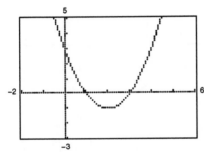

(b)

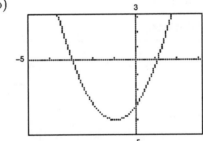

(c)

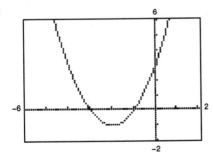

(d)

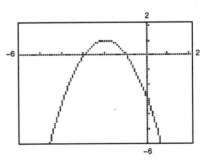

(e) None of these

2—M—Answer: c

24. Sketch the graph of $f(x) = 4x^2 - 8x + 4$.

(a)
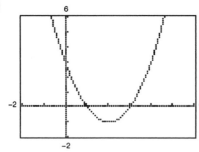

(b)
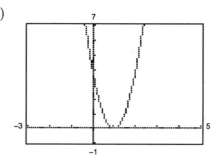

(c)
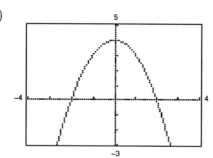

(d)
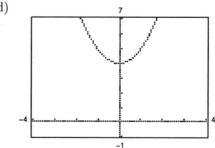

(e) None of these

2—M—Answer: b

25. Sketch the graph of $f(x) = -2x^2 - x + 3$.

2—O—Answer:

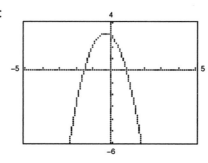

26. Find the minimum point on the graph of $y = 2x^2 + 8x + 9$.

(a) $(-2, \ 1)$ (b) $(2, 33)$ (c) $(2, 17)$ (d) $(-2, \ -17)$ (e) None of these

2—M—Answer: a

27. Find the minimum point on the graph of $f(x) = x^2 - 4x + 14$.

(a) $(2, \ 18)$ (b) $(-2, \ 18)$ (c) $(-2, \ 26)$ (d) $(2, \ 10)$ (e) None of these

2—M—Answer: d

28. Find the maximum point on the graph of $f(x) = -3x^2 + 12x + 1$.

    (a) $(6, -5)$ (b) $(-2, -19)$ (c) $(2, 13)$ (d) $(1, 14)$ (e) None of these

    2—M—Answer: c

29. Find the quadratic function that has a maximum point at $(-1, 17)$ and passes through $(7, 1)$.

    (a) $y = \frac{1}{4}(-x^2 - 2x + 16)$ (b) $y = -\frac{1}{4}(x + 1)^2 + 17$ (c) $y = (x - 7)^2 + 1$
    (d) $y = (x - 1)^2 + 17$ (e) None of these

    2—M—Answer: b

30. Find the quadratic function that has a minimum at $(1, -2)$ and passes through $(0, 0)$.

    (a) $y = 2(x - 1)^2 - 2$ (b) $y = 2(x + 1)^2 - 2$ (c) $y = -2(x - 1)^2 + 2$
    (d) $y = -2(x + 1)^2 + 2$ (e) None of these

    2—M—Answer: a

31. Find the quadratic function that has a maximum at $(-1, 2)$ and passes through $(0, 1)$.

    2—O—Answer: $f(x) = -(x + 1)^2 + 2$

32. Find the number of units that produce a maximum revenue, $R = 95x - 0.1x^2$, where R is the total revenue in dollars and x is the number of units sold.

    (a) 716   (b) 475   (c) 371   (d) 550   (e) None of these

    1—M—Answer: b

33. Find the number of units that produce a maximum revenue, $R = 400x - 0.01x^2$, where R is the total revenue in dollars and x is the number of units sold.

    (a) 15,000   (b) 32,000   (c) 4500   (d) 20,000   (e) None of these

    1—M—Answer: d

34. The profit for a company is given by the equation

    $$P = -0.0002x^2 + 140x - 250{,}000$$

    where x is the number of units produced. What production level will yield a maximum profit?

    (a) 700,000   (b) 350,000   (c) 893   (d) 350   (e) None of these

    2—M—Answer: b

35. The revenue R for a symphony concert is given by the equation

$$R = -\tfrac{1}{400}(x^2 - 4800x)$$

where x is the number of tickets sold. Determine the number of tickets that will yield maximum revenue.

(a) 4800   (b) 12   (c) 48,000   (d) 2400   (e) None of these

2—M—Answer: d

36. The perimeter of a rectangle is 300 feet. What is the width of the rectangle of maximum area?

(a) 100 feet   (b) 50 feet   (c) 75 feet   (d) 60 feet   (e) None of these

2—M—Answer: c

3.2 | Polynomial Functions of Higher Degree

1. Determine the left and right behavior of the graph: $y = 4x^2 - 2x + 1$

(a) Up to the left, down to the right   (b) Down to the left, up to the right

(c) Up to the left, up to the right   (d) Down to the left, down to the right

(e) None of these

1—M—Answer: c

2. Determine the left and right behavior of the graph: $f(x) = -x^5 + 2x^2 - 1$

(a) Up to the left, down to the right   (b) Down to the left, up to the right

(c) Up to the left, up to the right   (d) Down to the left, down to the right

(e) None of these

1—M—Answer: a

3. Determine the left and right behavior of the graph: $f(x) = 3x^5 - 7x^2 + 2$

(a) Down to the left, up to the right   (b) Up to the left, down to the right

(c) Up to the left, up to the right   (d) Down to the left, down to the right

(e) None of these

1—M—Answer: a

4. Determine the left and right behavior of the graph: $f(x) = -4x^3 + 3x^2 - 1$

1—O—Answer: Up to the left, down to the right

5. Determine the left and right behavior of the graph: $f(x) = 3x^4 + 2x^3 + 7x^2 + x - 1$

1—O—Answer: Up to the left and right

6. Determine the left and right behavior of the graph: $f(x) = -2x^4 + 3x^3 + 5x^2$

   (a) Up to the left, down to the right

   (b) Down to the left, up to the right

   (c) Up to the left, up to the right

   (d) Down to the left, down to the right

   (e) None of these

   1—M—Answer: d

7. Find all the real zeros of the polynomial function: $f(x) = x^3 - 3x^2 - 4x$

   (a) -1, 4   (b) -4, 1   (c) -1, 0, 4   (d) 0, 4   (e) None of these

   1—M—Answer: c

8. Find all the real zeros of the polynomial function: $f(x) = x^6 - x^2$

   (a) 0   (b) 0, 1   (c) 1   (d) 0, 1, -1 (e) None of these

   1—M—Answer: d

9. Find all the real zeros of the polynomial function: $f(x) = x^3 + x$

   (a) 0   (b) 0, 1   (c) 0, 1, -1 (d) 1, -1 (e) None of these

   1—M—Answer: a

10. Find all the real zeros of the polynomial function: $f(x) = x^4 - 5x^2 - 36$

    (a) 3, 2   (b) ± 3 (c) ± 3, ± 2 (d) ± 2 (e) None of these

    2—M—Answer: b

11. Find all the real zeros of the polynomial function: $g(t) = t^3 + 3t^2 - 16t - 48$

    (a) -3 (b) 3   (c) -4, -3, 4   (d) -3, 4   (e) None of these

    2—M—Answer: c

12. Find all the real zeros of the polynomial function: $f(x) = 9x^4 - 37x^2 + 4$

    1—O—Answer: ± 2, $\pm \frac{1}{3}$

13. Find a polynomial function with the given zeros: 0, -1, 2

    (a) $f(x) = x(x - 1)(x + 2)$

    (b) $f(x) = x(x + 1)(x - 2)$

    (c) $f(x) = (x + 1)(x - 2)$

    (d) $f(x) = (x + 1)^2(x - 2)$

    (e) None of these

    1—M—Answer: b

14. Find a polynomial function with the given zeros: $-2, -2, 1, 3$

(a) $f(x) = (x + 1)(x + 3)(x - 2)$ (b) $f(x) = (x - 2)^2(x - 1)(x - 3)$

(c) $f(x) = (x + 2)(x - 1)(x - 3)$ (d) $f(x) = (x + 2)^2(x - 1)(x - 3)$

(e) None of these

1—M—Answer: d

15. Find a polynomial function with zeros: $1, 0, -3$

(a) $f(x) = x(x - 3)^3(x + 1)^2$ (b) $f(x) = x^2(x - 1)(x + 3)$

(c) $f(x) = x(x - 3)(x - 1)$ (d) $f(x) = (x - 1)(x + 3)^2$

(e) None of these

1—M—Answer: b

16. Find a polynomial function with zeros: $0, 1, -2$

(a) $f(x) = x(x - 1)(x - 2)$ (b) $f(x) = x(x + 1)(x + 2)$

(c) $f(x) = (x - 1)(x + 2)$ (d) $f(x) = x^2(x - 1)(x + 2)$

(e) None of these

1—M—Answer: d

17. Determine the correct function for the given graph.

(a) $f(x) = x^5 + 2$ (b) $f(x) = -x^5 - 2$

(c) $f(x) = x^4 + 2$ (d) $f(x) = x^4 + 2x^2$

(e) None of these

2—M—Answer: a

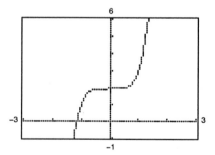

18. Determine the correct function for the given graph.

(a) $f(x) = x^3 + x^2 - 6$ (b) $f(x) = -x^3 - x^2 + 6x$

(c) $f(x) = x^3 + x^2 - 6x$ (d) $f(x) = x^4 + x^2 - 6x$

(e) None of these

2—M—Answer: c

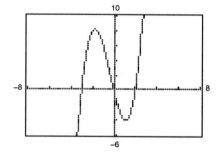

19. Determine the correct function for the given graph.

(a) $f(x) = 2x^3 - 3x^2$ (b) $f(x) = 3x^4 - 2x^3$

(c) $f(x) = 2x^3 + 3x^2$ (d) $f(x) = 3x^2 - 2x^3$

(e) None of these

2—M—Answer: d

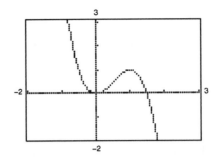

20. Determine the correct function for the given graph.

(a) $f(x) = 2x^4 + 8x^2$ (b) $f(x) = -2x^4 - 8x^2$

(c) $f(x) = 8x^2 - 2x^4$ (d) $f(x) = 2x^4 - 8x^2$

(e) None of these

2—M—Answer: d

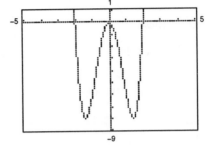

21. Sketch the graph of the function: $f(x) = 2x^3 - 3x^2$

2—O—Answer:

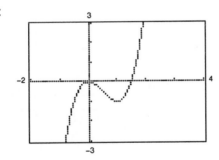

22. Sketch the graph of the function: $f(x) = -2x^4 + x$

(a)

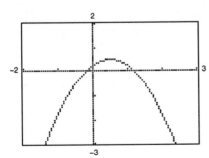

(b)

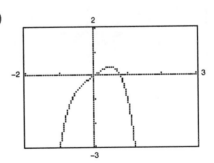

22. —CONTINUED—

(c)

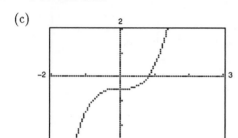

(d)

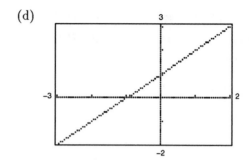

(e) None of these

2—M—Answer: b

23. Sketch the graph of the function: $f(x) = x^2 - 4x^4$

(a)

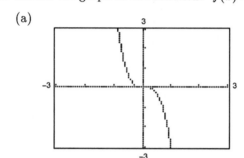

(b)

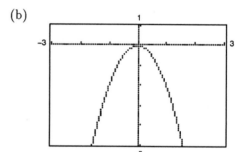

(c)

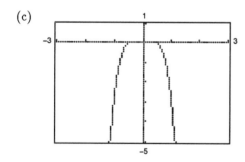

(d)

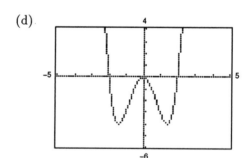

(e) None of these

2—M—Answer: c

24. Sketch the graph of the function: $f(x) = -x^5 + 4$

(a)

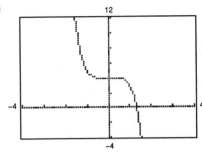

(b)

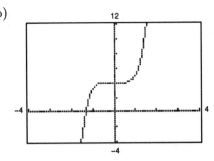

(c)

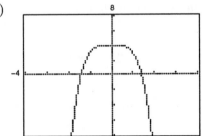

(d)

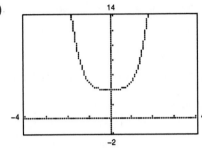

(e) None of these

2—M—Answer: a

25. Sketch the graph of the function: $f(x) = x^4 + 2x^3 + 1$

2—O—Answer:

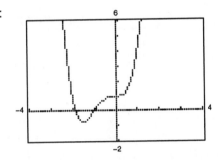

26. Which of the following viewing rectangles gives the best view of the basic characteristics of the graph of $f(x) = -\frac{1}{4}x^4 + x^3 - 1$?

(a)
```
RANGE
Xmin=-3
Xmax=3
Xscl=1
Ymin=-3
Ymax=3
Yscl=1
```

(b)
```
RANGE
Xmin=1
Xmax=4
Xscl=1
Ymin=0
Ymax=6
Yscl=1
```

(c)
```
RANGE
Xmin=-4
Xmax=6
Xscl=1
Ymin=-3
Ymax=7
Yscl=1
```

(d)
```
RANGE
Xmin=0
Xmax=6
Xscl=1
Ymin=-1
Ymax=7
Yscl=1
```

(e) None of these

1—M—Answer: c

27. Which of the following viewing rectangles gives the best view of the basic characteristics of the graph of $f(x) = 2x^3 + 3$?

(a)
```
RANGE
Xmin=0
Xmax=3
Xscl=1
Ymin=2
Ymax=5
Yscl=1
```
(b)
```
RANGE
Xmin=-4
Xmax=4
Xscl=1
Ymin=-1
Ymax=7
Yscl=1
```
(c)
```
RANGE
Xmin=-3
Xmax=0
Xscl=1
Ymin=-2
Ymax=1
Yscl=1
```
(d)
```
RANGE
Xmin=-2
Xmax=2
Xscl=1
Ymin=3
Ymax=7
Yscl=1
```

(e) None of these

1—M—Answer: b

28. Use the Intermediate Value Theorem to estimate the real zero in the interval $[0, 1]$:

$$f(x) = 3x^3 + 7x - 9$$

(a) Between 0.2 and 0.3   (b) Between 0.5 and 0.7   (c) Between 0.7 and 0.8

(d) Between 0.9 and 1.0   (e) None of these

2—M—Answer: d

29. Use the Intermediate Value Theorem to estimate the real zero in the interval $[1, 2]$:

$$f(x) = 3x^3 - 2x^2 - 2$$

(a) Between 1.0 and 1.1   (b) Between 1.1 and 1.2   (c) Between 1.3 and 1.4

(d) Between 0.7 and 0.8   (e) None of these

2—M—Answer: b

30. Use the Intermediate Value Theorem to estimate the real zero in the interval $[0, 1]$:

$$f(x) = 2x^3 + 7x^2 - 1$$

(a) Between 0.1 and 0.2   (b) Between 0.2 and 0.3   (c) Between 0.3 and 0.4

(d) Between 0.4 and 0.5   (e) None of these

2—M—Answer: c

31. Use the Intermediate Value Theorem to estimate the real zero in the interval $[1, 2]$:

$$f(x) = x^4 - 4x - 1$$

(a) Between 1.5 and 1.6   (b) Between 1.6 and 1.7   (c) Between 1.7 and 1.8

(d) Between 1.8 and 1.9   (e) None of these

2—M—Answer: b

32. Use the Intermediate Value Theorem to estimate the real zero in the interval $[1, 2]$.

$$f(x) = 3x^4 - 5x - 1$$

(a) Between 1.1 and 1.2   (b) Between 1.2 and 1.3   (c) Between 1.3 and 1.4

(d) Between 1.4 and 1.5   (e) None of these

2—M—Answer: b

33. The function $f(x)$ has a zero of 2 with multiplicity 3. We know

(a) since 3 is an odd number, the graph touches but does not cross the x-axis.

(b) since 3 is an odd number, the graph crosses the x-axis.

(c) since 2 is an even number, the graph touches but does not cross the x-axis.

(d) since 2 is an even number, the graph crosses the x-axis.

(e) None of these

1—M—Answer: b

34. The function $f(x)$ has a zero of -1 with multiplicity 1. We know

(a) since the multiplicity is 1, the graph crosses the x-axis.

(b) since the multiplicity is 1, the graph touches but does not cross the x-axis.

(c) since the zero is -1 the graph crosses the y-axis at -1.

(d) since the zero is -1, the graph goes down to the left.

(e) None of these

1—M—Answer: a

35. The function $f(x)$ has a zero of 3 with multiplicity 2. We know

(a) since the zero is 3, the graph crosses the y-axis at 3.

(b) since the zero is 3, the graph goes up to the right.

(c) since the multiplicity is 2, the graph crosses the x-axis.

(d) since the multiplicity is 2, the graph touches but does not cross the x-axis.

(e) None of these

1—M—Answer: d

36. An open box is made from a 16-inch square piece of material by cutting equal squares with sides of length, x, from all corners and turning up the sides. The volume of the box is $V(x) = 4x(8 - x)^2$. Estimate the value of x for which the volume is maximum.

(a) 2.7 inches   (b) 3.0 inches   (c) 1.9 inches   (d) 8 inches   (e) None of these

2—M—Answer: a

37. An open box is made from a 24-inch square piece of material by cutting equal squares with sides of length, x, from all corners and turning up the sides. The volume of the box is $V(x) = 4x(12 - x)^2$. Estimate the value of x for which the volume is maximum.

    (a) 12 inches   (b) 3 inches   (c) 6 inches   (d) 4 inches   (e) None of these

    2—M—Answer: d

38. An open box is made from a 10-inch square piece of material by cutting equal squares with sides of length, x, from all corners and turning up the sides. The volume of the box is $V(x) = 4x(5 - x)^2$. Estimate the value of x for which the volume is maximum.

    2—O—Answer: 1.7 inches

3.3 | Polynomial Division and Synthetic Division

1. Divide: $(9x^3 - 6x^2 - 8x - 3) \div (3x + 2)$

    (a) $3x^2 - \dfrac{8}{3}x - \dfrac{7/3}{3x + 2}$

    (b) $3x^2 - 4x - 2 + \dfrac{7}{3x + 2}$

    (c) $3x^2 - 4x - \dfrac{3}{3x + 2}$

    (d) $3x^2 - 4x - \dfrac{16}{3} + \dfrac{23/3}{3x + 2}$

    (e) None of these

    1—M—Answer: c

2. Divide: $(6x^3 + 7x^2 - 15x + 6) \div (2x - 1)$

    (a) $3x^2 + 2x - \dfrac{17}{2} - \dfrac{5}{2(2x - 1)}$

    (b) $3x^2 + 5x - 5 + \dfrac{1}{2x - 1}$

    (c) $3x^2 + 5x + 5 + \dfrac{11}{2x - 1}$

    (d) $3x^2 + 4x - 17 + \dfrac{29/2}{2x - 1}$

    (e) None of these

    1—M—Answer: b

3. Divide: $(3x^4 + 2x^3 - 3x + 1) \div (x^2 + 1)$

    (a) $3x^2 + 2x + 3 - \dfrac{5x + 2}{x^2 + 1}$

    (b) $3x^2 + 2x - 3 + \dfrac{-5x + 4}{x^2 + 1}$

    (c) $3x^2 - x^2 + x - 4 + \dfrac{5}{x^2 + 1}$

    (d) $3x^2 - x + 1 + \dfrac{-4x + 5}{x^2 + 1}$

    (e) None of these

    1—M—Answer: b

4. Divide: $(6x^4 - 4x^3 + x^2 + 10x - 1) \div (3x + 1)$

    1—O—Answer: $2x^3 - 2x^2 + x + 3 - \dfrac{4}{3x + 1}$

5. Divide: $(2x^4 + 7x - 2) \div (x^2 + 3)$

   2—O—Answer: $2x^2 - 6 + \dfrac{7x + 16}{x^2 + 3}$

6. Divide by long division: $(2x^3 - x^2 - 3x + 4) \div (2x + 1)$

   (a) $x^2 - x - 1 + \dfrac{5}{2x + 1}$
     (b) $x^2 - \dfrac{3}{2} + \dfrac{5}{2(2x + 1)}$
     (c) $x^2 - x - 1 + \dfrac{3}{2x + 1}$

   (d) $x^2 - x - 2 + \dfrac{6}{2x + 1}$
     (e) None of these

   1—M—Answer: a

7. Divide by long division: $(x^4 + 3x^3 - 3x^2 - 12x - 4) \div (x^2 + 3x + 1)$

   (a) $x^2 - 2 - \dfrac{6x + 2}{x^2 + 3x + 1}$
     (b) $x^2 - 4$
     (c) $x^2 + 2 - \dfrac{18x - 6}{x^2 + 3x + 1}$

   (d) $x^2 - 4x$
     (e) None of these

   1—M—Answer: b

8. Use synthetic division to divide: $(5x^4 - 2x^2 + 1) \div (x + 1)$

   (a) $5x^3 - 5x^2 + 3x - 3 + \dfrac{4}{x + 1}$
     (b) $5x^2 - 7x + 8$

   (c) $5x^2 + 3x + 4$
     (d) $5x^3 + 5x^2 + 3x + 3 + \dfrac{4}{x + 1}$

   (e) None of these

   1—M—Answer: a

9. Use synthetic division to divide: $(3x^4 + 4x^3 - 2x^2 + 1) \div (x + 2)$

   (a) $3x^3 + 10x^2 + 18x + 37$
     (b) $3x^3 - 2x^2 + 2x - 3$

   (c) $3x^3 - 2x^2 + 2x - 4 + \dfrac{9}{x + 2}$
     (d) $3x^3 + 10x^2 + 18x + 36 + \dfrac{73}{x + 2}$

   (e) None of these

   1—M—Answer: c

10. Use synthetic division to divide: $(x^4 + 2x^2 - x + 1) \div (x - 2)$

   1—O—Answer: $x^3 + 2x^2 + 6x + 11 + \dfrac{23}{x - 2}$

11. Divide: $(x^3 + 4x^2 + 4x + 3) \div (x + 3)$

   (a) $x^2 + 7x - 17 + \dfrac{54}{x + 3}$
     (b) $x^2 - x + 7 - \dfrac{21}{x + 3}$
     (c) $x^2 + x + 1$

   (d) $x^2 + x + 1 + \dfrac{6}{x + 3}$
     (e) None of these

   1—M—Answer: c

12. Divide: $(x^3 + 8) \div (x + 2)$

    (a) $x^2 - 2x + 4$ (b) $x^2 + 4$ (c) $x^2 + 2x + 4$

    (d) $x^2 + 2x - 4$ (e) None of these

    1—M—Answer: a

13. Divide by synthetic division: $(x^3 - 6x^2 - 3x + 1) \div (x + 2)$

    (a) $x^2 - 4x - 11 - \dfrac{21}{x + 2}$ (b) $x^2 - 8x + 13 - \dfrac{25}{x + 2}$ (c) $x^2 - 4x + 5 - \dfrac{9}{x + 2}$

    (d) $x^2 - 8x + 13 - \dfrac{27}{x + 2}$ (e) None of these

    1—M—Answer: b

14. Divide by synthetic division: $(2x^3 + 3x^2 - 19x - 1) \div (x + 4)$

    (a) $2x^2 - 5x + 1 - \dfrac{3}{x + 4}$ (b) $2x^2 - x - 15 + \dfrac{54}{x + 4}$ (c) $2x^2 - 5x + 1 - \dfrac{5}{x + 4}$

    (d) $2x^2 + 11x + 25 + \dfrac{99}{x + 4}$ (e) None of these

    1—M—Answer: c

15. Divide using synthetic division: $(x^3 - x - 6) \div (x - 2)$

    (a) $x^2 - x - 3$ (b) $x^2 + 2x + 3$ (c) $x^2 + x + 2 + \dfrac{2}{x - 2}$

    (d) $x^2 + 2x + 5$ (e) None of these

    1—M—Answer: b

16. Use synthetic division to determine which of the following is a solution of the equation:

    $$3x^4 - 2x^3 + 26x^2 - 18x - 9 = 0$$

    (a) 3   (b) 1   (c) -3 (d) $\frac{1}{3}$ (e) None of these

    2—M—Answer: b

17. Use synthetic division to determine which of the following are solutions of the equation:

    $$3x^3 - 11x^2 - 6x + 8 = 0$$

    (a) $\frac{2}{3}$ (b) -1 (c) 4   (d) All of these   (e) None of these

    1—M—Answer: d

18. Use synthetic division to determine which of the following is a solution of the equation:

    $$6x^4 - 11x^3 - 10x^2 + 19x - 6 = 0$$

    (a) 2   (b) 3   (c) -2 (d) -3 (e) None of these

    1—M—Answer: a

19. Use synthetic division to factor the polynomial $x^3 - x^2 - 10x - 8$ completely if -2 is a zero.

(a) $(x-2)(x-4)(x+1)$ (b) $-2,\ 4,\ -1$ (c) $(x+2)(x+1)(x-4)$

(d) $(x+2)(x+4)(x-1)$ (e) Does not factor

1—M—Answer: c

20. Use synthetic division to factor the polynomial $x^3 - 4x^2 - 7x + 10$ completely if -2 is a zero.

(a) $(x+2)(x+1)(x+5)$ (b) $-2,\ 1,\ 5$ (c) $(x+2)(x-1)(x-5)$

(d) $(x-2)(x-1)(x+5)$ (e) None of these

1—M—Answer: c

21. Use synthetic division to factor the polynomial $x^3 + 4x^2 + x - 6$ completely if 1 is a zero.

(a) $(x+1)(x+2)(x+3)$ (b) $(x-1)(x-2)(x-3)$ (c) $1,\ -2,\ -3$

(d) $(x-1)(x+2)(x+3)$ (e) Does not factor

1—M—Answer: d

22. Use synthetic division to factor the polynomial $2x^3 - 7x^2 + 7x - 2$ completely if $\frac{1}{2}$ is a zero.

(a) $2(x+\frac{1}{2})(x-1)(x-2)$ (b) $2(x-\frac{1}{2})(x+1)(x+2)$ (c) $2(x-\frac{1}{2})(x-1)(x-2)$

(d) $2(x+\frac{1}{2})(x+1)(x+2)$ (e) Does not factor

2—M—Answer: c

23. Factor the polynomial $x^3 + 3x^2 - 10x - 24$ completely knowing that $x - 3$ is a factor.

(a) $(x-3)(x+2)(x+4)$ (b) $(x-3)(x-2)(x-4)$ (c) $(x-3)(x+1)(x+7)$

(d) $(x-3)(x-1)(x+7)$ (e) None of these

1—M—Answer: a

24. Express $f(x) = 3x^4 - 2x^2 + x - 1$ in the form $f(x) = (x-k)q(x) + r$ for $k = -1$.

(a) $f(x) = (x-1)(3x^3 + 3x^2 + x + 2) + 1$ (b) $f(x) = (x+1)(3x^3 - 3x^2 + x) - 1$

(c) $f(x) = (x-1)(3x^3 + x^2 + 2x) + 1$ (d) $f(x) = (x+1)(3x^3 - 5x^2 + 6x) - 7$

(e) None of these

1—M—Answer: b

25. Express $f(x) = 2x^3 - 3x + 2$ in the form $f(x) = (x-k)q(x) + r$ for $k = -2$.

(a) $f(x) = (x-2)(2x^2 - x) + 4$ (b) $f(x) = (x+2)(2x^2 - 7x) + 16$

(c) $f(x) = (x-2)(2x^2 + 4x + 5) + 12$ (d) $f(x) = (x+2)(2x^2 - 4x + 5) - 8$

(e) None of these

1—M—Answer: d

26. Express $f(x) = 3x^4 - 7x^3 + x - 1$ in the form $f(x) = (x - k)q(x) + r$ for $k = 2$.

    (a) $f(x) = (x + 2)(3x^3 - 13x^2 + 26x - 51) + 101$ (b) $f(x) = (x - 2)(3x^3 - x^2 - 2x - 3) - 7$

    (c) $f(x) = (x + 2)(3x^3 - 13x^2 - 25x) + 49$ (d) $f(x) = (x - 2)(3x^3 - x^2 - x) - 3$

    (e) None of these

    1—M—Answer: b

27. Express $f(x) = 2x^3 - 5x^2 + 3$ in the form $f(x) = (x - k)q(x) + r$ for $k = -2$.

    (a) $f(x) = (x + 2)(2x^2 - 9x + 18) - 33$ (b) $f(x) = (x - 2)(2x^2 - x - 2) - 1$

    (c) $f(x) = (x + 2)(2x^2 - 9x) + 21$ (d) $f(x) = (x - 2)(2x^2 - x) + 1$

    (e) None of these

    1—M—Answer: a

28. Use synthetic division to find $f(-2)$: $f(x) = 4x^3 + 3x + 10$

    (a) 20   (b) −20   (c) 36   (d) −28   (e) None of these

    2—M—Answer: d

29. Use synthetic division to find $f(-3)$: $f(x) = 3x^3 + 2x^2 - 1$

    (a) 98   (b) $3x^2 - 7x + 21 - \dfrac{64}{x + 3}$ (c) −64

    (d) 20   (e) None of these

    1—M—Answer: c

30. Use synthetic division to find $f(3)$: $f(x) = x^4 + 2x^2 - x - 1$

    (a) $x^3 + 3x^2 + 11x + 32 + \dfrac{95}{x - 3}$ (b) 95   (c) 101

    (d) 122   (e) None of these

    1—M—Answer: b

31. Use synthetic division to find $f(-2)$: $f(x) = 3x^4 - 2x^2 + 1$

    (a) 23   (b) −16   (c) 17   (d) 21   (e) None of these

    1—M—Answer: e

32. Simplify the rational function: $f(x) = \dfrac{x^3 + 4x^2 - 3x + 10}{x + 5}$

    (a) 0   (b) $x^2 - x + 2$ (c) $5x^2 - 3x + 2$

    (d) $x^2 + 9x + 42$ (e) None of these

    1—M—Answer: b

33. Simplify the rational function: $f(x) = \dfrac{x^5 - 1}{x - 1}$

    (a) x^4

    (b) $x^4 + x^3 + x^2 + x$

    (c) $x^4 + x^3 + x^2 + x + 1$

    (d) $x^4 - x^3 + x^2 - x + 1$

    (e) None of these

    1—M—Answer: c

34. Simplify the rational expression: $\dfrac{2x^4 - x^3 - 4x^2 + x - 3}{2x + 3}$

    (a) $x^3 + x^2 - x + 1$

    (b) $x^3 - 2x^2 - 5x - 1$

    (c) $x^3 + x^2 - 5x - 1$

    (d) $x^3 - 2x^2 + x - 1$

    (e) None of these

    1—M—Answer: d

35. Simplify the rational expression: $\dfrac{4x^5 - 3x^4 + 8x^3 - 3x^2 + 6}{x^2 + 2}$

    (a) $4x^3 - 3x^2 + 6x + 3 + \dfrac{12x}{x^2 + 2}$

    (b) $4x^3 - 3x^2 + 3$

    (c) $4x^3 - 3x^2 - 9 + \dfrac{24}{x^2 + 2}$

    (d) $4x^3 + 5x^2 + 6$

    (e) None of these

    2—M—Answer: b

36. A rectangular room has a volume of $3x^3 - 2x^2 - 11x + 10$ cubic feet. The height of the room is $x - 1$. Find the algebraic expression for the number of square feet of floor space in the room.

    (a) 20

    (b) $3x^3 - 2x^2 - 10x + 9$

    (c) $3x^2 + x - 10$

    (d) $3x^2 - 5x - 5 + \dfrac{15}{x - 1}$

    (e) None of these

    2—M—Answer: c

3.4 Real Zeros of Polynomial Functions

1. Use Descartes's Rule of Signs to determine the possible number of positive and negative zeros: $f(x) = 5x^4 - 3x^3 - 4x + 2$

    (a) 2 positive, 2 negative

    (b) 2 or 0 positive, 0 negative

    (c) 4 positive, 0 negative

    (d) 0 positive, 4 negative

    (e) None of these

    1—M—Answer: b

2. Use Descartes's Rule of Signs to determine the possible number of positive and negative zeros: $f(x) = x^3 + 2x - 1$

(a) 1 positive, 0 negative

(b) 0 positive, 1 negative

(c) 3 or 1 positive, 0 or 2 negative

(d) 1 positive, 2 negative

(e) None of these

1—M—Answer: a

3. Use Descartes's Rule of Signs to determine the possible number of positive and negative zeros: $f(x) = 6x^5 - 6x^3 + 10x + 5$

(a) 4 or 2 or 0 positive, 1 negative

(b) 3 or 1 positive, 2 or 4 negative

(c) 2 or 0 positive, 3 or 1 negative

(d) 1 positive, 0 negative

(e) None of these

1—M—Answer: c

4. Use Descartes's Rule of Signs to determine the possible number of positive and negative zeros: $f(x) = x^3 + 1$

(a) 3 positive, 0 negative

(b) 0 positive, 1 negative

(c) 1 positive, 2 negative

(d) 1 positive, 0 negative

(e) None of these

1—M—Answer: b

5. Use Descartes's Rule of Signs to determine which of the following polynomial functions has a possible 0 or 2 positive zeros and 0 negative zeros.

(a) $f(x) = 5x^4 - 3x^3 - 4x + 2$

(b) $f(x) = 4x^4 + 3x^3 - x^2 + 1$

(c) $f(x) = 3x^4 - 4x^2 - 4x + 2$

(d) Both a and b

(e) Both b and c

1—M—Answer: a

6. Use Descartes's Rule of Signs to determine which of the following polynomial functions has a possible 0 or 2 negative zeros and 0 positive zeros.

(a) $f(x) = 3x^4 + x^3 + 4x^2 + x$

(b) $f(x) = 5x^4 + 3x^3 + x^2 + 1$

(c) $f(x) = 2x^4 - 4x^2 + x$

(d) Both a and b

(e) Both b and c

1—M—Answer: b

7. List the possible rational zeros of the function: $f(x) = 3x^5 + 2x^2 - 3x + 2$

   (a) $\pm 3, \pm 2, \pm \frac{3}{2}, \pm 1, \pm \frac{2}{3}$ (b) $\pm 3, \pm \frac{1}{3}, \pm 2, \pm \frac{1}{2}, \pm 1$

   (c) $\pm 2, \pm 1, \pm \frac{2}{3}, \pm \frac{1}{3}$ (d) $\pm 3, \pm 1, \pm \frac{3}{2}, \pm \frac{1}{2}$

   (e) None of these

   1—M—Answer: c

8. List the possible rational zeros of the function: $f(x) = 3x^5 - 2x^3 + 3x - 5$

   (a) $\pm \frac{5}{3}, \pm 3, \pm \frac{1}{3}, \pm 5, \pm 1, \pm \frac{1}{5}, \pm \frac{3}{5}$ (b) $\pm \frac{3}{5}, \pm 1, \pm \frac{1}{5}, \pm 3$

   (c) $\pm \frac{1}{3}, \pm 1, \pm \frac{5}{3}, \pm 5$ (d) $\pm 1, \pm 3, \pm \frac{3}{5}, \pm \frac{5}{3}$

   (e) None of these

   1—M—Answer: c

9. List the possible rational zeros of the function: $f(x) = 3x^5 + 7x^3 - 3x^2 + 2$

   (a) $\pm \frac{2}{3}, \pm \frac{3}{2}, \pm 2, \pm 3$ (b) $\pm \frac{1}{3}, \pm \frac{2}{3}, \pm 1, \pm 2$ (c) $\pm \frac{3}{2}, \pm \frac{1}{2}, \pm 3, \pm 1$

   (d) $\pm \frac{3}{2}, \pm \frac{2}{3}, \pm \frac{1}{2}, \pm \frac{1}{3}$ (e) None of these

   1—M—Answer: b

10. List the possible rational zeros of the function: $f(x) = 4x^4 - x^3 + 5x^2 + 2$

    (a) $\pm 1, \pm 2, \pm 4$ (b) $\pm \frac{1}{2}, \pm 2, \pm 4$ (c) $\pm \frac{1}{2}, \pm 1, \pm 2$

    (d) $\pm \frac{1}{4}, \pm \frac{1}{2}, \pm 1, \pm 2$ (e) None of these

    1—M—Answer: d

11. List the possible rational zeros of the function: $f(x) = 2x^4 - 3x^2 + 15$

    1—O—Answer: $\pm \frac{1}{2}, \pm 1, \pm \frac{3}{2}, \pm \frac{5}{2}, \pm 3, \pm 5, \pm \frac{15}{2}, \pm 15$

12. Given $f(x) = 3x^3 + 4x - 1$, determine whether $x = -2$ is an upper bound for the zeros of f, a lower bound for the zeros of f, or neither.

    2—O—Answer: Lower bound

13. Which of the following are upper bounds for the zeros of f:

    $$f(x) = x^5 + 2x^4 - x^3 - 2x^2 - 30x - 60$$

    (a) 1   (b) 2   (c) 3   (d) Both b and c   (e) None of these

    2—M—Answer: c

14. Which of the following are lower bounds for the zeros of f: $f(x) = 6x^4 + 3x^3 + 5x - 10$

    (a) 0   (b) −1   (c) −2   (d) Both −1 and −2   (e) None of these

    2—M—Answer: c

15. Which of the following are upper bounds for the zeros of f: $f(x) = 3x^3 + x^2 - 7x + 2$

    (a) 1　　　(b) 2　　　(c) 3　　　(d) Both b and c　　　(e) None of these

    2—M—Answer: d

16. Which of the following are lower bounds for the zeros of f: $f(x) = 3x^3 + x^2 - 11x - 5$

    (a) −3　　　(b) −2　　　(c) −1　　　(d) All of these　　　(e) None of these

    2—M—Answer: a

17. Which of the following are lower bounds for the zeros of f: $f(x) = 3x^4 + x^2 + 3x - 1$

    (a) −3　　　(b) −2　　　(c) −1　　　(d) All of these　　　(e) None of these

    2—M—Answer: d

18. Find all of the rational zeros of the function: $f(x) = 2x^3 + 14x^2 + 24x$

    (a) 0, 3, 4　　　(b) 3, 4　　　(c) −4, −3, 0　　　(d) 0, 1, 6　　　(e) None of these

    1—M—Answer: c

19. Find all of the rational zeros of the function: $f(x) = 3x^4 - 27x^3 + 54x^2$

    (a) 0, 3, 9, 2　　　(b) 0, 6, 3　　　(c) 0, 9, 2　　　(d) 0, 6　　　(e) None of these

    1—M—Answer: b

20. Find all of the rational zeros of the function: $f(x) = 6x^4 + 32x^3 - 70x^2$

    (a) 0, −1, 5　　　(b) 0, −7, $\frac{5}{3}$　　　(c) $\frac{7}{3}$, 5

    (d) 0, −1, −7, $\frac{5}{3}$　　　(e) None of these

    1—M—Answer: b

21. Find all of the rational zeros of the function: $f(x) = x^3 + 6x^2 + 12x + 7$

    (a) $\pm\frac{5}{2}$　　　(b) −1, $\pm\frac{5}{2}$　　　(c) −1　　　(d) −1, 7　　　(e) None of these

    2—M—Answer: c

22. Find all of the rational zeros of the function: $f(x) = 4x^3 - 3x - 1$

    (a) 1, $-\frac{1}{2}$　　　(b) 1, $\frac{1}{2}$, $-\frac{1}{2}$　　　(c) $\frac{1}{2}$, 1　　　(d) 1　　　(e) None of these

    2—M—Answer: a

23. Find all of the real solutions: $x^3 - 7x + 6 = 0$

    (a) −3, 1, 2　　　(b) −2, −1, 3　　　(c) −6, −1, 1

    (d) −1, 1, 6　　　(e) None of these

    1—M—Answer: a

24. Find all of the real solutions: $2x^3 + 5x^2 - x - 6 = 0$

(a) -3, -1, 1 (b) -1, $\frac{3}{2}$, 2 (c) -2, $-\frac{3}{2}$, 1

(d) -6, 2, 5 (e) None of these

1—M—Answer: c

25. Find all of the real solutions: $x^3 - 5x^2 + 5x - 1 = 0$

(a) 1, 2, $\pm 2\sqrt{3}$ (b) 1, $2 \pm \sqrt{3}$ (c) 1

(d) -1, $2 \pm 2\sqrt{3}$ (e) None of these

2—M—Answer: b

26. Find all of the real solutions: $x^3 - x^2 - 3x - 1 = 0$

(a) -1, 2 (b) 1, $1 \pm \sqrt{2}$ (c) 1, -2

(d) -1, $1 \pm \sqrt{2}$ (e) None of these

1—M—Answer: d

27. Find all of the real solutions: $3x^3 - 4x^2 + 3x - 4 = 0$

(a) -1, 1, $\frac{4}{3}$ (b) $-\frac{4}{3}$, -1, 1 (c) 1, $\frac{4}{3}$ (d) $\frac{4}{3}$ (e) None of these

1—M—Answer: d

28. Find all of the real solutions: $3x^4 - 4x^3 + 4x^2 - 4x + 1 = 0$

(a) -1, $\frac{1}{3}$, 1 (b) -1, $-\frac{1}{3}$, 1 (c) $\frac{1}{3}$, 1 (d) 1 (e) None of these

1—M—Answer: c

29. Find all of the real solutions: $x^3 + 8x^2 + 17x + 6 = 0$

(a) -3 (b) -3, $\dfrac{-5 \pm \sqrt{17}}{2}$ (c) -3, -1, 2

(d) -3, $\dfrac{-5 \pm \sqrt{33}}{2}$ (e) None of these

2—M—Answer: b

30. Find the real zeros of the function: $f(x) = x^3 - \frac{4}{3}x^2 - \frac{5}{3}x + \frac{2}{3}$

(a) -1, $\frac{1}{3}$, 2 (b) 1, $\frac{2}{3}$, -2 (c) -2, $-\frac{1}{3}$, 1

(d) -1, $\frac{2}{3}$, 1 (e) None of these

2—M—Answer: a

31. Find the real zeros of the function: $f(x) = x^3 - \dfrac{9}{2}x^2 + \dfrac{11}{2}x - \dfrac{3}{2}$

(a) $1, \ 4 \pm \sqrt{13}$

(b) $\dfrac{3}{2}, \ \dfrac{3 \pm \sqrt{13}}{2}$

(c) $\dfrac{3}{2}, \ \dfrac{3 \pm \sqrt{5}}{2}$

(d) $1, \ 4 \pm \sqrt{19}$

(e) None of these

2—M—Answer: c

32. Find all of the real zeros of the function: $f(x) = x^3 - \frac{11}{3}x^2 + \frac{5}{3}x + 1$

(a) $-\frac{1}{3}, \ 1, \ 3$

(b) $3, \ \pm 1$

(c) $1, \ \pm 3$

(d) $3, \ 1 \pm \sqrt{2}$

(e) None of these

2—M—Answer: a

33. Determine the number of rational and irrational zeros of the function: $f(x) = x^4 + 2x^3 + 7x^2 + 12x + 6$

(a) Rational zeros: 4
     Irrational zeros: 0

(b) Rational zeros: 2
     Irrational zeros: 2

(c) Rational zeros: 0
     Irrational zeros: 4

(d) Rational zeros: 1
     Irrational zeros: 1

(e) None of these

2—M—Answer: b

34. Determine the number of rational and irrational zeros of the function: $f(x) = x^5 - 3x^4 - 2x^3 + 6x^2 - 3x + 9$

(a) Rational zeros: 3
     Irrational zeros: 2

(b) Rational zeros: 1
     Irrational zeros: 4

(c) Rational zeros: 1
     Irrational zeros: 2

(d) Rational zeros: 2
     Irrational zeros: 3

(e) None of these

2—M—Answer: c

35. Use the Bisection Method to approximate the real zeros of the function in the interval $[-1, \ 0]$:

$f(x) = x^3 + x + 1$

(a) -0.83

(b) -0.68

(c) -0.48

(d) -0.23

(e) None of these

2—M—Answer: b

36. Use the Bisection Method to approximate the zero of the function in the interval $[0, \ 1]$:

$f(x) = 3x^3 + x^2 - 16x + 10$

(a) 0.58

(b) 0.65

(c) 0.73

(d) 0.94

(e) None of these

2—M—Answer: c

37. An open box is made from a square piece of material 12 inches on a side by cutting equal squares from each corner and turning up the sides. Find the dimensions of the box given that the volume is to be 128 cubic inches.

2—O—Answer: 8 in. × 8 in. × 2 in.

38. An open box is made from a rectangular piece of material 11 inches by 8 inches by cutting equal squares from each corner and turning up the sides. Find the dimensions of the box given that the volume is to be 56 cubic inches.

    2—O—Answer: 4 in. × 7 in. × 2 in.

3.5 Complex Numbers

1. Find b so that the equation is true: $(a + 3) + (2b - 1)i = 5 + 9i$

   (a) 2   (b) 4   (c) 5   (d) 8   (e) None of these

   1—M—Answer: c

2. Find a so that the equation is true: $(a + 6) + (3b + 1)i = 4 + 3i$

   (a) −2   (b) $\frac{2}{3}$ (c) 10   (d) $\frac{3}{2}$ (e) None of these

   1—M—Answer: a

3. Find b so that the equation is true: $(2a + 1) + (b - 2)i = 3 + 7i$

   (a) −1   (b) 1   (c) 5   (d) 9   (e) None of these

   1—M—Answer: d

4. Find b so that the equation is true: $(3a + 1) + (b - 6)i = 4 - 5i$

   (a) −1   (b) 1   (c) 7   (d) 5   (e) None of these

   1—M—Answer: b

5. Find b so that the equation is true: $(2a + 1) + (2b + 3)i = 4 - 7i$

   (a) $\frac{2}{3}$ (b) 5   (c) −5   (d) −2   (e) None of these

   1—M—Answer: c

6. Write in standard form: $3 + \sqrt{-9} - 16 + 2i^2$

   (a) $-15 - 3i$ (b) $-15 + 3i$ (c) -18

   (d) $-17 + 3i$ (e) None of these

   1—M—Answer: b

7. Write in standard form: $2i^3 - 3\sqrt{-16} + 2$

   (a) $2 - 14i$ (b) $14 - 2i$ (c) $2 + 10i$

   (d) $2 - 4i$ (e) None of these

   1—M—Answer: a

8. Write in standard form: $4 - \sqrt{-8}$

    (a) $4 - 2i$ (b) $4 + 2\sqrt{2}i$ (c) $4 - 2\sqrt{2}i$

    (d) 8 (e) None of these

    1—M—Answer: c

9. Write in standard form: $2i^4 + 7i^3$

    (a) $2 - 7i$ (b) $-2 + 7i$ (c) $7 - 2i$

    (d) $-7 + 2i$ (e) None of these

    1—M—Answer: a

10. Write in standard form: $(16 + 2i) - (3 + 4i^2)$

    (a) $9 + 2i$ (b) $13 - 2i$ (c) $15 + 2i$

    (d) $17 + 2i$ (e) None of these

    1—M—Answer: d

11. Simplify, then write your result in standard form: $(3 + 6i) - 2(i + 7) - \sqrt{-4}$

    (a) $1 + 4i$ (b) $-11 + 6i$ (c) $-11 + 2i$

    (d) $3 + 4i$ (e) None of these

    1—M—Answer: c

12. Simplify, then write your result in standard form: $(6 + \sqrt{-9}) - 2i + 10 - \sqrt{16}$

    (a) $16 - 3i$ (b) $13 - 6i$ (c) $9 - 2i$

    (d) $12 + i$ (e) None of these

    1—M—Answer: d

13. Simplify, then write your result in standard form: $(4 - \sqrt{-1}) - 2(3 + 2i)$

    (a) $-2 - 3i$ (b) $-2 + 5i$ (c) $-2 - 5i$

    (d) $-2 + i$ (e) None of these

    1—M—Answer: c

14. Simplify, then write your result in standard form: $(4 - \sqrt{-25}) + 2\sqrt{-9} - 4i + 7$

    (a) $11 - 3i$ (b) $13 - 12i$ (c) $15 - 4i$

    (d) $13 - 2i$ (e) None of these

    1—M—Answer: a

15. Simplify, then write your result in standard form: $3(2 - \sqrt{-9}) + 2i(4i - 7)$

    1—O—Answer: $-2 - 23i$

16. Write the conjugate: $4 - \sqrt{-3}$

  (a) $-4 + \sqrt{3}i$ (b) $16 - 3i$ (c) $4 + \sqrt{3}i$

  (d) $4 - \sqrt{3}i$ (e) None of these

  1—M—Answer: c

17. Write the conjugate: $6 + \sqrt{-16}$

  (a) $6 - 4i$ (b) $6 + 4i$ (c) $-6 - 4i$

  (d) $-6 + 4i$ (e) None of these

  1—M—Answer: a

18. Write the conjugate: $3 - \sqrt{-1}$

  (a) $-3 - i$ (b) $-3 + i$ (c) 4

  (d) $3 + i$ (e) None of these

  1—M—Answer: d

19. Write the conjugate: $\frac{1}{2} + 4i$

  (a) $\frac{1}{2} - 4i$ (b) $2 - \frac{1}{4}i$ (c) $-\frac{1}{2} + 4i$

  (d) $-2 - 4i$ (e) None of these

  1—M—Answer: a

20. Write the conjugate: $\dfrac{3 + 4i}{16}$

  (a) $\dfrac{3}{16} + \dfrac{1}{4}i$ (b) $\dfrac{16}{3 + 4i}$ (c) $\dfrac{3}{16} - \dfrac{1}{4}i$

  (d) $-\dfrac{3 + 4i}{16}$ (e) None of these

  1—M—Answer: c

21. Multiply: $(3 + 7i)(6 - 2i)$

  (a) $18 + 22i$ (b) $4 + 48i$ (c) $4 + 36i$

  (d) $32 + 36i$ (e) None of these

  1—M—Answer: d

22. Divide then write your answer in standard form: $\dfrac{6 + 10i}{2i}$

  (a) $\dfrac{3}{i} + 5$ (b) $5 - 3i$ (c) $5 + 3i$

  (d) $3 + 5i$ (e) None of these

  1—M—Answer: b

23. Multiply: $(3 - \sqrt{-4})(7 + \sqrt{-9})$

    (a) $15 + 23i$ (b) $27 - 5i$ (c) $27 + 5i$

    (d) $15 + 5i$ (e) None of these

    1—M—Answer: b

24. Divide, then write the result in standard form: $\dfrac{2 + 3i}{1 - i}$

    1—O—Answer: $-\dfrac{1}{2} + \dfrac{5}{2}i$

25. Multiply: $(4 - \sqrt{-9})^2$

    (a) 7   (b) $7 - 24i$ (c) $25 - 24i$

    (d) $7 - 12i$ (e) None of these

    1—M—Answer: b

26. Solve for x: $3x^2 = 4x - 2$

    (a) $\dfrac{2 \pm 2\sqrt{2}\,i}{3}$ (b) $\dfrac{2 \pm 2\sqrt{10}}{3}$ (c) $\dfrac{2 \pm \sqrt{2}\,i}{3}$

    (d) $\dfrac{2 \pm \sqrt{10}}{3}$ (e) None of these

    1—M—Answer: c

27. Solve for x: $3x^2 = x + 14$

    (a) $-7, \dfrac{2}{3}$ (b) $\dfrac{7}{3}, -2$ (c) $\dfrac{x + 14}{3x}$

    (d) $-\dfrac{1}{6} \pm \dfrac{\sqrt{167}}{6}i$ (e) None of these

    1—M—Answer: b

28. Solve for x: $8x^2 = 2x - 3$

    (a) $\dfrac{2x - 3}{8}$ (b) $\dfrac{1}{16} \pm \dfrac{\sqrt{23}}{16}i$ (c) $2 \pm \dfrac{\sqrt{23}}{16}i$

    (d) $\dfrac{1 \pm \sqrt{23}\,i}{8}$ (e) None of these

    1—M—Answer: d

29. Solve for x: $x^2 - 2x + 10 = 0$

    (a) $7, -1$ (b) $1 + 3i, -1 + 3i$ (c) $1 + 3i, 1 - 3i$

    (d) $4, -2$ (e) None of these

    1—M—Answer: c

30. Use the Quadratic Formula to solve for x: $5x^2 - 2x + 6 = 0$

1—O—Answer: $\frac{1}{5}(1 \pm \sqrt{29}\,i)$

31. Use the Quadratic Formula to solve for x: $2x^2 - 4x + 3 = 0$

1—O—Answer: $\frac{1}{2}(2 \pm \sqrt{2}\,i)$

32. Simplify: $(\sqrt{-25})^3$

    (a) -125 (b) $125i$ (c) $-125i$ (d) 125 (e) None of these

1—M—Answer: c

33. Simplify: $4i^{16} + 3i^{12}$

    (a) 7 (b) $4 - 3i$ (c) $7i$ (d) $-3 + 4i$ (e) None of these

1—M—Answer: a

34. Simplify: $6i^{17} + 4i^{20}$

    (a) $6 - 4i$ (b) $4 - 6i$ (c) $-6 + 4i$

    (d) $4 + 6i$ (e) None of these

1—M—Answer: d

35. Divide then write the result in standard form: $\dfrac{-4 + i}{1 + 4i}$

    (a) $-\dfrac{8}{17} + i$ (b) $-i$ (c) i

    (d) $\dfrac{8}{17} - i$ (e) None of these

2—M—Answer: c

36. Plot $2 - i$ in the complex plane.

(a)

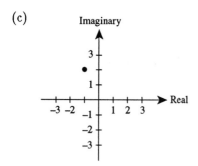

(b)

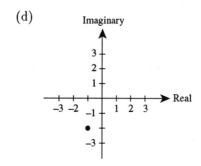

(c)

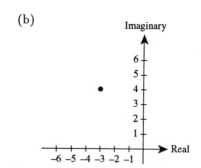

(d)

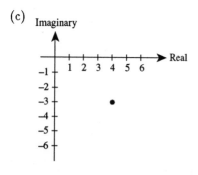

(e) None of these

1—M—Answer: a

37. Plot $-3 + 4i$ in the complex plane.

(a)

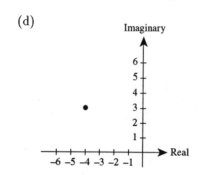

(b)

(c)

(d)

(e) None of these

1—M—Answer: b

38. Plot $1 - 3i$ in the complex plane.

1—O—Answer:

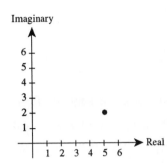

39. Plot $5 + 2i$ in the complex plane.

1—O—Answer:

3.6 Complex Zeros and the Fundamental Theorem of Algebra

1. Write as a product of linear factors: $x^4 + 25x^2 + 144$

(a) $(x^2 + 9)(x^2 + 16)$

(b) $(x + 3i)(x + 3i)(x + 4i)(x + 4i)$

(c) $(x + 3i)(x - 3i)(x + 4i)(x - 4i)$

(d) $(x - 3i)(x - 3i)(x - 4i)(x - 4i)$

(e) None of these

1—M—Answer: c

2. Write as a product of linear factors: $f(x) = x^4 - 3x^2 - 28$

(a) $(x^2 + 4)(x^2 - 7)$

(b) $(x - 2i)(x + 2i)(x - \sqrt{7})(x + \sqrt{7})$

(c) $(x + 2i)(x + 2i)(x + \sqrt{7})(x - \sqrt{7})$

(d) $(x - 2i)(x - 2i)(x - \sqrt{7})(x + \sqrt{7})$

(e) None of these

1—M—Answer: b

3. Write as a product of linear factors: $f(x) = x^4 - 5x^3 + 8x^2 - 20x + 16$

(a) $(x + 2)(x - 2)(x - 4)(x - 1)$

(b) $(x + 4)(x + 1)(x - 2i)(x + 2i)$

(c) $(x - 4)(x - 1)(x + 2i)(x - 2i)$

(d) $(x + 4)(x + 1)(x + 2i)(x + 2i)$

(e) None of these

2—M—Answer: c

4. Write as a product of linear factors: $x^4 - 16$

1—O—Answer: $(x + 2)(x - 2)(x + 2i)(x - 2i)$

5. Write as a product of linear factors: $f(x) = x^4 - 100$

1—O—Answer: $f(x) = (x + \sqrt{10})(x - \sqrt{10})(x + \sqrt{10}i)(x - \sqrt{10}i)$

6. Write as a product of linear factors: $f(x) = x^4 - 6x^3 - 4x^2 + 40x + 32$

   (a) $(x - 4)(x + 2)(x + 2 + \sqrt{8})(x + 2 - \sqrt{8})$ (b) $(x + 4)(x - 2)(x - 2 + \sqrt{8})(x - 2 - \sqrt{8})$

   (c) $(x - 4)(x - 2)(x - 2 + \sqrt{8})(x - 2 - \sqrt{8})$ (d) $(x + 4)(x + 2)(x + 2 + \sqrt{8})(x + 2 - \sqrt{8})$

   (e) None of these

   2—M—Answer: a

7. Write as a product of linear factors: $f(x) = x^4 + 2x^3 - 5x^2 - 18x - 36$

   (a) $(x + 3)(x + 3)(x + 1 + \sqrt{3})(x + 1 - \sqrt{3})$ (b) $(x - 3)(x - 3)(x - 1 + \sqrt{6})(x - 1 - \sqrt{6})$

   (c) $(x - 3)(x + 3)(x + 1 + \sqrt{3}\,i)(x + 1 - \sqrt{3}\,i)$ (d) $(x - 3)(x + 3)(x - 1 + \sqrt{3}\,i)(x - 1 - \sqrt{3}\,i)$

   (e) None of these

   2—M—Answer: c

8. Write as a product of linear factors: $f(x) = x^4 - 49$

   (a) $(x - \sqrt{7}\,i)(x + \sqrt{7}\,i)$ (b) $(x - 7i)^2(x + 7)^2$

   (c) $(x - \sqrt{7})^2(x + \sqrt{7})^2$ (d) $(x - \sqrt{7})(x + \sqrt{7})(x - \sqrt{7}\,i)(x + \sqrt{7}\,i)$

   (e) None of these

   1—M—Answer: d

9. Write as a product of linear factors: $f(x) = x^4 + 13x^2 + 36$

   (a) $(x - 2i)^2(x - 3i)^2$ (b) $(x - 2i)(x + 2i)(x - 3i)(x - 3i)$

   (c) $(x - \sqrt{2}\,i)(x + \sqrt{2}\,i)(x - \sqrt{3}\,i)(x + \sqrt{3}\,i)$ (d) $(x - \sqrt{2}\,i)^2(x - \sqrt{3}\,i)^2$

   (e) None of these

   1—M—Answer: b

10. Find a polynomial with real coefficients that has zeros: 0, 3, −3, i, and $-i$

    (a) $f(x) = x^5 - 8x^3 - 9x$ (b) $f(x) = x^5 - 10x^3 + 9x$ (c) $f(x) = x^3 - 4x^2 + 3$

    (d) $f(x) = x^5 - 9x$ (e) None of these

    1—M—Answer: a

11. Find a fourth degree polynomial function that has zeros: 1, −1, 0, and 2

    1—O—Answer: $f(x) = x^4 - 2x^3 - x^2 + 2x$

12. Find a fourth degree polynomial with real coefficients that has zeros: 1, −1, i, $-i$

    (a) $x^4 + 1$ (b) $x^4 - 1$ (c) $x^4 + 2x^2 + 1$

    (d) $x^4 - 2x^2 + 1$ (e) None of these

    1—M—Answer: b

13. Find a third degree polynomial with real coefficients that has zeros: 0, $2 - i$, $2 + i$

    (a) $x^3 - 5x^2 + 4x$ (b) $x^3 + 4x^2 - 5x$ (c) $x^3 - 4x^2 + 5x$

    (d) $x^3 + 5x$ (e) None of these

    1—M—Answer: c

14. Find a fourth degree polynomial with real coefficients that has zeros: 2, 3, $\sqrt{2}i$

    (a) $x^4 - 5x^3 + 8x^2 - 10x + 12$ (b) $x^4 - 5x^2 + 6$ (c) $x^4 - 5x^3 + 6x^2$

    (d) $x^4 - 5x^3 + 8x^2 - 10x - 12$ (e) None of these

    2—M—Answer: a

15. Find a fourth degree polynomial that has zeros: 1, -3, $2i$

    (a) $x^4 - 2x^3 + x^2 - 8x - 12$ (b) $x^4 + 2x^3 - 7x^2 - 8x + 12$

    (c) $x^4 + 2x^3 + x^2 + 8x - 12$ (d) $x^4 - 2x^3 - 7x^2 + 8x - 12$

    (e) None of these

    1—M—Answer: c

16. Find a fourth degree polynomial that has zeros: 3, -2, i

    (a) $x^4 - x^3 - 5x^2 - x - 6$ (b) $x^4 + x^3 + 5x^2 - x - 6$

    (c) $x^4 - x^3 + 5x^2 + x - 6$ (d) $x^4 + x^3 - 5x^2 + x - 6$

    (e) None of these

    1—M—Answer: a

17. Find a third degree polynomial that has zeros: -2, $-4i$

    (a) $x^3 - 4x^2 + 4x - 32$ (b) $x^3 + 4x^2 - 4x + 16$ (c) $x^3 - 2x^2 - 14x + 32$

    (d) $x^3 + 2x^2 + 16x + 32$ (e) None of these

    1—M—Answer: d

18. Find a third degree polynomial with zeros: 6 and $-2i$

    (a) $x^3 + 6x^2 + 2x + 12$ (b) $x^3 - 6x^2 + 4x - 24$ (c) $x^3 - 6x^2 + 2x - 12$

    (d) $x^3 + 6x^2 + 4x + 24$ (e) None of these

    1—M—Answer: b

19. Write the polynomial as a product of factors irreducible over the rational numbers:

$$f(x) = x^4 - 3x^2 - 28$$

(a) $(x^2 + 4)(x^2 - 7)$

(b) $(x - 2i)(x + 2i)(x - \sqrt{7})(x + \sqrt{7})$

(c) $(x^2 + 4)(x - \sqrt{7})(x + \sqrt{7})$

(d) $(x - 2i)(x + 2i)(x^2 - 7)$

(e) None of these

1—M—Answer: a

20. Write the polynomial as a product of factors irreducible over the rational numbers: $f(x) = x^4 + 4x^2 - 45$

(a) $(x^2 - 5)(x - 3i)(x + 3i)$

(b) $(x^2 - 5)(x^2 + 9)$

(c) $(x - \sqrt{5})(x + \sqrt{5})(x - 3i)(x + 3i)$

(d) $(x - \sqrt{5})(x + \sqrt{5})(x^2 + 9)$

(e) None of these

1—M—Answer: b

21. Write the polynomial as a product of factors irreducible over the rational numbers: $f(x) = x^4 - 1$

(a) $(x^2 - 1)(x^2 + 1)$

(b) $(x^2 - 1)(x - i)(x + i)$

(c) $(x - 1)(x + 1)(x - i)(x + i)$

(d) $(x - 1)(x + 1)(x^2 + 1)$

(e) None of these

1—M—Answer: d

22. Write the polynomial as a product of factors irreducible over the real numbers: $f(x) = x^4 - 3x^2 - 28$

(a) $(x^2 + 4)(x^2 - 7)$

(b) $(x - 2i)(x + 2i)(x - \sqrt{7})(x + \sqrt{7})$

(c) $(x^2 + 4)(x - \sqrt{7})(x + \sqrt{7})$

(d) $(x - 2i)(x + 2i)(x^2 - 7)$

(e) None of these

1—M—Answer: c

23. Write the polynomial as a product of factors irreducible over the real numbers: $f(x) = x^4 + 4x^2 - 45$

(a) $(x^2 - 5)(x - 3i)(x + 3i)$

(b) $(x^2 - 5)(x^2 + 9)$

(c) $(x - \sqrt{5})(x + \sqrt{5})(x - 3i)(x + 3i)$

(d) $(x - \sqrt{5})(x + \sqrt{5})(x^2 + 9)$

(e) None of these

1—M—Answer: d

24. Write the polynomial as a product of factors irreducible over the real numbers: $f(x) = x^4 + 23x^2 - 50$

(a) $(x^2 + 25)(x^2 - 2)$

(b) $(x^2 - 2)(x - 5i)(x + 5i)$

(c) $(x - \sqrt{2})(x + \sqrt{2})(x^2 + 25)$

(d) $(x - \sqrt{2})(x + \sqrt{2})(x - 5i)(x + 5i)$

(e) None of these

1—M—Answer: c

25. Write the polynomial in completely factored form: $f(x) = x^4 - 16$

(a) $(x^2 - 4)(x^2 + 4)$

(b) $(x - 2)(x + 2)(x^2 + 4)$

(c) $(x - 2)(x + 2)(x - 2i)(x + 2i)$

(d) $(x^2 - 4)(x - 2i)(x + 2i)$

(e) None of these

1—M—Answer: c

26. Write the polynomial f in completely factored form: $f(x) = 3x^4 - 4x^3 + 4x^2 - 4x + 1$

2—O—Answer: $f(x) = (x - 1)(3x - 1)(x + i)(x - i)$

27. Write the polynomial f in completely factored form: $f(x) = x^4 - 2x^3 - x^2 + 2x$

1—O—Answer: $f(x) = x(x - 1)(x + 1)(x - 2)$

28. Write the polynomial in completely factored form: $f(x) = x^3 - x + 6$

(a) $(x + 2)(x^2 - 2x + 3)$

(b) $(x + 2)(x - 1 + \sqrt{2}\,i)(x + 1 - \sqrt{2}\,i)$

(c) $(x + 2)(x - 1 - \sqrt{2}\,i)(x - 1 + \sqrt{2}\,i)$

(d) $(x + 2)(x + 1 - \sqrt{2}\,i)(x + 1 + \sqrt{2}\,i)$

(e) None of these

2—M—Answer: c

29. Use the fact that $3i$ is a zero of f to find the remaining zeros: $f(x) = x^4 - 6x^3 + 14x^2 - 54x + 45$

(a) $0, -3i$

(b) $-1, -5, -3i$

(c) $2, 3, -3i$

(d) $1, 5, -3i$

(e) None of these

2—M—Answer: d

30. Use the fact that i is a zero of f to find the remaining zeros: $f(x) = x^4 - 5x^3 + 7x^2 - 5x + 6$

2—O—Answer: $2, 3, -i$

31. Use the fact that $1 - 2i$ is a zero of f to find the remaining zeros: $f(x) = x^3 - 3x^2 + 7x - 5$

2—O—Answer: $1, 1 + 2i$

32. Use the fact that $2 + \sqrt{3}i$ is a zero of f to find the remaining zeros: $f(x) = x^4 - 6x^3 + 12x^2 - 2x - 21$

2—O—Answer: $-1, 3, 2 - \sqrt{3}i$

33. Find all of the zeros of the function: $f(x) = x^4 + 25x^2 + 144$

(a) $\pm 2\sqrt{3}, \pm 5$

(b) $-3i, -3i, -4i, -4i$

(c) $\pm 3i, \pm 4i$

(d) $3i, 3i, 4i, 4i$

(e) None of these

1—M—Answer: c

34. Find all of the zeros of the function: $f(x) = x^3 - \dfrac{9}{2}x^2 + \dfrac{11}{2}x - \dfrac{3}{2}$

(a) $\dfrac{3}{2}$, $\dfrac{3 \pm \sqrt{5}}{2}$

(b) 1, -2, 3

(c) $\dfrac{3}{2}$, $\dfrac{3 \pm \sqrt{5}i}{2}$

(d) $\dfrac{3}{2}$, $1 \pm i$

(e) None of these

1—M—Answer: a

35. Find all of the zeros of the function: $f(x) = x^3 + 6x^2 + 12x + 7$

(a) -1, 7

(b) -1, $\dfrac{-5 \pm \sqrt{3}}{2}$

(c) -1

(d) -1, $\dfrac{-5 \pm \sqrt{3}i}{2}$

(e) None of these

1—M—Answer: d

36. Find all of the zeros of the function: $f(x) = x^4 - 5x^3 + 8x^2 - 20x + 16$

(a) 1, 4, ± 2

(b) -4, -1, $\pm 2i$

(c) 1, 4, $\pm 2i$

(d) -4, -1, $-2i$, $-2i$

(e) None of these

2—M—Answer: c

37. Find all of the zeros of the function: $f(x) = 3x^4 - 7x^3 + 21x^2 - 63x - 54$

2—O—Answer: $-\frac{2}{3}$, 3, $\pm 3i$

C H A P T E R   F O U R
Rational Functions and Conic Sections

 Rational Functions and Asymptotes

1. Determine the horizontal asymptote of the graph of
   $f(x) = \dfrac{x}{x + 1}$ by using its graph at the right.

   (a) $y = -1$ (b) $y = 1$

   (c) $x = -1$ (d) $x = 1$

   (e) None of these

   1—M—Answer: b

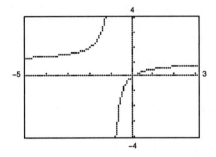

2. Determine the horizontal asymptote of the graph of
   $f(x) = \dfrac{2x^2 - 1}{x^2 + 3}$ by using its graph at the right.

   (a) $x = 2$ (b) $y = -\frac{1}{2}$

   (c) $y = 2$ (d) $x = -\frac{1}{2}$

   (e) None of these

   1—M—Answer: c

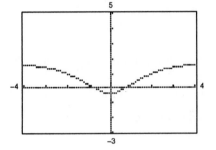

3. Find the vertical asymptote: $f(x) = \dfrac{7}{x + 2}$

   (a) $x = -2$ (b) $y = -2$ (c) $(0, -2)$ (d) $y = 0$ (e) None of these

   1—M—Answer: a

4. Find the vertical asymptote(s): $f(x) = \dfrac{1}{(x + 2)(x - 5)}$

   (a) $x = -2$, $x = 5$ (b) $y = 1$ (c) $y = 0$

   (d) $y = 1$, $y = 0$ (e) None of these

   1—M—Answer: a

5. Find the vertical asymptote(s): $f(x) = \dfrac{x + 3}{(x - 2)(x + 5)}$

   (a) $y = 2$, $y = -5$, $y = -3$ (b) $x = 2$, $x = -5$, $x = -3$, $x = 1$

   (c) $x = 1$ (d) $x = 2$, $x = -5$ (e) None of these

   1—M—Answer: d

6. Find the vertical asymptote(s): $f(x) = \dfrac{x+5}{x^2+4}$

    (a) $x = -2$, $x = 2$ (b) $x = -5$ (c) $x = 0$

    (d) $y = -2$, $y = 2$ (e) None of these

    1—M—Answer: e

7. Find the vertical asymptote(s): $f(x) = x + 2 - \dfrac{3}{x}$

    (a) $x = -2$, $x = 0$ (b) $y = 0$ (c) $y = -2$

    (d) $x = 0$ (e) None of these

    1—M—Answer: d

8. Find the vertical asymptote(s): $f(x) = \dfrac{x+2}{x^2-9}$

    (a) $x = 3$ (b) $x = -2$, $x = -3$, $x = 3$ (c) $y = 0$, $x = -2$

    (d) $x = -3$, $x = 3$ (e) None of these

    1—M—Answer: d

9. Find the horizontal asymptote(s): $f(x) = \dfrac{x^2-1}{x^2+9}$

    (a) $y = 1$ (b) $y = 0$ (c) $x = 1$ (d) $x = \pm1$ (e) None of these

    1—M—Answer: a

10. Find the horizontal asymptote(s): $f(x) = \dfrac{3x-1}{x+2}$

    (a) $y = 0$ (b) $x = -2$ (c) $x = \frac{1}{3}$ (d) $y = 3$ (e) None of these

    1—M—Answer: d

11. Find the horizontal asymptote(s): $f(x) = \dfrac{x^2-4}{x^2-9}$

    (a) $y = \pm3$ (b) $x = \pm3$ (c) $y = 1$ (d) $y = 0$ (e) None of these

    1—M—Answer: c

12. Find the horizontal asymptote(s): $f(x) = \dfrac{7}{x-4}$

    (a) $x = 4$ (b) $y = 0$ (c) $y = 7$ (d) $x = 0$ (e) None of these

    1—M—Answer: b

13. Find the horizontal asymptote(s): $f(x) = \dfrac{3x^2 + 2x - 16}{x^2 - 7}$

    (a) $x = \pm\sqrt{7}$ (b) $y = 3$ (c) $y = \pm 7$ (d) $y = 0$ (e) None of these

    1—M—Answer: b

14. Find the horizontal asymptote(s): $f(x) = \dfrac{x^2 - 3}{(x - 2)(x + 1)}$.

    1—O—Answer: $y = 1$

15. Find the domain: $f(x) = \dfrac{x + 2}{x^2 - 3x + 2}$

    (a) All reals except $x = -2,\ 1,\ 2$ (b) All reals except $x = -2$

    (c) All reals except $x = 1,\ 2$ (d) All reals

    (e) None of these

    1—M—Answer: c

16. Find the domain: $f(x) = \dfrac{3x - 1}{x^2 + 9}$

    (a) All reals   (b) All reals except $x = \pm 3$ (c) All reals except $x = \frac{1}{3}$

    (d) All reals except $x = \frac{1}{3},\ \pm 3$ (e) None of these

    1—M—Answer: a

17. Find the domain: $f(x) = \dfrac{x^2}{x + 1}$

    (a) All reals   (b) All reals except $x = -1$ (c) All reals except $x = 0$

    (d) All reals except $x = -1,\ 0$ (e) None of these

    1—M—Answer: b

18. Find the domain: $f(x) = \dfrac{x^3 - 1}{x^2 - 4}$

    (a) All reals   (b) All reals except $x = 2$ (c) All reals except $x = 1$

    (d) All reals except $x = 1,\ 2$ (e) None of these

    1—M—Answer: e

19. Find the domain: $f(x) = \dfrac{x^3 + 1}{x^2 + 4}$

    (a) All reals   (b) All reals except $x = -2$ (c) All reals except $x = -1$

    (d) All reals except $x = -2,\ -1$ (e) None of these

    1—M—Answer: a

20. Find the domain: $f(x) = \dfrac{3x^2 - 4x + 1}{x + 2}$

    (a) All reals (b) All reals except $x = \frac{1}{3}$, 1

    (c) All reals except $x = -2, \frac{1}{3}, 1$ (d) All reals except $x = -2$

    (e) None of these

    1—M—Answer: d

21. Find the domain: $f(x) = \dfrac{x}{x^2 + 3x - 4}$

    1—O—Answer: All reals except $x = -4$, 1

22. Find the domain: $f(x) = \dfrac{4 + x}{x^2 - 10}$

    1—O—Answer: All reals except $x = \pm\sqrt{10}$

23. Use a graphing utility with the given range setting to graph $f(x) = \dfrac{x + 1}{x - 3}$ and its horizontal asymptote(s).

    ```
    RANGE
    Xmin=-3
    Xmax=7
    Xscl=1
    Ymin=-5
    Ymax=5
    Yscl=1
    ```

    2—O—Answer:

    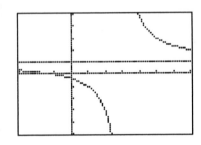

24. Use a graphing utility with the given range setting to graph $f(x) = \dfrac{x^2}{x^2 - 6x + 9}$ and its horizontal asymptote(s).

    ```
    RANGE
    Xmin=-12
    Xmax=16
    Xscl=2
    Ymin=-2
    Ymax=6
    Yscl=1
    ```

    2—O—Answer:

    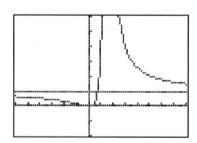

25. Find the x-intercept: $f(x) = \dfrac{2x - 1}{x^2 + 2}$

(a) $(-\sqrt{2},\ 0)$ (b) $(\tfrac{1}{2},\ 0)$ (c) $(-\sqrt{2},\ 0),\ (\tfrac{1}{2},\ 0)$

(d) $(\sqrt{2},\ 0)$ (e) None of these

1—M—Answer: b

26. Find the x-intercepts: $f(x) = \dfrac{x + 2}{x - 1}$

(a) $(1,\ 0)$ (b) $(-2,\ 0)(1,\ 0)$ (c) $(1,\ -2)$

(d) $(-2,\ 0)$ (e) None of these

1—M—Answer: d

27. Use a graphing utility to find the horizontal asymptote(s) of $f(x) = \dfrac{x - 3}{|x| - 2}$.

(a) $y = -1,\ y = 1$ (b) $y = 2$ (c) $x = 2$

(d) $x = -2,\ x = 2$ (e) None of these

2—M—Answer: a

28. Use a graphing utility to find the horizontal asymptote(s) of $f(x) = \dfrac{3x + 1}{2 + |x|}$.

(a) $y = -\tfrac{3}{2},\ y = \tfrac{3}{2}$ (b) $y = -3,\ y = 3$ (c) $x = -2,\ x = 2$

(d) $x = -3,\ x = 3$ (e) None of these

2—M—Answer: b

29. Check for symmetry: $y = \dfrac{x^2 + 3}{x - 1}$

(a) Symmetrical to x-axis   (b) Symmetrical to y-axis

(c) Symmetrical to origin   (d) None of these

1—M—Answer: d

30. Check for symmetry: $y = \dfrac{x^2 - 4}{x^2 + 9}$

(a) Symmetrical to x-axis   (b) Symmetrical to y-axis

(c) Symmetrical to the origin   (d) None of these

1—M—Answer: b

31. Suppose the cost C of removing $p\%$ of pollutants is

$$C = \frac{25{,}000p}{100 - p}, \quad 0 \le p < 100.$$

Find the cost of removing 60%.

(a) $167   (b) $25,000   (c) $37,500   (d) $375   (e) None of these

1—M—Answer: c

32. Suppose the cost C of removing $p\%$ of pollutants is

$$C = \frac{25{,}000p}{100 - p}, \quad 0 \le p < 100.$$

Find the cost of removing 90%.

(a) $225,000   (b) $2778   (c) $2   (d) $2250   (e) None of these

1—M—Answer: a

4.2   Graphs of Rational Functions

1. Find the intercepts: $f(x) = \dfrac{x^2 - 16}{x^2 - 9}$

(a) $(-4, 0)$, $(4, 0)$, $(0, -3)$, $(0, 3)$ (b) $(-4, 0)$, $(4, 0)$

(c) $(0, 1)$, $(-4, 0)$, $(4, 0)$ (d) $\left(0, \frac{16}{9}\right)$, $(-4, 0)$, $(4, 0)$

(e) None of these

1—M—Answer: d

2. Find the intercepts: $f(x) = \dfrac{x - 14}{2x + 7}$

(a) $(0, -2)$, $(14, 0)$ (b) $(-14, 0)$, $\left(\frac{1}{2}, 0\right)$ (c) $(14, 0)$, $\left(0, \frac{1}{2}\right)$

(d) $(14, 0)$, $\left(0, -\frac{7}{2}\right)$ (e) None of these

1—M—Answer: a

3. Find any horizontal and vertical asymptotes: $f(x) = \dfrac{x^2}{x^2 + 9}$

1—O—Answer: $y = 1$

4. Find any horizontal and vertical asymptotes: $f(x) = \dfrac{x}{x^3 - 1}$

1—O—Answer: $y = 0$, $x = 1$

5. Match the rational function with the correct graph: $f(x) = \dfrac{3+x}{x-1}$

(a)

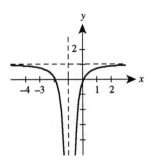

(b)

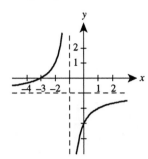

(c)

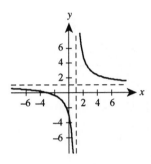

(d)

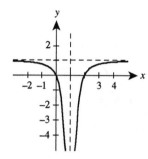

(e) None of these

1—M—Answer: c

6. Match the rational function with the correct graph: $f(x) = \dfrac{6}{x+2}$

(a)

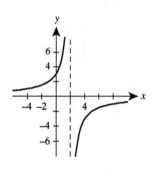

(b)

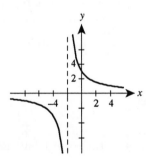

(c)

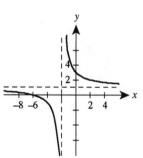

(d)

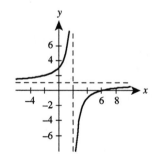

(e) None of these

1—M—Answer: b

7. Match the rational function with the correct graph: $f(x) = \dfrac{x^2}{x + 2}$

(a)

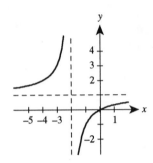

(b)

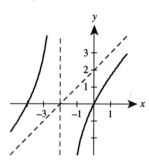

(c)

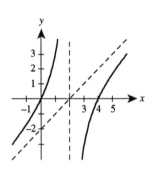

(d)

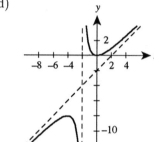

(e) None of these

2—M—Answer: d

8. Match the graph with the correct function.

(a) $f(x) = \dfrac{1}{2x + 1}$

(b) $f(x) = \dfrac{x - 1}{2x + 1}$

(c) $f(x) = \dfrac{x^2 + 2x + 2}{2x - 1}$

(d) $f(x) = \dfrac{x^3 + 2x^2 + x - 2}{2x + 1}$

(e) None of these

1—M—Answer: c

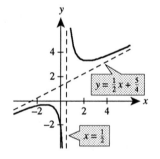

9. Match the graph with the correct function.

(a) $f(x) = \dfrac{x + 3}{x - 1}$

(b) $f(x) = x + 3$

(c) $f(x) = \dfrac{x - 1}{x^2 + 2x - 3}$

(d) $f(x) = \dfrac{x^2 + 2x - 3}{x - 1}$

(e) None of these

1—M—Answer: d

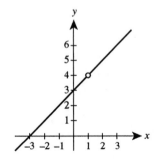

10. Match the graph with the correct function.

(a) $f(x) = \dfrac{x-5}{x+3}$ (b) $f(x) = \dfrac{5-x}{x+3}$

(c) $f(x) = -\dfrac{x+5}{x+3}$ (d) $f(x) = \dfrac{x+5}{x+3}$

(e) None of these

1—M—Answer: c

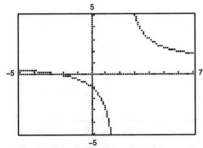

11. Use a graphing utility to graph $f(x) = \dfrac{x-2}{x+2}$.

(a)

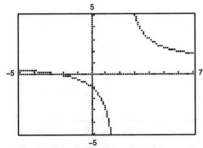

(b)

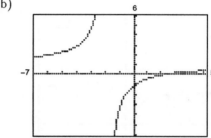

(c)

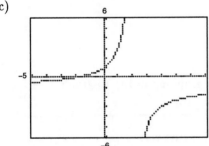

(d)

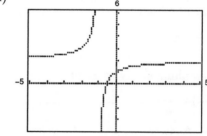

(e) None of these

1—M—Answer: b

12. Use a graphing utility to graph $f(x) = \dfrac{3x+1}{x}$.

(a)

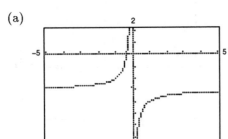

(b)

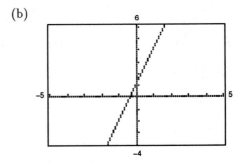

(c)

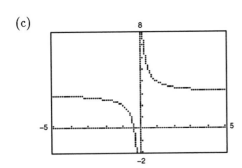

(d)

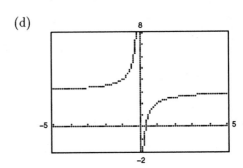

(e) None of these

1—M—Answer: c

13. Use a graphing utility to graph

$$f(x) = \frac{2}{x-1}.$$

1—O—Answer:

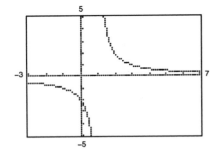

14. Use a graphing utility to graph

$$f(x) = \frac{x}{x^2-1}.$$

1—O—Answer:

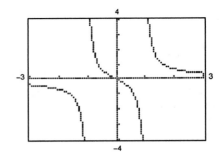

15. Match the graph with the correct function.

(a) $f(x) = \dfrac{3}{x-2}$ (b) $f(x) = \dfrac{3x}{x^2-4}$

(c) $f(x) = \dfrac{3}{x^2-4}$ (d) $f(x) = \dfrac{3}{x+2}$

(e) None of these

1—M—Answer: c

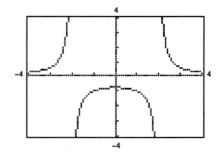

16. Match the graph with the correct function.

    (a) $f(x) = \dfrac{1}{x - 3}$ (b) $f(x) = \dfrac{1}{x + 3}$

    (c) $f(x) = \dfrac{x}{x - 3}$ (d) $f(x) = \dfrac{x}{x + 3}$

    (e) None of these

    1—M—Answer: d

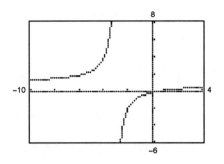

17. Find the slant asymptote: $f(x) = \dfrac{3x^2 + 2x - 1}{x - 1}$

    (a) $y = -3x + 5$ (b) $y = 3x + 5$ (c) $y = 3x - 5$

    (d) $y = -3x - 5$ (e) None of these

    1—M—Answer: b

18. Find the slant asymptote: $f(x) = x - 2 + \dfrac{3}{x + 4}$

    (a) $y = 0$ (b) $y = x + 4$ (c) $y = x - 2$

    (d) $y = x + 3$ (e) None of these

    1—M—Answer: c

19. Find the slant asymptote: $f(x) = \dfrac{x^3 + 7x^2 - 1}{x^2 + 1}$

    (a) $y = 1$ (b) $y = x + 7$ (c) $y = x - 8$

    (d) $y = x + 1$ (e) None of these

    1—M—Answer: b

20. Find the slant asymptote: $f(x) = \dfrac{x^2 + 2x - 1}{x - 1}$

    (a) $y = 1$ (b) $y = x - 1$ (c) $x = x + 1$

    (d) $y = x + 3$ (e) None of these

    1—M—Answer: d

21. Find the horizontal or slant asymptote: $f(x) = \dfrac{x^3 + 2x^2 - 3}{x + 1}$

    (a) $x = -1$ (b) $y = x^2 + x - 1$ (c) $y = 0$

    (d) $y = x^2 + 2x$ (e) None of these

    1—M—Answer: e

22. Find the horizontal or slant asymptote: $f(x) = \dfrac{x^2 + 3x + 1}{x + 1}$

  (a) $x = -1$ (b) $y = x + 3$ (c) $y = x + 2$ (d) $y = 0$ (e) None of these

  2—M—Answer: c

23. Find the vertical, horizontal, or slant asymptotes: $f(x) = \dfrac{x^3 - 2x^2 + 5}{x^2}$

  1—O—Answer: $x = 0$, $y = x - 2$

24. Find the vertical, horizontal, or slant asymptotes: $f(x) = \dfrac{x - 2}{x^2 - 2x - 3}$

  1—O—Answer: $x = -1$, $x = 3$, $y = 0$

25. Find the vertical, horizontal, or slant asymptotes: $f(x) = \dfrac{3x^2 - 2x + 4}{x - 3}$

  1—O—Answer: $x = 3$, $y = 3x + 7$

26. Label all intercepts and asymptotes, and sketch the graph: $f(x) = \dfrac{x + 2}{x + 1}$

  2—O—Answer:

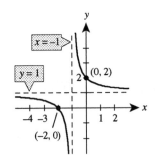

27. Label all intercepts and asymptotes, and sketch the graph: $f(x) = \dfrac{3x + 2}{x - 5}$

  2—O—Answer:

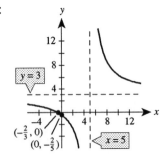

28. Label all intercepts and asymptotes and sketch the graph: $f(x) = \dfrac{x^2 + x - 2}{x - 3}$

2—O—Answer:

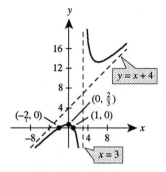

29. The concentration of a mixture is given by

$$C = \frac{2x + 9}{3(x + 12)}.$$

Use a graphing utility using the indicated range setting to determine what the concentration approaches.

(a) 33%   (b) 67%   (c) 50%

(d) 75%   (e) None of these

```
RANGE
Xmin=0
Xmax=280
Xscl=50
Ymin=0
Ymax=1
Yscl=.1
```

2—M—Answer: b

30. The concentration of a mixture is given by

$$C = \frac{3x + 8}{4(x + 8)}.$$

Use a graphing utility using the indicated range setting to determine what the concentration approaches.

(a) 75%   (b) 25%   (c) 50%

(d) 33%   (e) None of these

```
RANGE
Xmin=0
Xmax=200
Xscl=50
Ymin=0
Ymax=1
Yscl=.1
```

2—M—Answer: a

4.3 | Partial Fractions

1. Find the partial fraction decomposition: $\dfrac{1-x}{2x^2 + x}$

1—O—Answer: $\dfrac{1}{x} - \dfrac{3}{2x+1}$

2. Find the partial fraction decomposition: $\dfrac{7x-2}{3x^2 - x}$

1—O—Answer: $\dfrac{2}{x} + \dfrac{1}{3x-1}$

3. Find the partial fraction decomposition: $\dfrac{4x+23}{x^2 - x - 6}$

(a) $\dfrac{4x}{x+2} + \dfrac{23}{x-3}$ (b) $\dfrac{2}{x+2} - \dfrac{13}{x-3}$ (c) $\dfrac{5}{x-3} - \dfrac{2}{x+2}$

(d) $\dfrac{7}{x-3} - \dfrac{3}{x+2}$ (e) None of these

1—M—Answer: d

4. Find the partial fraction decomposition: $\dfrac{7}{3x^2 + 5x - 2}$

(a) $\dfrac{6}{(3x-2)} + \dfrac{1}{x-1}$ (b) $\dfrac{3}{3x-1} - \dfrac{1}{x+2}$ (c) $\dfrac{6}{x+2} - \dfrac{18}{3x-1}$

(d) $\dfrac{4}{3x-1} + \dfrac{2}{x+2}$ (e) None of these

1—M—Answer: b

5. Find the partial fraction decomposition: $\dfrac{5x+3}{x^2 - 3x - 10}$

(a) $\dfrac{2}{x+5} - \dfrac{7}{x-2}$ (b) $\dfrac{7}{x-5} - \dfrac{2}{x+2}$ (c) $\dfrac{2}{x-5} + \dfrac{3}{x+2}$

(d) $\dfrac{4}{x-5} + \dfrac{1}{x+2}$ (e) None of these

1—M—Answer: d

6. Find the partial fraction decomposition: $\dfrac{-5x-3}{x^2 - 9}$

(a) $\dfrac{-7}{x-3} + \dfrac{2x-3}{(x-3)^2}$ (b) $\dfrac{-3}{x-3} - \dfrac{2}{x+3}$ (c) $\dfrac{1}{x+3} - \dfrac{6}{x-3}$

(d) $\dfrac{4}{x-3} - \dfrac{9}{x+3}$ (e) None of these

1—M—Answer: b

7. Find the partial fraction decomposition: $\dfrac{x-7}{x^2-1}$

(a) $\dfrac{3}{x+1} - \dfrac{4}{x-1}$

(b) $-\dfrac{2}{x+1} + \dfrac{1}{x-1}$

(c) $\dfrac{3}{x+1} - \dfrac{2}{x-1}$

(d) $\dfrac{4}{x+1} - \dfrac{3}{x-1}$

(e) None of these

1—M—Answer: d

8. Find the partial fraction decomposition: $\dfrac{-3}{2x^2+3x}$

(a) $-\dfrac{1}{x} + \dfrac{2}{2x+3}$

(b) $\dfrac{3}{x} - \dfrac{9}{2x+3}$

(c) $\dfrac{-1}{x} - \dfrac{2}{2x+3}$

(d) $\dfrac{6}{2x+3} - \dfrac{9}{x}$

(e) None of these

1—M—Answer: a

9. Find the partial fraction decomposition: $\dfrac{3x^2-7x+1}{(x-1)^3}$

2—O—Answer: $\dfrac{3}{x-1} - \dfrac{1}{(x-1)^2} - \dfrac{3}{(x-1)^3}$

10. Find the partial fraction decomposition: $-\dfrac{2x+1}{(x+1)^2}$

(a) $\dfrac{-2}{x+1} + \dfrac{1}{(x+1)^2}$

(b) $\dfrac{1}{x+1} - \dfrac{2x}{(x+1)^2}$

(c) $\dfrac{-6}{x+1} - \dfrac{1}{(x+1)^2}$

(d) $\dfrac{-2}{x+1} + \dfrac{-2x+3}{(x+1)^2}$

(e) None of these

1—M—Answer: a

11. Find the partial fraction decomposition: $\dfrac{5x-2}{(x-1)^2}$

(a) $\dfrac{5}{x-1} + \dfrac{-2}{(x-1)^2}$

(b) $\dfrac{-2}{x-1} + \dfrac{5x}{(x-1)^2}$

(c) $\dfrac{5}{x-1} + \dfrac{3}{(x-1)^2}$

(d) $\dfrac{3}{(x-1)} + \dfrac{-2x+1}{(x-1)^2}$

(e) None of these

1—M—Answer: c

12. Find the partial fraction decomposition: $\dfrac{6x-13}{x^2-2x+1}$

(a) $\dfrac{6x}{(x-1)} - \dfrac{13}{(x-1)^2}$

(b) $\dfrac{6}{x-1} - \dfrac{7}{(x-1)^2}$

(c) $\dfrac{6}{x-1} - \dfrac{6x+7}{(x-1)^2}$

(d) $\dfrac{4}{x-1} + \dfrac{2}{(x-1)^2}$

(e) None of these

1—M—Answer: b

13. Find the partial fraction decomposition: $\dfrac{2x^2 - 9x + 11}{(x-2)^3}$

(a) $\dfrac{3}{x-2} + \dfrac{4}{(x-2)^2} - \dfrac{1}{(x-2)^3}$ (b) $\dfrac{2}{x-2} + \dfrac{4x+1}{(x-2)^2} + \dfrac{x^2 - 3x}{(x-2)^3}$

(c) $\dfrac{2}{x-2} + \dfrac{-1}{(x-2)^2} + \dfrac{1}{(x-2)^3}$ (d) $\dfrac{2x^2}{(x-2)^3} - \dfrac{9x}{(x-2)^2} - \dfrac{11}{(x-2)}$

(e) None of these

2—M—Answer: c

14. Find the partial fraction decomposition: $\dfrac{5x^2 + 12x + 10}{(x+1)^3}$

2—O—Answer: $\dfrac{5}{x+1} + \dfrac{2}{(x+1)^2} + \dfrac{3}{(x+1)^3}$

15. Find the partial fraction decomposition: $\dfrac{9x^2 + x - 1}{x^2(x+1)}$

(a) $\dfrac{2}{x} - \dfrac{1}{x^2} + \dfrac{7}{x+1}$ (b) $\dfrac{20}{x} - \dfrac{1}{x^2} - \dfrac{11}{x+1}$ (c) $\dfrac{9}{x} + \dfrac{1}{x^2} - \dfrac{1}{x+1}$

(d) $\dfrac{-1}{x^2} + \dfrac{9}{x+1}$ (e) None of these

2—M—Answer: a

16. Find the partial fraction decomposition: $\dfrac{-9}{(x+1)^2(x-2)}$

(a) $\dfrac{1}{x+1} + \dfrac{3}{(x+1)^2} - \dfrac{1}{x-2}$ (b) $\dfrac{10}{x+1} - \dfrac{4}{(x+1)^2} - \dfrac{15}{x-2}$

(c) $\dfrac{2}{x+1} - \dfrac{1}{(x+1)^2} - \dfrac{1}{x-2}$ (d) $\dfrac{1}{x+1} - \dfrac{3}{(x+1)^2} + \dfrac{5}{x-2}$

(e) None of these

2—M—Answer: a

17. Find the partial fraction decomposition: $\dfrac{-5x^2 - 19x - 28}{x^3 + 4x^2 + 4x}$

(a) $-\dfrac{5x^2}{x^3} - \dfrac{19x}{4x^2} - \dfrac{28}{4x}$ (b) $-\dfrac{5x^2}{x} - \dfrac{19x}{x+2} - \dfrac{28}{(x+2)^2}$

(c) $\dfrac{2}{x} - \dfrac{5}{x+2} + \dfrac{16}{(x+2)^2}$ (d) $-\dfrac{7}{x} + \dfrac{2}{x+2} + \dfrac{5}{(x+2)^2}$

(e) None of these

2—M—Answer: d

18. Find the partial fraction decomposition: $\dfrac{12x^2 - 13x - 3}{(x-1)^2(x+3)}$

2—O—Answer: $\dfrac{3}{x-1} - \dfrac{1}{(x-1)^2} + \dfrac{9}{x+3}$

19. Find the partial fraction decomposition: $\dfrac{2x^2 + 6x - 11}{(x-3)(x+2)^2}$

(a) $\dfrac{6}{x+2} + \dfrac{1}{(x+2)^2} - \dfrac{1}{x-3}$
(b) $\dfrac{-3}{x+2} + \dfrac{5}{(x+2)^2} - \dfrac{2}{x-3}$

(c) $\dfrac{2}{x+2} + \dfrac{7}{(x+2)^2} - \dfrac{11}{x-3}$
(d) $\dfrac{1}{x+2} + \dfrac{3}{(x+2)^2} + \dfrac{1}{x-3}$

(e) None of these

2—M—Answer: d

20. Find the partial fraction decomposition: $\dfrac{17x^2 - 14x + 3}{x^3 - x^2}$

(a) $\dfrac{5}{x} + \dfrac{2}{x^2} + \dfrac{5}{x-1}$
(b) $\dfrac{1}{x} + \dfrac{1}{x^2} + \dfrac{1}{x-1}$
(c) $\dfrac{11}{x} - \dfrac{3}{x^2} + \dfrac{6}{x-1}$

(d) $\dfrac{7}{x} + \dfrac{2}{x^2} - \dfrac{8}{x-1}$
(e) None of these

2—M—Answer: c

21. Find the partial fraction decomposition: $\dfrac{3x^2 - 31x - 25}{(x+1)(x^2 - 7x - 8)}$

2—O—Answer: $\dfrac{4}{x+1} - \dfrac{1}{(x+1)^2} - \dfrac{1}{x-8}$

22. Find the partial fraction decomposition: $\dfrac{-x^2 - 7x + 27}{x(x^2 + 9)}$

(a) $\dfrac{3}{x} + \dfrac{4}{x+3} - \dfrac{7}{x^2+9}$
(b) $\dfrac{3}{x} - \dfrac{4x+7}{x^2+9}$
(c) $\dfrac{2}{x} + \dfrac{3x+5}{x^2+9}$

(d) $\dfrac{2}{x} + \dfrac{3}{x+3} - \dfrac{5}{x^2+9}$
(e) None of these

2—M—Answer: b

23. Find the partial fraction decomposition: $\dfrac{5x^2 - 9x + 12}{(x-2)(x^2 + x + 1)}$

(a) $\dfrac{5x^2}{x-2} - \dfrac{9x+12}{x^2+x+1}$
(b) $-\dfrac{4/9}{x-2} + \dfrac{22/9}{x+1} - \dfrac{26/3}{(x+1)^2}$

(c) $\dfrac{2}{x-2} + \dfrac{3x-5}{x^2+x+1}$
(d) $\dfrac{5}{x-2} + \dfrac{2x-7}{x^2+x+1}$

(e) None of these

2—M—Answer: c

24. Find the partial fraction decomposition: $\dfrac{x^2 - x - 4}{x(x^2 + 2)}$

2—O—Answer: $-\dfrac{2}{x} + \dfrac{3x - 1}{x^2 + 2}$

25. Find the partial fraction decomposition: $\dfrac{4 - x}{x(x^2 + 4)}$

2—O—Answer: $\dfrac{1}{x} - \dfrac{x + 1}{x^2 + 4}$

26. Find the partial fraction decomposition: $\dfrac{x^2 - 4x + 1}{(x - 3)(x^2 + 1)}$

(a) $\dfrac{-1/5}{x - 3} + \dfrac{2}{x + 1} + \dfrac{4/5}{x + 1}$ (b) $\dfrac{1}{x - 3} + \dfrac{-4x + 1}{x^2 + 1}$

(c) $\dfrac{1}{x - 3} - \dfrac{4}{x + 1} + \dfrac{1}{x + 1}$ (d) $\dfrac{-1/5}{x - 3} + \dfrac{(6/5)x - (2/5)}{x^2 + 1}$

(e) None of these

2—M—Answer: d

27. Find the partial fraction decomposition: $\dfrac{7x^2 + 24x - 1}{(x^2 + 2)(x + 5)}$

(a) $\dfrac{2}{x + 5} + \dfrac{5x - 1}{x^2 + 2}$ (b) $\dfrac{3}{x + 5} + \dfrac{5x + 2}{x^2 + 2}$ (c) $\dfrac{3}{x + 5} - \dfrac{1}{x^2 + 2}$

(d) $\dfrac{1}{x + 5} - \dfrac{3x}{x^2 + 2}$ (e) None of these

2—M—Answer: a

28. Find the partial fraction decomposition: $\dfrac{x^2 + 11x + 2}{(x - 3)(x^2 + 2)}$

(a) $\dfrac{x - 6}{x^2 + 2} + \dfrac{4}{x - 3}$ (b) $\dfrac{7x - 5}{x^2 + 2} - \dfrac{1}{x - 3}$ (c) $\dfrac{-3x + 2}{x^2 + 2} + \dfrac{4}{x - 3}$

(d) $\dfrac{2x + 1}{x^2 + 2} + \dfrac{3}{x - 3}$ (e) None of these

2—M—Answer: c

29. Find the partial fraction decomposition: $\dfrac{x^2 - x + 2}{(x^2 + 2)^2}$

2—O—Answer: $\dfrac{1}{x^2 + 2} - \dfrac{x}{(x^2 + 2)^2}$

30. Find the partial fraction decomposition: $\dfrac{2x^3 - x^2 + 2x + 2}{(x^2 + 1)^2}$

(a) $\dfrac{x+1}{x^2+1} + \dfrac{x-1}{(x^2+1)^2}$

(b) $\dfrac{2x-1}{x^2+1} + \dfrac{3}{(x^2+1)^2}$

(c) $\dfrac{x-3}{x^2+1} + \dfrac{2x+5}{(x^2+1)^2}$

(d) $\dfrac{7}{x^2+1} + \dfrac{-3x+2}{(x^2+1)^2}$

(e) None of these

2—M—Answer: b

31. Find the partial fraction decomposition: $\dfrac{2x^2 - 6x + 4}{(x^2 + 1)^2}$

(a) $\dfrac{3x+1}{x^2+1} - \dfrac{x+1}{(x^2+1)^2}$

(b) $\dfrac{4}{x^2+1} - \dfrac{6x}{(x^2+1)^2}$

(c) $\dfrac{2x-6}{x^2+1} + \dfrac{4}{(x^2+1)^2}$

(d) $\dfrac{2}{x^2+1} - \dfrac{6x-2}{(x^2+1)^2}$

(e) None of these

1—M—Answer: d

32. Find the partial fraction decomposition: $\dfrac{3x^2 + 9x + 4}{(x^2 + x + 1)^2}$

(a) $\dfrac{3}{x^2+x+1} + \dfrac{6x+1}{(x^2+x+1)^2}$

(b) $\dfrac{2x-1}{x^2+x+1} + \dfrac{4x+7}{(x^2+x+1)}$

(c) $\dfrac{9x-1}{x^2+x+1} + \dfrac{4x}{(x^2+x+1)^2}$

(d) $\dfrac{3x+6}{x^2+x+1} + \dfrac{3x-6}{(x^2+x+1)^2}$

(e) None of these

1—M—Answer: a

33. Find the partial fraction decomposition: $\dfrac{6x^3 + 24x - 7}{(x^2 + 4)^2}$

(a) $\dfrac{-2x+1}{x^2+4} + \dfrac{16x-5}{(x^2+4)^2}$

(b) $\dfrac{-4x+3}{x^2+4} + \dfrac{x+1}{(x^2+4)^2}$

(c) $\dfrac{6x}{x^2+4} - \dfrac{7}{(x^2+4)^2}$

(d) $\dfrac{2-3x}{x^2+4} + \dfrac{4x-1}{(x^2+4)^2}$

(e) None of these

1—M—Answer: c

34. Find the partial fraction decomposition: $\dfrac{x^3 + x}{(x^2 + x + 1)^2}$

(a) $\dfrac{x+1}{x^2+x+1} - \dfrac{x+1}{(x^2+x+1)^2}$

(b) $\dfrac{x-1}{x^2+x+1} + \dfrac{x+1}{(x^2+x+1)^2}$

(c) $\dfrac{x+1}{x^2+x+1} + \dfrac{x-1}{(x^2+x+1)^2}$

(d) $\dfrac{x-1}{x^2+x+1} + \dfrac{x-1}{(x^2+x+1)^2}$

(e) None of these

1—M—Answer: b

35. Find the partial fraction decomposition: $\dfrac{5x^3 + 4x^2 + 7x + 3}{(x^2 + 2)(x^2 + 1)}$

2—O—Answer: $\dfrac{2x - 1}{x^2 + 1} + \dfrac{3x + 5}{x^2 + 2}$

36. Find the partial fraction decomposition: $\dfrac{5x + 5}{(x^2 + 1)(x^2 + 5)}$

2—O—Answer: $\dfrac{x + 1}{x^2 + 1} - \dfrac{x}{x^2 + 5}$

37. Find the partial fraction decomposition: $\dfrac{x^3 + x^2 + 2x - 2}{x^2 - 1}$

2—O—Answer: $x + 1 + \dfrac{1}{x - 1} + \dfrac{2}{x + 1}$

38. Find the partial fraction decomposition: $\dfrac{x^3 - x^2 + 4}{x^2 - 1}$

(a) $x - 1 + \dfrac{x}{x - 1} + \dfrac{1}{x + 1}$

(b) $x + 1 + \dfrac{4}{x + 1} + \dfrac{-2}{x - 1}$

(c) $x - 1 + \dfrac{2}{x - 1} - \dfrac{1}{x + 1}$

(d) $x + 1 - \dfrac{3}{x + 1} + \dfrac{1}{x - 1}$

(e) None of these

2—M—Answer: c

39. Find the partial fraction decomposition: $\dfrac{3x^4 + x^2 - 2}{x^2 - 1}$

(a) $3x^2 - 2 - \dfrac{2}{x - 1} + \dfrac{1}{x + 1}$

(b) $3x^2 - 2$

(c) $3x^2 - 4 + \dfrac{2}{x + 1} - \dfrac{1}{x - 1}$

(d) $3x^2 + 4 + \dfrac{1}{x - 1} - \dfrac{1}{x + 1}$

(e) None of these

2—M—Answer: d

4.4 Conic Sections and Graphs

1. Match the graph with the correct equation.

    (a) $\dfrac{x^2}{1} + \dfrac{y^2}{3} = 1$ (b) $\dfrac{x^2}{3} + \dfrac{y^2}{1} = 1$

    (c) $\dfrac{x^2}{9} + \dfrac{y^2}{1} = 1$ (d) $\dfrac{x^2}{2} + \dfrac{y^2}{9} = 1$

    (e) None of these

    1—M—Answer: e

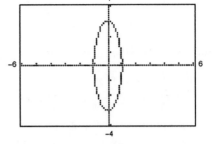

2. Match the graph with the correct equation.

    (a) $\dfrac{x^2}{16} - \dfrac{y^2}{4} = 1$ (b) $\dfrac{x^2}{4} - \dfrac{y^2}{16} = 1$

    (c) $\dfrac{y^2}{16} - \dfrac{x^2}{4} = 1$ (d) $\dfrac{y^2}{4} - \dfrac{x^2}{16} = 1$

    (e) None of these

    1—M—Answer: a

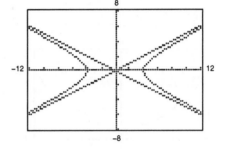

3. Match the graph with the correct equation.

    (a) $\dfrac{x^2}{4} + \dfrac{y^2}{2} = 1$ (b) $\dfrac{y^2}{4} + \dfrac{x^2}{2} = 1$

    (c) $\dfrac{x^2}{16} + \dfrac{y^2}{4} = 1$ (d) $\dfrac{y^2}{16} - \dfrac{x^2}{4} = 1$

    (e) None of these

    1—M—Answer: c

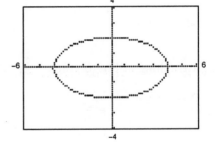

4. Match the graph with the correct equation.

    (a) $y = 2x^2$ (b) $y = -4x^2$

    (c) $x = 3y^2$ (d) $x = -2y^2$

    (e) None of these

    1—M—Answer: d

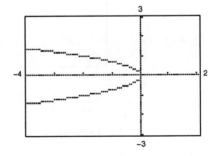

5. Match the graph with the correct equation.

(a) $\dfrac{x^2}{9} - \dfrac{y^2}{4} = 1$ (b) $\dfrac{x^2}{4} - \dfrac{y^2}{9} = 1$

(c) $\dfrac{y^2}{9} - \dfrac{x^2}{4} = 1$ (d) $\dfrac{y^2}{4} - \dfrac{x^2}{9} = 1$

(e) None of these

1—M—Answer: c

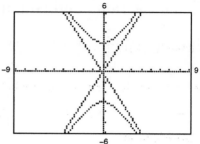

6. Use a graphing utility to graph:

$x^2 = 24(y - 2)$

1—O—Answer:

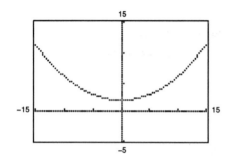

7. Use a graphing utility to graph:

$x^2 + 5y^2 = 5$

1—O—Answer:

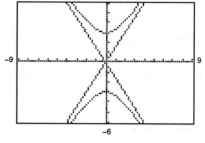

8. Use a graphing utility to graph: $\dfrac{x^2}{9} - \dfrac{y^2}{4} = 1$

1—O—Answer:

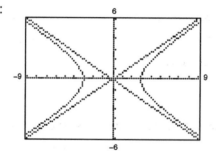

9. Find the focus of the parabola: $y^2 = -32x$

(a) (8, 0)   (b) (−8, 0)   (c) (0, 8)   (d) (0, −8)   (e) None of these

1—M—Answer: b

10. Find the directrix of the parabola: $y^2 = x$

(a) $y = \frac{1}{4}$ (b) $x = \frac{1}{4}$ (c) $y = -\frac{1}{4}$ (d) $x = -\frac{1}{4}$ (e) None of these

1—M—Answer: d

11. Find the focus of the parabola: $x = -16y^2$

   (a) $(-4, 0)$ (b) $\left(-\frac{1}{64}, 0\right)$ (c) $(0, -4)$ (d) $\left(0, -\frac{1}{64}\right)$ (e) None of these

   1—M—Answer: b

12. Determine the directrix of the parabola: $x = -4y^2$

   (a) $x = 1$ (b) $y = 1$ (c) $x = \frac{1}{16}$ (d) $y = \frac{1}{16}$ (e) None of these

   1—M—Answer: c

13. Determine the focus of the parabola: $y = -16x^2$

   (a) $\left(-\frac{1}{64}, 0\right)$ (b) $\left(0, -\frac{1}{64}\right)$ (c) $(-4, 0)$ (d) $(0, -4)$ (e) None of these

   1—M—Answer: b

14. Find an equation of the parabola with vertex at $(0, 0)$ and focus at $(-3, 0)$.

   (a) $x^2 = -12y$ (b) $y^2 = -12x$ (c) $x^2 = 12y$

   (d) $y^2 = 12x$ (e) None of these

   1—M—Answer: b

15. Find the standard equation of the parabola with vertex at $(0, 0)$ and directrix $x = 7$.

   (a) $x^2 = -28y$ (b) $x^2 = \frac{7}{4}y$ (c) $y^2 = -\frac{4}{7}x$

   (d) $y^2 = -28x$ (e) None of these

   1—M—Answer: d

16. Find the standard equation of the parabola with vertex at $(0, 0)$ and directrix $x = -5/2$.

   (a) $x^2 = 10y$ (b) $y^2 = 10x$ (c) $x^2 = -\frac{5}{8}y$

   (d) $y^2 = \frac{8}{5}x$ (e) None of these

   1—M—Answer: b

17. Find the standard equation of the parabola with a horizontal axis, the vertex at $(0, 0)$ and passes through the point $(2, -4)$.

   2—O—Answer: $y^2 = 8x$

18. Find an equation of the parabola with vertex $(0, 0)$ and focus $(0, 1)$.

   (a) $y = \frac{1}{4}x^2$ (b) $y = 4x^2$ (c) $x = -\frac{1}{4}y^2$

   (d) $x = -4y^2$ (e) None of these

   1—M—Answer: a

19. Find the foci of the ellipse: $\dfrac{x^2}{81} + \dfrac{y^2}{225} = 1$

    (a) $(0, 12)$, $(0, -12)$ (b) $(12, 0)$, $(-12, 0)$ (c) $(0, 3\sqrt{34})$, $(0, -3\sqrt{34})$

    (d) $(3\sqrt{34}, 0)$, $(-3\sqrt{34}, 0)$ (e) None of these

    1—M—Answer: a

20. Find the length of the minor axis: $\dfrac{x^2}{9} + \dfrac{y^2}{16} = 1$

    (a) 3   (b) 4   (c) 8   (d) $\sqrt{7}$ (e) None of these

    1—M—Answer: e

21. If the length of each latus rectum of an ellipse is $\dfrac{2b^2}{a}$, determine the combined length of the 2 latus recta of the ellipse $\dfrac{x^2}{4} + y^2 = 1$.

    (a) 1   (b) 2   (c) 4   (d) 64   (e) None of these

    2—M—Answer: b

22. Find the vertices: $9x^2 + 4y^2 = 36$

    (a) $(3, 0)$, $(-3, 0)$ (b) $(0, 2)$, $(0, -2)$ (c) $(0, 3)$, $(0, -3)$

    (d) $(0, \sqrt{5})$, $(0, -\sqrt{5})$ (e) None of these

    1—M—Answer: c

23. Find the foci: $\dfrac{x^2}{9} + \dfrac{y^2}{5} = 1$

    (a) $(-2, 0)$, $(2, 0)$ (b) $(0, -2)$, $(0, 2)$ (c) $(4, 0)$, $(-4, 0)$

    (d) $(0, 4)$, $(0, -4)$ (e) None of these

    1—M—Answer: a

24. Find the standard equation of the ellipse with center at $(0, 0)$, one focus at $(3, 0)$, and has a major axis of length 12.

    1—O—Answer: $\dfrac{x^2}{36} + \dfrac{y^2}{27} = 1$

25. Find the standard equation of the ellipse with vertices at $(\pm 4, 0)$, and foci at $(\pm 3, 0)$.

    (a) $\dfrac{x^2}{7} + \dfrac{y^2}{16} = 1$ (b) $\dfrac{x^2}{16} + \dfrac{y^2}{9} = 1$ (c) $\dfrac{x^2}{16} + \dfrac{y^2}{7} = 1$

    (d) $\dfrac{x^2}{16} - \dfrac{y^2}{9} = 1$ (e) None of these

    1—M—Answer: c

26. Find the standard equation of an ellipse with vertices at $(0, \pm7)$ and foci at $(0, \pm\sqrt{13})$.

   (a) $\dfrac{x^2}{13} + \dfrac{y^2}{49} = 1$ (b) $\dfrac{x^2}{49} + \dfrac{y^2}{36} = 1$ (c) $\dfrac{x^2}{36} + \dfrac{y^2}{13} = 1$

   (d) $\dfrac{x^2}{36} + \dfrac{y^2}{49} = 1$ (e) None of these

   2—M—Answer: d

27. Find the standard equation of the ellipse that passes through the point $(2, 6\sqrt{2})$ and has end points of $(\pm6, 0)$ on the minor axis.

   2—O—Answer: $\dfrac{x^2}{36} + \dfrac{y^2}{81} = 1$

28. Find the standard equation of the ellipse with center at $(0, 0)$, a focus at $(2\sqrt{35}, 0)$ and minor axis of length 4.

   (a) $\dfrac{x^2}{70} + \dfrac{y^2}{16} = 1$ (b) $\dfrac{x^2}{70} + \dfrac{y^2}{144} = 1$ (c) $\dfrac{x^2}{4} + \dfrac{y^2}{70} = 1$

   (d) $\dfrac{x^2}{144} + \dfrac{y^2}{4} = 1$ (e) None of these

   1—M—Answer: d

29. Find the foci of the hyperbola: $2y^2 - 9x^2 - 18 = 0$

   (a) $(\pm\sqrt{11}, 3)$ (b) $(0, \pm\sqrt{7})$ (c) $(0, \pm\sqrt{11})$ (d) $(\pm\sqrt{7}, 0)$ (e) None of these

   1—M—Answer: c

30. Find the foci of the hyperbola: $\dfrac{x^2}{144} - \dfrac{y^2}{36} = 1$

   (a) $(\pm6\sqrt{5}, 0)$ (b) $(0, \pm6\sqrt{5})$ (c) $(\pm6\sqrt{3}, 0)$ (d) $(0, \pm6\sqrt{3})$ (e) None of these

   1—M—Answer: a

31. Find the vertices: $\dfrac{y^2}{81} - \dfrac{x^2}{144} = 1$

   (a) $(\pm9, 0)$ (b) $(0, \pm9)$ (c) $(\pm12, 0)$ (d) $(0, \pm12)$ (e) None of these

   1—M—Answer: b

32. Find the vertices: $\dfrac{x^2}{36} - \dfrac{y^2}{25} = 1$

   (a) $(\pm5, 0)$ (b) $(0, \pm5)$ (c) $(0, \pm6)$ (d) $(\pm6, 0)$ (e) None of these

   1—M—Answer: d

33. Find the equations of the asymptotes of the hyperbola: $\dfrac{x^2}{25} - \dfrac{y^2}{81} = 1$

    (a) $y = \pm\dfrac{5}{9}x$ (b) $y = \pm\dfrac{\sqrt{106}}{5}x$ (c) $y = \pm\dfrac{9}{5}x$

    (d) $y = \pm\dfrac{5\sqrt{106}}{106}x$ (e) None of these

    1—M—Answer: c

34. Find the equations of the asymptotes of the hyperbola: $\dfrac{y^2}{36} - \dfrac{x^2}{25} = 1$

    (a) $y = \pm\dfrac{5}{6}x$ (b) $y = \pm\dfrac{6}{5}x$ (c) $y = \pm\dfrac{\sqrt{11}}{6}x$

    (d) $y = \dfrac{\sqrt{11}}{5}x$ (e) None of these

    1—M—Answer: b

35. Find an equation of the hyperbola with center at $(0, 0)$, vertices at $(\pm 3, 0)$, and foci at $(\pm 3\sqrt{5}, 0)$.

    (a) $\dfrac{x^2}{9} - \dfrac{y^2}{45} = 1$ (b) $\dfrac{y^2}{9} - \dfrac{x^2}{45} = 1$ (c) $\dfrac{x^2}{9} - \dfrac{y^2}{36} = 1$

    (d) $\dfrac{x^2}{9} - \dfrac{y^2}{54} = 1$ (e) None of these

    1—M—Answer: c

36. Find an equation of the hyperbola with center $(0, 0)$, vertices $(0, \pm 9)$, and asymptotes $y = \pm\dfrac{9}{2}x$.

    (a) $\dfrac{x^2}{2} - \dfrac{y^2}{9} = 1$ (b) $\dfrac{x^2}{81} - \dfrac{y^2}{4} = 1$ (c) $\dfrac{y^2}{81} - \dfrac{x^2}{4} = 1$

    (d) $\dfrac{x^2}{77} - \dfrac{y^2}{4} = 1$ (e) None of these

    2—M—Answer: c

37. Find an equation of the hyperbola with vertices $(\pm 12, 0)$ and foci $(\pm 13, 0)$.

    (a) $\dfrac{x^2}{144} - \dfrac{y^2}{169} = 1$ (b) $\dfrac{x^2}{169} - \dfrac{y^2}{144} = 1$ (c) $\dfrac{y^2}{169} - \dfrac{x^2}{25} = 1$

    (d) $\dfrac{x^2}{144} - \dfrac{y^2}{25} = 1$ (e) None of these

    1—M—Answer: d

38. The width of an elliptical window is 6 feet. The height is 4 feet. Find an equation for the elliptical shape of the window.

(a) $\dfrac{x^2}{4} + \dfrac{y^2}{36} = 1$ (b) $\dfrac{x^2}{9} + \dfrac{y^2}{4} = 1$ (c) $\dfrac{x^2}{36} + \dfrac{y^2}{9} = 1$

(d) $\dfrac{x^2}{4} = \dfrac{y^2}{9} = 1$ (e) None of these

2—M—Answer: b

39. The width of an elliptical window is 4 feet. The height of the window is 8 feet. Find an equation for the elliptical shape of the window.

(a) $\dfrac{x^2}{4} + \dfrac{y^2}{16} = 1$ (b) $\dfrac{x^2}{4} + \dfrac{y^2}{8} = 1$ (c) $\dfrac{x^2}{64} + \dfrac{y^2}{16} = 1$

(d) $\dfrac{x^2}{16} + \dfrac{y^2}{64} = 1$ (e) None of these

2—M—Answer: a

4.5 | Conic Sections and Translations

1. Match the graph with the correct equation.

(a) $\dfrac{(x-1)^2}{4} + (y+2) = 1$

(b) $\dfrac{(x-1)^2}{4} + \dfrac{(y+2)^2}{1} = 1$

(c) $\dfrac{(x-1)^2}{4} - \dfrac{(y+2)^2}{1} = 1$

(d) $\dfrac{(x+1)}{4} + \dfrac{(y+2)^2}{1} = 1$

(e) None of these

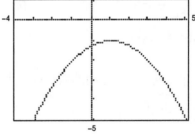

1—M—Answer: a

2. Match the graph with the correct equation.

(a) $\dfrac{(x+2)^2}{4} - \dfrac{(y+2)^2}{9} = 1$

(b) $\dfrac{(x+2)^2}{4} + \dfrac{(y+2)^2}{9} = 1$

(c) $\dfrac{(x+2)^2}{9} + \dfrac{(y+2)^2}{4} = 1$

(d) $\dfrac{(x+2)^2}{9} - \dfrac{(y+2)^2}{4} = 1$

(e) None of these

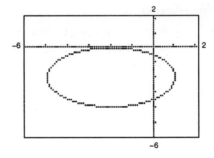

1—M—Answer: c

3. Use a graphing utility to graph

$$\frac{(x-3)^2}{1} - \frac{(y+4)^2}{4} = 1$$

and its asymptotes.

2—O—Answer:

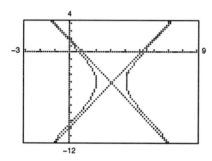

4. Use a graphing utility to graph

$$\frac{(x+3)^2}{16} + \frac{(y-1)^2}{25} = 1.$$

2—O—Answer:

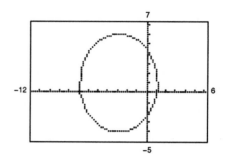

5. Write in standard form: $x^2 + 4x - 8y + 4 = 0$

(a) $y = \frac{1}{8}(x+2)^2$

(b) $x(x+4) = 8\left(y - \frac{1}{2}\right)$

(c) $(x+2)^2 = 4(2)y$

(d) $\frac{(x+2)^2}{8y} = 1$

(e) None of these

1—M—Answer: c

6. Write in standard form: $4x^2 + 9y^2 - 8x + 72y + 4 = 0$

(a) $\frac{(x-1)^2}{36} + \frac{(y+4)^2}{16} = 1$

(b) $\frac{(x-1)^2}{144} + \frac{(y+8)^2}{64} = 1$

(c) $\frac{(x-1)^2}{13/4} + \frac{(y+4)^2}{13/9} = 1$

(d) $\frac{(x-4)^2}{327} + \frac{(y+36)^2}{436/3} = 1$

(e) None of these

2—M—Answer: a

7. Write in standard form: $9x^2 - 4y^2 - 54x + 8y + 41 = 0$

(a) $\frac{(y+1)^2}{41/4} - \frac{(x-3)^2}{41/9} = 1$

(b) $\frac{(x-3)^2}{31/9} - \frac{(y-1)^2}{31/4} = 1$

(c) $\frac{(x-3)^2}{4} - \frac{(y-1)^2}{9} = 1$

(d) $\frac{(y+1)^2}{14} - \frac{(x-3)^2}{63/2} = 1$

(e) None of these

2—M—Answer: c

8. Write in standard form: $4x^2 - 5y^2 - 16x - 30y - 9 = 0$

   (a) $\dfrac{(x-4)^2}{11} - \dfrac{(y-3)^2}{4} = 1$ (b) $\dfrac{(y+3)^2}{4} - \dfrac{(x-2)^2}{5} = 1$

   (c) $\dfrac{(y-3)^2}{6} - \dfrac{(x+2)^2}{9} = 1$ (d) $\dfrac{(x+2)^2}{4} - \dfrac{(y+3)^2}{6} = 1$

   (e) None of these

   2—M—Answer: b

9. Find the vertex of the parabola: $(x+3)^2 - 8(y+6) = 0$

   (a) $(3,\ 6)$ (b) $(-3,\ -6)$ (c) $(-3,\ -4)$ (d) $(-1,\ -6)$ (e) None of these

   1—M—Answer: b

10. Find the directrix: $y = \frac{1}{2}(x-2)^2$

    (a) $y = -\frac{1}{2}$ (b) $y = \frac{1}{8}$ (c) $x = 2$ (d) $x = -8$ (e) None of these

    1—M—Answer: a

11. Find the focus of a parabola with directrix $x = 2$ and vertex $(6,\ 2)$.

    (a) $(8,\ 2)$ (b) $(6,\ 4)$ (c) $(10,\ 2)$ (d) $(6,\ 6)$ (e) None of these

    1—M—Answer: c

12. Find the vertex: $(y-2)^2 - 8(x+1) = 0$

    (a) $(-2,\ -1)$ (b) $(-1,\ -2)$ (c) $(2,\ -1)$ (d) $(-1,\ 2)$ (e) None of these

    1—M—Answer: d

13. Find an equation of the parabola with vertex $(2,\ -3)$ and focus $(2,\ 0)$.

    (a) $y^2 + 6y - 12x + 33 = 0$ (b) $x^2 - 4x + 12y + 40 = 0$ (c) $x^2 - 4x - 12y - 32 = 0$

    (d) $y^2 + 6y + 12x - 15 = 0$ (e) None of these

    2—M—Answer: c

14. Find the equation of the parabola with vertex $(1,\ -1)$ and focus $(1,\ 0)$.

    (a) $x^2 - 2x - 4y - 3 = 0$ (b) $x^2 + 2x - 4y + 5 = 0$ (c) $y^2 - 4x - 2y - 2 = 0$

    (d) $y^2 - 4x - 2y - 3 = 0$ (e) None of these

    2—M—Answer: a

15. Find the equation of the parabola with focus $(-8,\ 1)$ and directrix $x = 0$.

    (a) $(y-1)^2 = 4(x-4)$ (b) $(x-4)^2 = -16(y+1)$ (c) $(y-1)^2 = -16(x+4)$

    (d) $(x+4)^2 = 2(y-1)$ (e) None of these

    2—M—Answer: c

16. Find the equation of the parabola with vertex $(2, -3)$ and directrix $y = 1$.

(a) $(x - 2)^2 = -16(y + 3)$ (b) $(x - 2)^2 = -8(y + 3)$ (c) $(x + 2)^2 = 8(y - 3)$

(d) $(y + 3)^2 = 4(x - 2)$ (e) None of these

1—M—Answer: a

17. Find the center of the ellipse: $9x^2 + 4y^2 - 36x - 24y - 36 = 0$

(a) $(2, 3)$ (b) $(3, -2)$ (c) $(2\sqrt{3}, 3\sqrt{3})$ (d) $(6, 48)$ (e) None of these

2—M—Answer: a

18. Find the center of the ellipse: $5x^2 + 2y^2 - 20x + 24y + 82 = 0$

2—O—Answer: $(2, -6)$

19. Find the vertices of the ellipse: $\dfrac{(x - 1)^2}{4} + \dfrac{(y + 3)^2}{9} = 1$

(a) $(-1, 0)$, $(-1, 6)$ (b) $(1, 0)$, $(1, -6)$ (c) $(-1, -1)$, $(-1, 5)$

(d) $(1, -5)$, $(1, -1)$ (e) None of these

2—M—Answer: b

20. Find the vertices of the ellipse: $\dfrac{(x + 5)^2}{25} + \dfrac{(y - 2)^2}{9} = 1$

(a) $(5, 0)$, $(5, 10)$ (b) $(-5, 0)$, $(-5, 10)$ (c) $(-10, 2)$, $(0, 2)$

(d) $(-8, 2)$, $(-2, 2)$ (e) None of these

2—M—Answer: c

21. Find an equation of the ellipse with center at $(-1, 3)$, vertex at $(3, 3)$, and has a minor axis of length 2.

(a) $\dfrac{x^2}{16} + \dfrac{y^2}{4} = 1$ (b) $\dfrac{x^2}{4} + \dfrac{y^2}{16} = 1$

(c) $\dfrac{(x + 1)^2}{1} + \dfrac{(y - 3)^2}{16} = 1$ (d) $\dfrac{(x + 1)^2}{16} + \dfrac{(y - 3)^2}{1} = 1$

(e) None of these

2—M—Answer: d

22. Find an equation of the ellipse with foci at $(0, 2)$ and $(0, 8)$ and vertices at $(0, 0)$ and $(0, 10)$.

2—O—Answer: $25x^2 + 16y^2 - 160y = 0$

23. Determine an equation of the ellipse with foci $(-4, -1)$ and $(-4, -3)$ and vertices $(-4, 0)$ and $(-4, -4)$.

(a) $\dfrac{(x-4)^2}{3} + \dfrac{(y-4)^2}{4} = 1$

(b) $\dfrac{(x+4)^2}{3} + \dfrac{(y+2)^2}{4} = 1$

(c) $\dfrac{(x+4)^2}{9} + \dfrac{(y+2)^2}{4} = 1$

(d) $\dfrac{(x-4)^2}{4} + \dfrac{(y-4)^2}{1} = 1$

(e) None of these

2—M—Answer: b

24. Determine an equation of the ellipse with vertices $(-1, 10)$ and $(-1, 2)$ and minor axis with length 6.

(a) $\dfrac{(x-1)^2}{16} + \dfrac{(y-6)^2}{9} = 1$

(b) $\dfrac{(x+1)^2}{64} + \dfrac{(x-6)^2}{36} = 1$

(c) $\dfrac{(x+1)^2}{16} + \dfrac{(y-4)^2}{9} = 1$

(d) $\dfrac{(x+1)^2}{9} + \dfrac{(y-6)^2}{16} = 1$

(e) None of these

1—M—Answer: d

25. Find the center of the hyperbola: $3x^2 - 4y^2 - 6x - 16y + 7 = 0$

(a) $(1, -2)$ (b) $(4, 3)$ (c) $(1, -8)$ (d) $(3, -8)$ (e) None of these

2—M—Answer: a

26. Find the vertices of the hyperbola: $\dfrac{(x-2)^2}{9} - \dfrac{(y+7)^2}{12} = 1$

(a) $(5, -7), (-1, -7)$ (b) $(2, -4), (2, -10)$ (c) $(-2, 10), (-2, 4)$

(d) $(1, 7), (-5, 7)$ (e) None of these

1—M—Answer: a

27. Determine the vertices: $\dfrac{(x+1)^2}{16} - \dfrac{(y-6)^2}{25} = 1$

(a) $(-5, 6), (3, 6)$ (b) $(-6, 6), (4, 6)$ (c) $(-1, 2), (-1, 10)$

(d) $(-1, 1), (-1, 11)$ (e) None of these

1—M—Answer: a

28. Determine the foci: $\dfrac{(x+1)^2}{16} - \dfrac{(y-6)^2}{25} = 1$

(a) $(-1, 6), (1, -6)$

(b) $(-1, 9), (-1, 3)$

(c) $(-1 - \sqrt{41}, 6), (-1 + \sqrt{41}, 6)$

(d) $(-1, 6 - \sqrt{41}), (-1, 6 + \sqrt{41})$

(e) None of these

2—M—Answer: c

29. Find the equation of the hyperbola with vertices at $(0, -1)$ and $(4, -1)$, and foci at $(-2, -1)$ and $(6, -1)$.

    (a) $\dfrac{(x-2)^2}{16} - \dfrac{(y+1)^2}{4} = 1$

    (b) $\dfrac{(x-2)^2}{4} - \dfrac{(y+1)^2}{12} = 1$

    (c) $\dfrac{(y+1)^2}{12} - \dfrac{(x-2)^2}{4} = 1$

    (d) $\dfrac{(x+2)^2}{4} - \dfrac{(y-1)^2}{12} = 1$

    (e) None of these

    2—M—Answer: b

30. Find the standard equation of the hyperbola with center at $(2, 5)$, one focus at $(2, 15)$, and has a transverse axis of length 12.

    2—O—Answer: $\dfrac{(y-5)^2}{36} - \dfrac{(x-2)^2}{64} = 1$

31. Find an equation of the hyperbola with foci $(-3, -4)$ and $(-3, 4)$ and transverse axis of length 6.

    (a) $\dfrac{(x+3)^2}{16} - \dfrac{y^2}{9} = 1$

    (b) $\dfrac{y^2}{16} - \dfrac{(x+3)^2}{9} = 1$

    (c) $\dfrac{y^2}{9} - \dfrac{(x+3)^2}{7} = 1$

    (d) $\dfrac{(x+3)^2}{9} - \dfrac{y^2}{7} = 1$

    (e) None of these

    2—M—Answer: c

32. Find an equation of the hyperbola with foci $(-7, -7)$ and $(-1, -7)$ and vertices $(-6, -7)$ and $(-2, -7)$.

    (a) $\dfrac{(x-4)^2}{9} - \dfrac{(y-7)^2}{4} = 1$

    (b) $\dfrac{(y+7)^2}{4} - \dfrac{(x+4)^2}{9}$

    (c) $\dfrac{(y-7)^2}{4} - \dfrac{(x-4)^2}{5} = 1$

    (d) $\dfrac{(x+4)^2}{4} - \dfrac{(y+7)^2}{5} = 1$

    (e) None of these

    2—M—Answer: d

33. Classify the graph of $3x^2 + 6x - 4y + 12 = 0$.

    (a) Circle   (b) Hyperbola   (c) Ellipse

    (d) Parabola   (e) None of these

    1—M—Answer: d

34. Classify the graph of $2x^2 - 5y^2 + 4x - 6 = 0$.

    (a) Circle   (b) Parabola   (c) Ellipse

    (d) Hyperbola   (e) None of these

    1—M—Answer: d

35. Classify the graph of $3x^2 + 3y^2 - 4x + 5y - 16 = 0$.

(a) Circle   (b) Parabola   (c) Ellipse

(d) Hyperbola   (e) None of these

1—M—Answer: a

36. Classify the graph of $3x^2 + 3y^2 - 6x + 18y + 10 = 0$.

1—O—Answer: Circle

37. Classify the graph of $x^2 + 2x + 4y^2 + 1 = 0$.

1—O—Answer: Ellipse

38. For a science project you plan to demonstrate the elliptical orbit of a planet with the sun at one of the foci. If the center of the ellipse is (0, 0), and the length of the major axis is 120 cm, what is the smallest distance from the planet to the sun, if the sun is located at the point (1, 0)?

(a) 61 cm   (b) 59 cm   (c) 119 cm   (d) 59.99 cm   (e) None of these

2—M—Answer: b

39. For a science project you plan to demonstrate the elliptical orbit of a planet with the sun at one of the foci. If the center of the ellipse is (0, 0), the length of the major axis is 120 cm, and the sun is located at (1, 0), what is the equation in standard form of the ellipse?

2—O—Answer: $\dfrac{x^2}{3600} + \dfrac{y^2}{3599} = 1$

C H A P T E R   F I V E
Exponential and Logarithmic Functions

$\boxed{5.1}$ Exponential Functions and Their Graphs

1. Evaluate: $5.1(1.32)^{\sqrt{2}}$ Round your answer to 2 decimal places.

   (a) 14.83   (b) 27.69   (c) 9.52   (d) 7.55   (e) None of these

   1—M—Answer: d

2. Evaluate: $4.7e^{\sqrt{3}}$ Round your answer to 2 decimal places.

   (a) 82.48   (b) 74.10   (c) 26.57   (d) 22.13   (e) None of these

   1—M—Answer: c

3. Evaluate: $\sqrt[3]{e}$ Round your answer to 2 decimal places.

   (a) 0.91   (b) 1.40   (c) 0.05   (d) 20.09   (e) None of these

   1—M—Answer: b

4. Evaluate: $(2)(4^{2e})$ Round your answer to 2 decimal places.

   (a) 86.99   (b) 81,228.08   (c) 12,343.03   (d) 3751.18   (e) None of these

   1—M—Answer: d

5. Evaluate when $t = 15$: $300e^{-0.076t}$

   (a) 95.95   (b) 39.31   (c) 0.000479718   (d) −1906.12   (e) None of these

   1—M—Answer: a

6. Evaluate: $\dfrac{3e^{(0.0721)(52)}}{(1 - 0.0721)}$

   (a) 4.2727   (b) 180.6908   (c) 137.3653   (d) −410.3055   (e) None of these

   1—M—Answer: c

7. Evaluate when $t = 3$: $y = \dfrac{300}{1 + e^{-2t}}$

   (a) 299.2582   (b) 213.3704   (c) 300.0025   (d) 107.4591   (e) None of these

   1—M—Answer: a

8. Evaluate when $x = 65$: $200 - 5e^{0.002x}$

1—O—Answer: 194.3059

9. Evaluate when $x = -20$: $16e^{-0.015x}$

1—O—Answer: 21.5977

10. Match the graph with the correct function:

(a) $f(x) = 4^x - 5$ (b) $f(x) = 4^x + 5$

(c) $f(x) = 4^{-x} + 5$ (d) $f(x) = 4^{-x} - 5$

(e) None of these

1—M—Answer: a

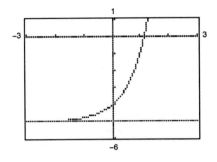

11. Match the graph with the correct function.

(a) $f(x) = 3^{x-1}$ (b) $f(x) = 3^x - 1$

(c) $f(x) = 3^{1-x}$ (d) $f(x) = 4^{-x}$

(e) None of these

1—M—Answer: b

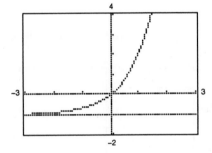

12. Match the graph with the correct function.

(a) $f(x) = \left(\frac{1}{2}\right)^x - 1$ (b) $f(x) = 3^{-x^2} - 1$

(c) $f(x) = 3^{x+1}$ (d) $f(x) = 4^{-x}$

(e) None of these

2—M—Answer: d

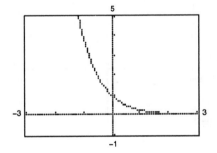

13. Without using a graphing utility, sketch the graph of $f(x) = 3^x - 5$.

1—O—Answer:

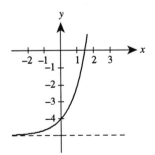

14. Without using a graphing utility, sketch the graph of $f(x) = 3^x - 2$.

1—O—Answer:

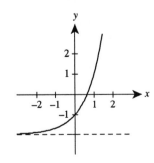

15. Without using a graphing utility, sketch the graph of $f(x) = e^{-x}$.

1—O—Answer:

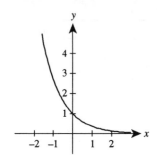

16. Use a graphing utility to graph $f(x) = 2 - 3^x$.

1—O—Answer:

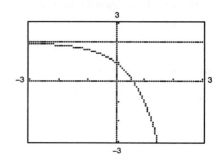

17. Match the exponential function with the correct graph: $y = 2 - e^x$

(a)

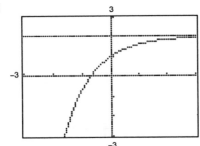

(b)

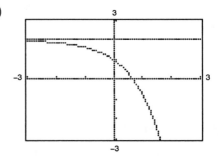

(c)

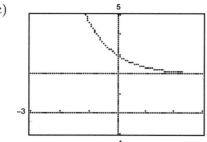

(d)

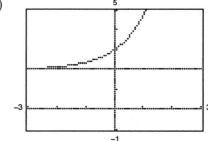

(e) None of these

1—M—Answer: b

18. Match the exponential function with the correct graph: $y = \left(\frac{1}{5}\right)^x + 1$

(a)

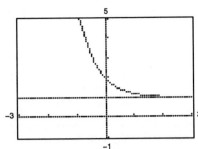

(b)

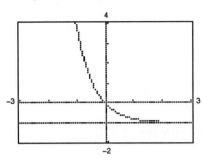

(c)

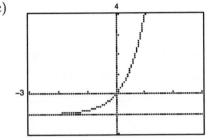

(d)

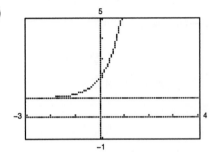

(e) None of these

1—M—Answer: a

19. The domain of $f(x) = 1 + e^{-x}$ is:

(a) $(-\infty, \infty)$ (b) $(0, \infty)$ (c) $(-1, \infty)$ (d) $(1, \infty)$ (e) None of these

1—M—Answer: a

20. The domain of $f(x) = 3 - e^x$ is:

(a) $(3, \infty)$ (b) $[0, \infty)$ (c) $(-\infty, \infty)$ (d) $(-\infty, 3)$ (e) None of these

1—M—Answer: c

21. The range of $f(x) = 1 + e^{-x}$ is:

(a) $(-\infty, \infty)$ (b) $(0, \infty)$ (c) $(-1, \infty)$ (d) $(1, \infty)$ (e) None of these

2—M—Answer: d

22. The range of $f(x) = 3 - e^x$ is:

(a) $(3, \infty)$ (b) $[0, \infty)$ (c) $(-\infty, \infty)$ (d) $(-\infty, 3)$ (e) None of these

2—M—Answer: d

23. $1500 is invested at a rate of 8% compounded quarterly. What is the balance at the end of 5 years?

    (a) $1624.67   (b) $2237.74   (c) $2228.92   (d) $2226.04   (e) None of these

    1—M—Answer: c

24. $1500 is invested at a rate of 10% compounded monthly. What is the balance at the end of 12 years?

    (a) $1657.70   (b) $3512.55   (c) $4955.47   (d) $4980.18   (e) None of these

    1—M—Answer: c

25. $2100 is invested at a rate of 7% compounded monthly. What is the balance at the end of 10 years?

    1—O—Answer: $4220.29

26. $3500 is invested at a rate of 9% compounded continuously. What is the balance at the end of 18 years?

    (a) $68,932.98   (b) $17,685.82   (c) $17,493.53   (d) $8608.61   (e) None of these

    1—M—Answer: b

27. $3500 is invested at a rate of $4\frac{1}{2}$% compounded continuously. What is the balance at the end of 10 years?

    (a) $315,059.96   (b) $5472.45   (c) $5221.39   (d) $5489.09   (e) None of these

    1—M—Answer: d

28. $2000 is invested at a rate of $7\frac{1}{2}$% compounded continuously. What is the balance at the end of 20 years?

    1—O—Answer: $8963.38

29. Determine the amount of money that should be invested at a rate of 8% compounded quarterly to produce a final balance of $20,000 in 10 years.

    (a) $16,406.97   (b) $9057.81   (c) $18,463.80   (d) $9081.26   (e) None of these

    2—M—Answer: b

30. Determine the amount of money that should be invested at a rate of $6\frac{1}{2}$% compounded monthly to produce a final balance of $15,000 in 20 years.

    (a) $4102.34   (b) $5216.07   (c) $2458.83   (d) $14,056.14   (e) None of these

    2—M—Answer: a

31. Determine the amount of money that should be invested at a rate of 7% compounded continuously to produce a final balance of $15,000 in 20 years.

    2—O—Answer: $3698.95

32. A certain population decreases according to the equation $y = 300 - 5e^{0.2t}$. Find the initial population and the population (to the nearest integer) when $t = 10$.

2—O—Answer: 295, 263

33. A certain population grows according to the equation $y = 40e^{0.025t}$. Find the initial population and the population (to the nearest integer) when $t = 50$.

2—O—Answer: 40, 140

34. A certain population increases according to the model $P(t) = 250e^{0.47t}$. Use the model to determine the population when $t = 5$. Round your answer to the nearest integer.

(a) 400   (b) 1597   (c) 1998   (d) 2621   (e) None of these

1—M—Answer: d

35. A certain population increases according to the model $P(t) = 250e^{0.47t}$. Use the model to determine the population when $t = 10$. Round your answer to the nearest integer.

(a) 400   (b) 4091   (c) 27,487   (d) 23,716   (e) None of these

1—M—Answer: c

5.2 Logarithmic Functions and Their Graphs

1. Evaluate: $\log_7 7$

(a) 1   (b) 0   (c) 2   (d) 49   (e) None of these

1—M—Answer: a

2. Evaluate: $\log_a a^3$

(a) a^3 (b) a (c) 3   (d) $3a$ (e) None of these

1—M—Answer: c

3. Evaluate: $\log_a \dfrac{1}{a}$

(a) 1   (b) -1 (c) a (d) $\dfrac{1}{a}$ (e) None of these

1—M—Answer: b

4. Evaluate: $\ln e^{1-x}$

(a) e^{1-x} (b) e (c) $1 - x$ (d) $\ln(1 - x)$ (e) None of these

1—M—Answer: c

5. Evaluate: $\ln 3.76$

   (a) 1.3244   (b) 0.5752   (c) 42.9484   (d) 5754.3994   (e) None of these

   1—M—Answer: a

6. Evaluate: $\log \sqrt{18}$

   (a) $\sqrt{18}$ (b) 4.2426   (c) 1.4452   (d) 0.6276   (e) None of these

   1—M—Answer: d

7. Evaluate: $\ln(1 + \sqrt{2})$

   (a) 0.3828   (b) 0.8814   (c) 0.3466   (d) 0.1505   (e) None of these

   1—M—Answer: b

8. Evaluate: $\log(1 + \sqrt{2})$

   (a) 0.3828   (b) 0.8814   (c) 0.3466   (d) 0.1505   (e) None of these

   1—M—Answer: a

9. Write in logarithmic form: $4^3 = 64$

   (a) $4 \log 3 = 64$ (b) $\log_4 64 = 3$ (c) $\log_3 4 = 64$

   (d) $\log_3 64 = 4$ (e) None of these

   1—M—Answer: b

10. Write in logarithmic form: $5^2 = 25$

    (a) $5 \log 2 = 25$ (b) $\log_2 25 = 5$ (c) $\log_5 25 = 2$

    (d) $\log_2 5 = 25$ (e) None of these

    1—M—Answer: c

11. Write in logarithmic form: $3^5 = 243$

    1—O—Answer: $\log_3 243 = 5$

12. Write in exponential form: $\log_b 37 = 2$

    (a) $37^2 = b$ (b) $2^b = 37$ (c) $b = 10$

    (d) $b^2 = 37$ (e) None of these

    1—M—Answer: d

13. Write in exponential form: $\log_b 7 = 13$

    (a) $7^{13} = b$ (b) $b^{13} = 7$ (c) $b^7 = 13$

    (d) $7^b = 13$ (e) None of these

    1—M—Answer: b

14. Write in exponential form: $\log_7 b = 12$

    (a) $7^{12} = b$ (b) $b^7 = 12$ (c) $7^b = 12$

    (d) $b^{12} = 7$ (e) None of these

    1—M—Answer: a

15. Evaluate: $\dfrac{15 \ln 23}{\ln 7 - \ln 2}$

    (a) 37.5429   (b) 23.4767   (c) 34.8698   (d) 22, 218, 828.26   (e) None of these

    1—M—Answer: a

16. Evaluate: $\dfrac{3 \ln 5}{7 \ln 6 - 2 \ln 7}$

    (a) -3.8222 (b) -2.6559 (c) 0.5582   (d) -11.6058 (e) None of these

    1—M—Answer: c

17. Evaluate: $\dfrac{16 \ln 5}{1 + 2 \ln 3}$

    (a) 918.3228   (b) 27.9482   (c) 8.0542   (d) 22.5538   (e) None of these

    1—M—Answer: c

18. Evaluate: $\dfrac{16 \ln(1/2)}{3 \ln 10}$

    1—O—Answer: -1.6055

19. Find the domain of the function: $f(x) = \ln(3x + 1)$

    (a) $(-\infty, \infty)$ (b) $(-\frac{1}{3}, \infty)$ (c) $(0, \infty)$

    (d) $(\frac{1}{3}, \infty)$ (e) None of these

    1—M—Answer: b

20. Find the domain of the function: $f(x) = 3 \log(5x - 2)$

    (a) $(-\infty, \infty)$ (b) $(0, \infty)$ (c) $(\frac{2}{5}, \infty)$

    (d) $(0.064, \infty)$ (e) None of these

    1—M—Answer: c

21. Find the domain of the function: $f(x) = 3 + \ln(x - 1)$

    (a) $(-\infty, \infty)$ (b) $(0, \infty)$ (c) $(1, \infty)$

    (d) $(3, \infty)$ (e) None of these

    1—M—Answer: c

22. Find the domain of the function: $f(x) = 3 - \log(x^2 - 1)$

    2—O—Answer: $(-\infty, -1), (1, \infty)$

23. Find the domain of the function: $f(x) = \log_3(x^2 - 4)$

    2—O—Answer: $(-\infty, -2), (2, \infty)$

24. Find the vertical asymptote: $f(x) = \ln(x + 2)$

    (a) $x = 2$ (b) $x = 0$ (c) $y = 2$ (d) $x = -2$ (e) None of these

    2—M—Answer: d

25. Find the vertical asymptote: $f(x) = 2 + \ln x$

    (a) $x = 2$ (b) $y = 2$ (c) $x = 0$ (d) $x = -2$ (e) None of these

    2—M—Answer: c

26. Match the graph with the correct function.

    (a) $f(x) = -3 + \ln x$ (b) $f(x) = 3 + \ln x$

    (c) $f(x) = \ln(x - 3)$ (d) $f(x) = \ln(x + 3)$

    (e) None of these

    1—M—Answer: d

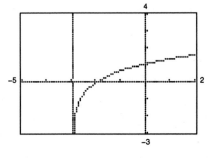

27. Match the graph with the correct function.

    (a) $f(x) = 3 + \log x$ (b) $f(x) = \log(x + 3)$

    (c) $f(x) = \frac{1}{3}\log x$ (d) $f(x) = 3\log x$

    (e) None of these

    1—M—Answer: a

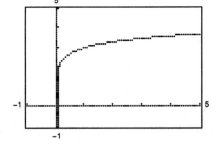

28. Match the graph with the correct function.

    (a) $f(x) = e^x$ (b) $f(x) = e^{x-1}$

    (c) $f(x) = \ln x$ (d) $f(x) = \ln(x - 1)$

    (e) None of these

    1—M—Answer: d

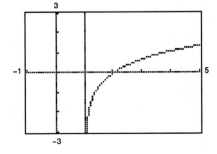

29. Sketch the graph: $f(x) = 1 + \log_5 x$

   1—O—Answer:

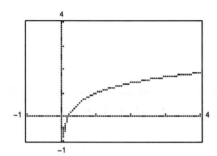

30. Sketch the graph: $f(x) = \ln(1 - x)$

   1—O—Answer:

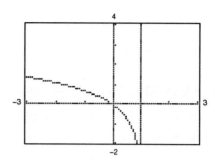

31. Students in an algebra class were given an exam and then tested monthly with an equivalent exam. The average score for the class was given by the human memory model

$$f(t) = 85 - 16 \log_{10}(t + 1), \quad 0 \le t \le 12$$

where t is the time in months. What is the average score after 3 months?

(a) 77   (b) 67   (c) 75   (d) 63   (e) None of these

   2—M—Answer: c

32. Students in an algebra class were given an exam and then tested monthly with an equivalent exam. The average score for the class was given by the human memory model

$$f(t) = 85 - 16 \log_{10}(t + 1), \quad 0 \le t \le 12$$

where t is the time in months. What is the average score after 5 months?

(a) 73   (b) 74   (c) 59   (d) 56   (e) None of these

   2—M—Answer: a

33. Students in an algebra class were given an exam and then tested monthly with an equivalent exam. The average score for the class was given by the human memory model

$$f(t) = 85 - 16 \log_{10}(t + 1), \quad 0 \le t \le 12$$

where t is the time in months. What is the average score after 10 months?

(a) 69   (b) 48   (c) 47   (d) 68   (e) None of these

   2—M—Answer: d

34. A principal P invested at $7\frac{1}{2}\%$ interest compounded continuously increases to an amount K times the original principal after t years, where t is given by $t = \dfrac{\ln K}{0.075}$. Determine the number of years necessary to triple the investment (Hint: $K = 3$).

(a) 6.4   (b) 14.6   (c) 12.8   (d) 8.2   (e) None of these

   2—M—Answer: b

35. A principal P invested at $6\frac{1}{2}\%$ interest compounded continuously increases to an amount K times the original principal after t years, where t is given by $t = \dfrac{\ln K}{0.065}$. Determine the number of years necessary to triple the investment (Hint: $K = 3$).

    (a) 7.3   (b) 9.2   (c) 14.8   (d) 16.9   (e) None of these

    2—M—Answer: d

36. A principal P invested at $8\frac{1}{2}\%$ interest compounded continuously increases to an amount K times the original principal after t years, where t is given by $t = \dfrac{\ln K}{0.085}$. Determine the number of years necessary to triple the investment (Hint: $K = 3$).

    (a) 5.6   (b) 8.2   (c) 12.9   (d) 15.1   (e) None of these

    2—M—Answer: c

5.3 | Properties of Logarithms

1. Use the change of base formula to identify the expression that is equivalent to $\log_7 16$.

   (a) $\dfrac{\log 7}{\log 16}$ (b) $\dfrac{\ln 16}{\ln 7}$ (c) $16 \log 7$

   (d) $\log \dfrac{16}{7}$ (e) None of these

   1—M—Answer: b

2. Use the change of base formula to identify the expression that is equivalent to $\log_3 5$.

   (a) $\dfrac{\log 5}{\log 3}$ (b) $\dfrac{\ln 3}{\ln 5}$ (c) $5 \ln 3$

   (d) $\log \dfrac{5}{3}$ (e) None of these

   1—M—Answer: a

3. Use the change of base formula to identify the expression that is equivalent to $\log_3 10$.

   (a) $\dfrac{\ln 3}{\ln 10}$ (b) $10 \log 3$ (c) $\ln \dfrac{10}{3}$

   (d) $\dfrac{1}{\log 3}$ (e) None of these

   2—M—Answer: d

4. Evaluate $\log_4 7$ using the change of base formula.

   (a) 0.2430   (b) 0.5596   (c) 0.7124   (d) 1.4037   (e) None of these

   2—M—Answer: d

5. Evaluate $\log_{1/2} 13$ using the change of base formula.

(a) 2.5649 (b) 1.1139 (c) -0.2702 (d) -3.7004 (e) None of these

2—M—Answer: d

6. Evaluate $\log_7 15$ using the change of base formula.

(a) 1.3917 (b) 12.6765 (c) 2.1429 (d) 0.7186 (e) None of these

2—M—Answer: a

7. Evaluate $\log_5 22$ using the change of base formula.

2—O—Answer: 1.9206

8. Evaluate $\log_5 17$ using the change of base formula.

2—O—Answer: 1.7604

9. Write as a sum, difference, or multiple of logarithms: $\log \sqrt[3]{\dfrac{a^2 b}{c}}$

(a) $\sqrt[3]{\dfrac{2\log a + \log b}{\log c}}$ (b) $\dfrac{1}{3}\left(\dfrac{2\log a + \log b}{\log c}\right)$ (c) $\dfrac{1}{3}(2\log a + \log b - \log c)$

(d) $\sqrt[3]{2\log a^2 + \log b - \log c}$ (e) None of these

1—M—Answer: c

10. Write as a sum, difference, or multiple of logarithms: $\log_b\left(\dfrac{x^3 y^2}{\sqrt{w}}\right)$

(a) $x^3 + y^3 - \sqrt{w}$ (b) $\dfrac{1}{3}\log_b x + \dfrac{1}{2}\log_b y - 2\log_b w$

(c) $3\log_b x + 2\log_b y - \dfrac{1}{2}\log_b w$ (d) $\dfrac{3\log x + 2\log y}{(1/2)\log w}$

(e) None of these

1—M—Answer: c

11. Write as a sum, difference, or multiple of logarithms: $\ln \dfrac{5x}{\sqrt[3]{x^2+1}}$

1—O—Answer: $\ln 5 + \ln x - \dfrac{1}{3}\ln(x^2+1)$

12. The expression $\log_2 \sqrt{\dfrac{x^2}{y}}$ is equivalent to:

    (a) $\dfrac{1}{2}\left[\log_2 x - \log_2 y\right]$

    (b) $\log_2 x - \dfrac{1}{2}\log_2 y$

    (c) $\dfrac{1}{2}\left[\log_2 x + \log_2 y\right]$

    (d) $\log_2 x + \dfrac{1}{2}\log_2 y$

    (e) None of these

    1—M—Answer: b

13. Write as the logarithm of a single quantity: $\frac{1}{4}\log_b 16 - 2\log_b 5 + \log_b 7$

    (a) $\frac{14}{25}$

    (b) $\log_b \frac{2}{175}$

    (c) 1

    (d) $\log_b \frac{14}{25}$

    (e) None of these

    1—M—Answer: d

14. Write as the logarithm of a single quantity: $\dfrac{1}{5}[3\log(x+1) + 2\log(x-1) - \log 7]$

    2—O—Answer: $\log \sqrt[5]{\dfrac{(x+1)^3(x-1)^2}{7}}$

15. Write as the logarithm of a single quantity: $\frac{1}{2}[\ln(x+1) + 2\ln(x-1)] + \frac{1}{3}\ln x$

    (a) $\ln \sqrt[3]{x}\sqrt{(x+1)(x^2-1)}$

    (b) $\ln \sqrt[3]{x}\sqrt{x^2-1}$

    (c) $\ln \sqrt{x(x^2-1)}$

    (d) $\ln \sqrt[3]{x(x+1)(x-1)^2}$

    (e) None of these

    2—M—Answer: e

16. Write as the logarithm of a single quantity: $\log_2(x-2) + \log_2(x+2)$

    (a) $-2 + 2\log_2 x$

    (b) $\log_2(x^2-4)$

    (c) $2\log_2 x$

    (d) $\log_2 2x$

    (e) None of these

    1—M—Answer: b

17. Evaluate $\log_a 24$, given that $\log_a 2 = 0.4307$ and $\log_a 3 = 0.6826$.

    (a) 0.8820   (b) 1.9747   (c) 0.2940   (d) 1.1133   (e) None of these

    2—M—Answer: b

18. Evaluate $\log_b \left(\dfrac{14}{3b}\right)$, given that $\log_b 2 = 0.2789$, $\log_b 3 = 0.4421$, and $\log_b 7 = 0.7831$.

    (a) -0.3801 (b) 0.6199   (c) 0.5119   (d) 0.7364   (e) None of these

    2—M—Answer: a

19. Evaluate $\log_b \sqrt{10b}$, given that $\log_b 2 = 0.3562$ and $\log_b 5 = 0.8271$.

    2—O—Answer: 1.09165

20. Simplify: $\ln 5e^3$

    (a) $3 + \ln 5$ (b) $3 \ln 5$ (c) $3 + 3 \ln 5$

    (d) $5e^3$ (e) None of these

    2—M—Answer: a

21. Simplify: $\log_b b$ **22.** Simplify: $\log_b \left(\dfrac{m}{n} \right)$

    1—O—Answer: 1   **1—O—Answer:** $\log_b m - \log_b n$

23. Simplify: $b^{\log_b x}$

    1—O—Answer: x

24. Simplify: $\log_a \sqrt[3]{a}$

    (a) 1   (b) -3 (c) 0   (d) $\frac{1}{3}$ (e) None of these

    1—M—Answer: d

25. Simplify: $\ln \sqrt[3]{e^2 x}$

    (a) $\dfrac{2e}{3} + \dfrac{1}{3} \ln x$ (b) $\dfrac{2}{3} + \ln \dfrac{x}{3}$ (c) $\dfrac{2}{3} + \dfrac{1}{3} \ln x$

    (d) $\dfrac{2e}{3} + \ln \dfrac{x}{3}$ (e) None of these

    2—M—Answer: c

26. Simplify: $\ln \sqrt[4]{e^3 x}$

    (a) $\dfrac{3}{4} + \dfrac{1}{4} \ln x$ (b) $\dfrac{3}{4} + \ln \dfrac{x}{4}$ (c) $\dfrac{3e}{4} + \dfrac{1}{4} \ln x$

    (d) $\dfrac{3e}{4} + \ln \dfrac{x}{4}$ (e) None of these

    2—M—Answer: a

27. Simplify: $\ln \sqrt[5]{e^3 x}$

    (a) $\dfrac{3e}{5} + \dfrac{1}{5} \ln x$ (b) $\dfrac{3e}{5} + \ln \dfrac{x}{5}$ (c) $\dfrac{3}{5} + \ln \dfrac{x}{5}$

    (d) $\dfrac{3}{5} + \dfrac{1}{5} \ln x$ (e) None of these

    2—M—Answer: d

28. Evaluate: $\log_a 16$, given that $\log_a 2 = 0.4307$

    (a) 0.0344   (b) 1.7228   (c) 4.4307   (d) 1.8168   (e) None of these

1—M—Answer: b

29. Evaluate: $\log_a 18$, given $\log_a 2 = 0.2789$, $\log_a 3 = 0.4421$

    (a) 1.1631   (b) 0.2466   (c) 0.0349   (d) 1.4420   (e) None of these

1—M—Answer: a

30. Evaluate: $\log_a \frac{9}{2}$, given $\log_a 2 = 0.2789$, $\log_a 3 = 0.4421$

    (a) −0.0834   (b) 1.1631   (c) −0.3264   (d) 0.6053   (e) None of these

1—M—Answer: d

31. Simplify: $\log_6 \sqrt{6}$

    (a) 2.4495   (b) −2   (c) 1   (d) $\frac{1}{2}$ (e) None of these

1—M—Answer: d

32. Simplify: $\log_2 \frac{1}{16}$

    (a) 4   (b) −4   (c) 8   (d) $\frac{1}{2}$ (e) None of these

1—M—Answer: b

33. Simplify: $\ln \sqrt{e^3}$

    (a) $\ln \frac{3}{2}$ (b) $\ln \frac{2}{3}$ (c) $\frac{3}{2}$ (d) $\frac{2}{3}$ (e) None of these

1—M—Answer: c

34. Simplify: $\log_b 3b^4$

    (a) $4 \log_b 3 + 1$ (b) $4 + 4 \log_b 3$ (c) $4 + \log_b 3$

    (d) 12   (e) None of these

1—M—Answer: c

35. Simplify: $\log_b \sqrt{4b^3}$

    (a) $\log_b 2 + \sqrt{b^3}$ (b) $\frac{3}{2} + \frac{3}{2} \log_b 4$ (c) $\frac{3}{2} + 3 \log_b 2$

    (d) $\frac{3}{2} + \log_b 2$ (e) None of these

1—M—Answer: d

5.4 | Solving Exponential and Logarithmic Equations

1. Solve for x: $3^{2x} = 81$

   (a) $x = 13.5$ (b) $x = \frac{1}{4}$ (c) $x = 4$ (d) $x = 2$ (e) None of these

   1—M—Answer: d

2. Solve for x: $16 = 2^{7x-5}$

   (a) 0.1143   (b) −0.3010   (c) $\frac{13}{7}$ (d) $\frac{9}{7}$ (e) None of these

   1—M—Answer: d

3. Solve for x: $27^x = 81$

   (a) $\frac{3}{4}$ (b) $-\frac{1}{3}$ (c) $\frac{4}{3}$ (d) $\frac{2}{3}$ (e) None of these

   1—M—Answer: c

4. Solve for x: $\log_x 8 = -3$

   (a) 2   (b) 512   (c) $\frac{1}{2}$ (d) −2   (e) None of these

   1—M—Answer: c

5. Solve for x: $\ln e^{4x} = 60$

   (a) 2.7832   (b) 15   (c) 1.0236   (d) 2.7081   (e) None of these

   1—M—Answer: b

6. Solve for x: $\ln e^{2x+1} = 9$

   (a) $\dfrac{-1 + \ln 9}{2}$ (b) $\dfrac{9}{2\ln e} - \dfrac{1}{2}$ (c) 23

   (d) 4   (e) None of these

   1—M—Answer: d

7. Solve for x: $25^{x-2} = 5^{3x}$

   1—O—Answer: −4

8. Solve for x: $2x + \ln e^{4x} = 12$

   1—O—Answer: 2

9. Which of the following equations is not true?

   (a) $b^{\log_b c} = c$ (b) $\log_1 b = b$ (c) $\log_b b = 1$

   (d) All of these equations are false.   (e) All of these equations are true.

   1—M—Answer: b

10. Simplify: $e^{3\ln 2}$

    (a) 6   (b) 8   (c) 9   (d) 5   (e) None of these

    1—M—Answer: b

11. Simplify: $e^{2\ln(x+1)}$

    (a) $(x+1)^2$ (b) $2(x+1)$ (c) $e^2\ln(x+1)$

    (d) $x+1$ (e) None of these

    1—M—Answer: a

12. Simplify: $3e^{2\ln x}$

    (a) $3x$ (b) $3xe^2$ (c) $3x^2$

    (d) $\ln x^3$ (e) None of these

    1—M—Answer: c

13. Simplify: $2e^{3\ln(x+1)}$

    (a) $2(x+1)e^3$ (b) $6(x+1)$ (c) $3(x+1)\ln 2$

    (d) $2(x+1)^3$ (e) None of these

    1—M—Answer: d

14. Simplify: $3 + \ln e^{5x}$

    (a) $\dfrac{\ln 3}{5x}$ (b) $\ln 3 + 5x$ (c) $3 + 5x$

    (d) $5x\ln 3$ (e) None of these

    1—M—Answer: c

15. Simplify: $7 + 2\ln e^{5x}$

    (a) $7 + 10x$ (b) $7 + 2^{5x}$ (c) $45x$

    (d) $7 + 2e^{5x}$ (e) None of these

    1—M—Answer: a

16. Simplify: $7 + \ln e^{5x}$

    (a) $5x + \ln 7$ (b) $7 + 5x$ (c) $\dfrac{\ln 7}{5x}$

    (d) $35x$ (e) None of these

    1—M—Answer: b

17. Solve for x: $3^{5x+1} = 5$

    (a) 0.1022   (b) 0.0930   (c) 0.1333   (d) 0.2218   (e) None of these

    1—M—Answer: b

18. Solve for t: $e^{-0.0097t} = 12$

    (a) -256.1759 (b) -1237.1134 (c) $16,778,844.47$

    (d) -2.5886 (e) None of these

    1—M—Answer: a

19. Solve for x: $3^{2x} = 5^{x-1}$

    (a) -0.5563 (b) -1 (c) -2.7381 (d) 15.2755   (e) None of these

    2—M—Answer: c

20. Solve for x: $2^{x-1} = 5^{2x+6}$ **21.** Solve for x: $16^x = 8^{2x-1}$

    2—O—Answer: -4.0977 **2—O—Answer:** $\frac{3}{2}$

22. Solve for x: $3^{1-x} = 5^x$

    (a) $\ln \dfrac{1}{5}$ (b) $\ln \dfrac{3}{5}$ (c) $\dfrac{\ln 3}{\ln 15}$

    (d) $(\ln 3)\ln(15)$ (e) None of these

    2—M—Answer: c

23. Solve for x: $2^{1-x} = 3^x$

    (a) $\dfrac{\ln 2}{\ln 6}$ (b) $\ln \dfrac{1}{3}$ (c) $\ln \dfrac{2}{3}$

    (d) $\ln 3 + \ln 2$ (e) None of these

    2—M—Answer: a

24. Solve for x: $\ln x = 5.3670$ **25.** Solve for x: $\log_x 16 = 5$

    1—O—Answer: 214.2192   **2—O—Answer:** 1.7411

26. Solve for x: $\log(3x + 7) + \log(x - 2) = 1$

    (a) $\frac{8}{3}$ (b) $3, -\frac{8}{3}$ (c) 2

    (d) $2, -\frac{5}{3}$ (e) None of these

    2—M—Answer: a

27. Solve for x: $\ln(7 - x) + \ln(3x + 5) = \ln(24x)$

   (a) $\frac{6}{11}$ (b) $\frac{7}{3}$ (c) $\frac{7}{3}$, -5

   (d) $\frac{6}{11}$, 5   (e) None of these

   2—M—Answer: b

28. Solve for x: $\log(7 - x) - \log(3x + 2) = 1$

   (a) $\frac{19}{31}$ (b) $-\frac{13}{31}$ (c) $-\frac{27}{29}$ (d) $\frac{9}{4}$ (e) None of these

   2—M—Answer: b

29. Solve for x: $\log x + \log(x + 3) = 1$ **30.** Solve for x: $x^2 - 4x = \log_2 32$

   2—O—Answer: 2   **2—O—Answer:** $-1, 5$

31. Solve for x: $\log_3(x^2 + 5) = \log_3(4x^2 - 2x)$

   1—O—Answer: $-1, \frac{5}{3}$

32. Find the number of years required for a $3000 investment to double at a 7% interest rate compounded continuously.

   2—O—Answer: 9.9 years

33. Find the number of years required for a $2000 investment to triple at an 8% interest rate compounded continuously.

   (a) 12.6   (b) 13.7   (c) 11.2   (d) 15.1   (e) None of these

   2—M—Answer: b

34. Find the number of years required for a $2000 investment to triple at a $9\frac{1}{2}$% interest rate compounded continuously.

   (a) 12.6   (b) 13.7   (c) 11.6   (d) 15.1   (e) None of these

   2—M—Answer: c

35. The yield V (in millions of cubic feet per acre) for a forest at age t years is given by $V = 6.7e^{-48.1/t}$. Find the time necessary to have a yield of 1.7 million cubic feet.

   2—O—Answer: 35 years

36. The yield V (in millions of cubic feet per acre) for a forest at age t years is given by $V = 6.7e^{-48.1/t}$. Find the time necessary to have a yield of 2.1 million cubic feet.

   (a) 22.1 years   (b) 25.2 years   (c) 39.8 years   (d) 41.5 years   (e) None of these

   2—M—Answer: d

5.5 Applications of Exponential and Logarithmic Equations

1. If \$3700 is invested at $11\frac{1}{2}\%$ interest compounded continuously, find the balance, B, in the account after 5 years.

  (a) \$3918.99   (b) \$20,754.65   (c) \$6575.38

  (d) \$7376.75   (e) None of these

  1—M—Answer: c

2. If \$9200 is invested at $9\frac{1}{2}\%$ interest compounded continuously, find the balance, B, in the account after 10 years.

  (a) \$22,628.35   (b) \$25,040.56   (c) \$17,940.00

  (d) \$23,788.53   (e) None of these

  1—M—Answer: d

3. Find the balance B after 10 years if \$800 is invested in an account that pays $11\frac{1}{2}\%$ interest compounded monthly.

  1—O—Answer: \$2512.76

4. Find the balance after 15 years if \$1500 is invested in an account that pays $8\frac{1}{2}\%$ compounded quarterly.

  (a) \$5273.72   (b) \$5296.82   (c) \$1978.13

  (d) \$1632.98   (e) None of these

  1—M—Answer: b

5. Find the balance after 10 years if \$1500 is invested in an account that pays $7\frac{1}{2}\%$ compounded quarterly.

  (a) \$3153.52   (b) \$4151.16   (c) \$2625.00

  (d) \$2997.10   (e) None of these

  1—M—Answer: a

6. Determine the principal P that must be invested at a rate of 8% compounded quarterly so that the balance B in 40 years will be \$200,000.

  (a) \$90,578.10   (b) \$47,539.00   (c) \$12,416.00

  (d) \$8414.00   (e) None of these

  1—M—Answer: d

7. Determine the principal that must be invested at a rate of $7\frac{1}{2}\%$ compounded quarterly so that the balance in 20 years will be \$35,000.

  (a) \$2333.33   (b) \$14,000.00   (c) \$9635.17

  (d) \$7918.78   (e) None of these

  1—M—Answer: d

8. Determine the principal that must be invested at a rate of 9% compounded monthly so that the balance at the end of 20 years is $35,000.

   (a) $12,500.00   (b) $9470.02   (c) $6914.23

   (d) $5824.45   (e) None of these

   1—M—Answer: d

9. Determine the principal that must be invested at a rate of $9\frac{1}{2}\%$ compounded quarterly so that the balance in 15 years will be $40,000.

   1—O—Answer: $9781.94

10. An initial deposit of $2000 is compounded continuously at an annual percentage rate of 9%. Find the effective yield.

   (a) 9.4%   (b) 9.2%   (c) $188.00   (d) $180.00   (e) None of these

   2—M—Answer: a

11. An initial deposit of $3000 is compounded continuously at an annual percentage rate of $7\frac{1}{2}\%$. Find the effective yield.

   (a) $225.00   (b) $3233.65   (c) 7.8%   (d) 8.0%   (e) None of these

   2—M —Answer: c

12. An initial deposit of $3000 is compounded continuously at an annual percentage rate of $6\frac{1}{2}\%$. Find the effective yield.

   (a) $3201.48   (b) $195.00   (c) 6.9%   (d) 6.7%   (e) None of these

   2—M—Answer: d

13. An initial deposit of $2500 is compounded continuously at 7% interest. Find the effective yield.

   2—O—Answer: 7.25%

14. An initial deposit of $3000 is made in a savings account for which the interest is compounded continuously. The balance will double in seven years. What is the annual rate of interest for this account?

   (a) 4.3%   (b) 6.2%   (c) 8.1%   (d) 9.9%   (e) None of these

   2—M—Answer: d

15. An initial deposit of $4000 is made in a savings account for which the interest is compounded continuously. The balance will triple in 15 years. What is the annual rate of interest for this account?

   (a) 6.2%   (b) 7.3%   (c) 7.9%   (d) 8.2%   (e) None of these

   2—M—Answer: b

16. An initial deposit of $2800 is made in a savings account for which the interest is compounded continuously. The balance will triple in eight years. What is the annual rate of interest for this account?

(a) 6.9%   (b) 13.7%   (c) 11.6%   (d) 9.9%   (e) None of these

2—M—Answer: b

17. Determine the annual rate of interest compounded continuously for the sum of money in an account to double in 10 years.

(a) 6.9%   (b) 7.4%   (c) 8.2%   (d) 9.9%   (e) None of these

2—M—Answer: a

18. Determine the annual rate of interest compounded continuously for the sum of money in an account to become four times the original amount in 15 years.

2—O—Answer: 9.2%

19. Determine the annual rate of interest compounded continuously for the sum of money in an account to become triple the original amount in 10 years.

2—O—Answer: 11%

20. The ice trays in a freezer are filled with water at 68° F. The freezer maintains a temperature of 20° F. According to Newton's Law of Cooling, the water temperature T is related to the time t (in hours) by the equation

$$kt = \ln \frac{T - 20}{68 - 20}.$$

After 1 hour, the water temperature in the ice trays is 49° F. Use the fact that $T = 49$ when $t = 1$ to find how long it takes the water to freeze (water freezes at 32° F).

(a) 3.27 hours   (b) 2.75 hours   (c) 5.10 hours

(d) 1.17 hours   (e) None of these

2—M—Answer: b

21. The ice trays in a freezer are filled with water at 60° F. The freezer maintains a temperature of 20° F. According to Newton's Law of Cooling, the water temperature T is related to the time t (in hours) by the equation

$$kt = \ln \frac{T - 20}{60 - 20}.$$

After 1 hour, the water temperature in the ice trays is 44° F. Use the fact that $T = 44$ when $t = 1$ to find how long it takes the water to freeze (water freezes at 32° F).

(a) 2.4 hours   (b) 3.2 hours   (c) 1.7 hours

(d) 5.1 hours   (e) None of these

2—M—Answer: a

22. The ice trays in a freezer are filled with water at 50° F. The freezer maintains a temperature of 0° F According to Newton's Law of Cooling, the water temperature T is related to the time t (in hours) by the equation

$$kt = \ln \frac{T}{50}.$$

After 1 hour the water temperature in the ice trays is 43° F. Use the fact that $T = 43$ when $t = 1$ to find how long it takes the water to freeze (water freezes at 32° F).

(a) 2.4 hours   (b) 3.0 hours   (c) 3.6 hours

(d) 2.1 hours   (e) None of these

2—M—Answer: b

23. The ice trays in a freezer are filled with water at 60° F. The freezer maintains a temperature of 0° F. According to Newton's Law of Cooling the water temperature T is related to the time t (in hours) by the equation

$$kt = \ln \frac{T}{60}.$$

After 1 hour, the water temperature in the ice trays is 51° F. Use the fact that $T = 51$ when $t = 1$ to find how long it takes the water to freeze (water freezes at 32° F).

2—O—Answer: 3.9 hours

24. The spread of a flu virus through a certain population is modeled by

$$y = \frac{1000}{1 + 990e^{-0.7t}},$$

where y is the total number infected after t days. In how many days will 820 people be infected with the virus?

(a) 10 days   (b) 11 days   (c) 12 days

(d) 13 days   (e) None of these

2—M—Answer: c

25. The spread of a flu virus through a certain population is modeled by

$$y = \frac{1000}{1 + 990e^{-0.7t}},$$

where y is the total number infected after t days. In how many days will 690 people be infected with the virus?

(a) 10 days   (b) 11 days   (c) 12 days

(d) 13 days   (e) None of these

2—M—Answer: b

26. The spread of a flu virus through a certain population is modeled by

$$y = \frac{1000}{1 + 990e^{-0.7t}},$$

where y is the total number infected after t days. In how many days will 900 people be infected with the virus?

(a) 11 days   (b) 13 days   (c) 15 days

(d) 17 days   (e) None of these

2—M—Answer: b

27. The spread of a flu virus through a certain population is modeled by

$$y = \frac{1000}{1 + 990e^{-0.7t}},$$

where y is the total number infected after t days. In how many days will 530 people be infected with the virus?

(a) 13 days   (b) 12 days   (c) 11 days

(d) 10 days   (e) None of these

2—M—Answer: d

28. The spread of a flu virus through a certain population is modeled by

$$y = \frac{1000}{1 + 990e^{-0.7t}},$$

where y is the total number infected after t days. In how many days will 612 people be infected with the virus?

2—O—Answer: $10\frac{1}{2}$ days

29. The relationship between the level of sound β, in decibels, and the intensity of sound, I, in watts per centimeter squared is given by

$$\beta = 10 \log_{10}\left(\frac{I}{10^{-16}}\right).$$

Determine the level of sound when $I = 10^{-12}$.

(a) 93   (b) 74   (c) 56   (d) 40   (e) None of these

1—M—Answer: d

30. The relationship between the level of sound β, in decibels, and the intensity of sound, I, in watts per centimeter squared is given by

$$\beta = 10 \log_{10}\left(\frac{I}{10^{-16}}\right).$$

Determine the level of sound when $I = 10^{-10}$.

(a) 92   (b) 60   (c) 51   (d) 100   (e) None of these

1—M—Answer: b

31. The relationship between the level of sound β, in decibels, and the intensity of sound, I, in watts per centimeter squared is given by

$$\beta = 10 \log_{10} \left(\frac{I}{10^{-16}} \right).$$

Determine the level of sound when $I = 10^{-8}$.

(a) 50   (b) 60   (c) 70   (d) 80   (e) None of these

1—M—Answer: d

32. The relationship between the level of sound β, in decibels, and the intensity of sound, I, in watts per centimeter squared is given by

$$\beta = 10 \log_{10} \left(\frac{I}{10^{-16}} \right).$$

Determine the level of sound when $I = 10^{-6}$.

(a) 100   (b) 90   (c) 80   (d) 70   (e) None of these

1—M—Answer: a

33. The relationship between the level of sound β, in decibels, and the intensity of sound, I, in watts per centimeter squared is given by

$$\beta = 10 \log_{10} \left(\frac{I}{10^{-16}} \right).$$

Determine the level of sound when $I = 10^{-5}$.

(a) 100   (b) 110   (c) 120   (d) 125   (e) None of these

1—M—Answer: b

34. The pH of a solution is determined by pH $= -\log_{10} [\text{H}^+]$ where pH is a measure of the hydrogen ion concentration $[\text{H}^+]$, measured in moles per liter. Find the pH of a solution for which $[\text{H}^+] = 7.61 \times 10^{-6}$.

(a) −5.12   (b) 5.12   (c) −11.79   (d) 11.79   (e) None of these

2—M—Answer: b

35. The pH of a solution is determined by pH $= -\log_{10}[\text{H}^+]$ where pH is a measure of the hydrogen ion concentration $[\text{H}^+]$, measured in moles per liter. Find the pH of a solution for which $[\text{H}^+] = 5.93 \times 10^{-7}$.

2—O—Answer: 6.23

36. The demand equation for a certain product is given by $p = 450 - 0.4e^{0.007x}$. Find the demand x if the price charged is $300.

1—O—Answer: 847

37. The demand equation for a certain product is given by $p = 450 - 0.4e^{0.007x}$. Find the demand x if the price charged is $250.

1—O—Answer: 888

38. Find the constant k so that the exponential function $y = 3e^{kt}$ passes through the points $(0, 3)$ and $(3, 5)$.

   2—O—Answer: $K = \frac{1}{3} \ln \frac{5}{3}$

39. Find the constant k so that the exponential function $y = 2e^{kt}$ passes through the points $(0, 2)$ and $(2, 5)$.

   2—O—Answer: $k = \frac{1}{2} \ln \frac{5}{2}$

40. The population P of a city is given by $P = 2000e^{kt}$. Let $t = 0$ correspond to the year 1960 and suppose the population in 1950 was 1500. Find the value of k (to 3 decimal places) and then predict the population in 1990.

   2—O—Answer: $k = 0.029$, In 1990, $P = 4774$

41. The number N of bacteria in a culture is given by $N = 200e^{kt}$. If $N = 300$ when $t = 4$ hours, find k (to the nearest tenth) and then determine approximately how long it will take for the number of bacteria to triple in size.

   2—O—Answer: $k = 0.1$, $t \approx 11$ hours

42. Write an equation for the amount Q of a radioactive substance with a half-life of 30 days, if 10 grams are present when $t = 0$.

   2—O—Answer: $Q(t) = 10e^{-0.0231t}$

43. Write an equation for the amount Q of a radioactive substance with a half-life of 60 days, if 25 grams are present when $t = 0$.

   2—O—Answer: $Q(t) = 25e^{-0.0116t}$

CHAPTER SIX
Trigonometry

6.1 Angles and Their Measure

1. Determine the quadrant in which the terminal side of an angle of $\dfrac{6\pi}{5}$ lies.

   (a) I   (b) II   (c) III

   (d) IV   (e) The terminal side lies on one of the axes.

   1—M—Answer: c

2. Determine the quadrant in which the terminal side of an angle of 395° lies.

   (a) I   (b) II   (c) III

   (d) IV   (e) The terminal side lies on one of the axes.

   1—M—Answer: a

3. Determine the quadrant in which the terminal side of an angle of $\dfrac{17\pi}{2}$ lies.

   (a) I   (b) II   (c) III

   (d) IV   (e) The terminal side lies on one of the axes.

   1—M—Answer: e

4. Determine the quadrant in which the terminal side of an angle of 215° lies.

   (a) I   (b) II   (c) III

   (d) IV   (e) The terminal side lies on one of the axes.

   1—M—Answer: c

5. Which of the following angles is coterminal to $\theta = -\dfrac{7\pi}{12}$?

   (a) $\dfrac{5\pi}{12}$ (b) $\dfrac{17\pi}{12}$ (c) $-\dfrac{19\pi}{12}$ (d) Both **a** and **c**   (e) None of these

   1—M—Answer: b

6. Find an angle θ that is coterminal to $\dfrac{11\pi}{4}$ such that $0 \le \theta < 2\pi$.

   1—O—Answer: $\dfrac{3\pi}{4}$

7. Determine which angle is coterminal to $\theta = -\dfrac{5\pi}{6}$.

   (a) $\dfrac{5\pi}{6}$ (b) $\dfrac{7\pi}{6}$ (c) $\dfrac{\pi}{6}$ (d) $\dfrac{11\pi}{6}$ (e) None of these

   1—M—Answer: b

8. Which of the following angles is coterminal to $\theta = -73°$?

   (a) $107°$ (b) $287°$ (c) $-253°$ (d) $17°$ (e) None of these

   1—M—Answer: b

9. Find an angle θ that is coterminal to $-423°$ such that $0 \le \theta < 360°$.

   1—O—Answer: $297°$

10. Find an angle θ that is coterminal to $-495°$ such that $0 \le \theta < 360°$.

    1—O—Answer: $225°$

11. Determine which of the following angles is complementary to $\theta = \dfrac{\pi}{6}$.

    (a) $\dfrac{5\pi}{6}$ (b) $\dfrac{13\pi}{6}$ (c) $\dfrac{\pi}{3}$ (d) $-\dfrac{11\pi}{6}$ (e) None of these

    1—M—Answer: c

12. Determine which of the following angles is complementary to $\theta = \dfrac{\pi}{12}$.

    (a) $\dfrac{5\pi}{12}$ (b) $\dfrac{11\pi}{12}$ (c) $\dfrac{13\pi}{12}$ (d) $\dfrac{25\pi}{12}$ (e) None of these

    1—M—Answer: a

13. Determine which of the following angles is complementary to $\theta = \dfrac{2\pi}{7}$.

    (a) $\dfrac{5\pi}{7}$ (b) $\dfrac{16\pi}{7}$ (c) $-\dfrac{10\pi}{7}$ (d) $\dfrac{3\pi}{14}$ (e) None of these

    1—M—Answer: d

14. Determine which of the following angles is supplementary to $\theta = \dfrac{2\pi}{5}$.

    (a) $\dfrac{3\pi}{5}$ (b) $\dfrac{3\pi}{10}$ (c) $\dfrac{7\pi}{5}$ (d) $-\dfrac{8\pi}{5}$ (e) None of these

    1—M—Answer: a

15. Determine which of the following angles is supplementary to $\theta = \dfrac{\pi}{15}$.

    (a) $\dfrac{16\pi}{15}$ (b) $\dfrac{14\pi}{15}$ (c) $\dfrac{13\pi}{30}$ (d) $\dfrac{29\pi}{15}$ (e) None of these

    1—M—Answer: b

16. Determine which of the following angles is supplementary to $\theta = \dfrac{\pi}{4}$.

    (a) $\dfrac{3\pi}{4}$ (b) $\dfrac{\pi}{4}$ (c) $\dfrac{5\pi}{4}$ (d) $\dfrac{9\pi}{4}$ (e) None of these

    1—M—Answer: a

17. Convert to degrees: $\dfrac{5\pi}{12}$

    (a) 82°   (b) 150°   (c) 36°   (d) 75°   (e) None of these

    1—M—Answer: d

18. Convert to degrees: 2.5 radians

    (a) 143.24°   (b) 0.04°   (c) 286.48°   (d) 450.00°   (e) None of these

    1—M—Answer: a

19. Convert to degrees: $\theta = \dfrac{3\pi}{5}$ radians

    (a) 0.0329°   (b) 108°   (c) 216°   (d) 54°   (e) None of these

    1—M—Answer: b

20. Convert to radians: 240°

    (a) $\dfrac{3\pi}{4}$ (b) $\dfrac{43200}{\pi}$ (c) $\dfrac{3\pi}{2}$ (d) $\dfrac{4\pi}{3}$ (e) None of these

    1—M—Answer: d

21. Convert to radians: 25°

    (a) $\dfrac{5\pi}{36}$ (b) $\dfrac{36}{5\pi}$ (c) $\dfrac{4500}{\pi}$ (d) $\dfrac{5\pi}{18}$ (e) None of these

    1—M—Answer: a

22. Convert to radians: 330°

    1—O—Answer: $\dfrac{11\pi}{6}$

23. Convert to radians: 42° 15′

    (a) 0.7374   (b) 0.7346   (c) 2420.7467   (d) 0.7357   (e) None of these

    1—M—Answer: a

24. Convert to (degree) decimal form: $-13°42'15''$

(a) $-13.95°$ (b) $-12.05°$ (c) $-13.7042°$ (d) $-12.2958°$ (e) None of these

1—M—Answer: c

25. Convert to (degree) decimal form: $72°15''$

(a) $72.25°$ (b) $72.0042°$ (c) $72.09°$ (d) $72.00054°$ (e) None of these

1—M—Answer: b

26. Convert to (degree) decimal form: $128°35'18''$

1—O—Answer: $128.5883°$

27. Convert to degrees, minutes, and seconds: $178.463°$

(a) $178°77'50''$ (b) $178°46'30''$ (c) $178°7'12''$ (d) $178°27'47''$ (e) None of these

1—M—Answer: d

28. Convert to degrees, minutes, and seconds: $12.4762°$

1—O—Answer: $12°28'34''$

29. Convert to degrees, minutes, and seconds: $17.3872°$

(a) $17°23'14''$ (b) $17°29'17''$ (c) $17°42'06''$ (d) $17°38'72''$ (e) None of these

1—M—Answer: a

30. A central angle θ of a circle with radius 16 inches subtends an arc 19.36 inches. Find θ.

(a) $47.3519°$ (b) $1.21°$ (c) $69.3279°$ (d) $0.8264°$ (e) None of these

1—M—Answer: c

31. The central angle θ of a circle with radius 9 inches subtends an arc of 20 inches. Find θ.

(a) $2.22°$ (b) $127.32°$ (c) $0.45°$ (d) $25.78°$ (e) None of these

1—M—Answer: b

32. The central angle θ of a circle with radius 5 inches subtends an arc of 15 inches. Find θ.

(a) $168.2°$ (b) $171.9°$ (c) $166.1°$ (d) $177.9°$ (e) None of these

1—M—Answer: b

33. Find the arc length s shown in the figure.

1—O—Answer: 24.1 inches

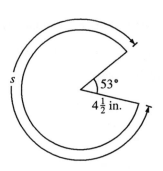

34. A bicycle wheel with an 18 inch diameter rotates 120°. What distance has the bicycle traveled?

1—O—Answer: $6\pi \approx 18.85$ inches

35. Find the arc length s shown in the figure.

(a) 3.49″   (b) 37.22″   (c) 27.93″

(d) 17.41″   (e) None of these

1—M—Answer: c

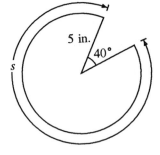

36. A circle of radius r has a central angle of 15° which subtends an arc of 23″. Find r.

(a) 105.27″   (b) 41.16″   (c) 94.98″   (d) 87.85″   (e) None of these

1—M—Answer: d

37. A circle of radius r has a central angle of $\theta = 45°$ which subtends an arc of 16 inches. Find r.

(a) 0.3556 inch   (b) 12.5664 inches   (c) 2.8125 inches

(d) 20.3718 inches   (e) None of these

1—M—Answer: d

38. Assuming that the earth is a sphere of radius 4000 miles, what is the difference in latitude of 2 cities, one of which is 500 miles due north of the other?

(a) 7°9′43″   (b) 4°10′51″   (c) 6°49′44″   (d) 5°7′48″   (e) None of these

1—M—Answer: a

39. Assuming that the earth is a sphere of radius 4000 miles, what is the difference in latitude of 2 cities, one of which is 1500 miles due north of the other?

(a) 10°17′6″   (b) 21°29′9″   (c) 12°15′42″   (d) 19°44′7″   (e) None of these

1—M—Answer: b

6.2 Right Triangle Trigonometry

1. In the triangle shown at the right, use the fact that $\sin \theta = \dfrac{2}{5}$ to find $\tan \theta$.

1—O—Answer: $\dfrac{2\sqrt{21}}{21}$

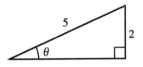

2. Using the right triangle, find $\cot \theta$.

(a) $\dfrac{4}{7}$ (b) $\dfrac{7}{4}$ (c) $\dfrac{\sqrt{33}}{4}$

(d) $\dfrac{4}{\sqrt{33}}$ (e) None of these

1—M—Answer: c

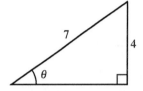

3. Using the right triangle, find $\sec \theta$.

(a) $\dfrac{9}{5}$ (b) $\dfrac{9\sqrt{14}}{28}$ (c) $\dfrac{\sqrt{106}}{5}$

(d) $\dfrac{\sqrt{106}}{9}$ (e) None of these

1—M—Answer: b

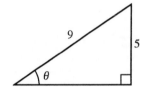

4. A right triangle has an acute angle θ such that $\cot \theta = 15$. Find $\cos \theta$.

(a) $\sqrt{226}$ (b) $\dfrac{\sqrt{226}}{226}$ (c) $\dfrac{15\sqrt{226}}{226}$ (d) $\dfrac{\sqrt{226}}{15}$ (e) None of these

1—M—Answer: c

5. A right triangle has an acute angle θ such that $\csc \theta = \dfrac{7}{3}$. Find $\tan \theta$.

(a) $\dfrac{2\sqrt{10}}{7}$ (b) $\dfrac{3\sqrt{10}}{20}$ (c) $\dfrac{2\sqrt{10}}{3}$ (d) $\dfrac{3}{7}$ (e) None of these

1—M—Answer: b

6. A right triangle has an acute angle θ such that $\sin\theta = \dfrac{7}{9}$. Find $\tan\theta$.

(a) $\dfrac{7\sqrt{2}}{8}$ (b) $\dfrac{4\sqrt{2}}{7}$ (c) $\dfrac{\sqrt{130}}{7}$ (d) $\dfrac{9\sqrt{130}}{130}$ (e) None of these

1—M—Answer: a

7. Given $\sec\theta = 3$, find $\csc(90° - \theta)$.

(a) $\dfrac{1}{3}$ (b) $\dfrac{3\sqrt{2}}{4}$ (c) 3 (d) $\dfrac{2\sqrt{2}}{3}$ (e) None of these

1—M—Answer: c

8. Given $\sec\theta = 5$, find $\csc(90° - \theta)$.

(a) $\dfrac{5\sqrt{6}}{12}$ (b) 5 (c) $\dfrac{1}{5}$ (d) $\dfrac{2\sqrt{6}}{5}$ (e) None of these

1—M—Answer: b

9. Given $\cos\theta = \dfrac{1}{2}$, find $\csc(90° - \theta)$.

(a) 2 (b) $\dfrac{1}{2}$ (c) $\sqrt{3}$ (d) $\dfrac{2}{\sqrt{3}}$ (e) None of these

1—M—Answer: a

10. Evaluate: $\sec\left(\dfrac{\pi}{3}\right)$

(a) $\dfrac{\sqrt{2}}{2}$ (b) $\dfrac{\sqrt{3}}{2}$ (c) $\dfrac{\sqrt{3}}{3}$ (d) 2 (e) None of these

1—M—Answer: d

11. Evaluate: $\cot\left(\dfrac{\pi}{3}\right)$

1—O—Answer: $\dfrac{\sqrt{3}}{3}$

12. Evaluate: $\cot\left(\dfrac{\pi}{6}\right)$

(a) $\sqrt{3}$ (b) $\dfrac{1}{2}$ (c) $\dfrac{\sqrt{3}}{2}$ (d) $\dfrac{\sqrt{3}}{3}$ (e) None of these

1—M—Answer: a

13. Evaluate: $\csc 45°$

(a) $\dfrac{1}{2}$ (b) $\sqrt{2}$ (c) $\dfrac{\sqrt{2}}{2}$ (d) 1 (e) None of these

1—M—Answer: b

14. Evaluate: tan 60°

(a) $\dfrac{1}{2}$ (b) $\dfrac{1}{3}$ (c) $\dfrac{\sqrt{3}}{3}$ (d) $\sqrt{3}$ (e) None of these

1—M—Answer: d

15. Evaluate: cos 60°

(a) $\sqrt{3}$ (b) $\dfrac{1}{2}$ (c) 2   (d) $\dfrac{\sqrt{3}}{2}$ (e) None of these

1—M—Answer: b

16. Evaluate: csc 14°

(a) 4.0960   (b) 4.1336   (c) 1.0306   (d) 0.9999   (e) None of these

1—M—Answer: b

17. Evaluate: cot 15°

(a) 3.7321   (b) 0.0012   (c) 86.1859   (d) 1.0353   (e) None of these

1—M—Answer: a

18. Evaluate: sec(4° 15′ 42″)

(a) 13.4569   (b) 0.9999   (c) 1.0028   (d) 13.8043   (e) None of these

1—M—Answer: c

19. Evaluate: cot 49°

1—O—Answer: 0.8693

20. Evaluate: sec 1.2

(a) 0.6724   (b) 1.0002   (c) 2.7597   (d) 0.9999   (e) None of these

1—M—Answer: c

21. Evaluate: csc 1.32

(a) 2.0132   (b) 1.0323   (c) 0.0230   (d) 0.6872   (e) None of these

1—M—Answer: b

22. Evaluate: cot 1.14

(a) 0.4596   (b) 1.2028   (c) 50.2528   (d) 0.0153   (e) None of these

1—M—Answer: a

23. Find the acute angle θ if $\tan \theta = 1$.

    (a) $\dfrac{\pi}{3}$ (b) $\dfrac{\pi}{4}$ (c) $\dfrac{\pi}{5}$ (d) $\dfrac{\pi}{6}$ (e) None of these

    1—M—Answer: b

24. Find the acute angle θ, if $\sin \theta = \dfrac{1}{2}$.

    (a) $\dfrac{\pi}{3}$ (b) $\dfrac{\pi}{4}$ (c) $\dfrac{\pi}{5}$ (d) $\dfrac{\pi}{6}$ (e) None of these

    1—M—Answer: d

25. Find the acute angle θ, if $\sin \theta = \dfrac{\sqrt{3}}{2}$.

    (a) $\dfrac{\pi}{2}$ (b) $\dfrac{\pi}{3}$ (c) $\dfrac{\pi}{4}$ (d) $\dfrac{\pi}{6}$ (e) None of these

    1—M—Answer: b

26. Find θ such that $0 \le \theta < \dfrac{\pi}{2}$ and $\csc \theta = 1.4736$.

    1—O—Answer: 0.7459

27. Given $\tan \theta = 1.2617$, find θ.

    (a) 0.0220   (b) 0.9006   (c) 1.0145   (d) 0.3193   (e) None of these

    1—M—Answer: b

28. Given $\cos \theta = 0.9872$, find θ.

    (a) 80.8229°   (b) 0.9998°   (c) 9.1771°   (d) 1.0001°   (e) None of these

    1—M—Answer: c

29. Find x for the triangle shown at the right.

    (a) $7\sqrt{3}$ (b) $\dfrac{7}{\sqrt{3}}$ (c) 14

    (d) $\dfrac{7}{2}$ (e) None of these

    1—M—Answer: a

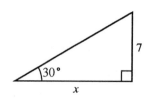

30. Find x for the triangle shown at the right.

1—O—Answer: $\dfrac{15\sqrt{3}}{2}$

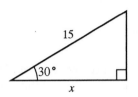

31. Find x for the right triangle shown at the right.

(a) $15\sqrt{2}$ (b) $15\sqrt{3}$ (c) 30

(d) $\frac{15}{2}$ (e) None of these

1—M—Answer: c

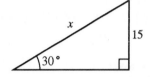

32. Find x for the triangle shown at the right.

(a) 0.1047   (b) 11.9638   (c) 5.4256

(d) 9.5547   (e) None of these

1—M—Answer: d

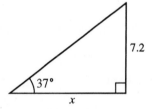

33. Find x for the triangle shown at the right.

1—O—Answer: 6.5756

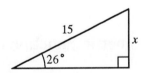

34. Find x for the right triangle shown at the right.

(a) 9.7174   (b) 15.4411   (c) 14.8188

(d) 7.5518   (e) None of these

1—M—Answer: a

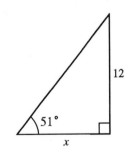

35. A man that is 6 feet tall casts a shadow 14 feet long. Find the angle of elevation of the sun.

    (a) 23.2°   (b) 66.8°   (c) 25.4°   (d) 64.6°   (e) None of these

    1—M—Answer: a

36. The pilot of an airplane flying at 12,000 feet sights a water tower. The angle of depression to the base of the tower is 25°. What is the length of the line of sight from the plane to the tower?

    (a) 28,394 feet   (b) 27,962 feet   (c) 23,662 feet   (d) 13,241 feet   (e) None of these

    2—M—Answer: a

37. A 16-foot ladder leaning against the side of a house reaches 12 feet up the side of the house. What angle does the ladder make with the ground?

    (a) 57.7°   (b) 63.1°   (c) 42.9°   (d) 48.6°   (e) None of these

    2—M—Answer: d

38. Complete the following Pythagorean identity: $\tan^2 \theta = $ _____

    (a) $1 - \sec^2 \theta$ (b) $1 - \csc^2 \theta$ (c) $\csc^2 \theta + 1$ (d) $\sec^2 \theta - 1$ (e) None of these

    1—M—Answer: d

39. Complete the following Pythagorean identity: $\sec^2 \theta = $ _____

    (a) $1 - \tan^2 \theta$ (b) $1 + \tan^2 \theta$ (c) $1 + \csc^2 \theta$ (d) $\csc^2 \theta - 1$ (e) None of these

    1—M—Answer: b

40. Complete the following Pythagorean identity: $\cos^2 \theta = $ _____

    (a) $\sec^2 \theta + 1$ (b) $1 - \sin^2 \theta$ (c) $\sin^2 \theta + 1$ (d) $1 - \sec^2 \theta$ (e) None of these

    1—M—Answer: b

$\boxed{6.3}$ Trigonometric Functions of Any Angle or Real Number

1. Find $\tan \theta$, for the angle θ shown at the right.

   (a) $-\dfrac{9\sqrt{130}}{7}$ (b) $\dfrac{\sqrt{130}}{7}$ (c) $-\dfrac{7}{9}$

   (d) $-\dfrac{9}{7}$ (e) None of these

   1—M—Answer: d

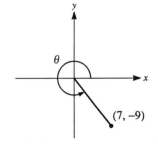

2. Find $\csc \theta$ for the angle θ shown at the right.

1—O—Answer: $-\dfrac{\sqrt{113}}{7}$

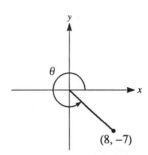

3. Determine the exact value of $\cos \theta$, if θ is in standard position and its terminal side passes through the point $(-3, 3)$.

1—O—Answer: $-\dfrac{\sqrt{2}}{2}$

4. Determine the quadrant in which θ lies: $\sin \theta < 0$, $\cos \theta < 0$

(a) I   (b) II   (c) III   (d) IV   (e) None of these

1—M—Answer: c

5. Determine the quadrant in which θ lies: $\tan \theta < 0$, $\cos \theta > 0$

(a) I   (b) II   (c) III   (d) IV   (e) None of these

1—M—Answer: d

6. Determine the quadrant in which θ lies: $\tan \theta < 0$, $\sin \theta > 0$

(a) I   (b) II   (c) III   (d) IV   (e) None of these

1—M—Answer: b

7. Given $\sin \theta = -\dfrac{1}{5}$ and $\tan \theta < 0$, find $\cos \theta$.

(a) $-\dfrac{\sqrt{26}}{5}$ (b) $\dfrac{\sqrt{26}}{5}$ (c) $-\dfrac{2\sqrt{6}}{5}$ (d) $\dfrac{2\sqrt{6}}{5}$ (e) None of these

1—M—Answer: d

8. Given $\sin \theta = \dfrac{7}{13}$, and $\tan \theta < 0$, find $\tan \theta$.

(a) $-\dfrac{7\sqrt{3}}{2}$ (b) $-\dfrac{2\sqrt{3}}{7}$ (c) $-\dfrac{2\sqrt{3}}{13}$ (d) $-\dfrac{7\sqrt{30}}{60}$ (e) None of these

1—M—Answer: d

9. Given $\tan \theta = -\dfrac{7}{8}$ and $\cos \theta > 0$, find $\csc \theta$.

1—O—Answer: $-\dfrac{\sqrt{113}}{7}$

10. Given $\sin\theta = -\dfrac{2}{9}$, and $\tan\theta > 0$, find $\cos\theta$.

1—O—Answer: $-\dfrac{\sqrt{77}}{9}$

11. Find the reference angle for $\theta = 305°$.

(a) $35°$ (b) $-55°$ (c) $55°$ (d) $125°$ (e) None of these

1—M—Answer: c

12. Find the reference angle for $\theta = -155°$.

1—O—Answer: $25°$

13. Find the reference angle for $\theta = \dfrac{19\pi}{15}$.

(a) $\dfrac{4\pi}{15}$ (b) $\dfrac{7\pi}{30}$ (c) $\dfrac{11\pi}{30}$ (d) $\dfrac{49\pi}{15}$ (e) None of these

1—M—Answer: a

14. Find the reference angle for $\theta = \dfrac{7\pi}{3}$.

(a) $\dfrac{\pi}{3}$ (b) $\dfrac{2\pi}{3}$ (c) $\dfrac{\pi}{6}$ (d) $\dfrac{\pi}{2}$ (e) None of these

1—M—Answer: a

15. Find the reference angle for $\theta = \dfrac{17\pi}{15}$.

(a) $\dfrac{32\pi}{15}$ (b) $\dfrac{13\pi}{15}$ (c) $\dfrac{2\pi}{15}$ (d) $\dfrac{11\pi}{30}$ (e) None of these

1—M—Answer: c

16. Find the exact value of $\cot(-150°)$.

(a) $\sqrt{3}$ (b) $-\dfrac{1}{2}$ (c) $-\dfrac{1}{\sqrt{3}}$ (d) 1 (e) None of these

1—M—Answer: a

17. Find the exact value of $\csc(225°)$.

(a) 2 (b) $\dfrac{\sqrt{3}}{2}$ (c) $-\sqrt{2}$ (d) $-\dfrac{\sqrt{3}}{2}$ (e) None of these

1—M—Answer: c

18. Find the exact value of $\tan(-210°)$.

(a) 1   (b) $-\dfrac{\sqrt{3}}{3}$ (c) $-\sqrt{3}$ (d) $\dfrac{1}{2}$ (e) None of these

1—M—Answer: b

19. Find the exact value of $\tan 870°$.

(a) $\sqrt{3}$ (b) $\dfrac{\sqrt{3}}{3}$ (c) $-\dfrac{\sqrt{3}}{3}$ (d) $-\sqrt{3}$ (e) None of these

1—M—Answer: c

20. Find the exact value of $\sin\left(-\dfrac{8\pi}{3}\right)$.

(a) $\dfrac{\sqrt{3}}{2}$ (b) $\dfrac{1}{2}$ (c) $-\dfrac{1}{2}$ (d) $-\dfrac{\sqrt{3}}{2}$ (e) None of these

1—M—Answer: d

21. Find the exact value of $\sec\dfrac{7\pi}{4}$.

(a) $\sqrt{2}$ (b) $\dfrac{\sqrt{3}}{2}$ (c) $\dfrac{1}{\sqrt{3}}$ (d) 1   (e) None of these

1—M—Answer: a

22. Find the exact value of $\tan\dfrac{5\pi}{6}$.

(a) $\dfrac{\sqrt{3}}{2}$ (b) $\sqrt{3}$ (c) -1 (d) $-\dfrac{\sqrt{3}}{3}$ (e) None of these

1—M—Answer: d

23. Find the exact value of $\sin\dfrac{7\pi}{6}$.

(a) $-\dfrac{1}{2}$ (b) $-\dfrac{\sqrt{3}}{2}$ (c) $\dfrac{\sqrt{3}}{3}$ (d) $\dfrac{\sqrt{2}}{2}$ (e) None of these

1—M—Answer: a

24. Find two radian values of θ $(0 \le \theta < 2\pi)$ that satisfy $\cos\theta = 0.7833$. (Round answer to 3 decimal places.)

2—O—Answer: 0.671 and 5.612

25. Find two values of θ $(0 \le \theta < 2\pi)$ that satisfy $\cot\theta = -1$. (Answers rounded to 3 decimal places.)

(a) 2.356 and 5.498   (b) -0.785 and 3.927   (c) -0.785 and 5.498

(d) 0.785 and 2.356   (e) None of these

2—M—Answer: a

26. Find two values of θ ($0 \leq \theta < 2\pi$) that satisfy $\sec \theta = 5.1258$. (Round to 3 decimal places.)

    (a) 1.767 and 4.516   (b) 1.374 and 4.909

    (c) 1.134 and 1.767   (d) 1.767 and 4.909

    2—M—Answer: b

27. Find two values of θ ($0 \leq \theta < 360°$) that satisfy $\csc \theta = 2.5593$.

    (a) 23° and 157°   (b) 67° and 293°   (c) 157° and 293°

    (d) 23° and 203°   (e) None of these

    2—M—Answer: a

28. Find two values of θ ($0 \leq \theta < 360°$) that satisfy $\cot \theta = -0.2679$.

    (a) 165° and 345°   (b) 75° and 285°   (c) 15° and 165°

    (d) 105° and 285°   (e) None of these

    2—M—Answer: d

29. Given $\cos \theta = -\dfrac{7}{8}$, $\dfrac{\pi}{2} \leq \theta \leq \pi$, find $\tan \theta$.

    (a) $-\dfrac{7\sqrt{15}}{15}$ (b) $-\dfrac{7\sqrt{113}}{113}$ (c) $-\dfrac{\sqrt{15}}{7}$ (d) $-\dfrac{1}{7}$ (e) None of these

    1—M—Answer: c

30. Given $\csc \theta = -\dfrac{16}{5}$, $\pi \leq \theta \leq \dfrac{3\pi}{2}$, find $\tan \theta$.

    (a) $-\dfrac{16\sqrt{281}}{281}$ (b) $\dfrac{5\sqrt{231}}{231}$ (c) $\dfrac{\sqrt{231}}{5}$ (d) $-\dfrac{16\sqrt{231}}{231}$ (e) None of these

    1—M—Answer: b

31. Given $\sin \theta = -\dfrac{4}{7}$, $\dfrac{3\pi}{2} \leq \theta \leq 2\pi$, find $\sec \theta$.

    (a) $\dfrac{\sqrt{33}}{7}$ (b) $\dfrac{7\sqrt{33}}{7}$ (c) $-\dfrac{\sqrt{65}}{4}$ (d) $\dfrac{7\sqrt{65}}{65}$ (e) None of these

    1—M—Answer: b

32. Two similar triangles are shown at the right. Find a.

    (a) $\dfrac{15\sqrt{6}}{6}$ (b) $\dfrac{\sqrt{74}}{30}$

    (c) $\dfrac{15\sqrt{74}}{37}$ (d) $\dfrac{21\sqrt{74}}{37}$

    (e) None of these

    2—M—Answer: c

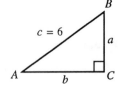

33. Two similar triangles are shown at the right. Find b.

1—O—Answer: $\frac{56}{3}$

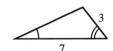 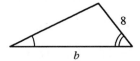

34. Two similar triangles are shown at the right. Find a.

(a) $\frac{35}{12}$ (b) $\frac{84}{5}$

(c) $\frac{60}{7}$ (d) 17

(e) None of these

1—M—Answer: b

 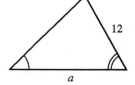

35. The ramp approaching a loading platform that is 6 feet off the ground is to have an angle of 20° with the ground. Find length l of the ramp. Round to two decimal places.

(a) 31.02 feet   (b) 19.37 feet

(c) 16.48 feet   (d) 17.54 feet

(e) None of these

1—M—Answer: d

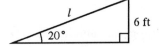

36. The height of a tree can be determined by measuring the length of the shadow of the tree and the angle of elevation of the sun from the tip of the shadow. Find the height of a tree that casts a 20 foot shadow when the angle of elevation is 60°.

(a) $10\sqrt{3}$ feet   (b) $20\sqrt{3}$ feet

(c) 30 feet   (d) $20\sqrt{2}$ feet

(e) None of these

1—M—Answer: b

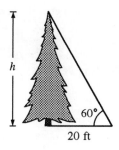

6.4   Graphs of Sine and Cosine Functions

1. Determine the amplitude: $f(x) = \sin\left(\dfrac{x}{4} - \pi\right)$

   (a) 1   (b) π (c) π^2 (d) 0   (e) None of these

   1—M—Answer: a

2. Determine the amplitude: $f(x) = -3\cos\left(\dfrac{x}{2} + \pi\right)$

   (a) 0   (b) -2π (c) 3π (d) 3   (e) None of these

   1—M—Answer: d

3. Determine the amplitude: $f(x) = -\dfrac{2}{3}\sin(4x)$

   (a) $\dfrac{2}{3}$ (b) $\dfrac{3}{2}$ (c) 4   (d) $\dfrac{\pi}{2}$ (e) None of these

   1—M—Answer: a

4. Determine the amplitude: $f(x) = 4\cos(3x)$

   (a) 3   (b) $\frac{1}{3}$ (c) 4   (d) -4 (e) None of these

   1—M—Answer: c

5. Determine the amplitude: $f(x) = \dfrac{2}{3}\sin\left(4x - \dfrac{\pi}{2}\right)$

   (a) $\dfrac{\pi}{2}$ (b) 4   (c) $\dfrac{2}{3}$ (d) 2π (e) None of these

   1—M—Answer: c

6. Determine the period: $f(x) = 3\sin(4x - \pi)$

   (a) 3π (b) $\dfrac{\pi}{2}$ (c) 2π (d) $\dfrac{3\pi}{2}$ (e) None of these

   1—M—Answer: b

7. Determine the period: $f(x) = -\dfrac{2}{3}\cos\left(\dfrac{x}{3} - \dfrac{1}{2}\right)$

   (a) 6π (b) $\dfrac{2\pi}{3}$ (c) $\dfrac{2}{3}$ (d) $\dfrac{1}{2}$ (e) None of these

   1—M—Answer: a

8. Determine the period: $f(x) = -\dfrac{1}{2}\sin\left(\dfrac{3x}{2} - \dfrac{1}{2}\right)$

    (a) $\dfrac{1}{2}$ (b) $\dfrac{1}{2}\pi$ (c) $\dfrac{3\pi}{4}$ (d) $\dfrac{4\pi}{3}$ (e) None of these

    1—M—Answer: d

9. Determine the period of the function: $y = \dfrac{1}{2}\sin\left(\dfrac{x}{3} - \pi\right)$

    (a) $\dfrac{1}{2}$ (b) $\dfrac{2\pi}{3}$ (c) 6π (d) 3π (e) None of these

    1—M—Answer: c

10. Determine the period and amplitude of the function: $f(x) = -7\cos 3x$

    1—O—Answer: Period: $\dfrac{2\pi}{3}$, Amplitude: 7

11. Determine the period and amplitude of the function: $f(x) = 5\cos\dfrac{x}{2}$

    1—O—Answer: Period: 4π, Amplitude: 5

12. Describe the horizontal shift of the graph of g with respect to the graph of f:

    $$g(x) = 4\sin\left(2x - \dfrac{\pi}{3}\right) \quad\text{and}\quad f(x) = 4\sin(2x)$$

    (a) $\dfrac{\pi}{6}$ units to the left   (b) $\dfrac{\pi}{6}$ units to the right   (c) $\dfrac{2\pi}{3}$ units to the left

    (d) $\dfrac{2\pi}{3}$ units to the right   (e) None of these

    1—M—Answer: b

13. Describe the horizontal shift of the graph of g with respect to the graph of f:

    $$g(x) = 3\sin\left(2x - \dfrac{\pi}{4}\right) \quad\text{and}\quad f(x) = 3\sin(2x)$$

    (a) $\dfrac{\pi}{4}$ units to the left   (b) $\dfrac{\pi}{8}$ units to the right   (c) $\dfrac{\pi}{4}$ units to the right

    (d) $\dfrac{\pi}{8}$ units to the left   (e) None of these

    1—M—Answer: b

14. Describe the horizontal shift of the graph of g with respect to the graph of f:

    $$g(x) = 4\cos\left(3x + \dfrac{\pi}{4}\right) \quad\text{and}\quad f(x) = 4\cos(3x)$$

    (a) $\dfrac{\pi}{4}$ units to the right   (b) $\dfrac{\pi}{4}$ units to the left   (c) $\dfrac{\pi}{12}$ units to the right

    (d) $\dfrac{\pi}{12}$ units to the left   (e) None of these

    1—M—Answer: d

15. Describe the horizontal shift of the graph of g with respect to the graph of f:

$$g(x) = 3\cos(\pi x + 3) \quad \text{and} \quad f(x) = 3\cos(\pi x)$$

(a) $\dfrac{3}{\pi}$ units to the left

(b) $\dfrac{\pi}{3}$ units to the left

(c) $\dfrac{2\pi}{3}$ units to the right

(d) $\dfrac{3}{2\pi}$ units to the right

(e) None of these

1—M—Answer: a

16. Describe the horizontal shift of the graph of g with respect to the graph of f:

$$g(x) = \frac{1}{2}\cos\left(\pi x - \frac{\pi}{2}\right) \quad \text{and} \quad f(x) = \frac{1}{2}\cos(\pi x)$$

(a) $\dfrac{\pi}{2}$ units to the right

(b) $\dfrac{\pi}{2}$ units to the left

(c) $\dfrac{1}{2}$ units to the right

(d) $\dfrac{1}{2}$ units to the left

(e) None of these

1—M—Answer: c

17. Describe the horizontal shift of the graph of g with respect to the graph of f:

$$g(x) = 4\sin\left(3x - \frac{3}{2}\pi\right) \quad \text{and} \quad f(x) = 4\sin 3x$$

(a) $\dfrac{3\pi}{2}$ units to the left

(b) $\dfrac{3\pi}{2}$ units to the right

(c) $\dfrac{\pi}{2}$ units to the left

(d) $\dfrac{\pi}{2}$ units to the right

(e) None of these

1—M—Answer: d

18. Describe the shifts in the graph of g with respect to the graph of f:

$$g(x) = 1 + \cos\left(2x + \frac{\pi}{2}\right) \quad \text{and} \quad f(x) = \cos 2x$$

(a) $\dfrac{\pi}{2}$ right, down 1

(b) $\dfrac{\pi}{4}$ right, up 1

(c) $\dfrac{\pi}{4}$ left, up 1

(d) $\dfrac{\pi}{2}$ left, up 1

(e) None of these

1—M—Answer: c

19. Describe the shifts in the graph of g with respect to the graph of f:

$$g(x) = -3 + \sin\left(4x + \frac{\pi}{2}\right) \quad \text{and} \quad f(x) = \sin(4x)$$

(a) $\dfrac{\pi}{8}$ left, 3 down

(b) $\dfrac{\pi}{8}$ right, 3 down

(c) $\dfrac{\pi}{2}$ left, 3 down

(d) $\dfrac{\pi}{2}$ right, 3 up

(e) None of these

1—M—Answer: a

20. Describe the shifts in the graph of g with respect to the graph of f:

$$g(x) = 2 - \sin\left(3x - \frac{\pi}{4}\right) \quad \text{and} \quad f(x) = -\sin(3x)$$

(a) $\frac{\pi}{4}$ right, 2 down

(b) $\frac{\pi}{12}$ left, 2 down

(c) $\frac{\pi}{12}$ right, 2 up

(d) $\frac{\pi}{4}$ left, 2 up

(e) None of these

1—M—Answer: c

21. Describe the shifts in the graph of g with respect to the graph of f:

$$g(x) = 1 - \cos\left(\frac{2x}{\pi} - \pi\right) \quad \text{and} \quad f(x) = -\cos\frac{2x}{\pi}$$

(a) π right, 1 up

(b) $\frac{1}{2}$ right, 1 up

(c) $\frac{2}{\pi}$ left, 1 down

(d) $\frac{\pi^2}{2}$ right, 1 up

(e) None of these

1—M—Answer: d

22. Match the graph with the correct function.

(a) $f(x) = 2\sin\frac{3x}{2}$

(b) $f(x) = 2\cos\frac{3x}{2}$

(c) $f(x) = 2\sin\frac{2x}{3}$

(d) $f(x) = 2\cos\frac{2x}{3}$

(e) None of these

1—M—Answer: b

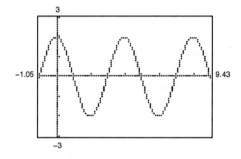

23. Match the graph with the correct function.

(a) $f(x) = 4\sin 2x$

(b) $f(x) = 2\sin 4x$

(c) $f(x) = 4\cos 4x$

(d) $f(x) = 2\cos 2x$

(e) None of these

1—M—Answer: e

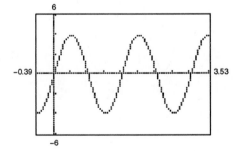

24. Match the graph with the correct function.

(a) $f(x) = 3\cos\left(\frac{x}{2}\right)$

(b) $y = 3\sin\left(\frac{x}{2}\right)$

(c) $f(x) = 3\cos 2x$

(d) $y = 3\sin 2x$

(e) None of these

1—M—Answer: a

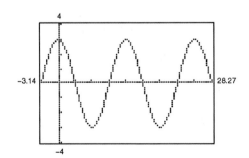

25. Match the graph with the correct function.

(a) $f(x) = 4\cos\left(2x - \dfrac{\pi}{3}\right)$

(b) $f(x) = 4\sin\left(2x - \dfrac{\pi}{3}\right)$

(c) $f(x) = -4\sin\left(3x - \dfrac{\pi}{2}\right)$

(d) $f(x) = 4\cos\left(3x + \dfrac{\pi}{2}\right)$

(e) None of these

2—M—Answer: d

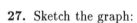

26. Match the graph with the correct function.

(a) $f(x) = \dfrac{1}{2}\cos\left(\dfrac{2x}{3}\right)$ (b) $f(x) = \dfrac{1}{2}\sin\left(\dfrac{2x}{3}\right)$

(c) $f(x) = \dfrac{1}{2}\cos\left(\dfrac{3x}{2}\right)$ (d) $f(x) = \dfrac{1}{2}\sin\left(\dfrac{3x}{2}\right)$

(e) None of these

1—M—Answer: a

27. Sketch the graph:

$$f(x) = 3\sin 4x$$

1—O—Answer:

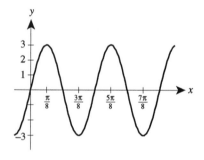

28. Sketch the graph:

$$f(x) = 4\cos\left(2x + \dfrac{\pi}{3}\right)$$

2—O—Answer:

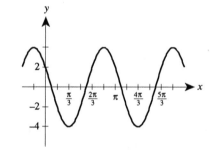

29. Sketch the graph: $f(x) = 2 \sin 3x$

(a)

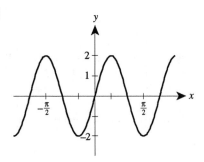

(b)

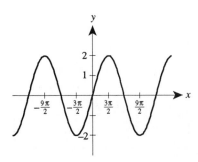

(c)

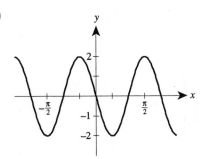

(d)

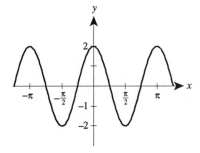

(e) None of these

1—M—Answer: a

30. Use a graphing utility to graph: $y = -4 \cos\left(\frac{1}{2}x\right)$

(a)

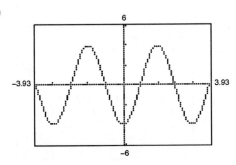

(b)

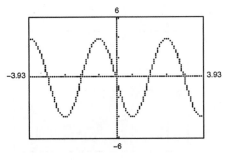

(c)

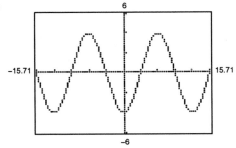

(d)

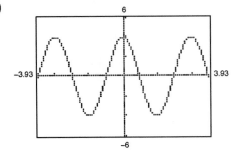

(e) None of these

1—M—Answer: c

31. Use a graphing utility to graph: $y = \cos\left(2x - \dfrac{\pi}{3}\right)$

(a)

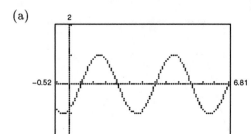

(b)

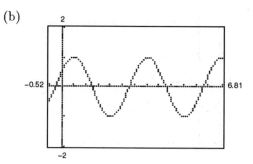

(c)

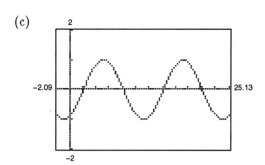

(d)

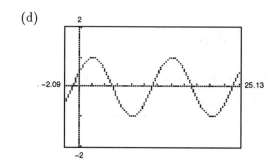

(e) None of these

1—M—Answer: b

32. Use a graphing utility to graph: $y = \sin\left(3x - \dfrac{\pi}{4}\right)$

(a)

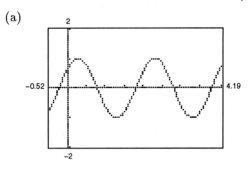

(b)

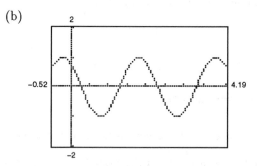

32. —CONTINUED—

(c)

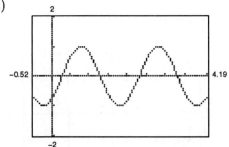

(d)

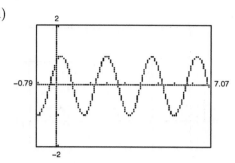

(e) None of these

1—M—Answer: c

33. Use a graphing utility to graph: $y = 4\sin(2x - \pi)$

1—O—Answer:

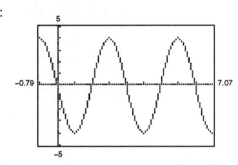

34. A buoy oscillates in simple harmonic motion as waves move past. An equation that describes this motion is $d = \dfrac{7}{4}\cos\dfrac{\pi t}{5}$. Find the period of the function.

(a) 5   (b) 10   (c) $\dfrac{2\pi^2}{5}$ (d) $\dfrac{2}{5}$ (e) None of these

1—M—Answer: b

35. A buoy oscillates in simple harmonic motion as waves move past. An equation that describes this motion is $d = 2\cos\dfrac{\pi t}{6}$. Find the period of the function.

(a) 12   (b) $\dfrac{\pi^2}{3}$ (c) $\dfrac{1}{3}$ (d) 3   (e) None of these

1—M—Answer: a

6.5 Graphs of Other Trigonometric Functions

1. Match the correct graph with the function: $f(x) = \csc 3x$

(a)
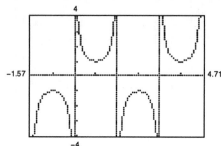

(b)
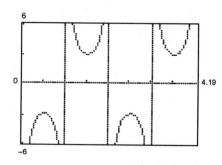

(c)
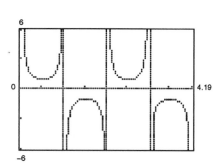

(d)
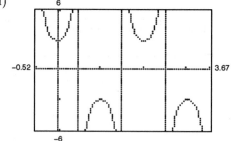

(e) None of these

1—M—Answer: c

2. Match the correct graph with the function: $f(x) = \sec 2x$

(a)
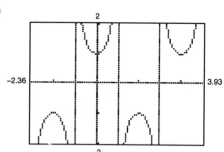

(b)
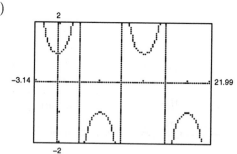

2. —CONTINUED—

(c)

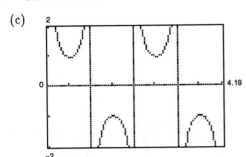

(d)

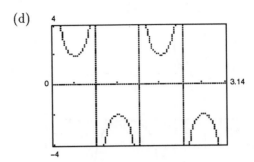

(e) None of these

1—M—Answer: a

3. Match the correct graph with the function: $f(x) = -\tan 3x$

(a)

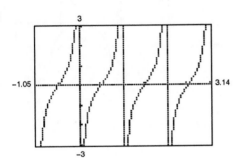

(b)

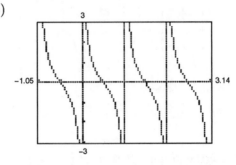

(c)

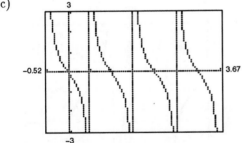

(d)

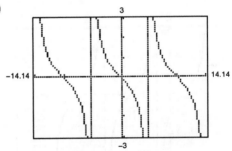

(e) None of these

1—M—Answer: c

4. Sketch the graph: $f(x) = 1 + \sec 2x$

(a)

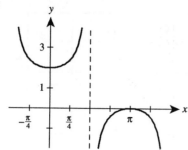

(b)

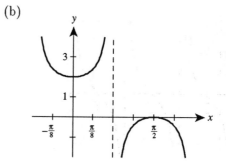

(c)

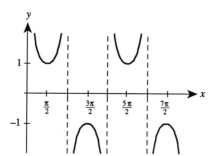

(d)

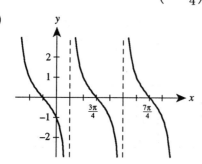

(e) None of these

1—M—Answer: b

5. Sketch the graph: $f(x) = \cot\left(x - \dfrac{\pi}{4}\right)$

(a)

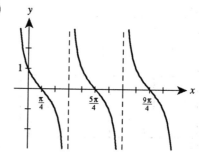

(b)

5. —CONTINUED—

(c)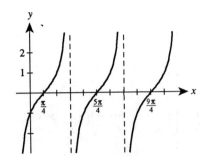

(d)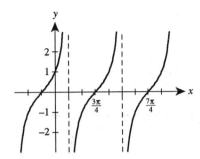

(e) None of these

1—M—Answer: a

6. Use a graphing utility to graph the function: $f(x) = 2 \csc \pi x$

(a)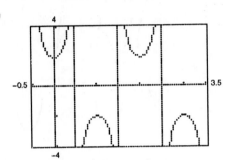

(b)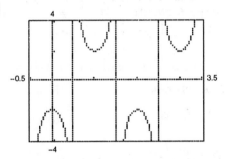

(c)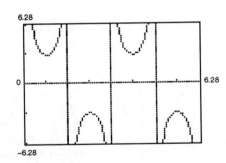

(d)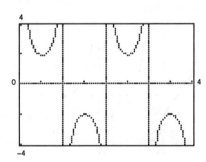

(e) None of these

1—M—Answer: d

7. Match the correct function with the graph.

(a) $y = \cot\left(x - \dfrac{\pi}{4}\right)$

(b) $y = \tan\left(x - \dfrac{\pi}{4}\right)$

(c) $y = -\cot(4x)$

(d) $y = \tan 4x$

(e) None of these

1—M—Answer: c

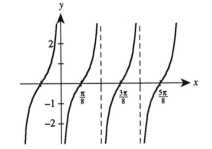

8. Match the correct function with the graph.

(a) $y = 3 \csc 2x$ (b) $y = 3 \sec 2x$

(c) $y = -3 \sec 2x$ (d) $y = -3 \csc 2x$

(e) None of these

1—M—Answer: a

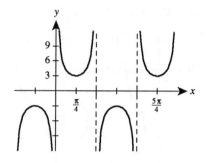

9. Match the correct function with the graph.

(a) $y = 2 \cot 3\pi x$ (b) $y = -2 \tan \dfrac{\pi x}{3}$

(c) $y = 2 \cot \dfrac{\pi x}{3}$ (d) $y = -2 \tan 3\pi x$

(e) None of these

1—M—Answer: c

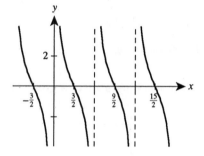

10. Match the correct equation with the graph.

(a) $y = -\sec \pi x$ (b) $y = -\csc \pi x$

(c) $y = \sec \left(x - \dfrac{\pi}{2} \right)$ (d) $y = -\csc \left(x + \dfrac{1}{2} \right)$

(e) None of these

1—M—Answer: a

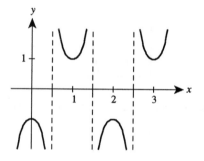

11. Match the correct equation with the graph.

(a) $y = -\csc 3x$ (b) $y = \sec 3x$

(c) $y = -\sec \dfrac{x}{3}$ (d) $y = -\csc \dfrac{x}{3}$

(e) None of these

1—M—Answer: d

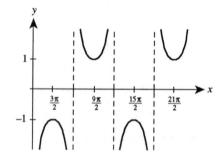

12. Sketch the graph of the function:

$$f(x) = \frac{1}{2}\sec\left(x - \frac{\pi}{2}\right)$$

2—O—Answer:

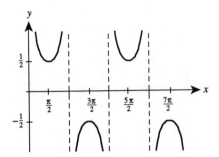

13. Sketch the graph of the function:

$$f(x) = \cot\left(x - \frac{\pi}{6}\right)$$

2—O—Answer:

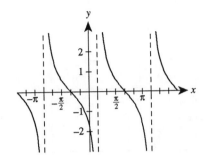

14. Match the graph with the correct function.

(a) $y = 3 - \sec x$ (b) $y = x + \csc x$

(c) $y = x + \sec x$ (d) $y = 3 + \csc x$

(e) None of these

1—M—Answer: d

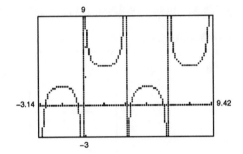

15. Match the graph with the correct function.

(a) $y = 2\sec 2\pi x$ (b) $y = -2\csc\left(\frac{\pi x}{2}\right)$

(c) $y = -2\cot\left(\frac{\pi x}{4}\right)$ (d) $y = -\sin\left(\frac{x}{2}\right)$

(e) None of these

1—M—Answer: b

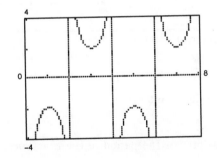

16. Use a graphing utility to graph:

$$f(x) = -\csc\left(x + \frac{\pi}{3}\right)$$

2—O—Answer:

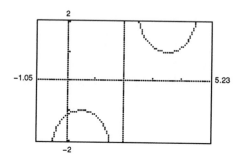

17. Use a graphing utility to graph:

$$f(x) = -\csc(2x - \pi)$$

2—O—Answer:

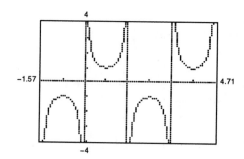

18. Use a graphing utility to graph: $f(x) = -\sec\left(3x - \frac{\pi}{2}\right)$

2—O—Answer:

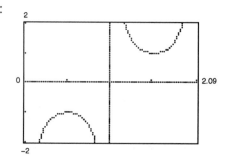

19. Determine the period of the function: $y = 3\tan 7x$

(a) $\frac{\pi}{3}$ (b) $\frac{\pi}{7}$ (c) $\frac{2\pi}{7}$ (d) 6π (e) None of these

1—M—Answer: b

20. Determine the period of the function: $f(x) = \frac{1}{5}\tan\left(3x + \frac{\pi}{2}\right)$

1—O—Answer: $\frac{\pi}{3}$

21. Determine the period of the function: $f(x) = 3\cot 4x$

(a) $\frac{\pi}{2}$ (b) $\frac{\pi}{4}$ (c) 2π (d) 4π (e) None of these

1—M—Answer: b

22. Determine the period of the function: $f(x) = 2\tan(3x - \pi)$

(a) $\frac{\pi}{3}$ (b) $\frac{2\pi}{3}$ (c) 6π (d) 3π (e) None of these

1—M—Answer: a

23. Determine the period of the function: $f(x) = -\sec\left(\dfrac{x}{2} - \dfrac{\pi}{3}\right)$

(a) $\dfrac{\pi}{2}$ (b) π (c) 2π (d) 4π (e) None of these

1—M—Answer: d

24. Determine the period of the function: $f(x) = \csc\left(\dfrac{x}{3} - \dfrac{\pi}{2}\right)$

(a) 3π (b) $\dfrac{\pi}{2}$ (c) $\dfrac{2\pi}{3}$ (d) 6π (e) None of these

1—M—Answer: d

25. Determine the period of the function: $f(x) = \tan\left(\dfrac{x}{2}\right)$

(a) π (b) 2π (c) $\dfrac{\pi}{2}$ (d) 4π (e) None of these

1—M—Answer: b

26. To sketch the graph of the cosecant function, it is convenient to first sketch the graph of the _____ function.

(a) sine   (b) cosine   (c) tangent

(d) cotangent   (e) secant

1—M—Answer: a

27. To sketch the graph of the secant function, it is convenient to first sketch the graph of the _____ function.

(a) sine   (b) cosine   (c) tangent

(d) cotangent   (e) secant

1—M—Answer: b

28. Which of the following is a vertical asymptote to the graph of $y = \csc 3x$?

(a) $x = \dfrac{\pi}{2}$ (b) $x = \dfrac{3\pi}{2}$ (c) $x = \dfrac{\pi}{3}$

(d) $x = \dfrac{\pi}{4}$ (e) None of these

1—M—Answer: c

29. Which of the following is a vertical asymptote to the graph of $y = -\tan\left(x - \dfrac{\pi}{3}\right)$?

(a) $x = \dfrac{\pi}{3}$ (b) $x = \dfrac{\pi}{2}$ (c) $x = \dfrac{3\pi}{2}$

(d) $x = \dfrac{5\pi}{6}$ (e) None of these

1—M—Answer: d

30. Which of the following is a vertical asymptote to the graph of $y = \tan\left(2x - \dfrac{\pi}{3}\right)$?

    (a) $x = \dfrac{5\pi}{6}$ (b) $x = \dfrac{5\pi}{12}$ (c) $x = \dfrac{6\pi}{5}$

    (d) $x = \dfrac{\pi}{2}$ (e) None of these

    1—M—Answer: b

31. Determine which of the following is a vertical asymptote to the graph of $y = -2\csc\left(3x - \dfrac{\pi}{3}\right)$.

    (a) $x = \dfrac{2\pi}{3}$ (b) $x = \dfrac{5\pi}{12}$ (c) $x = \dfrac{7\pi}{9}$

    (d) $x = \dfrac{8\pi}{15}$ (e) None of these

    1—M—Answer: c

32. Determine which of the following is a vertical asymptote to the graph of $y = \dfrac{1}{2}\sec\left(2x - \dfrac{\pi}{4}\right)$.

    (a) $x = \dfrac{\pi}{8}$ (b) $x = \dfrac{9\pi}{8}$ (c) $x = \dfrac{7\pi}{8}$

    (d) $x = \dfrac{\pi}{4}$ (e) None of these

    1—M—Answer: c

33. Determine which of the following is a vertical asymptote to the graph of $y = -\cot\left(\dfrac{x}{2}\right)$.

    (a) $x = \pi$ (b) $x = 2\pi$ (c) $x = \dfrac{\pi}{2}$

    (d) $x = \dfrac{\pi}{4}$ (e) None of these

    1—M—Answer: b

34. Standing on a dock 50 feet above the water line, you sight a ship heading directly toward you. Let x be the angle of depression to the ship and d the distance from shore to the ship. Write d as a function of x.

    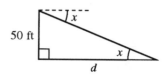

    (a) $d = 50\sin x$ (b) $d = 50\tan x$

    (c) $d = \dfrac{\tan x}{50}$ (d) $d = 50\cot x$

    (e) None of these

    1—M—Answer: d

35. Standing on a dock 100 feet above the water line, you sight a ship heading directly toward you. Let x be the angle of depression to the ship and d the distance from shore to the ship. Write d as a function of x.

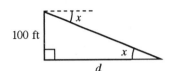

(a) $d = \dfrac{\tan x}{100}$ (b) $d = 100 \cot x$

(c) $d = \dfrac{\cot x}{100}$ (d) $d = 100 \tan x$

(e) None of these

1—M—Answer: b

6.6 Advanced Graphing Techniques

1. Sketch the graph of
$$f(x) = 3 + \sin\left(x + \frac{\pi}{2}\right).$$
1—O—Answer:

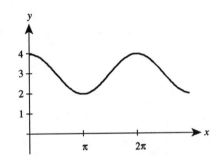

2. Sketch the graph of
$$f(x) = -2 + \cos\left(x + \frac{\pi}{2}\right).$$
1—O—Answer:

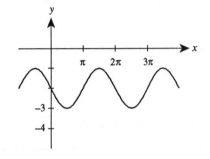

3. Sketch the graph of
$$f(x) = -2 + \sin\left(x + \frac{3\pi}{2}\right).$$
1—O—Answer:

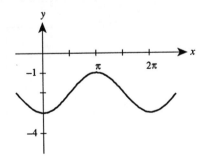

4. Sketch the graph of
$$f(x) = 2 - \cos(x + \pi).$$
1—O—Answer:

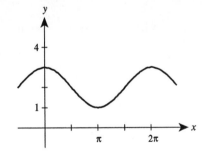

5. Sketch the graph of

$$f(x) = 2 + \sin\left(x + \frac{\pi}{2}\right).$$

1—O—Answer:

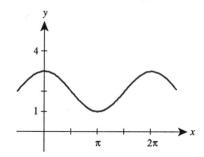

6. Sketch the graph of

$$f(x) = 2 - \sin(x - \pi).$$

1—O—Answer:

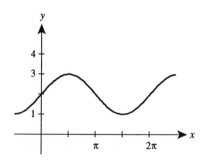

7. Match the graph with the correct function.

(a) $y = \cos 2x + \sin x$ (b) $y = \cos x + \sin 2x$

(c) $y = 2\cos x + \sin x$ (d) $y = \cos x + 2\sin x$

(e) None of these

1—M—Answer: d

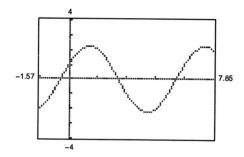

8. Match the graph with the correct function.

(a) $y = x \sin x$ (b) $y = -x \sin x$

(c) $y = -x + \sin x$ (d) $y = -x - \sin x$

(e) None of these

1—M—Answer: c

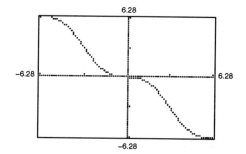

9. Match the graph with the correct function.

(a) $y = x - \sin x$ (b) $y = x - \cos x$

(c) $y = x + \sin x$ (d) $y = x + \cos x$

(e) None of these

1—M—Answer: b

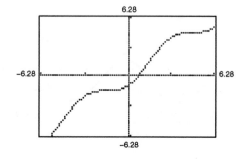

10. Match the graph with the correct function.

    (a) $y = \frac{1}{3}x - \cos x$ (b) $y = \frac{1}{3}x - \sin x$

    (c) $y = \frac{1}{3}x + \cos x$ (d) $y = \frac{1}{3}x + \sin x$

    (e) None of these

    1—M—Answer: a

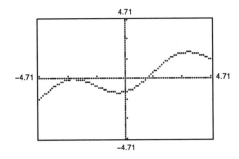

11. Match the graph with the correct function.

    (a) $y = 2x \cos x$ (b) $y = 2x \sin x$

    (c) $y = 2x + \cos x$ (d) $y = 2x + \sin x$

    (e) None of these

    1—M—Answer: b

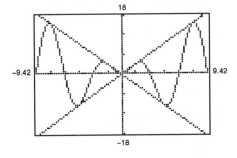

12. Match the graph with the correct function.

    (a) $y = |x| \cos x$ (b) $y = 2^x \sin x$

    (c) $y = |x| \sin 2x$ (d) $y = x \sin x$

    (e) None of these

    1—M—Answer: c

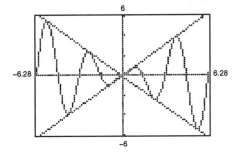

13. Match the graph with the correct function.

    (a) $y = |x| \sin 2x$ (b) $y = x \sin x$

    (c) $y = |x| \cos 2x$ (d) $y = x \cos x$

    (e) None of these

    1—M—Answer: c

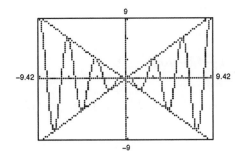

14. Match the graph with the correct function.

    (a) $y = e^x \cos x$ (b) $y = x \cos x$

    (c) $y = x \sin x$ (d) $y = e^x \sin x$

    (e) None of these

    1—M—Answer: a

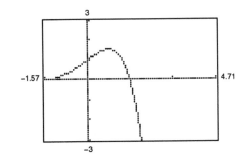

15. Match the graph with the correct function.

(a) $y = e^x \cos x$ (b) $y = x \cos x$

(c) $y = x \sin x$ (d) $y = e^x \sin x$

(e) None of these

1—M—Answer: d

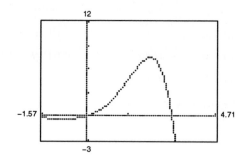

16. Match the graph with the correct function.

(a) $y = x \sin x$ (b) $y = \dfrac{1}{x} \sin x$

(c) $y = \sin^2 x$ (d) $y = \dfrac{1}{x} \cos x$

(e) None of these

1—M—Answer: d

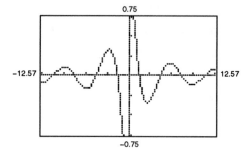

17. Match the graph with the correct function.

(a) $y = \sin^2 x$ (b) $y = \cos^2 x$

(c) $y = \sin x^2$ (d) $y = \cos x^2$

(e) None of these

1—M—Answer: a

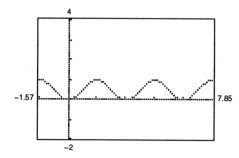

18. Find the period of the function: $f(x) = \sin 2x + \cos x$

(a) π (b) 2π (c) $\dfrac{\pi}{2}$ (d) 2   (e) None of these

1—M—Answer: b

19. Find the period of the function: $f(x) = \sin \dfrac{x}{2} + \cos \dfrac{x}{3}$

(a) 6π (b) 2π (c) $\dfrac{\pi}{6}$ (d) 12π (e) None of these

1—M—Answer: d

20. Find the period of the function: $f(x) = 3 \cos 2x - \sin \dfrac{x}{2}$

(a) π (b) 2π (c) 4π (d) $\dfrac{\pi}{4}$ (e) None of these

1—M—Answer: c

21. Use a graphing utility to approximate any relative minimum and relative maximum of the function $f(x) = \sin 3x - \cos x$ in the interval $[0, 2\pi)$.

2—O—Answer: $(0.59, 0.15)$, $(1.42, -1.05)$, $(2.67, 1.88)$

22. Use a graphing utility to approximate any relative minimum and relative maximum of the function $f(x) = |\cos x|$ in the interval $\left(-\dfrac{\pi}{2}, \dfrac{3\pi}{2}\right)$.

2—O—Answer: $(0, 1)$, $(1.57, 0)$, $(3.14, 1)$

23. Use a graphing utility to approximate any zeros of the function $f(x) = 2x - \sin x$.

(a) $x = 2$ (b) $x = 0$ (c) $x = \frac{1}{2}$ (d) $x = -1$ (e) None of these

1—M—Answer: b

24. Use a graphing utility to approximate any zeros of the function $f(x) = 3x - \cos x$.

(a) $x = 0.32$ (b) $x = 0$ (c) $x = -0.95$ (d) $x = 0.02$ (e) None of these

1—M—Answer: a

25. Find the domain of the function: $f(x) = \frac{1}{2}x - \sin 3x$

(a) All real numbers   (b) All real numbers, $x = 0$

(c) All real numbers, $x \geq 0$ (d) All real numbers between -1 and 1

(e) None of these

1—M—Answer: a

26. Find the domain of the function: $f(x) = x \cos |x|$

1—O—Answer: All real numbers

27. Find the range of the function: $f(x) = -x + \cos x$

(a) All real numbers   (b) All real numbers between -1 and 1

(c) All real numbers, $x \neq 0$ (d) All real numbers, $x \geq 0$

(e) None of these

1—M—Answer: a

28. Find the range of the function: $f(x) = |\cos x|$

(a) All real numbers   (b) $0 \leq x \leq 1$ (c) $0 \leq y \leq 1$

(d) $y \geq 0$ (e) None of these

1—M—Answer: c

29. Find the range of the function: $f(x) = x \cos x$

1—O—Answer: All real numbers

30. Find the damping factor of $f(x) = 2x \sin 4x$.

    (a) $4x$ (b) x (c) $2x$ (d) 2 (e) None of these

    1—M—Answer: c

31. Find the damping factor of $f(x) = \dfrac{1}{x} \cos x^2$.

    (a) x (b) $\dfrac{1}{x}$ (c) x^2 (d) $2x$ (e) None of these

    1—M—Answer: b

32. Find the damping factor of $f(x) = e^{2x} \sin \dfrac{x}{4}$.

    1—O—Answer: e^{2x}

33. Find the damping factor of $f(x) = 2^{-x} \cos 3x$.

    1—O—Answer: 2^{-x}

34. Describe the behavior of the function $f(x) = e^{-x} \sin x$ as x increases.

    2—O—Answer: Functional values approach zero

35. Describe the behavior of the function $f(x) = x|\cos x|$ as x approaches zero.

    2—O—Answer: Functional values approach zero

36. Describe the behavior of the function $f(x) = \cos\left(\dfrac{2}{x}\right)$ as x approaches zero.

    2—O—Answer: Functional values oscillate between -1 and 1

37. Use a graphing utility to graph $f(x) = \frac{1}{3}x - \cos x$ and its algebraic component.

    2—O—Answer:

    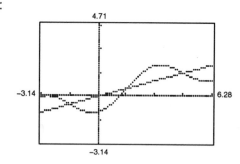

38. Use a graphing utility to graph $f(x) = x \sin 2x$ and the lines $y = x$ and $y = -x$.

2—O—Answer:

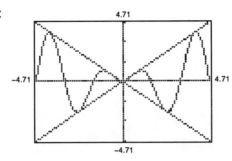

39. Use a graphing utility to graph $f(x) = 7 + \tan x$.

1—O—Answer:

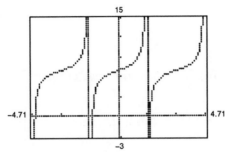

40. Use a graphing utility to graph the function: $f(x) = e^{-x} \sin x$

1—O—Answer:

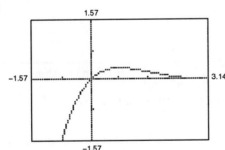

41. Use a graphing utility to graph the function $f(x) = \frac{1}{2}x + \sin x$ and its algebraic component.

2—O—Answer:

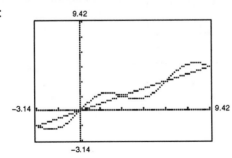

42. Use a graphing utility to graph the function $f(x) = \sin 2x + 2\cos x$.

1—O—Answer:

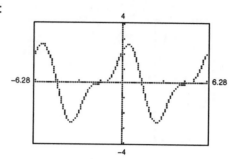

6.7 Inverse Trigonometric Functions

1. Evaluate: $\arccos\left(-\dfrac{1}{2}\right)$

(a) $\dfrac{\pi}{6}$ (b) $\dfrac{\pi}{3}$ (c) $-\dfrac{\pi}{3}$ (d) $\dfrac{2\pi}{3}$ (e) None of these

1—M—Answer: d

2. Evaluate: $\arcsin 0$

(a) $\dfrac{\pi}{2}$ (b) π (c) 0   (d) $-\dfrac{\pi}{2}$ (e) None of these

1—M—Answer: c

3. Evaluate: $\arctan(-1)$

(a) $\dfrac{\pi}{4}$ (b) $-\dfrac{\pi}{4}$ (c) $\dfrac{3\pi}{4}$ (d) $\dfrac{7\pi}{4}$ (e) None of these

1—M—Answer: b

4. Evaluate: $\arcsin\left(-\dfrac{1}{2}\right)$

(a) $-\dfrac{\pi}{6}$ (b) $\dfrac{11\pi}{6}$ (c) $\dfrac{5\pi}{6}$ (d) $\dfrac{\pi}{6}$ (e) None of these

1—M—Answer: a

5. Evaluate: $\arccos(2)$

(a) $\dfrac{\pi}{3}$ (b) $\dfrac{\pi}{4}$ (c) $\dfrac{\pi}{2}$ (d) $-\dfrac{\pi}{6}$ (e) None of these

1—M—Answer: e

6. Evaluate: $\arctan(2.41)$

(a) 1.1775   (b) −0.8978   (c) 0.4149   (d) 0.9732   (e) None of these

1—M—Answer: a

7. Evaluate: $\arccos(-0.4777)$

   (a) -1.0049 (b) 1.0728 (c) 2.0934 (d) 2.0688 (e) None of these

   1—M—Answer: d

8. Evaluate: $\arcsin(-0.7182)$

   (a) -0.5771 (b) 1.3924 (c) -0.8012 (d) 4.2318 (e) None of these

   1—M—Answer: c

9. Evaluate: $\arccos(-0.923)$

   (a) -1.1758 (b) -0.3950 (c) 2.7466 (d) 1.1758 (e) None of these

   1—M—Answer: c

10. Evaluate: $\arctan(5.572)$

    (a) 1.3932 (b) 1.784 (c) 0.1795 (d) -0.8616 (e) None of these

    1—M—Answer: a

11. Evaluate: $\arccos(-0.8923)$

    1—O—Answer: 2.6732 radians

12. Evaluate: $\arctan(-3)$

    1—O—Answer: -1.2490 radians

13. Evaluate: $\sec[\arctan 3]$

    (a) $\sqrt{10}$ (b) $\dfrac{\sqrt{2}}{4}$ (c) $2\sqrt{2}$ (d) $\dfrac{\sqrt{10}}{3}$ (e) None of these

    1—M—Answer: a

14. Evaluate: $\cos\left[\arctan\left(-\dfrac{2}{3}\right)\right]$

    (a) $3\sqrt{13}$ (b) $\dfrac{3\sqrt{13}}{13}$ (c) $-\dfrac{2\sqrt{13}}{13}$ (d) $\dfrac{2\sqrt{13}}{13}$ (e) None of these

    1—M—Answer: b

15. Evaluate: $\sin\left[\arccos\left(-\dfrac{2}{7}\right)\right]$

    (a) $\dfrac{\sqrt{53}}{7}$ (b) $-\dfrac{\sqrt{53}}{7}$ (c) $\dfrac{3\sqrt{5}}{7}$ (d) $-\dfrac{3\sqrt{5}}{7}$ (e) None of these

    1—M—Answer: c

16. Find the exact value: $\cos\left[\arctan\left(-\dfrac{3}{10}\right)\right]$

    1—O—Answer: $\dfrac{10\sqrt{109}}{109}$

17. Find the exact value: $\sin(\arctan 3)$

1—O—Answer: $\dfrac{3\sqrt{10}}{10}$

18. Evaluate: $\sin\left(\arctan\dfrac{3}{8}\right)$

(a) $\dfrac{8}{3}$ (b) $\dfrac{\sqrt{73}}{8}$ (c) $\dfrac{3\sqrt{55}}{55}$ (d) $\dfrac{3\sqrt{73}}{73}$ (e) None of these

1—M—Answer: d

19. Evaluate: $\tan\left(\arcsin\dfrac{1}{3}\right)$

(a) $-\dfrac{\sqrt{2}}{2}$ (b) $2\sqrt{2}$ (c) $\sqrt{2}$ (d) $\dfrac{\sqrt{2}}{4}$ (e) None of these

1—M—Answer: d

20. Evaluate: $\tan\left(\arccos\dfrac{3}{7}\right)$

(a) $\dfrac{3\sqrt{10}}{20}$ (b) $\dfrac{2\sqrt{10}}{3}$ (c) $\dfrac{\sqrt{58}}{7}$ (d) $\dfrac{\sqrt{58}}{3}$ (e) None of these

1—M—Answer: b

21. Evaluate: $\sec\left[\arctan\left(-\dfrac{2}{5}\right)\right]$

(a) $-\dfrac{5\sqrt{21}}{21}$ (b) $-\dfrac{\sqrt{21}}{2}$ (c) $\dfrac{\sqrt{21}}{5}$ (d) $\dfrac{\sqrt{29}}{2}$ (e) None of these

1—M—Answer: e

22. Evaluate: $\tan\left[\arcsin\left(-\dfrac{\sqrt{7}}{7}\right)\right]$

(a) $\sqrt{8}$ (b) $\sqrt{6}$ (c) $-\dfrac{\sqrt{6}}{6}$ (d) $-\dfrac{\sqrt{8}}{8}$ (e) None of these

1—M—Answer: c

23. Evaluate: $\sin\left[\arccos\left(-\dfrac{4}{9}\right)\right]$

(a) $\dfrac{\sqrt{65}}{9}$ (b) $-\dfrac{\sqrt{65}}{9}$ (c) $-\dfrac{9\sqrt{97}}{97}$ (d) $\dfrac{4\sqrt{97}}{97}$ (e) None of these

1—M—Answer: a

24. Evaluate: $\sin\left(\arctan\dfrac{x}{5}\right)$

(a) $\dfrac{x}{x+5}$ (b) $\dfrac{x}{\sqrt{x^2+25}}$ (c) $\dfrac{5}{\sqrt{x^2+25}}$ (d) $\dfrac{\sqrt{25-x^2}}{5}$ (e) None of these

1—M—Answer: b

25. Evaluate: $\csc\left(\arccos\dfrac{x}{5}\right)$

(a) $\dfrac{\sqrt{25-x^2}}{5}$ (b) $\dfrac{\sqrt{25+x^2}}{x}$ (c) $\dfrac{5}{\sqrt{25-x^2}}$ (d) $\dfrac{x}{x+5}$ (e) None of these

1—M—Answer: c

26. Evaluate: $\cot\left(\arcsin\dfrac{1}{x-1}\right)$

(a) $2x-x^2$ (b) $x-1$ (c) $\dfrac{1}{\sqrt{x^2+2x+2}}$ (d) $\sqrt{x^2-2x}$ (e) None of these

1—M—Answer: d

27. Write an algebraic expression for $\tan[\arcsin x]$.

(a) $\dfrac{x\sqrt{1+x^2}}{1+x^2}$ (b) $\dfrac{1}{x}$ (c) $\dfrac{\sqrt{1-x^2}}{x}$ (d) $\dfrac{x\sqrt{1-x^2}}{1-x^2}$ (e) None of these

2—M—Answer: d

28. Write an algebraic expression for $\csc[\operatorname{arcsec} x]$.

(a) $\dfrac{\sqrt{1-x}}{1-x}$ (b) $\sqrt{1-x}$ (c) $\sqrt{1+x}$ (d) $\dfrac{\sqrt{1+x}}{1+x}$ (e) None of these

2—M—Answer: a

29. Write an algebraic expression for $\cot[\arccos x]$.

2—O—Answer: $\dfrac{x\sqrt{1-x}}{1-x}$

30. Write an algebraic expression for $\sec[\arcsin x]$.

2—O—Answer: $\dfrac{\sqrt{1-x}}{1-x}$

31. Match the graph with the correct function.

(a) $y=\arctan(x-1)$ (b) $y=\operatorname{arccot}(x+1)$

(c) $y=\arcsin x$ (d) $y=\arcsin(x+1)$

(e) None of these

1—M—Answer: a

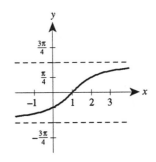

32. Match the graph with the correct function.

(a) $y = \arctan(x - 1)$ (b) $y = \arcsin(x - 1)$

(c) $y = \arcsin x$ (d) $y = \arctan x$

(e) None of these

1—M—Answer: b

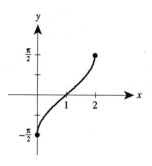

33. Match the graph with the function.

(a) $y = \arccos(x - 2)$ (b) $y = \arcsin(x + 2)$

(c) $y = \arccos\left(\dfrac{x}{2}\right)$ (d) $y = \arccos(2x)$

(e) None of these

1—M—Answer: c

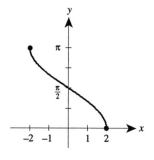

34. Match the graph with the correct function.

(a) $y = \arctan(x - 1)$ (b) $y = \arctan 2x$

(c) $y = \arccos\dfrac{x}{2}$ (d) $y = \arcsin\dfrac{x}{2}$

(e) None of these

1—M—Answer: d

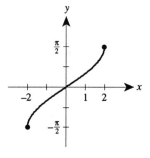

35. Use a graphing utility to graph the function: $f(x) = \arctan 2x$

1—O—Answer:

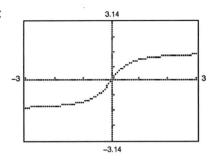

36. Use a graphing utility to graph the function: $f(x) = 2 + \arctan 4x$

1—O—Answer:

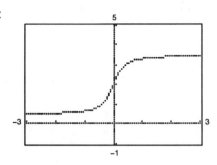

37. Use a graphing utility to graph the function: $f(x) = \arccos\left(\dfrac{x}{2}\right)$

1—O—Answer:

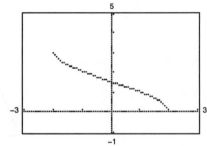

38. Use a graphing utility to graph the function: $f(x) = 1 - \arccos 2x$

1—O—Answer:

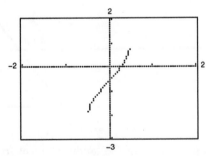

39. A boat is d feet from shore. A person standing on the dock is 25 feet above water level. The angle of depression to the boat from the dock is θ. Write θ as a function of d.

(a) $\theta = \arcsin 25d$ (b) $\theta = \arctan \dfrac{25}{d}$

(c) $\theta = \arcsin \dfrac{d}{25}$ (d) $\theta = \arctan 25d$

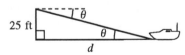

(e) None of these

1—M—Answer: b

40. A boat is d feet from shore. A person standing on the dock is 60 feet above water level. The angle of depression from the dock to the boat is θ. Write θ as a function of d.

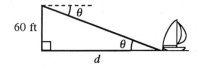

(a) $\theta = 60 \arcsin d$

(b) $\theta = \dfrac{\arctan d}{60}$

(c) $\theta = \arcsin \dfrac{d}{60}$

(d) $\theta = \arctan \dfrac{60}{d}$

(e) None of these

1—M—Answer: d

6.8 Applications of Trigonometry

1. A 40-foot extension ladder leans against the side of a building. Find the distance, h, up the side of the building if the angle of elevation of the ladder is 68°.

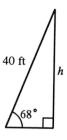

(a) 35 feet

(b) 36 feet

(c) 37 feet

(d) 38 feet

(e) None of these

1—M—Answer: c

2. A 40-foot extension ladder leans against the side of a building. Find the distance, h, up the side of the building if the angle of elevation of the ladder is 52°.

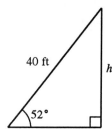

(a) 19.6 feet

(b) 51.2 feet

(c) 29.7 feet

(d) 31.5 feet

(e) None of these

1—M—Answer: d

3. A ladder is leaning against the side of a house. The base of the ladder is 5 feet from the wall and makes an angle of 39° with the ground. Find the length of the ladder.

(a) 3.89 feet   (b) 6.43 feet   (c) 4.05 feet   (d) 7.95 feet   (e) None of these

1—M—Answer: b

4. A boy and his father are walking on a street with their backs to the sun. The father is 5′8″ tall and casts a shadow 9 feet long. The boy is 4′9″ tall. How long is his shadow?

(a) 6.7 feet   (b) 7.5 feet   (c) 5.9 feet   (d) 8.2 feet   (e) None of these

1—M—Answer: b

5. A lamp post that is 8 feet high casts a shadow 5 feet long. How tall is the person standing beside the lamp post if his shadow is $3\frac{1}{2}$ feet long?

   (a) 5'7"   (b) 5'5"   (c) 5'3"   (d) 5'1"   (e) None of these

   1—M—Answer: a

6. The angle of depression from the top of one building to the foot of a building across the street is 63°. The angle of depression to the top of the same building is 33°. The two buildings are 40 feet apart. What is the height of the shorter building?

   2—O—Answer: 52.5 feet

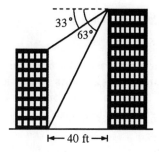

7. From a point 300 feet from a building, the angle of elevation to the base of an antenna on the roof is 26.6° and the angle of elevation to the top of the antenna is 31.5°. Determine the height, h, of the antenna.

   (a) 42.0 feet   (b) 29.4 feet
   (c) 33.6 feet   (d) 45.1 feet
   (e) None of these

   1—M—Answer: c

8. From a point on a cliff 75 feet above water level an observer can see a ship. The angle of depression to the ship is 4°. How far is the ship from the base of the cliff?

   1—O—Answer: 1072.5 feet

9. The pilot of an airplane flying at an altitude of 3000 feet sights two ships traveling in the same direction as the plane. The angle of depression of the farther ship is 20° and the angle of depression of the other ship is 35°. Find the distance between the two ships.

   (a) 470 feet   (b) 3541 feet   (c) 3958 feet   (d) 1009 feet   (e) None of these

   2—M—Answer: c

10. The sun is 30° above the horizon. Find the length of a shadow cast by a person 6 feet tall.

    (a) 7.9 feet   (b) 8 feet
    (c) 9.6 feet   (d) 10.4 feet
    (e) None of these

    1—M—Answer: d

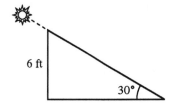

11. A silo is 40 feet high and 16 feet across. Find the angle of depression from the top edge of the silo to the floor on the opposite side.

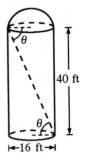

(a) 68.2°   (b) 55.1°

(c) 62.5°   (d) 58.8°

(e) None of these

1—M—Answer: a

12. A surveyor wishes to find the distance across a river. The bearings from 2 points 70 feet apart on the same bank of the river to a tree on the opposite bank are N and N34°W. Find the width of the river.

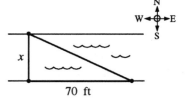

(a) 93.4′   (b) 100.9′

(c) 103.8′   (d) 111.4′

(e) None of these

2—M—Answer: c

13. A ship is 90 miles south and 20 miles east of port. If the captain wants to travel directly to port, what bearing should be taken?

(a) S77.5°E   (b) N12.5°W   (c) N77.5°E   (d) S12.5°W   (e) None of these

1—M—Answer: b

14. A ship leaves port and travels due west for 30 nautical miles, then changes course to S30°W and travel 50 more nautical miles. Find the bearing to the port of departure.

(a) N74°E   (b) N38.2°E   (c) N51.8°E   (d) N16°E   (e) None of these

2—M—Answer: c

15. A ship leaves port and travels due east 15 nautical miles, then changes course to N20°W and travels 40 more nautical miles. Find the bearing to the port of departure.

(a) S21.8°W   (b) S43.7°W   (c) N15.2°E   (d) S68.3°W   (e) None of these

2—M—Answer: a

16. A ship leaves port and travels 30 nautical miles due north, then changes course to N15°E and travels for 10 nautical miles. Find the ships bearing from the port of departure.

(a) N18.2°E   (b) N86.3°E   (c) S21.2°W   (d) N3.7°E   (e) None of these

2—M—Answer: d

17. A guy wire attached to the top of a 90 foot antenna is fastened to the ground 40 feet from the base of the antenna. Find the angle of elevation of the wire with the ground.

(a) 50°   (b) 66°   (c) 75°   (d) 79°   (e) None of these

1—M—Answer: b

18. The length of the shadow of a 200 foot tower is 70 feet. Find the angle of elevation of the sun.

(a) 65.4°   (b) 70.7°   (c) 73.2°   (d) 75.1°   (e) None of these

1—M—Answer: b

19. The pilot of an airplane flying at an elevation of 5000 feet sights two towers that are 300 feet apart. If an angle of depression to the tower closer to him is 30°, determine the angle of depression to the second tower.

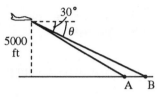

(a) 29.2°   (b) 28.9°   (c) 28.7°

(d) 27.6°   (e) None of these

2—M—Answer: a

20. An airplane flying at 600 miles per hour has a bearing of S34° E. After flying 3 hours, how far south has the plane traveled from its point of departure? (Round to the nearest mile)

(a) 1007 miles   (b) 1720 miles   (c) 1947 miles   (d) 1492 miles   (e) None of these

1—M—Answer: d

21. An airplane flying 550 miles per hour has a bearing of S15°W. After flying 2 hours, how far south has the plane traveled from its point of departure? (Round to the nearest mile)

(a) 1063 miles   (b) 285 miles   (c) 531 miles   (d) 719 miles   (e) None of these

1—M—Answer: a

22. A regular pentagon is inscribed in a circle of radius 36 inches. Find the length of the sides of the pentagon. (Round to three decimal places)

(a) 38.892 in.   (b) 39.431 in.   (c) 42.321 in.   (d) 44.472 in.   (e) None of these

1—M—Answer: c

23. A regular pentagon is inscribed in a circle of radius 10 inches. Find the length of the sides of the pentagon. (Round to three decimal places)

(a) 9.771   (b) 10.235   (c) 11.222   (d) 11.756   (e) None of these

1—M—Answer: d

24. A regular octagon is inscribed in a circle of radius 36 inches. Find the length of sides of the octagon. (Round to three decimal places)

(a) 27.553 in.   (b) 27.731 in.   (c) 28.448 in.   (d) 29.432 in.   (e) None of these

1—M—Answer: a

25. A regular octagon is inscribed in a circle of radius 10 inches. Find the length of sides of the octagon. (Round to three decimal places)

(a) 7.239 in.   (b) 7.654 in.   (c) 9.447 in.   (d) 9.571 in.   (e) None of these

1—M—Answer: b

26. Find the frequency of the simple harmonic motion described by $d = 7\cos 16\pi t$.

(a) $3\frac{1}{2}$ (b) 7   (c) 16   (d) 8   (e) None of these

1—M—Answer: d

27. Find the frequency of a simple harmonic motion described by $d = 4\sin 8\pi t$.

(a) 2   (b) 4   (c) 8π (d) 8   (e) None of these

1—M—Answer: b

28. Find the frequency of a simple harmonic motion described by $d = 4\cos \pi t$.

(a) 4   (b) π (c) 2   (d) 4   (e) None of these

1—M—Answer: e

29. Find the frequency of a simple harmonic motion described by $d = 5\cos 16\pi t$.

(a) 16   (b) 8   (c) 4   (d) 2   (e) None of these

1—M—Answer: b

30. Find the maximum displacement for the simple harmonic motion described by $d = 2\cos 40\pi t$.

1—O—Answer: 2

31. Find the maximum displacement for the simple harmonic motion described by $d = 4\cos \pi t$.

(a) 4   (b) 8   (c) $\frac{1}{2}$ (d) 2   (e) None of these

1—M—Answer: a

32. Find the maximum displacement for the simple harmonic motion described by $d = 5\cos 16\pi t$.

(a) 8   (b) 10   (c) 5   (d) $2\frac{1}{2}$ (e) None of these

1—M—Answer: c

33. Find the maximum displacement for the simple harmonic motion described by $d = 7\cos 8\pi t$.

(a) $3\frac{1}{2}$ (b) 14   (c) 4   (d) 7   (e) None of these

1—M—Answer: d

34. Find the least possible value of t for which $d = 0$: $d = 7\cos 8\pi t$

(a) $\frac{1}{2}$ (b) $\frac{1}{4}$ (c) $\frac{1}{8}$ (d) $\frac{1}{16}$ (e) None of these

1—M—Answer: d

35. Find the least possible value of t for which $d = 0$: $d = 5\cos 4\pi t$

(a) $\frac{1}{2}$ (b) $\frac{1}{4}$ (c) $\frac{1}{8}$ (d) $\frac{1}{16}$ (e) None of these

1—M—Answer: c

36. Find the least possible value of t for which $d = 0$: $d = 7\cos 16\pi t$

(a) $\frac{1}{32}$ (b) $\frac{1}{16}$ (c) $\frac{1}{8}$ (d) $\frac{1}{4}$ (e) None of these

1—M—Answer: a

CHAPTER SEVEN
Analytic Trigonometry

7.1 Applications of Fundamental Identities

1. Given $\sin x = \dfrac{4}{7}$ and $\cos x = \dfrac{-\sqrt{33}}{7}$, find $\cot x$.

   1—O—Answer: $\dfrac{-\sqrt{33}}{4}$

2. Given $\cos\left(\dfrac{\pi}{2} - x\right) = \dfrac{2}{7}$, find $\sin x$.

   (a) $\dfrac{3\sqrt{5}}{7}$ (b) $\dfrac{7}{2}$ (c) $\dfrac{3\sqrt{5}}{2}$ (d) $\dfrac{2}{7}$ (e) None of these

   1—M—Answer: d

3. Given $\csc x = -3$ and $\tan x > 0$, find $\cos x$.

   (a) $\dfrac{2\sqrt{2}}{3}$ (b) $\dfrac{-3\sqrt{2}}{2}$ (c) $\dfrac{-2\sqrt{2}}{3}$ (d) $\dfrac{3\sqrt{2}}{2}$ (e) None of these

   1—M—Answer: c

4. Given $\cot x$ is undefined and $\cos x > 0$, find $\csc x$.

   (a) 0   (b) 1   (c) −1   (d) Undefined   (e) None of these

   1—M—Answer: d

5. Given $\cos(-x) = \dfrac{3}{4}$ and $\tan x = \dfrac{\sqrt{7}}{3}$, find $\sin(-x)$.

   1—O—Answer: $-\dfrac{\sqrt{7}}{4}$

6. Simplify: $\sec x \cos\left(\dfrac{\pi}{2} - x\right)$

   (a) 1   (b) $\dfrac{1}{\cos^2 x}$ (c) $\tan x$ (d) $\cot x$ (e) None of these

   1—M—Answer: c

7. Simplify: $\dfrac{\csc x}{\tan x + \cot x}$

   (a) $\cos x + \tan x$ (b) $\sin^2 + \cos x$ (c) $\csc^2 x \sec$

   (d) $\cos x$ (e) None of these

   1—M—Answer: d

8. Simplify: $\sin\left(\dfrac{\pi}{2} - x\right)\cos(-x)$

   1—O—Answer: $\cos^2 x$

9. Simplify: $\dfrac{\cos^4 x - \sin^4 x}{\cos^2 x - \sin^2 x}$

   (a) $1 - 2\sin^2 x$ (b) $2\cos^2 x - 1$ (c) 1

   (d) -1 (e) None of these

   1—M—Answer: c

10. Simplify: $\dfrac{\csc x \cos^2 x}{1 + \csc x}$

    (a) $\csc x + 1$ (b) $1 - \sin x$ (c) $\sin x - 1$

    (d) $1 + \sin x$ (e) None of these

    2—M—Answer: b

11. Simplify: $\dfrac{\sin^2 x}{\sec^2 x - 1}$

    (a) $\sin^2 x \tan^2 x$ (b) $\sec^2 x$ (c) $\cos^2 x$

    (d) 1 (e) None of these

    1—M—Answer: c

12. Simplify: $\dfrac{\cos(-x)}{\sin(-x)}$

    (a) $\tan x$ (b) $-\tan x$ (c) $\cot x$ (d) $-\cot x$ (e) None of these

    1—M—Answer: d

13. Factor and simplify: $\cos^2 x - \sin^2 x \cos^2 x$

    (a) $\cos^4 x$ (b) $-\cos^4 x$ (c) $1 - \sin^2 x$

    (d) $2\cos x$ (e) None of these

    1—M—Answer: a

14. Factor and simplify: $\cot^4 x + 2\cot^2 x + 1$

(a) $\tan^4 x$ (b) $\csc^2 x$ (c) $\sec^4 x$

(d) $\csc^4 x$ (e) None of these

1—M—Answer: d

15. Factor and simplify: $2\sin^2 x - 2\sin^4 x$

(a) $2\tan^2 x$ (b) 0 (c) $2\sin^2 x \cos^2 x$

(d) $2\cos^4 x$ (e) None of these

1—M—Answer: c

16. Factor and simplify: $\sec^2 x \csc^2 x - \sec^2 x - \csc^2 x + 1$

(a) 1 (b) $\cot^4 x$ (c) $\cot^2 x (\sec^2 x + 1)$

(d) $\tan^4 x$ (e) None of these

2—M—Answer: a

17. Perform the addition and simplify: $\dfrac{\tan x}{\csc x} + \dfrac{\sin x}{\tan x}$ Use a graphing utility to verify your result.

(a) $\cos x$ (b) $\csc^2 x$ (c) $\sec^2 x$

(d) $\sec x$ (e) None of these

2—M—Answer: d,

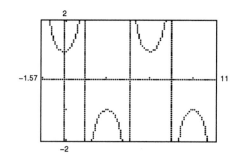

18. Perform the subtraction and simplify: $\dfrac{\sec x}{\sin x} - \dfrac{\sin x}{\cos x}$ Use a graphing utility to verify your result.

(a) $\csc x$ (b) $\tan x$ (c) $\cot x$

(d) $\cos^2 x$ (e) None of these

1—M—Answer: c,

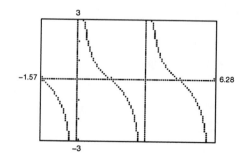

19. Perform the addition and simplify: $\dfrac{1}{1+\sin x} + \dfrac{1}{1-\sin x}$

(a) 2

(b) $2\sec^2 x$

(c) $2\cos^2 x$

(d) 0

(e) None of these

1—M—Answer: b

20. Perform the subtraction and simplify: $\csc x - \dfrac{\cos^2 x}{\sin x}$ Use a graphing utility to verify your result.

(a) 1

(b) $\sin x$

(c) $\sin^2 x$

(d) $-\sin x$

(e) None of these

1—M—Answer: b,

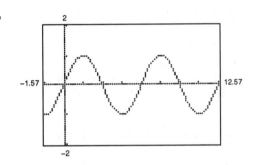

21. Rewrite the expression so that it is not in fractional form: $\dfrac{\sin x}{\cos x - 1}$

(a) $-\cot x + 1$

(b) $-\cot x - \csc x$

(c) $\sin x \cos x + \sin x$

(d) $-\tan x + 1$

(e) None of these

2—M—Answer: b

22. Rewrite the expression so that it is not in fractional form: $\dfrac{1}{\csc x + 1}$

(a) $\sin x + 1$

(b) $\tan x \sec x - \tan^2 x$

(c) $\cot x \cos x - \cot^2 x$

(d) $\csc x - 1$

(e) None of these

2—M—Answer: b

23. Rewrite the expression so that it is not in fraction form: $\dfrac{\cos x}{\sec x - 1}$

(a) $\cot^2 x + \cot^2 x \cos x$

(b) $2\sin^2 x$

(c) $1 - \cos x$

(d) $\csc^2 x + \cos^4 x$

(e) None of these

2—M—Answer: a

24. Use the substitution $x = 3\cos\theta$ to write the algebraic expression $\sqrt{9 - x^2}$ as a trigonometric expression involving θ, where $0 < \theta < \dfrac{\pi}{2}$.

(a) $3\cos\theta$ (b) $-3\sin\theta$ (c) $3(1 - \sin\theta)$

(d) $3\sin\theta$ (e) None of these

1—M—Answer: d

25. Use the substitution $x = 2\csc\theta$ to write the algebraic expression $\sqrt{x^2 - 4}$ as a trigonometric expression involving θ, where $0 < \theta < \dfrac{\pi}{2}$.

(a) $2(\csc x - 1)$ (b) $2\cot\theta$ (c) $2\tan\theta$

(d) $-2\cot\theta$ (e) None of these

1—M—Answer: b

26. Use the substitution $x = \dfrac{1}{2}(\sin\theta + 1)$ to write the algebraic expression $\sqrt{1 - (2x - 1)^2}$ as a trigonometric expression involving θ, where $0 < \theta < \dfrac{\pi}{2}$.

2—O—Answer: $\cos\theta$

27. For what values of θ, $0 \le \theta < 2\pi$ is it true that $\sin\theta = -\sqrt{1 - \cos^2\theta}$?

(a) $\dfrac{\pi}{2} \le \theta \le \pi$, $\dfrac{3\pi}{2} < \theta < 2\pi$ (b) $0 \le \theta \le \pi$ (c) $\dfrac{\pi}{2} \le \theta \le 3\dfrac{\pi}{2}$

(d) $\pi \le \theta \le 2\pi$ (e) None of these

1—M—Answer: d

28. For what value of x, $0 \le x < 2\pi$ is it true that $\csc x = \sqrt{\cot^2 x + 1}$?

(a) $0 < x < \pi$ (b) $\pi < x < 2\pi$ (c) $\dfrac{\pi}{2} \le x \le 3\dfrac{\pi}{2}$

(d) $0 \le x < \dfrac{\pi}{2}$, $\pi < x \le \dfrac{3\pi}{2}$ (e) None of these

1—M—Answer: a

29. For what values of θ, $0 \le \theta < 2\pi$ is it true that $\cos\theta = -\sqrt{1 - \sin^2\theta}$?

1—O—Answer: $\dfrac{\pi}{2} \le \theta \le \dfrac{3\pi}{2}$

30. For what values of θ, $0 \le \theta < 2\pi$ is it true $2\sec\theta = \sqrt{4 + 4\tan^2\theta}$?

1—O—Answer: $0 \le \theta < \dfrac{\pi}{2}$, $\dfrac{3\pi}{2} < \theta < 2\pi$

31. Simplify: $\dfrac{1 + \tan x}{\sin x} - \sec x$ Use a graphing utility to verify your result.

(a) $\csc x$ (b) $\tan x \csc x$ (c) $\tan x$

(d) 1   (e) None of these

1—M—Answer: a,

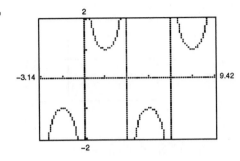

32. Simplify: $\dfrac{1 - \cos^4 x}{1 + \cos^2 x}$ Use a graphing utility to verify your result.

(a) $1 + \cos^2 x$ (b) $\sin^2 x$ (c) $\sin^2 x + \tan^2 x$

(d) $\sin^4 x$ (e) None of these

1—M—Answer: b,

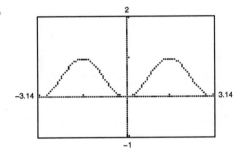

33. Simplify: $\dfrac{1}{\cot \theta} + \dfrac{1}{\tan \theta}$

(a) 1   (b) $\sec x \csc x$ (c) 0

(d) $\sin x \cos x$ (e) None of these

2—M—Answer: b

34. Simplify: $2\sin^2 \theta + \cos^2 \theta - 1$ Use a graphing utility to verify your result.

1—O—Answer:

$2\sin^2 \theta + \cos^2 \theta - 1 = \sin^2 \theta + \sin^2 \theta + \cos^2 \theta - 1$

$ = \sin^2 \theta + 1 - 1$

$ = \sin^2 \theta$

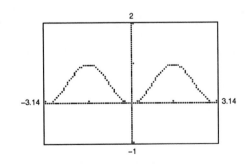

35. Simplify: $\sin^2 x \cot^2 x + \sin^2 x$ Use a graphing utility to verify your result.

2—O—Answer:

$$\sin^2 x \cot^2 x + \sin^2 x = \sin^2 x(\cot^2 x + 1)$$
$$= \sin^2 x \csc^2 x$$
$$= 1$$

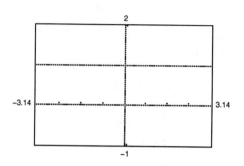

36. Simplify: $\dfrac{1 - \csc x}{\csc x}$ Use a graphing utility to verify your result.

1—O—Answer:

$$\frac{1 - \csc x}{\csc x} = \frac{1}{\csc x} - \frac{\csc x}{\csc x}$$
$$= \sin x - 1$$

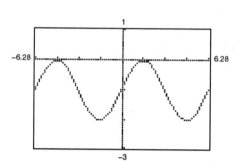

37. Rewrite the expression so that it is *not* in fractional form. Use a graphing utility to verify your result.

$$\frac{\cos^2 x}{1 - \sin x}$$

2—O—Answer:

$$\frac{\cos^2 x}{1 - \sin x} = \frac{\cos^2 x}{1 - \sin x} \cdot \frac{1 + \sin x}{1 + \sin x}$$
$$= \frac{\cos^2 x(1 + \sin x)}{1 - \sin^2 x}$$
$$= \frac{\cos^2 x(1 + \sin x)}{\cos^2 x}$$
$$= 1 + \sin x$$

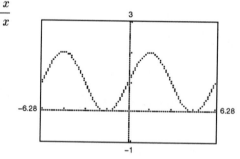

38. In determining the path of a radiated particle moving through a charged field it is necessary to determine a constant, K, which equals the expression $2\sec^2 x - 2\sec^2 x \sin^2 x - \sin^2 x - \cos^2 x$. Find this constant, K.

2—O—Answer: $K = 2\sec^2 - 2\sec^2 x \sin^2 x - \sin^2 x - \cos^2 x$

$$= 2\sec^2 x(1 - \sin^2 x) - (\sin^2 x + \cos^2 x)$$

$$= 2\sec^2 x(\cos^2 x) - 1$$

$$= 2\sec^2 x \frac{1}{\sec^2 x} - 1$$

$$= 2 - 1$$

$$K = 1$$

39. The intensity of a bright spotlight at a certain point on a stage is given by $I = \dfrac{k \tan \theta}{d^2 \sec \theta}$. In the formula, k is a constant, and d is the distance from the spotlight to that point on the stage at which I is measured. Simplify the formula for I.

2—O—Answer: $\dfrac{k \tan \theta}{d^2 \sec \theta} = \dfrac{k\dfrac{\sin \theta}{\cos \theta}}{\dfrac{d^2}{\cos \theta}} = k\dfrac{\sin \theta}{\cos \theta}\dfrac{\cos \theta}{d^2} = \dfrac{k \sin \theta}{d^2}$

7.2 | Verifying Trigonometric Identities

1. Simplify: $\dfrac{\tan x}{\csc x + \cot x}$

(a) $\sec x - 1$　　　(b) $\sec x + 1$　　　(c) $\tan x \csc x + \tan x \cot x$

(d) $1 - \dfrac{1}{\cos x}$　　　(e) None of these

1—M—Answer: a

2. Simplify: $\dfrac{1}{\sec x + 1} + \dfrac{1}{\sec x - 1}$

(a) $\dfrac{2\sin^2 x}{\cos^4 x}$　　　(b) $2\cot x \csc x$　　　(c) $2\csc x$

(d) $\dfrac{\cos x}{2\sin^2 x}$　　　(e) None of these

2—M—Answer: b

3. Simplify: $\dfrac{\cot^2 \theta + 1}{\cos^2 \theta - 1}$

(a) $-\dfrac{1}{\sin^4 \theta}$　　　(b) -1　　　(c) $\csc^4 \theta$

(d) $\cot^2 \theta$　　　(e) None of these

1—M—Answer: a

4. Simplify: $\dfrac{\cos x}{1 + \sin x}$

   (a) $\cos x + \cot x$ (b) $\sec x - \tan x$ (c) $\sec x - \cot x$

   (d) $\cos x + \tan x$ (e) None of these

   1—M—Answer: b

5. Simplify: $\dfrac{\tan^2 x}{\csc^2 x - 1}$

   (a) -1 (b) 1 (c) $\tan^4 x$

   (d) $-\cot^4 x$ (e) None of these

   1—M—Answer: c

6. Simplify: $\dfrac{\tan x}{1 - \sec x}$

   (a) $-\cot x(1 + \sec x)$ (b) $\dfrac{1 + \sec x}{\tan x}$ (c) $\cot x$

   (d) $1 - \sin x \sec^2 x$ (e) None of these

   2—M—Answer: a

7. Add and simplify: $\dfrac{1 + \cos \theta}{\sin \theta} + \dfrac{\sin \theta}{1 + \cos \theta}$

   (a) $\dfrac{1 + \cos \theta + \sin \theta}{\sin \theta + \sin \theta \cos \theta}$ (b) $1 + 2 \cos \theta + \cos^2 \theta$ (c) $\dfrac{2}{\sin \theta}$

   (d) $\cos^2 \theta$ (e) None of these

   1—M—Answer: c

8. Add and simplify: $\dfrac{1}{1 + \cos x} + \dfrac{1}{1 - \cos x}$

   (a) $\dfrac{2}{1 - \cos x}$ (b) 0 (c) $2 \cot x \csc x$

   (d) $2 \csc^2 x$ (e) None of these

   1—M—Answer: d

9. Simplify: $1 + \dfrac{1}{\csc^2 x - 1}$

   (a) $\sin^2 x$ (b) $1 - \cot^2 x$ (c) $\sec^2 x$

   (d) $\cos^2 x$ (e) None of these

   1—M—Answer: c

10. Simplify: $\sin\left(\dfrac{\pi}{2} - x\right)[\tan(-x) + \cot(-x)]$

    (a) $\sin x - \cot^2 x \csc x$ (b) $-\csc x$ (c) $\sin^2 x - \cos^2 x$

    (d) $\dfrac{1}{\sin x}$ (e) None of these

    2—M—Answer: b

11. Simplify: $\cos\left(\dfrac{\pi}{2} - x\right)\sec x + \dfrac{1}{\cos x \cdot \sec\left(\dfrac{\pi}{2} - x\right)}$

    (a) 0   (b) $\sec^2 x$ (c) $2\tan x$

    (d) 2   (e) None of these

    2—M—Answer: c

12. Simplify: $1 - 2\csc x + \csc^4 x$

    (a) $\tan^2 x$ (b) $-\cot^2$ (c) $-\cot^4 x$

    (d) $\cot^4 x$ (e) None of these

    2—M—Answer: d

13. Simplify: $\sin x - \sin x \cos^2 x$

    (a) $\sin^2 x$ (b) $\csc x$ (c) $\sin^3 x$

    (d) $-\sin^3 x$ (e) None of these

    1—M—Answer: c

14. Verify the identity: $\dfrac{\sec^2 x}{\cot x} - \tan^3 x = \tan x$

    (a) $\dfrac{\sec^2 x}{\cot x} - \tan^3 x = \sec^2 x \tan x - \tan^3 x$

                       $= \tan x(\sec^2 x - \tan^2 x)$

                       $= \tan x(1)$

                       $= \tan x$

    (b) $\dfrac{\sec^2 x}{\cot x} - \tan^3 x = \dfrac{\sec^2 x - \tan^3 x(\cot x)}{\cot x}$

                       $= \dfrac{\sec^2 x - \tan^3 x\left(\dfrac{1}{\tan x}\right)}{\cot x}$

                       $= \dfrac{\sec^2 x - \tan^2 x}{\cot x}$

                       $= \dfrac{1}{\cot x}$

                       $= \tan x$

14. —CONTINUED—

(c) $\dfrac{\sec^2 x}{\cot x} - \tan^3 x = \dfrac{1 + \tan^2 x}{\cot x} - \tan^3 x$

$= \dfrac{1}{\cot x} + \dfrac{\tan^2 x}{\cot x} - \tan^3 x$

$= \tan x + \tan^3 x - \tan^3 x$

$= \tan x$

(d) All of these are correct verifications.

(e) None of these

2—M—Answer: d

15. Verify the identity: $\dfrac{\cos x \csc x}{\cot^2 x} = \tan x$

(a) $\dfrac{\cos x \csc x}{\cot^2 x} = \cos x \left(\dfrac{1}{\sin x}\right) \tan^2 x$

$= \dfrac{\cos x}{\sin x} \dfrac{\sin^2 x}{\cos^2 x}$

$= \dfrac{\sin x}{\cos x}$

$= \tan x$

(b) $\dfrac{\cos x \csc x}{\cot^2 x} = \dfrac{\cos x \csc x}{1 - \csc^2 x}$

$= \dfrac{\cos x}{1} - \dfrac{\csc x}{\csc^2 x}$

$= \cos x - \dfrac{1}{\csc x}$

$= \dfrac{\cos x}{\sin x}$

$= \tan x$

(c) $\dfrac{\cos x \csc x}{\cot^2 x} = \dfrac{\cos x \csc x}{1 - \tan^2 x}$

$= \cos x - \dfrac{\csc x}{\tan^2 x}$

$= \cos x - \dfrac{\left(\dfrac{1}{\sin x}\right)}{\left(\dfrac{\sin x}{\cos x}\right)}$

$= \cos x - \dfrac{1}{\sin x} \cdot \dfrac{\cos x}{\sin x}$

$= \dfrac{\cos x}{\sin x}$

$= \tan x$

(d) All of these are correct verifications.

(e) None of these

2—M—Answer: a

16. Verify the identity: $\tan^2 x \cos^2 x + \cot^2 x \sin^2 x = 1$

(a) $\tan^2 x \cos^2 + \cot^2 x \sin^2 x = \dfrac{\cos^2 x}{\sin^2 x} \cdot \cos^2 x + \dfrac{\sin^2 x}{\cos^2 x} \cdot \sin^2 x$

$$= \frac{\cos^4 x + \sin^4 x}{\sin^2 x + \cos^2 x}$$

$$= \frac{(\cos^2 x + \sin^2 x)^2}{(\sin^2 x + \cos^2 x)}$$

$$= \frac{(1)^2}{(1)} = 1$$

(b) $\tan^2 x \cos^2 x + \cot^2 x \sin^2 x = (1 - \sec^2 x)\cos^2 x + (1 - \csc^2 x)\sin^2 x$

$$= \cos^2 x - \cos^2 x \sec^2 + \sin^2 x - \sin^2 x \csc^2 x$$

$$= \cos^2 x - \cos^2 x \left(\frac{1}{\cos^2 x}\right) + \sin^2 x - \sin^2 x \left(\frac{1}{\sin^2 x}\right)$$

$$= \cos^2 x + \sin^2 x = 1$$

(c) $\tan^2 x \cos^2 x + \cot^2 x \sin^2 x = \dfrac{\sin^2 x}{\cos^2 x} \cdot \cos^2 x + \dfrac{\cos^2 x}{\sin^2 x} \cdot \sin^2 x$

$$= \sin^2 x + \cos^2 x = 1$$

(d) All of these are correct verifications.

(e) None of these

1—M—Answer: c

17. Verify the identity: $\dfrac{\sec x - \cos x}{\tan x} = \sin x$

(a) $\dfrac{\sec x - \cos x}{\tan x} = \dfrac{\sec x - \cos x}{\dfrac{\sin x}{\cos x}}$

$$= (\sec x - \cos x)\left(\frac{\cos x}{\sin x}\right)$$

$$= \sec x \sin x - \cos^2 x$$

$$= 1 - \cos^2 x$$

$$= \sin x$$

(b) $\dfrac{\sec x - \cos x}{\tan x} = \dfrac{\sec x - \cos x}{\dfrac{1}{\cot x}}$

$$= (\sec x - \cos x)(\cot x)$$

$$= \sec x \cot x - \cos x \cot x$$

$$= \frac{1}{\cos x}\left(\frac{\sin x}{\cos x}\right) - \cos x \left(\frac{\sin x}{\cos x}\right)$$

$$= \frac{\sin x}{\cos x} - \sin x$$

$$= \sin x - \sin x \cos x$$

$$= \sin x (1 - \cos x)$$

$$= \sin x (1) = \sin x$$

17. —CONTINUED—

(c) $\dfrac{\sec x - \cos x}{\tan x} = \dfrac{\sec x - \cos x}{\dfrac{1}{\cot x}}$

(d) All of these are correct verifications.

(e) None of these

$$= (\sec x - \cos x)(\cot x)$$

$$= \dfrac{1}{\cos x}\left(\dfrac{\cos x}{\sin x}\right) - \cos x\left(\dfrac{\cos x}{\sin x}\right)$$

$$= \dfrac{1}{\sin x} - \dfrac{\cos^2 x}{\sin x}$$

$$= \dfrac{1 - \cos^2 x}{\sin x}$$

$$= \dfrac{\sin^2 x}{\sin x} = \sin x$$

2—M—Answer: c

18. Verify the identity: $\dfrac{\csc x}{\sin x} - \dfrac{\cot x}{\tan x} = 1$

(a) $\dfrac{\csc x}{\sin x} - \dfrac{\cot x}{\tan x} = \csc x \tan x - \sin x \cot x$

$$= \dfrac{1}{\sin x} \cdot \dfrac{\sin x}{\cos x} - \sin x \cdot \dfrac{\cos x}{\sin x}$$

$$= \dfrac{1 - \cos x}{\cos x}$$

$$= 1 - \dfrac{\cos x}{\cos x} = 1$$

(b) $\dfrac{\csc x}{\sin x} - \dfrac{\cot x}{\tan x} = \dfrac{\csc x}{\left(\dfrac{1}{\csc x}\right)} - \dfrac{\cot x}{\left(\dfrac{1}{\cot x}\right)}$

$$= \csc^2 x - \cot^2 x = 1$$

(c) $\dfrac{\csc x}{\sin x} - \dfrac{\cot x}{\tan x} = \dfrac{\left(\dfrac{1}{\sin x}\right)}{\sin x} - \dfrac{\left(\dfrac{1}{\tan x}\right)}{\tan x}$

$$= \dfrac{1}{\sin^2 x} - \dfrac{1}{\tan^2 x}$$

$$= \dfrac{\tan^2 x - \sin^2 x}{\sin^2 x \tan^2 x}$$

$$= \dfrac{\dfrac{\sin^2 x}{\cos^2 x} - \sin^2 x}{\sin^2 x \left(\dfrac{\sin^2 x}{\cos^2 x}\right)}$$

$$= \dfrac{\sin^2 x - \sin^2 x \cos^2 x}{\cos^2 x} \cdot \dfrac{\cos^2 x}{\sin^4 x}$$

$$= \dfrac{\sin^2 x (1 - \cos^2 x)}{\sin^4 x}$$

$$= \dfrac{\sin^2 x \cdot \sin^2 x}{\sin^4 x}$$

$$= \dfrac{\sin^4 x}{\sin^4 x} = 1$$

(d) Both **b** and **c** are correct verifications.

(e) None of these

2—M—Answer: d

19. Verify the identity: $\dfrac{1+\tan x}{\sin x} - \sec x = \csc x$

(a) $\dfrac{1+\tan x}{\sin x} - \sec x = 1 + \tan x - \sin x \sec x$

$= 1 + \dfrac{\sin x}{\cos x} - \dfrac{\sin x}{\cos x}$

$= 1 \ne \csc x$

Therefore, this is not an identity.

(b) $\dfrac{1+\tan x}{\sin x} - \sec x = \dfrac{1 + \tan x - \sin x \sec s}{\sin x}$

$= \dfrac{1 + \tan x - \sin x \left(\dfrac{1}{\cos x}\right)}{\sin x}$

$= \dfrac{1 + \tan x - \tan x}{\sin x}$

$= \dfrac{1}{\sin x} = \csc x$

(c) $\dfrac{1+\tan x}{\sin x} - \sec x = 1 + \tan x - \sin x \sec x$

$= 1 + \tan x - \sin x \left(\dfrac{1}{\sin x}\right)$

$= 1 + \tan x$

$= \csc x$

(d) Both **b** and **c** are correct verifications.

(e) None of these

1—M—Answer: b

20. Verify the identity: $\dfrac{1+\sin x}{\cos x \sin x} = \sec x(\csc x + 1)$

1—O—Answer: $\dfrac{1+\sin x}{\cos x \sin x} = \dfrac{1}{\cos x \sin x} + \dfrac{\sin x}{\cos x \sin x}$

$= \sec x \csc x + \sec x$

$= \sec x(\csc x + 1)$

21. Simplify: $\sin x + \sin x \cot^2 x$ Use a graphing utility to verify your results.

(a) $\sin x \tan x$

(b) $\csc x$

(c) $\sin x \tan^2 x$

(d) $\csc^3 x$

(e) None of these

1—M—Answer: b

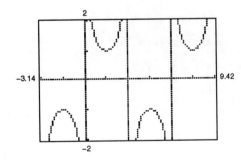

22. Verify the identity: $\sin x \left(\dfrac{\sin x}{1 - \cos x} + \dfrac{1 - \cos x}{\sin x} \right) = 2$

2—O—Answer: $\sin x \left(\dfrac{\sin x}{1 - \cos x} + \dfrac{1 - \cos x}{\sin x} \right) = \dfrac{\sin^2 x}{1 - \cos x} + 1 - \cos x$

$$= \dfrac{1 - \cos^2 x}{1 - \cos x} + 1 - \cos x$$

$$= \dfrac{(1 + \cos x)(1 - \cos x)}{1 - \cos x} + 1 - \cos x$$

$$= (1 + \cos x) + 1 - \cos x = 2$$

23. Simplify: $\sec^4 x + \sec^2 x - 2$

(a) $2 \tan^4 x$ (b) $(\sec^2 x + 2)(\tan^2 x)$ (c) $2 \tan^2 x$

(d) $\tan^2 x + 2$ (e) None of these

1—M—Answer: b

24. Simplify: $\dfrac{\tan x}{\cot x} - \dfrac{\sin x}{\csc x}$

(a) $\sec x - \cos x$ (b) $\tan^2 x \sin^2 x$ (c) $\tan^2 x - \sin^2 x$

(d) **b** and **c**   (e) None of these

2—M—Answer: d

25. Simplify: $\csc^4 x + 2 \csc^2 x - 3$

(a) $4 \cot^2 x$ (b) $\tan^2 x (\csc^2 x + 3)$ (c) $(\cot^2 x)(\csc^2 x + 3)$

(d) $2 \csc^2 x - 2$ (e) None of these

2—M—Answer: c

26. Find the missing factor to complete the verification.

$$\sin x \cos x (\tan x + \csc x) = \sin^2 x + \cos x$$

$$\sin x \cos x \tan x + \sin x \cos x \csc x = \sin^2 x + \cos x$$

$$\sin x \cos x (\quad) + \sin x \cos x (\quad) = \sin^2 x + \cos x$$

$$\sin^2 x + \cos x = \sin^2 x + \cos^2 x$$

(a) $\dfrac{\cos x}{\sin x}, \dfrac{1}{\sin x}$ (b) $\dfrac{\sin x}{\cos x}, \dfrac{1}{\cos x}$ (c) $\dfrac{\cos x}{\sin x}, \dfrac{1}{\cos x}$

(d) $\dfrac{\sin x}{\cos x}, \dfrac{1}{\sin x}$ (e) None of these

1—M—Answer: d

27. Simplify: $\sec x + \tan(-x)\sin x$ Use a graphing utility to verify your results.

(a) $\cos^2 x$ 　　　　　　　(b) $\cos x$ 　　　　　　　(c) $-\cos x$

(d) $-\tan x$ 　　　　　　　(e) None of these

2—M—Answer: b

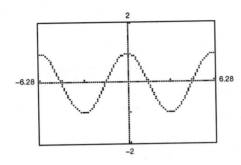

28. Verify the identity: $\sec\left(\dfrac{\pi}{2} - x\right) - \tan\left(\dfrac{\pi}{2} - x\right)\sin\left(\dfrac{\pi}{2} - x\right) = \sin x$

2—O—Answer: $\sec\left(\dfrac{\pi}{2} - x\right) - \tan\left(\dfrac{\pi}{2} - x\right)\sin\left(\dfrac{\pi}{2} - x\right) = \csc x - \cot x \cos x$

$$= \frac{1}{\sin x} - \frac{\cos x}{\sin x} \cdot \cos x$$

$$= \frac{1 - \cos^2 x}{\sin x}$$

$$= \frac{\sin^2 x}{\sin x}$$

$$= \sin x$$

29. Find the missing factor to rewrite the expression with a monomial denominator.

$$\frac{1}{\csc x - \cot x} \cdot (\qquad)$$

(a) $\dfrac{\csc x - \cot x}{\csc x - \cot x}$ 　　　　(b) $\dfrac{\csc x + \cot x}{\csc x + \cot x}$ 　　　　(c) $\sin x + \tan x$

(d) $\dfrac{1}{\sin x} - \dfrac{1}{\tan x}$ 　　　　(e) None of these

1—M—Answer: b

30. Verify the identity:

$$\frac{\sqrt{\sec x - 1}}{\sqrt{\sec x + 1}} = \frac{\sec x - 1}{|\tan x|}$$

(a) $\dfrac{\sqrt{\sec - 1}}{\sqrt{\sec x + 1}} \cdot \dfrac{\sqrt{\sec + 1}}{\sqrt{\sec x + 1}} = \dfrac{\sqrt{\sec^2 x - 1}}{\sqrt{(\sec^2 x + 1)^2}} = \dfrac{\sec x - 1}{\sec^2 x + 1} = \dfrac{\sec x - 1}{|\tan x|}$

(b) $\dfrac{\sqrt{\sec x - 1}}{\sqrt{\sec x + 1}} \cdot \dfrac{\sqrt{\sec x - 1}}{\sqrt{\sec x - 1}} = \dfrac{\sqrt{(\sec x - 1)^2}}{\sqrt{\sec^2 x - 1}} = \dfrac{\sec x - 1}{\sqrt{\tan^2 x}} = \dfrac{\sec x - 1}{|\tan x|}$

(c) Both **a** and **b** are correct verifications.

(d) Neither **a** nor **b** is a correct verification.

(e) The identity is not true. $\dfrac{\sqrt{\sec x - 1}}{\sqrt{\sec x + 1}} \neq \dfrac{\sec x - 1}{|\tan x|}$

2—M—Answer: b

31. Verify the identity and confirm it graphically.

$$\frac{\sin^2 x \cos^2 x}{\sin^2 x - 1} + \tan^2 x = \tan^2 x \sin^2 x$$

2—O—Answer:

$$\frac{\sin^2 x \cos^2 x}{\sin^2 x - 1} + \tan^2 x = \frac{\sin^2 x \cos^2 x}{-(1 - \sin^2 x)} + \tan^2 x$$

$$= \frac{\sin^2 x \cos^2 x}{-\cos^2 x} + \frac{\sin^2 x}{\cos^2 x}$$

$$= \frac{\sin^2 x}{\cos^2 x} - \sin^2 x$$

$$= \frac{\sin^2 x - \sin^2 x \cos^2 x}{\cos^2 x}$$

$$= \frac{\sin^2 x (1 - \cos^2 x)}{\cos^2 x}$$

$$= \frac{\sin^2 x}{\cos^2 x} \sin^2 x$$

$$= \tan^2 x \sin^2 x$$

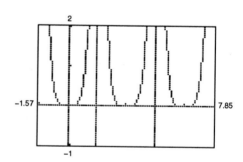

32. Simplify: $\dfrac{\sin^3 x + \cos^3 x}{\sin x + \cos x}$

(a) $\sin^2 x + 2 \sin x \cos x + \cos^2 x$ 　　　　(b) $1 + 2 \sin x \cos x$

(c) $1 - \sin x \cos x$ 　　　(d) Both **a** and **b** 　　　(e) None of these

1—M—Answer: c

33. Verify the identity: $\dfrac{\tan^2 x + 1}{\tan^2 x} = \csc^2 x$

1—O—Answer: $\dfrac{\tan^2 x + 1}{\tan^2 x} = 1 + \dfrac{1}{\tan^2 x} = 1 + \cot^2 x = \csc^2 x$

34. Verify the identity: $\sec x \csc^2 x - \csc^2 x = \dfrac{\sec x}{1 + \cos x}$

2—O—Answer: $\sec x \csc^2 x - \csc^2 x = \csc^2 x(\sec x - 1) = \dfrac{1}{\sin^2 x}\left(\dfrac{1}{\cos x} - 1\right)$

$$= \dfrac{1}{\sin^2 x}\left(\dfrac{1 - \cos x}{\cos x}\right)$$

$$= \dfrac{1}{1 - \cos^2 x}\left(\dfrac{1 - \cos x}{\cos x}\right)$$

$$= \dfrac{1}{(1 + \cos x)\cos x}$$

$$= \dfrac{\sec x}{1 + \cos x}$$

35. Verify the identity and confirm it graphically.

$$\sin\left(\dfrac{\pi}{2} - x\right)\cos(-x) = \cos^2 x$$

2—O—Answer:

$$\sin\left(\dfrac{\pi}{2} - x\right)\cos(-x) = \cos^2 x$$

$$\cos x \cos x = \cos^2 x$$

$$\cos^2 x = \cos^2 x$$

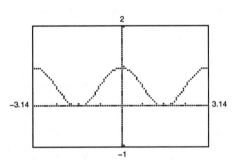

36. Verify the identity and confirm it graphically.

$$\sin x + \dfrac{\cos^2 x}{\sin x} = \csc x$$

1—O—Answer:

$$\sin x + \dfrac{\cos^2 x}{\sin x} = \csc x$$

$$\dfrac{\sin^2 x + \cos^2 x}{\sin x} = \csc x$$

$$\dfrac{1}{\sin x} = \csc x$$

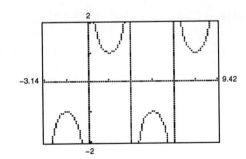

37. Verify the identity and confirm it graphically.

$$\frac{\cos x}{1 - \sin^2 x} = \sec x$$

1—O—Answer: $\dfrac{\cos x}{1 - \sin^2 x} = \sec x$

$$\frac{\cos x}{\cos^2 x} = \sec x$$

$$\frac{1}{\cos x} = \sec x$$

$$\sec x = \sec x$$

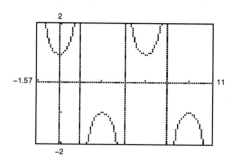

38. While drawing the plans for the plumbing of your new home, the contractor finds its necessary for two water pipes of radius, R and r, to be joined at right angles. The expression

$$(r \cos x)^2 + (R - r)(R + r)$$

is used. Show that this expression can be written $R^2 - r^2 \sin^2 x$.

2—O—Answer: $(r \cos x)^2 + (R - r)(R + r) = r^2 \cos^2 x + R^2 - r^2$

$$= R^2 + r^2 \cos^2 x - r^2$$

$$= R^2 + r^2(\cos^2 x - 1)$$

$$= R^2 + r^2[-(1 - \cos^2 x)]$$

$$= R^2 + r^2[-\sin^2 x]$$

$$= R^2 - r^2 \sin^2 x$$

39. In the study of the motion of a projectile, the expression

$$\sqrt{0.36 \cos^2 \beta t - 0.36 + 2.0 \sin^2 \beta t}$$

arises. Simplify the expression.

2—O—Answer: $\sqrt{0.36 \cos^2 \beta t - 0.36 + 2.0 \sin^2 \beta t} = \sqrt{-0.36(1 - \cos^2 \beta t) + 2.0 \sin^2 \beta t}$

$$= \sqrt{-0.36 \sin^2 \beta t + 2.0 \sin^2 \beta t}$$

$$= \sqrt{1.44 \sin^2 \beta t}$$

$$= 1.2 \sin \beta t$$

7.3 | Solving Trigonometric Equations

1. Find all solutions in the interval $[0, 2\pi)$: $2 \cos x - \sqrt{3} = 0$

(a) $\dfrac{\pi}{6}, \dfrac{11\pi}{6}$ (b) $\dfrac{5\pi}{6}, \dfrac{7\pi}{6}$ (c) $\dfrac{\pi}{3}, \dfrac{5\pi}{3}$

(d) $\dfrac{2\pi}{3}, \dfrac{4\pi}{3}$ (e) None of these

1—M—Answer: a

2. Find all solutions in the interval $[0, 2\pi)$: $\cos x - 1 = 0$

(a) $\dfrac{\pi}{4}, \dfrac{7\pi}{4}$ (b) $\dfrac{\pi}{2}, \dfrac{3\pi}{2}$ (c) 0

(d) π (e) None of these

1—M—Answer: c

3. Find all solutions in the interval $[0, 2\pi)$: $\csc x + 2 = 0$

(a) $\dfrac{\pi}{3}, \dfrac{2\pi}{3}$ (b) $\dfrac{\pi}{6}, \dfrac{5\pi}{6}$ (c) $\dfrac{4\pi}{3}, \dfrac{5\pi}{3}$

(d) $\dfrac{7\pi}{6}, \dfrac{11\pi}{6}$ (e) None of these

1—M—Answer: d

4. Find all solutions in the interval $[0, 2\pi)$: $\sin 2x = 0$ Use a graphing utility to verify your results.

(a) $0, \pi$ (b) $0, \dfrac{\pi}{2}, \pi, \dfrac{3\pi}{2}$ (c) $\dfrac{\pi}{2}, \dfrac{3\pi}{2}$

(d) $\dfrac{\pi}{4}, \dfrac{3\pi}{4}, \dfrac{5\pi}{4}, \dfrac{7\pi}{4}$ (e) None of these

1—M—Answer: b

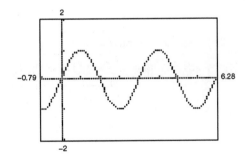

5. Find all solutions in the interval $[0, 2\pi)$: $3 \tan x - 3 = 0$

(a) $0, \pi$ (b) $\dfrac{\pi}{2}, \dfrac{3\pi}{2}$ (c) $\dfrac{\pi}{4}, \dfrac{5\pi}{4}$

(d) $\dfrac{3\pi}{4}, \dfrac{7\pi}{4}$ (e) None of these

1—M—Answer: c

6. Find all solutions in the interval $[0, 2\pi)$: $\cos^2 x + \sin x = 1$ Use a graphing utility to verify your results.

(a) $0, \pi$

(b) $\dfrac{\pi}{2}$

(c) $\dfrac{\pi}{2}, \dfrac{3\pi}{2}$

(d) $0, \dfrac{\pi}{2}, \pi$

(e) None of these

1—M—Answer: d

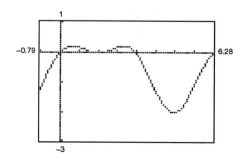

7. Find all solutions in the interval $[0, 2\pi)$: $\sec^2 x = \sec x + 2$

(a) $\dfrac{\pi}{2}, \dfrac{2\pi}{3}, \dfrac{4\pi}{3}, \dfrac{3\pi}{2}$

(b) $\dfrac{\pi}{3}, \pi, \dfrac{5\pi}{3}$

(c) $\dfrac{2\pi}{3}, \dfrac{4\pi}{3}$

(d) $\dfrac{\pi}{6}, \pi, \dfrac{11\pi}{6}$

(e) None of these

1—M—Answer: b

8. Find all solutions in the interval $[0, 2\pi)$: $\sin x = \dfrac{1}{4 \sin x}$

(a) $\dfrac{\pi}{6}, \dfrac{5\pi}{6}$

(b) $\dfrac{7\pi}{6}, \dfrac{11\pi}{6}$

(c) $\dfrac{\pi}{3}, \dfrac{2\pi}{3}, \dfrac{4\pi}{3}, \dfrac{5\pi}{3}$

(d) $\dfrac{\pi}{6}, \dfrac{5\pi}{6}, \dfrac{7\pi}{6}, \dfrac{11\pi}{6}$

(e) None of these

1—M—Answer: d

9. Find all solutions in the interval $[0, 2\pi)$: $\sec^2 x - 3 \tan x = 5$

(a) $1.1578, 4.299, \dfrac{3\pi}{4}, \dfrac{7\pi}{4}$

(b) $1.3258, 4.4674, \dfrac{3\pi}{4}, \dfrac{7\pi}{4}$

(c) $0.0699, \dfrac{3\pi}{4}, \dfrac{7\pi}{4}$

(d) $\dfrac{3\pi}{4}, \dfrac{7\pi}{4}$

(e) None of these

2—M—Answer: b

10. Find all solutions in the interval $[0, 2\pi)$: $6 \sin^2 x - \sin x - 2 = 0$

(a) $0.6667, 0.5$

(b) $0.7297, 2.4119, \dfrac{7\pi}{6}, \dfrac{11\pi}{6}$

(c) $\dfrac{\pi}{6}, \dfrac{11\pi}{6}$

(d) $0.7297, 3.871$

(e) None of these

2—M—Answer: b

11. Find all solutions in the interval $[0, 2\pi)$: $\tan 3t = \sqrt{3}$

    (a) $\dfrac{\pi}{9}, \dfrac{4\pi}{9}$

    (b) $\dfrac{\pi}{9}, \dfrac{4\pi}{9}, \dfrac{7\pi}{9}, \dfrac{10\pi}{9}, \dfrac{13\pi}{9}, \dfrac{16\pi}{9}$

    (c) $\dfrac{\pi}{3}, \dfrac{4\pi}{3}$

    (d) $\dfrac{\pi}{6}, \dfrac{7\pi}{6}$

    (e) None of these

    1—M—Answer: b

12. Find all solutions in the interval $[0, 2\pi)$: $2\cos x \csc x - 4\cos x - \csc x + 2 = 0$

    (a) $\dfrac{\pi}{3}, \dfrac{5\pi}{3}$

    (b) $\dfrac{\pi}{6}, \dfrac{\pi}{3}, \dfrac{5\pi}{3}, \dfrac{11\pi}{6}$

    (c) $\dfrac{\pi}{6}, \dfrac{\pi}{3}, \dfrac{5\pi}{6}, \dfrac{5\pi}{3}$

    (d) $\dfrac{\pi}{6}, \dfrac{2\pi}{3}, \dfrac{5\pi}{6}, \dfrac{5\pi}{3}$

    (e) None of these

    1—M—Answer: c

13. Find all solutions in the interval $[0, 2\pi)$: $5\sin^2 x + 8\sin x - 4 = 0$

    (a) 0.4115, 2.7301

    (b) $\dfrac{\pi}{6}, \dfrac{5\pi}{6}$

    (c) 0.4, 2.7416

    (d) 3.5531, 5.8717

    (e) None of these

    2—M—Answer: a

14. Find all solutions in the interval $[0, 2\pi)$: $6\cos^2 x - 5\sin x - 2 = 0$

    (a) $-1.3333, -4.4749, \dfrac{\pi}{6}, \dfrac{5\pi}{6}$

    (b) $\dfrac{\pi}{6}, \dfrac{5\pi}{6}$

    (c) 2.0000, 5.1416

    (d) $\dfrac{7\pi}{6}, \dfrac{11\pi}{6}$

    (e) None of these

    1—M—Answer: b

15. Find all solutions in the interval $[0, 2\pi)$: $\cot^2 x - \tan^2 x = 0$

    (a) $0, \pi$

    (b) $0, \dfrac{\pi}{4}, \dfrac{3\pi}{4}, \pi, \dfrac{5\pi}{4}, \dfrac{7\pi}{4}$

    (c) $\dfrac{\pi}{4}, \dfrac{3\pi}{4}, \dfrac{5\pi}{4}, \dfrac{7\pi}{4}$

    (d) $\dfrac{\pi}{4}, \dfrac{3\pi}{4}, \dfrac{5\pi}{4}, \dfrac{7\pi}{4}$

    (e) None of these

    2—M—Answer: d

16. Find all solutions in the interval $[0, 2\pi)$: $2\cos^2 x + (1 + 2\sqrt{3})\cos x + \sqrt{3} = 0$

    (a) $\dfrac{2\pi}{3}, \dfrac{5\pi}{6}, \dfrac{7\pi}{6}, \dfrac{4\pi}{3}$

    (b) $\dfrac{2\pi}{3}, \dfrac{4\pi}{3}$

    (c) $\dfrac{\pi}{3}, \dfrac{5\pi}{3}$

    (d) $-1.7321, -4.8736$

    (e) None of these

    1—M—Answer: b

17. Find all solutions in the interval $[0, 2\pi)$: $8\sin\left(\frac{x}{2}\right) - 8 = 0$

    (a) $\frac{\pi}{2}, \frac{3\pi}{2}$ (b) $\frac{\pi}{4}, \frac{3\pi}{4}, \frac{5\pi}{4}, \frac{7\pi}{4}$ (c) π

    (d) 0 (e) None of these

    1—M—Answer: c

18. Find all solutions in the interval $[0, 2\pi)$: $2\sin^2\left(\frac{x}{4}\right) - 3\cos\left(\frac{x}{4}\right) = 0$

    (a) $\frac{\pi}{3}, \frac{5\pi}{3}$ (b) $\frac{4\pi}{3}$ (c) $\frac{4\pi}{3}, \frac{2\pi}{3}$

    (d) $\frac{\pi}{6}, \frac{\pi}{3}$ (e) None of these

    2—M—Answer: b

19. Find all solutions in the interval $[0, 2\pi)$: $1 + \tan^2\theta + \tan^4\theta = 1$

    (a) $0, \frac{\pi}{2}, \pi, \frac{3\pi}{2}$ (b) $0, \pi$ (c) $0, \frac{\pi}{4}, \frac{3\pi}{4}, \pi, \frac{5\pi}{4}, \frac{3\pi}{2}, \frac{7\pi}{4}$

    (d) $\frac{\pi}{2}, \frac{3\pi}{2}$ (e) None of these

    1—M—Answer: b

20. Find all solutions in the interval $[0, 2\pi)$: $2\sin^2 x - 5\sin x = -3$

    (a) $0.7297, 2.4119, \frac{3\pi}{2}$ (b) $\frac{\pi}{2}, \frac{3\pi}{2}$ (c) $\frac{3}{2}, 1$

    (d) $\frac{\pi}{2}$ (e) None of these

    1—M—Answer: d

21. Find all solutions in the interval $[0, 2\pi)$: $\sec^4 x - 2\sec^2 x \tan^2 x + \tan^4 x = \tan^2 x$

    (a) $\frac{\pi}{2}, \frac{3\pi}{2}$ (b) $0, \pi$ (c) $\frac{\pi}{4}, \frac{3\pi}{4}, \frac{5\pi}{4}, \frac{7\pi}{4}$

    (d) $\frac{\pi}{4}, \frac{5\pi}{4}$ (e) None of these

    1—M—Answer: c

22. Find all solutions in the interval $[0, 2\pi)$: $\csc^2 x - (\cos^4 x + 2\cos^2 x \sin^2 x + \sin^4 x) = 0$

    (a) $\frac{\pi}{2}, \frac{3\pi}{2}$ (b) $0, \pi$ (c) $\frac{\pi}{4}, \frac{3\pi}{4}, \frac{5\pi}{4}, \frac{7\pi}{4}$

    (d) $\frac{\pi}{2}$ (e) None of these

    1—M—Answer: a

23. Find all solutions in the interval $[0, 2\pi)$: $\sec 3x = \sqrt{2}$

   (a) $\dfrac{\pi}{4}, \dfrac{7\pi}{4}$

   (b) $\dfrac{\pi}{12}, \dfrac{7\pi}{12}, \dfrac{9\pi}{12}, \dfrac{15\pi}{12}, \dfrac{17\pi}{12}, \dfrac{23\pi}{12}$

   (c) $\dfrac{\pi}{12}, \dfrac{5\pi}{12}, \dfrac{7\pi}{12}, \dfrac{9\pi}{12}, \dfrac{11\pi}{12}, \dfrac{13\pi}{12}, \dfrac{15\pi}{12}, \dfrac{17\pi}{12}, \dfrac{19\pi}{12}, \dfrac{23\pi}{12}$

   (d) $\dfrac{\pi}{12}, \dfrac{7\pi}{12}$

   (e) None of these

   1—M—Answer: b

24. Find all solutions in the interval $[0, 2\pi)$: $\tan \dfrac{x}{4} = \dfrac{\sqrt{3}}{3}$

   (a) $\dfrac{2\pi}{3}$ (b) $\dfrac{10\pi}{3}$ (c) $\dfrac{\pi}{4}$

   (d) $\dfrac{\pi}{4}, \dfrac{5\pi}{4}$ (e) None of these

   1—M—Answer: a

25. Find all solutions in the interval $[0, 2\pi)$: $2 \sin x \cos x + \cos x = 0$

   (a) $\dfrac{\pi}{6}, \dfrac{\pi}{2}, \dfrac{5\pi}{6}, \dfrac{3\pi}{2}$ (b) $\dfrac{\pi}{2}, \dfrac{7\pi}{6}, \dfrac{3\pi}{2}, \dfrac{11\pi}{6}$ (c) $\dfrac{5\pi}{6}, \dfrac{11\pi}{6}$

   (d) $0, \pi$ (e) None of these

   1—M—Answer: b

26. Find all solutions in the interval $[0, 2\pi)$: $2 \sin^3 x + \sin^2 x = 0$

   (a) $\dfrac{5\pi}{6}, \dfrac{11\pi}{6}$ (b) $\dfrac{4\pi}{3}, \dfrac{5\pi}{3}$ (c) $0, \dfrac{7\pi}{6}, \pi, \dfrac{11\pi}{6}$

   (d) $0, \dfrac{\pi}{2}, \pi, \dfrac{4\pi}{3}, \dfrac{3\pi}{2}, \dfrac{5\pi}{3}$ (e) None of these

   1—M—Answer: c

27. Find all solutions in the interval $[0, 2\pi)$: $2\cos^2(2\theta) - 1 = 0$ Use a graphing utility to verify your results.

(a) $\dfrac{\pi}{4}, \dfrac{3\pi}{4}, \dfrac{5\pi}{4}, \dfrac{7\pi}{4}$

(b) $\dfrac{\pi}{8}, \dfrac{3\pi}{8}, \dfrac{5\pi}{8}, \dfrac{7\pi}{8}, \dfrac{9\pi}{8}, \dfrac{11\pi}{8}, \dfrac{13\pi}{8}, \dfrac{15\pi}{8}$

(c) $\dfrac{\pi}{8}, \dfrac{\pi}{4}, \dfrac{3\pi}{8}, \dfrac{3\pi}{4}$

(d) $\dfrac{\pi}{2}, \dfrac{\pi}{4}, \dfrac{3\pi}{2}, \dfrac{3\pi}{4}, \dfrac{5\pi}{2}, \dfrac{5\pi}{4}, \dfrac{7\pi}{2}, \dfrac{7\pi}{4}$

(e) None of these

1—M—Answer: b

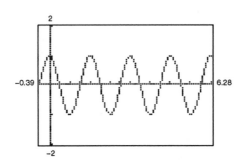

28. Find all solutions in the interval $[0, 2\pi)$: $3\tan^2 2x - 1 = 0$

1—O—Answer: $\dfrac{\pi}{12}, \dfrac{5\pi}{12}, \dfrac{7\pi}{12}, \dfrac{11\pi}{12}, \dfrac{13\pi}{12}, \dfrac{17\pi}{12}, \dfrac{19\pi}{12}, \dfrac{23\pi}{12}$

29. Find all solutions in the interval $[0, 2\pi)$: $2\sin^2 x = \sin x$

1—O—Answer: $0, \dfrac{\pi}{6}, \dfrac{5\pi}{6}, \pi$

30. Find all solutions in the interval $[0, 2\pi)$: $\tan^2\theta \csc\theta = \tan^2\theta$

1—O—Answer: $0, \dfrac{\pi}{2}, \pi$

31. Find all solutions in the interval $[0, 2\pi)$: $2\sin^2 2x + 5\sin 2x - 3 = 0$

1—O—Answer: $\dfrac{\pi}{12}, \dfrac{5\pi}{12}, \dfrac{13\pi}{12}, \dfrac{17\pi}{12}$

32. Find all solutions in the interval $[0, 2\pi)$: $2\cos\left(\dfrac{x}{2}\right) - \sqrt{3} = 0$

1—O—Answer: $\dfrac{\pi}{3}$

33. Find all solutions in the interval $[0, 2\pi)$: $4\sin^2 x + 2(1 - \sqrt{3})\sin x - \sqrt{3} = 0$

(a) $\dfrac{\pi}{3}, \dfrac{2\pi}{3}, \dfrac{7\pi}{6}, \dfrac{11\pi}{6}$

(b) $\dfrac{\pi}{6}, \dfrac{5\pi}{6}, \dfrac{4\pi}{3}, \dfrac{5\pi}{3}$

(c) $\dfrac{\pi}{6}, \dfrac{\pi}{3}, \dfrac{2\pi}{3}, \dfrac{5\pi}{6}$

(d) $\dfrac{7\pi}{6}, \dfrac{4\pi}{3}, \dfrac{5\pi}{3}, \dfrac{11\pi}{6}$

(e) None of these

2—M—Answer: a

34. Use a graphing utility to approximate the solutions of $5\cos^2 x - 3 = 0$ in the interval $[0,\ \pi)$ to ± 0.01 radians.

2—O—Answer: $x \approx 0.68,\ 2.46$

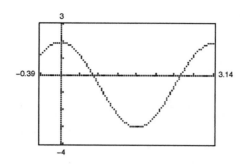

35. Use a graphing utility to approximate the solutions of $4\sin(2x) - 3 = 0$ in the interval $[0,\ \pi)$ to ± 0.01 radians by graphing the function.

2—O—Answer: $x \approx 0.42,\ 1.15$

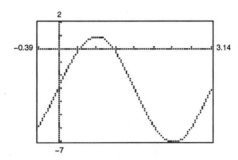

36. A professional quarterback completes a pass to a receiver 75 yards away. The football was thrown with a velocity of 88 feet per second. Find the angle θ that the ball was thrown, if the range

$$r = \frac{1}{32}V_0{}^2 \sin 2\theta.$$

2—O—Answer:

$$\sin 2\theta = \frac{32r}{V_0{}^2} \implies \theta = \frac{\sin^{-1}\left(\dfrac{32r}{V_0{}^2}\right)}{2}$$

$$\theta = \sin^{-1} = \frac{\left(\dfrac{32(75 \cdot 3)}{(88)^2}\right)}{2}$$

$$\theta = 34.20° \text{ or } 55.80°$$

37. You just received a new water gun for your birthday, and directly drench your little brother standing 100 feet away. You had pumped the gun to maximum pressure, which the manufacturer states is 60 feet per second. Find the angle θ which you must have directed the stream of water, if range

$$r = \frac{1}{32}V_0{}^2 \sin 2\theta.$$

2—O—Answer: $\sin 2\theta = \dfrac{32r}{V_0{}^2}$

$$\theta = \frac{\sin^{-1}\left(\dfrac{32r}{V_0{}^2}\right)}{2}$$

$$\theta = \sin^{-1}\frac{\left(\dfrac{32(100)}{(60)^2}\right)}{2}$$

$$\theta = 31.37° \text{ or } 58.63°$$

7.4 Sum and Difference Formulas

1. Evaluate: $\sin 105°$ (Use the fact that $105° = 60° + 45°$.)

   (a) $\dfrac{\sqrt{6} + \sqrt{2}}{4}$ (b) $\dfrac{\sqrt{6} - \sqrt{2}}{4}$ (c) $\dfrac{\sqrt{2} - \sqrt{6}}{4}$

   (d) $\dfrac{1 + \sqrt{3}}{2}$ (e) None of these

   1—M—Answer: a

2. Evaluate: $\sin 255°$ (Use the fact that $255° = 210° + 45°$.)

   (a) $\dfrac{\sqrt{6} - \sqrt{2}}{4}$ (b) $\dfrac{\sqrt{2} - \sqrt{6}}{4}$ (c) $-\dfrac{\sqrt{2} + \sqrt{6}}{4}$

   (d) $\dfrac{\sqrt{2} + \sqrt{6}}{4}$ (e) None of these

   1—M—Answer: c

3. Evaluate: $\tan \dfrac{13\pi}{12}$ $\left(\text{Use the fact that } \dfrac{13\pi}{12} = \dfrac{4\pi}{3} - \dfrac{\pi}{4}.\right)$

   (a) 1   (b) $1 + \sqrt{3}$ (c) $\sqrt{3} - 1$

   (d) $2 - \sqrt{3}$ (e) None of these

   1—M—Answer: d

4. Evaluate: $\tan 165°$ (Use the fact that $165° = 210° - 45°$.)

   (a) $3 + 2\sqrt{3}$ (b) $-2 + \sqrt{3}$ (c) $2 - \sqrt{3}$

   (d) $-3 - 2\sqrt{3}$ (e) None of these

   1—M—Answer: b

5. Evaluate: $\sin \dfrac{\pi}{12}$ $\left(\text{Use the fact that } \dfrac{\pi}{12} = \dfrac{\pi}{4} - \dfrac{\pi}{6}.\right)$

(a) $\dfrac{\sqrt{2}-1}{2}$

(b) $\dfrac{\sqrt{6}-\sqrt{2}}{2}$

(c) $\dfrac{1}{2}$

(d) $\dfrac{\sqrt{6}-\sqrt{2}}{4}$

(e) None of these

1—M—Answer: d

6. Evaluate: $\cos 285°$ (Use the fact that $285° = 330° - 45°$.)

(a) $\dfrac{\sqrt{6}+\sqrt{2}}{4}$

(b) $\dfrac{\sqrt{6}-\sqrt{2}}{4}$

(c) $\dfrac{\sqrt{3}-\sqrt{2}}{2}$

(d) $-\dfrac{\sqrt{3}+\sqrt{2}}{2}$

(e) None of these

1—M—Answer: b

7. Evaluate: $\tan 240°$ (Use the fact that $240° = 180° + 60°$.)

(a) $-\sqrt{3}$

(b) $\dfrac{\sqrt{3}}{1-\sqrt{3}}$

(c) 0

(d) $\sqrt{3}$

(e) None of these

1—M—Answer: d

8. Simplify: $\dfrac{\tan 37° - \tan 13°}{1 + (\tan 37°)(\tan 13°)}$

(a) $\tan 50°$

(b) $\tan 24°$

(c) $\cot 50°$

(d) $\cot 24°$

(e) None of these

1—M—Answer: b

9. Simplify: $\sin 8x \cos 2x + \cos 8x \sin 2x$

(a) $\sin 10x$

(b) $\sin 6x$

(c) $\cos 10x$

(d) $\cos 6x$

(e) None of these

1—M—Answer: a

10. Find the exact value: $\dfrac{\tan 325° - \tan 25°}{1 + \tan 325° \tan 25°}$

1—O—Answer: $-\sqrt{3}$

11. Simplify: $\dfrac{\tan 7x + \tan 5x}{1 - \tan 7x \tan 5x}$

1—O—Answer: $\tan 12x$

12. Simplify: $\sin 8x \cos 3x + \cos 8x \sin 3x$

    (a) $\sin 5x$ (b) $\sin 11x$ (c) $\cos 5x$

    (d) $\cos 11x$ (e) None of these

    1—M—Answer: b

13. Simplify: $\cos 146° \cos 11° + \sin 146° \sin 11°$

    (a) $-\dfrac{\sqrt{2}}{2}$ (b) -0.9205 (c) $\dfrac{\sqrt{2}}{2}$

    (d) 0.3907 (e) None of these

    1—M—Answer: a

14. Simplify: $\dfrac{\tan(2x-1)+\tan(1-x)}{1-\tan(2x-1)\tan(1-x)}$

    (a) $-\tan x$ (b) $\tan(3x-3)$ (c) $\tan(-2x^2+5x-2)$

    (d) $\tan x$ (e) None of these

    1—M—Answer: d

15. Given $\tan u = \dfrac{3}{4}$, $0 < u < \dfrac{\pi}{2}$ and $\sec v = \dfrac{25}{24}$, $\dfrac{3\pi}{2} < v < 2\pi$, find $\sin(u+v)$.

    (a) $\dfrac{8}{25}$ (b) $\dfrac{44}{125}$ (c) $\dfrac{22}{25}$ (d) $\dfrac{4}{5}$ (e) None of these

    1—M—Answer: b

16. Given $\sin u = -\dfrac{5}{13}$, $\pi < u < \dfrac{3\pi}{2}$ and $\csc v = \dfrac{\sqrt{10}}{3}$, $\dfrac{\pi}{2} < v < \pi$, find $\cos(u-v)$.

    (a) $\dfrac{-3\sqrt{10}}{130}$ (b) $\dfrac{-27\sqrt{10}}{130}$ (c) $\dfrac{27\sqrt{10}}{130}$

    (d) $\dfrac{-120+13\sqrt{10}}{130}$ (e) None of these

    1—M—Answer: a

17. Given $\cot u = \dfrac{2}{5}$, $0 < u < \dfrac{\pi}{2}$ and $\cos v = -\dfrac{3}{5}$, $\pi < v < \dfrac{3\pi}{2}$, find $\tan(u+v)$.

    (a) $\dfrac{7}{26}$ (b) $\dfrac{23}{26}$ (c) $-\dfrac{1}{2}$ (d) $-\dfrac{23}{14}$ (e) None of these

    1—M—Answer: d

18. Simplify: $\sin\left(\dfrac{3\pi}{2} + x\right)$

(a) $-\sin x$ (b) $-\cos x$ (c) $\sin\dfrac{3\pi}{2} + \sin x$

(d) $-\cos x - \sin x$ (e) None of these

1—M—Answer: b

19. Simplify: $\sin\left(x - \dfrac{\pi}{6}\right)$

(a) $\dfrac{1}{2}\sin x + \dfrac{\sqrt{3}}{2}\cos x$ (b) $\dfrac{\sqrt{3}}{2}\sin x + \dfrac{1}{2}\cos x$ (c) $\sin x - \dfrac{1}{2}$

(d) $\dfrac{\sqrt{3}}{2}\sin x - \dfrac{1}{2}\cos x$ (e) None of these

1—M—Answer: d

20. Simplify: $2\sin(x + \theta) - \sin(x - \theta)$

(a) $3\cos x \sin\theta + \sin x \cos\theta$ (b) $\sin x \cos\theta + \cos x \sin\theta$ (c) $2\cos x \sin\theta + \sin x \cos\theta$

(d) $\sin x + 3\sin\theta$ (e) None of these

1—M—Answer: a

21. Simplify: $\tan\left(\dfrac{\pi}{4} + \theta\right)$

(a) $\dfrac{\sqrt{2} + 2\tan\theta}{2 - \sqrt{2}\tan\theta}$ (b) $\dfrac{1 - \tan\theta}{1 + \tan\theta}$ (c) 1

(d) $\dfrac{1 + \tan\theta}{1 - \tan\theta}$ (e) None of these

1—M—Answer: d

22. Write the trigonometric expression as an algebraic expression: $\sin(\arctan x - \arccos 2x)$

(a) $\dfrac{x}{\sqrt{1 + x^2}} - \sqrt{1 - 4x^2}$ (b) $\dfrac{2x^2 - \sqrt{1 - 4x^2}}{\sqrt{1 + x^2}}$ (c) $\dfrac{-2x^2 - 1}{(1 + x^2)}$

(d) $\dfrac{2x - x\sqrt{1 - 4x^2}}{\sqrt{1 + x^2}}$ (e) None of these

2—M—Answer: a

23. Simplify: $\dfrac{\sin\left(\dfrac{\pi}{2} + h\right) - \sin\left(\dfrac{\pi}{2}\right)}{h}$

(a) $\dfrac{\sin h}{h}$ (b) $\dfrac{\sin h - 1}{h}$ (c) 1

(d) $\dfrac{\cos h - 1}{h}$ (e) None of these

2—M—Answer: d

24. Find all solutions in the interval $[0, 2\pi)$: $2\sin^2\left(x + \dfrac{\pi}{2}\right) = 1$

(a) $\dfrac{\pi}{6}, \dfrac{5\pi}{6}$

(b) $\dfrac{\pi}{6}, \dfrac{\pi}{4}, \dfrac{3\pi}{4}, \dfrac{5\pi}{6}$

(c) $\dfrac{\pi}{4}, \dfrac{3\pi}{4}, \dfrac{5\pi}{4}, \dfrac{7\pi}{4}$

(d) $0, \pi$

(e) None of these

2—M—Answer: c

25. Use the formula $a\sin B\theta + b\cos B\theta = \sqrt{a^2 + b^{2}}\,\sin(B\theta + c)$ where $c = \arctan\dfrac{b}{a}$, to write the expression $\sin 2\theta + \sqrt{3}\cos 2\theta$ in the form $\sqrt{a^2 + b^2}\,\sin(B\theta + c)$.

2—O—Answer: $\sin 2\theta + \sqrt{3}\cos 2\theta \Rightarrow a = 1,\; b = \sqrt{3} \Rightarrow \sqrt{a^2 + b^2} = 2$

$$B = 2$$

$$c = \arctan\dfrac{\sqrt{3}}{1} \Rightarrow c = \dfrac{\pi}{3}$$

Therefore, $\sin 2\theta + \sqrt{3}\cos 2\theta = 2\sin\left(2\theta + \dfrac{\pi}{3}\right).$

26. Use the formula $a\sin B\theta + b\cos B\theta = \sqrt{a^2 + b^2}\,\sin(B\theta + c)$ where $c = \arctan\dfrac{b}{a}$, to write the expression $3\sin\left(\theta + \dfrac{\pi}{6}\right)$ in the form $a\sin B\theta + b\cos B\theta$.

1—O—Answer: $3\sin\left(\theta + \dfrac{\pi}{6}\right)$

$$3\sin\theta\cos\dfrac{\pi}{6} + 3\cos\theta\sin\dfrac{\pi}{6}$$

$$3\sin\theta\left(\dfrac{\sqrt{3}}{2}\right) + 3\cos\theta\left(\dfrac{1}{2}\right)$$

$$\dfrac{3\sqrt{3}}{2}\sin\theta + \dfrac{3}{2}\cos\theta$$

27. Simplify: $\cos(2x - y)\cos y - \sin(2x - y)\sin y$

(a) $\sin 2x$

(b) $\sin(2x - 2y)$

(c) $\cos(2x - 2y)$

(d) $\cos 2x$

(e) None of these

1—M—Answer: d

28. Simplify: $\sin\left(\dfrac{4\pi}{3} - x\right) + \cos\left(x + \dfrac{5\pi}{6}\right)$

(a) $\cos x - \sin x$

(b) $-\sqrt{3}\cos x$

(c) $\sin x - \sqrt{3}\cos x$

(d) $\sin x$

(e) None of these

1—M—Answer: b

29. Simplify: $\tan\left(\theta + \dfrac{\pi}{3}\right) + \tan\left(\theta - \dfrac{\pi}{3}\right)$

2—O—Answer:

$$\tan\left(\theta + \frac{\pi}{3}\right) + \tan\left(\theta - \frac{\pi}{3}\right) = \frac{\tan\theta + \tan\dfrac{\pi}{3}}{1 - \tan\theta\tan\dfrac{\pi}{3}} + \frac{\tan\theta - \tan\dfrac{\pi}{3}}{1 + \tan\theta\tan\dfrac{\pi}{3}}$$

$$= \frac{\tan\theta + \sqrt{3}}{1 - \sqrt{3}\tan\theta} + \frac{\tan\theta - \sqrt{3}}{1 + \sqrt{3}\tan\theta}$$

$$= \frac{(\tan\theta + \sqrt{3})(1 + \sqrt{3}\tan\theta) + (\tan\theta - \sqrt{3})(1 - \sqrt{3}\tan\theta)}{(1 - \sqrt{3}\tan\theta)(1 + \sqrt{3}\tan\theta)}$$

$$= \frac{8\tan\theta}{1 - 3\tan^2\theta}$$

30. Simplify: $\cos(x + y)\cos y + \sin(x + y)\sin y$

(a) $\cos x + \sin x$ (b) $\cos x \cos^2 y + \sin x \sin^2 y$ (c) $\cos x$

(d) $\cos x + 2\sin x \sin y \cos y$ (e) None of these

1—M—Answer: c

31. Find all solutions in the interval $[0, 2\pi)$: $\sin\left(x + \dfrac{\pi}{4}\right) + \sin\left(x - \dfrac{\pi}{4}\right) = 1$

(a) $\dfrac{\pi}{4}, \dfrac{3\pi}{4}$ (b) $\dfrac{\pi}{4}, \dfrac{\pi}{2}$ (c) $\dfrac{\pi}{6}, \dfrac{5\pi}{6}$

(d) $\dfrac{\pi}{4}$ (e) None of these

1—M—Answer: a

32. Simplify, then find all solutions in the interval $0 \le x < 2\pi$:

$\cos(x - y)\cos y - \sin(x - y)\sin y = 0$

(a) No solutions   (b) $\dfrac{\pi}{2}, \dfrac{3\pi}{2}$ (c) $0, \pi$

(d) $0, \dfrac{\pi}{2}, \pi, \dfrac{3\pi}{2}$ (e) None of these

2—M—Answer: b

33. Find all solutions in the interval $[0,\ 2\pi)$: $\quad 3\sin(2t-\pi)=3$

1—O—Answer:

$$3\sin(2t-\pi)=3$$

$$\sin(2t-\pi)=1$$

$$\sin 2t\cos\pi - \cos 2t\sin\pi = 1$$

$$\sin 2t(-1) - \cos 2t(0) = 1$$

$$-\sin 2t = 1$$

$$\sin 2t = -1$$

$$2t = \frac{3\pi}{2} + 2n\pi$$

$$t = \frac{3\pi}{4} + n\pi \ \Rightarrow\ t = \frac{3\pi}{4},\ \frac{7\pi}{4}$$

34. Verify the following identity used in calculus: $\quad \dfrac{\sin(x+h)-\sin x}{h} = \dfrac{\sin x(\cos h - 1)}{h} + \dfrac{\cos x\sin h}{h}$

1—O—Answer: $\dfrac{\sin(x+h)-\sin x}{h} = \dfrac{\sin x\cos h + \cos x\sin h - \sin x}{h}$

$$= \frac{\sin x\cos h - \sin x + \cos x\sin h}{h}$$

$$= \frac{\sin x(\cos h - 1) + \cos x\sin h}{h}$$

$$= \frac{\sin x(\cos h - 1)}{h} + \frac{\cos x\sin h}{h}$$

35. The drive system of a compact disc player uses an equation $\tan x = \dfrac{\sin y}{r+\cos y}$, where r is the ratio of two gears. Show that $r = \dfrac{\sin(y-x)}{\sin x}$.

1—O—Answer:

$$\tan x = \frac{\sin y}{r+\cos y}$$

$$\tan x(r+\cos y) = \sin y$$

$$r+\cos y = \frac{\sin y}{\tan x}$$

$$r = \frac{\sin y}{\tan x} - \cos y$$

$$r = \frac{\sin y}{\dfrac{\sin x}{\cos x}} - \cos y$$

$$r = \sin y\frac{\cos x}{\sin x} - \cos y$$

$$r = \frac{\sin y\cos x - \cos y\sin x}{\sin x}$$

$$r = \frac{\sin(y-x)}{\sin x}$$

36. For picking up heavy machinery, a type of jack called a screw jack can be used. The formula $aF = Wr\tan(x - \theta)$ is used, where F is the effort necessary to obtain equilibrium with pitch angle, x, and load, W. If the pitch angle, x, is $\dfrac{\pi}{4}$, express F as a function of θ (the angle of friction).

1—O—Answer: $aF = Wr\tan\left(\dfrac{\pi}{4} - \theta\right)$

$$aF = Wr\dfrac{\left(\tan\dfrac{\pi}{4} - \tan\theta\right)}{\left(1 + \tan\dfrac{\pi}{4}\tan\theta\right)}$$

$$aF = Wr\dfrac{(1 - \tan\theta)}{(1 + (1)\tan\theta)}$$

$$aF = Wr\dfrac{1 - \tan\theta}{1 + \tan\theta}$$

$$F = \dfrac{Wr}{a} \cdot \dfrac{1 - \tan\theta}{1 + \tan\theta}$$

37. Sketch the graph of $y = 1 + \cos\left(x - \dfrac{\pi}{2}\right)$. Simplify the right hand side and verify your result graphically.

2—O—Answer:

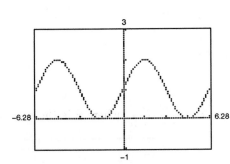

$$y = 1 + \cos\left(x - \dfrac{\pi}{2}\right)$$

$$y = 1 + \cos x\cos\dfrac{\pi}{2} + \sin x\sin\dfrac{\pi}{2}$$

$$y = 1 + \cos x(0) + \sin x(1)$$

$$y = 1 + \sin x$$

38. Sketch the graph of $y = 1 + \sin(x + \pi)$. Simplify the right hand side and verify your result graphically.

2—O—Answer:

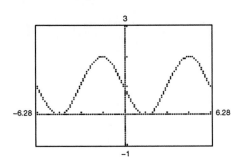

$$y = 1 + \sin(x + \pi)$$

$$y = 1 + \sin x\cos\pi + \cos x\sin\pi$$

$$y = 1 + \sin x(-1) + \cos x(0)$$

$$y = 1 - \sin x$$

7.5 | Multiple-Angle and Product-to-Sum Formulas

1. Find all solutions in the interval $[0,\ 2\pi)$: $\cos 2x + \sin x = 0$

(a) $0,\ \dfrac{\pi}{4},\ \dfrac{3\pi}{4}$

(b) $\dfrac{\pi}{2},\ \dfrac{7\pi}{6},\ \dfrac{11\pi}{6}$

(c) $\dfrac{\pi}{6},\ \dfrac{5\pi}{6},\ \dfrac{3\pi}{2}$

(d) $0,\ \dfrac{\pi}{4},\ \dfrac{3\pi}{4},\ \dfrac{5\pi}{4},\ \dfrac{7\pi}{4}$

(e) None of these

1—M—Answer: b

2. Find all solutions in the interval $[0,\ 2\pi)$: $\sin 2x + \sin x = 0$

(a) $\dfrac{\pi}{2},\ \dfrac{3\pi}{2},\ \dfrac{2\pi}{3},\ \dfrac{4\pi}{3}$

(b) $0,\ \dfrac{\pi}{3},\ \pi,\ \dfrac{5\pi}{3}$

(c) $0,\ \dfrac{\pi}{3}$

(d) $0,\ \pi,\ \dfrac{2\pi}{3},\ \dfrac{4\pi}{3}$

(e) None of these

1—M—Answer: d

3. Find all solutions in the interval $[0,\ 2\pi)$: $\cos^2 x - \cos 2x = 0$

(a) $0,\ \dfrac{\pi}{2},\ \dfrac{3\pi}{2}$

(b) $0,\ \pi$

(c) ± 1

(d) $\dfrac{\pi}{6},\ \dfrac{5\pi}{6},\ \dfrac{7\pi}{6},\ \dfrac{11\pi}{6}$

(e) None of these

1—M—Answer: b

4. Find all solutions in the interval $[0,\ 2\pi)$: $2\sin 3x \cos 3x = 1$

(a) $\dfrac{\pi}{18},\ \dfrac{\pi}{9}$

(b) $\dfrac{\pi}{12}$

(c) $\dfrac{\pi}{12},\ \dfrac{5\pi}{12},\ \dfrac{3\pi}{4},\ \dfrac{13\pi}{12},\ \dfrac{17\pi}{12},\ \dfrac{7\pi}{4}$

(d) $\dfrac{\pi}{18},\ \dfrac{\pi}{9},\ \dfrac{5\pi}{18},\ \dfrac{5\pi}{9}$

(e) None of these

1—M—Answer: c

5. Rewrite the function and sketch its graph:

$f(x) = 6\cos^2 x - 3$

1—O—Answer: $f(x) = 3(2\cos^2 x - 1)$

$= 3\cos 2x$

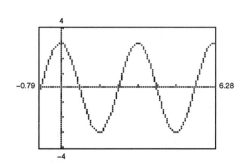

6. Rewrite the function and sketch its graph:

$$g(x) = (1 - \sqrt{2}\sin x)(1 + \sqrt{2}\sin x)$$

> **1—O—Answer:** $g(x) = (1 - \sqrt{2}\sin x)(1 + \sqrt{2}\sin x)$
>
> $$= 1 - 2\sin^2 x$$
>
> $$= \cos 2x$$

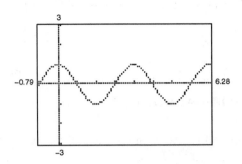

7. Rewrite the function and sketch its graph:

$$f(x) = 4\sin x \cos x(1 - 2\sin^2 x)$$

> **1—O—Answer:** $f(x) = 4\sin x \cos x(1 - 2\sin^2 x)$
>
> $$= 4\sin x \cos x \cos 2x$$
>
> $$= 2(2\sin x \cos x)\cos 2x$$
>
> $$= 2\sin 2x \cos 2x$$
>
> $$= \sin 4x$$

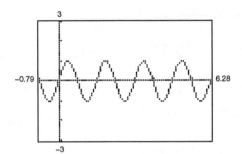

8. Rewrite the function and sketch its graph:

$$g(x) = \frac{\sin 3x}{\sin x} + \frac{\cos 3x}{\cos x}$$

> **2—O—Answer:** $g(x) = \dfrac{\sin 3x}{\sin x} + \dfrac{\cos 3x}{\cos x}$
>
> $$= \frac{\sin 3x \cos x + \sin x \cos 3x}{\sin x \cos x}$$
>
> $$= \frac{\sin(4x)}{\sin x \cos x}$$
>
> $$= \frac{2\sin 2x \cos 2x}{\sin x \cos x}$$
>
> $$= \frac{2(2\sin x \cos x)\cos 2x}{\sin x \cos x}$$
>
> $$= 4\cos 2x$$

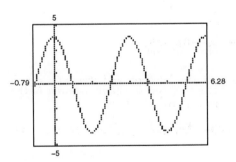

9. Given $\cos u = -\dfrac{4}{7}$, find $\cos 2u$. (Assume $\pi < u < 3\pi/2$.)

    (a) $\dfrac{\sqrt{33}}{7}$ (b) $-\dfrac{17}{49}$ (c) $-\dfrac{4\sqrt{33}}{14}$ (d) $-\dfrac{33}{49}$ (e) None of these

> **1—M—Answer:** b

10. Given $\cos\theta = -\dfrac{7}{9}$ and $\tan\theta < 0$, find $\sin 2\theta$.

    (a) $-\dfrac{14}{9}$ (b) $-\dfrac{56\sqrt{2}}{81}$ (c) $-\dfrac{32}{81}$ (d) $\dfrac{49}{81}$ (e) None of these

    1—M—Answer: b

11. Given $\tan\theta = \dfrac{3}{4}$ and $\sin\theta < 0$, find $\tan 2\theta$.

    (a) $\dfrac{1}{3}$ (b) $\dfrac{\sqrt{5}}{3}$ (c) $\dfrac{5}{9}$ (d) $\dfrac{24}{7}$ (e) None of these

    1—M—Answer: d

12. Given $\sin x = -\dfrac{1}{8}$ and $\tan x < 0$, find $\sin 2x$.

    (a) $-\dfrac{3\sqrt{7}}{32}$ (b) $-\dfrac{\sqrt{65}}{32}$ (c) $\dfrac{3\sqrt{7}}{32}$ (d) $-\dfrac{1}{4}$ (e) None of these

    1—M—Answer: a

13. Rewrite in terms of the first power of the cosine: $\sin^4 2x$

    (a) $\frac{1}{2}(1 - \cos 4x)$ (b) $\frac{1}{4}(1 - 2\cos 4x + \cos 16x)$ (c) $\frac{1}{4}(1 - \cos 4x)$

    (d) $\frac{1}{8}(3 - 4\cos 4x + \cos 8x)$ (e) None of these

    1—M—Answer: d

14. Rewrite in terms of the first power of the cosine: $\sin^2 x \cos^2 2x$

    (a) $\frac{1}{4}(1 - \cos 2x + \cos 4x - \cos 2x \cos 4x)$ (b) $\frac{1}{4}(1 - \cos 2x + \cos 4x - \cos 8x)$

    (c) $\frac{1}{4}(1 + \cos 2x - \cos 8x)$ (d) $\frac{1}{4}(1 + \cos 2x - \cos 4x - \cos 2x \cos 4x)$

    (e) None of these

    1—M—Answer: a

15. Rewrite in terms of the first power of the cosine: $\cos^2 2x \sin^2 2x$

    1—O—Answer: $\dfrac{1 - \cos 8x}{8}$

16. Rewrite in terms of the first power of the cosine: $\tan^4 2x$

    1—O—Answer: $\dfrac{3 - 4\cos 4x + \cos 8x}{3 + 4\cos 4x + \cos 8x}$

17. Find the exact value of $\sin \dfrac{7\pi}{12}$. $\left(\text{Use the fact that } \dfrac{1}{2}\left(\dfrac{7\pi}{6}\right) = \dfrac{7\pi}{12}.\right)$

(a) $\dfrac{\sqrt{2 - \sqrt{3}}}{2}$
(b) $\dfrac{\sqrt{2 + \sqrt{3}}}{2}$
(c) $-\dfrac{\sqrt{2 + \sqrt{3}}}{2}$

(d) $-\dfrac{\sqrt{2 - \sqrt{3}}}{2}$
(e) None of these

1—M—Answer: b

18. Find the exact value of $\cos 157°30'$. $\left(\text{Use the fact that } \dfrac{1}{2}(315°) = 157°30'.\right)$

(a) $\dfrac{\sqrt{2 + \sqrt{2}}}{2}$
(b) $-\dfrac{\sqrt{1 + \sqrt{2}}}{2}$
(c) $-\dfrac{\sqrt{2 - \sqrt{2}}}{2}$

(d) $-\dfrac{\sqrt{2 + \sqrt{2}}}{2}$
(e) None of these

1—M—Answer: d

19. Given $\sin u = -\dfrac{8}{13}$, find $\cos\left(\dfrac{u}{2}\right)$. $\left(\text{Assume } \dfrac{3\pi}{2} < u < 2\pi.\right)$

(a) $-\sqrt{\dfrac{13 - \sqrt{105}}{26}}$
(b) $-\sqrt{\dfrac{13 + \sqrt{105}}{26}}$
(c) $-\sqrt{\dfrac{13 - \sqrt{233}}{26}}$

(d) $\sqrt{\dfrac{13 + \sqrt{105}}{26}}$
(e) None of these

2—M—Answer: b

20. Given $\tan u = -\dfrac{1}{3}$, and $\sin u < 0$, find $\sin\left(\dfrac{u}{2}\right)$. $\left(\text{Assume } 0 \leq u < 2\pi.\right)$

(a) $-\sqrt{\dfrac{10 + 3\sqrt{10}}{20}}$
(b) $\sqrt{\dfrac{10 - 3\sqrt{10}}{20}}$
(c) $\sqrt{\dfrac{10 + 3\sqrt{10}}{20}}$

(d) $-\sqrt{\dfrac{10 - 3\sqrt{10}}{20}}$
(e) None of these

2—M—Answer: b

21. Given $\cos x = -\dfrac{3}{7}$ and $\dfrac{\pi}{2} < x < \pi$, find $\cos\left(\dfrac{x}{2}\right)$.

1—O—Answer: $\dfrac{\sqrt{14}}{7}$

22. Given $\cos x = \dfrac{2}{3}$ and $\dfrac{3\pi}{2} < x < 2\pi$, find $\cos\left(\dfrac{x}{2}\right)$.

1—O—Answer: $-\dfrac{\sqrt{30}}{6}$

23. Simplify: $y^2 = \sqrt{\dfrac{1 - \cos 16x}{2}}$

   (a) $y^2 = \sin 32x$ (b) $y^2 = \cos 32x$ (c) $y^2 = \sin 8x$

   (d) $y^2 = \cos 8x$ (e) None of these

   1—M—Answer: c

24. Simplify: $\sqrt{\dfrac{4 + 4\cos 2x}{2}}$

   (a) $2\cos x$ (b) $\cos 4x$ (c) $2\sin x$

   (d) $\sqrt{2}\cos x$ (e) None of these

   1—M—Answer: a

25. Rewrite as a sum: $9\sin 3x \cos 7x$

   (a) $\frac{9}{2}(\cos 4x + \cos 10x)$ (b) $\frac{9}{2}(\sin 10x + \sin 4x)$ (c) $\frac{9}{2}(\cos 4x - \cos 10x)$

   (d) $\frac{9}{2}(\sin 10x - \sin 4x)$ (e) None of these

   1—M—Answer: d

26. Rewrite as a sum: $\sin 3x \cos 4y$

   (a) $\frac{1}{2}[\sin(3x + 4y) + \sin(3x - 4y)]$ (b) $\frac{1}{2}[\sin(3x + 4y) - \sin(3x - 4y)]$

   (c) $2[\cos(3x + 4y) + \cos(3x - 4y)]$ (d) $2[\sin(3x - 4y) + \cos(3x - 4y)]$

   (e) None of these

   1—M—Answer: a

27. Rewrite as a sum: $\sin 7x \sin 3x$

   (a) $\frac{1}{2}(\sin 4x + \cos 10x)$ (b) $\frac{1}{2}(\sin 10x + \sin 4x)$ (c) $\frac{1}{2}(\cos 4x - \cos 10x)$

   (d) $\sin 2x + \cos 5x$ (e) None of these

   1—M—Answer: c

28. Rewrite as a sum: $\dfrac{1}{4}\cos 12x \cos 4x$

   1—O—Answer: $\dfrac{\cos 8x + \cos 16x}{8}$

29. Rewrite as a sum: $3\cos 5x \sin(-2x)$

   1—O—Answer: $\dfrac{3(\sin 3x - \sin 7x)}{2}$

30. Rewrite as a product: $\sin x + \sin 3x$

   (a) $2\sin 2x \cos x$ (b) $-2\sin x \cos 2x$ (c) $-2\cos 2x \cos x$

   (d) $2\sin 2x \sin x$ (e) None of these

   1—M—Answer: a

31. Rewrite as a product: $\sin 7\theta - \sin 3\theta$

   (a) $2\sin 5\theta \cos 2\theta$ (b) $2\cos 5\theta \sin 2\theta$ (c) $2\cos 5\theta \cos 2\theta$

   (d) $-2\sin 5\theta \cos 2\theta$ (e) None of these

   1—M—Answer: b

32. Rewrite as a product: $\cos(x + 2y) - \cos(x - 2y)$

   1—O—Answer: $-2\sin x \sin 2y$

33. Rewrite as a sum: $\sin\left(\dfrac{5x + 3y}{2}\right)\cos\left(\dfrac{5x - 3y}{2}\right)$

   (a) $\dfrac{1}{2}(\cos 5x - \cos 3y)$ (b) $\dfrac{1}{2}(\sin 5x - \sin 3y)$ (c) $\dfrac{1}{2}(\cos 5x = \cos 3y)$

   (d) $\dfrac{1}{2}(\sin 5x + \sin 3y)$ (e) None of these

   1—M—Answer: d

34. Find all solutions in the interval $[0,\ 2\pi)$: $\sin 5x + \sin x = \sin 3x$

   2—O—Answer:

   $$\sin 5x - \sin 3x + \sin x = 0$$
   $$2\cos\left(\frac{5x + 3x}{2}\right)\sin\left(\frac{5x - 3x}{2}\right) + \sin x = 0$$
   $$2\cos 4x \sin x + \sin x = 0$$
   $$\sin x(2\cos 4x + 1) = 0$$
   $$\sin x = 0 \text{ or } 2\cos 4x = -1$$
   $$x = 0,\ \pi \quad \cos 4x = -\frac{1}{2}$$
   $$4x = \frac{2\pi}{3},\ \frac{4\pi}{3}$$
   $$x = \frac{\pi}{6},\ \frac{\pi}{3},\ \frac{2\pi}{3},\ \frac{5\pi}{6},\ \frac{7\pi}{6},\ \frac{4\pi}{3},\ \frac{5\pi}{3},\ \frac{11\pi}{6}$$
   $$x = 0,\ \frac{\pi}{6},\ \frac{\pi}{3},\ \frac{2\pi}{3},\ \frac{5\pi}{6},\ \pi,\ \frac{7\pi}{6},\ \frac{4\pi}{3},\ \frac{5\pi}{3},\ \frac{11\pi}{6}$$

35. Find all solutions in the interval $[0,\ 2\pi)$: $\cos 4x + \cos 2x = 0$

   1—O—Answer:

   $$\cos 4x + \cos 2x = 0$$
   $$2\cos\left(\frac{4x + 2x}{2}\right)\cos\left(\frac{4x - 2x}{2}\right) = 0$$
   $$2\cos 3x \cos x = 0$$
   $$\cos 3x \cos x = 0$$
   $$\cos 3x = 0 \text{ or } \cos x = 0$$
   $$3x = \frac{\pi}{2}, \frac{3\pi}{2} \qquad x = \frac{\pi}{2}, \frac{3\pi}{2}$$
   $$x = \frac{\pi}{6},\ \frac{\pi}{2},\ \frac{5\pi}{6},\ \frac{7\pi}{6},\ \frac{3\pi}{2},\ \frac{11\pi}{6}$$

36. The expression $\sqrt{\sin^2 x + (1 - \cos x)^2}$ is used in the study of gases. Simplify this expression using a half angle formula.

1—O—Answer:
$$
\begin{aligned}
\sqrt{\sin^2 x + (1 - \cos x)^2} &= \sqrt{\sin^2 x + 1 - 2\cos x + \cos^2 x} \\
&= \sqrt{\sin^2 x + \cos^2 x + 1 - 2\cos x} \\
&= \sqrt{1 + 1 - 2\cos x} \\
&= \sqrt{2 - 2\cos x} \\
&= \sqrt{2(1 - \cos x)} \\
&= \sqrt{\tfrac{2}{2}2(1 - \cos x)} \\
&= \sqrt{\frac{4(1 - \cos x)}{2}} \\
&= 2\sqrt{\frac{1 - \cos x}{2}} \\
&= 2\sin\left(\frac{x}{2}\right)
\end{aligned}
$$

37. In the study of electronics the function $f(t) = \sin(200t + \pi) + \sin(200t - \pi)$ is used. First simplify the function using a sum-to-product formula, then graph the simplified function.

1—O—Answer:
$$ f(x) = \sin(200t + \pi) + \sin(200t - \pi) $$
$$ f(x) = 2\sin\left[\frac{(200t + \pi) + (200t - \pi)}{2}\right]\cos\left[\frac{(200t + \pi) - (200t - \pi)}{2}\right] $$
$$ f(x) = 2(\sin 200t)(\cos \pi) $$
$$ f(x) = 2(\sin 200t)(-1) $$
$$ f(x) = -2\sin 200t $$

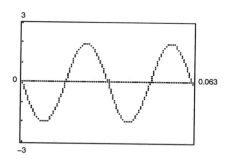

CHAPTER EIGHT
Additional Topics in Trigonometry

8.1 Law of Sines

1. Given triangle with $A = 41°$, $B = 72°$, and $a = 15$, find c.

    (a) 19.6   (b) 10.7   (c) 21.0   (d) 7.8   (e) None of these

    1—M—Answer: c

2. Given triangle with $B = 87°$, $C = 24°$, and $a = 113$, find b.

    (a) 120.9   (b) 142.7   (c) 49.2   (d) 94.4   (e) None of these

    1—M—Answer: a

3. Given triangle with $A = 20°$, $C = 110°$, and $a = 5$, find b.

    (a) 2.2   (b) 50.0   (c) 11.2   (d) 13.7   (e) None of these

    1—M—Answer: c

4. Given triangle with $A = 10°$, $B = 30°$, and $b = 14$, find c.

    (a) 27.4   (b) 18.0   (c) 65.3   (d) 34.1   (e) None of these

    1—M—Answer: b

5. Given triangle with $A = 42°$, $C = 88°$, and $a = 71$, find b.

    (a) 87.6   (b) 50.0   (c) 20.3   (d) 81.3   (e) None of these

    1—M—Answer: d

6. Given triangle with $C = 72°$, $A = 15°$, and $b = 342.6$, find a.

    (a) 1258.92   (b) 88.79   (c) 6323.1   (d) 326.28   (e) None of these

    1—M—Answer: b

7. Given triangle with $A = 39°$, $B = 106°$, and $c = 78$, find a.

    (a) 71.1   (b) 85.6   (c) 74.0   (d) 82.2   (e) None of these

    1—M—Answer: b

8. Given triangle with $A = 102°$, $B = 23°$, and $c = 576.1$, find a.

    (a) 687.9   (b) 208.8   (c) 1442.2   (d) 274.8   (e) None of these

    1—M—Answer: a

9. Given a triangle with $A = 61°$, $B = 49°$, and $c = 5396$, find a, b, and C.

   1—O—Answer: $C = 70°$, $a = 5022.33$, $b = 4333.77$

10. Given triangle $A = 47°$, $B = 63°$, and $c = 123$, find a.

    (a) 88.6   (b) 95.7   (c) 82.6   (d) 112.1   (e) None of these

    1—M—Answer: b

11. Given triangle $a = 12$, $b = 19$, and $A = 82°$, find c.

    (a) 16.2 and 1.4   (b) 4.3   (c) No solution

    (d) 7.6   (e) None of these

    1—M—Answer: c

12. Given triangle $a = 123$, $c = 86$, and $C = 52°$, find b.

    (a) No solution   (b) 96.9   (c) 71.2, 8.4

    (d) 74.4   (e) None of these

    1—M—Answer: a

13. Given triangle $b = 120$, $c = 142$, and $B = 78°$, find a.

    (a) 138.9   (b) 71.6, 113.4   (c) 157.8

    (d) No solution   (e) None of these

    1—M—Answer: d

14. Given triangle $a = 27$, $b = 46$, and $A = 71°$, find B.

    (a) No solution   (b) 1.6°   (c) 100.0°

    (d) 87.2°, 102.1°   (e) None of these

    1—M—Answer: a

15. Given triangle $a = 83$, $b = 98$, and $A = 110°$, find C.

    (a) 57°   (b) 41°   (c) No solution

    (d) 62°, 28°   (e) None of these

    1—M—Answer: c

16. Given triangle with $C = 80.3°$, $c = 52.7$, and $b = 41.6$, find B.

    (a) 77.7°   (b) 82.4°   (c) 51.1°   (d) 0.8°   (e) None of these

    1—M—Answer: c

17. Given triangle $a = 18$, $b = 23$, and $B = 97°$, find C.

(a) 51.0°   (b) 32.0°   (c) 39.2°   (d) 13.8°   (e) None of these

1—M—Answer: b

18. Given triangle $a = 56$, $b = 71$, and $B = 100°$, find c.

(a) 29.0   (b) 44.2   (c) 47.9   (d) 51.1   (e) None of these

2—M—Answer: a

19. Given triangle $b = 71$, $c = 63$, and $B = 110°$, find a.

(a) 38.7   (b) 21.2   (c) 15.4   (d) 17.6   (e) None of these

2—M—Answer: d

20. Given triangle $a = 17$, $c = 51$, and $C = 100°$, find b.

(a) 47.9   (b) 45.2   (c) 41.7   (d) 35.2   (e) None of these

2—M—Answer: b

21. Given triangle $a = 146$, $b = 148$, and $A = 78°$, find B.

(a) 82.5°, 97.5°   (b) 4.5°, 19.5°   (c) 82.5°

(d) No solution   (e) None of these

1—M—Answer: a

22. Given triangle $a = 112$, $b = 130$, and $A = 56°$, find c.

(a) 61.2   (b) 42.2 and 103.2   (c) 98.1

(d) No solution   (e) None of these

2—M—Answer: b

23. Given a triangle with $B = 61°$, $c = 18$, and $b = 17$, find A. If there are two solutions, find both A_1 and A_2.

(a) 6.8°, 173.2°   (b) 51.2°   (c) 112.2°

(d) 6.8°, 51.2°   (e) None of these

1—M—Answer: d

24. Given a triangle with $A = 74°$, $a = 59.2$, and $c = 60.3$, find the two possible values of B.

(a) 78.3°, 101.7°   (b) 4.3°, 27.7°   (c) 73.7°, 106.3°

(d) 32.3°, 0.3°   (e) None of these

1—M—Answer: b

25. Given a triangle with $B = 56°$, $a = 98$ and $b = 85$, find the two possible values of C.

1—O—Answer: $C = 51.09°$ or $16.91°$

26. Given a triangle with $A = 12°$, $a = 12$, and $c = 37$, find the two possible values of b.

    (a) 3.04, 14.95   (b) 44.30, 45.40   (c) 7.57, 10.85

    (d) 26.98, 45.40   (e) None of these

    2—M—Answer: d

27. Given a triangle with $c = 24.19$, $a = 91.6$, and $B = 37°$, find the area.

    (a) 1769.6 square units   (b) 666.8 square units   (c) 1107.9 square units

    (d) 1333.5 square units   (e) None of these

    1—M—Answer: b

28. Given a triangle with $a = 72$, $b = 51$, and $A = 27°$, find the area.

    (a) 833.5 square units   (b) 1315.3 square units   (c) 1635.9 square units

    (d) 2630.6 square units   (e) None of these

    2—M—Answer: b

29. Given a triangle with $A = 98°$, $a = 27$, and $b = 16$, find the area.

    (a) 155.56 square units   (b) 149.86 square units   (c) 311.11 square units

    (d) 213.90 square units   (e) None of these

    2—M—Answer: a

30. Given a triangle with $A = 37°$, $B = 78°$, and $c = 250$, find the area.

    2—O—Answer: $20,297.5$ square units

31. Given a triangle with $A = 71°$, $b = 10$, and $c = 19$, find the area.

    1—O—Answer: 89.8 square units

32. Given a triangle with $c = 634$, $b = 600$, and $B = 78°$, find the number of solutions for a.

    (a) 0   (b) 1   (c) 2   (d) 3   (e) 6

    1—M—Answer: a

33. Determine the number of solutions for each of the following triangles.

    (a) $C = 58°$, $c = 50$, $a = 67$

    (b) $A = 107°$, $b = 17$, $a = 25$

    (c) $B = 27°$, $a = 78$, $b = 28$

    1—O—Answer: (a) 0 solutions   (b) 1 solution   (c) 0 solutions

34. A television antenna sits on the roof. Two 78-foot guy wires are positioned on opposite sides of the antenna. The angle of elevation each makes with the ground is 23°. How far apart are the ends of the two guy wires?

(a) 71.8 feet   (b) 76.3 feet   (c) 143.6 feet

(d) 152.6 feet   (e) None of these

1—M—Answer: c

35. From firetower A a fire with a bearing N 78° E is sighted. The same fire is sighted from tower B at N 51° W. Tower B is 70 miles east of tower A. How far is it from tower A to the fire?

2—O—Answer: 56.7 miles

36. A surveyor wishes to find the distance from a rock on the east side of a river to a tree on the opposite bank. On the east side of the river he locates a second rock 135 feet from the first one. From each rock he measures the angle between the line connecting the two rocks and the tree. The angle from the first rock is 87° and from the second rock is 82°. Find the desired distance.

2—O—Answer: 700.6 feet

37. Find the height of a giant helium balloon used in a Thanksgiving Day parade given that two guy wires are attached as shown in the figure at the right.

2—O—Answer: 115.9 ft

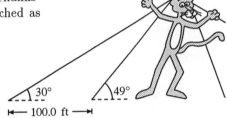

30°   49°

├── 100.0 ft ──┤

38. Two hunters, Paul, P, and Richard, R, are sitting in tree stands 100 yards apart. If Paul spots a deer, D, at an angle $RPD = 25°50'$ and Richard spots the same deer at an angle $PRD = 32°45'$, how far is the deer from Paul? From Richard?

2—O—Answer: 63.4 yards from Paul
                51.5 yards from Richard

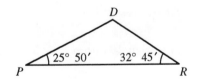

8.2 Law of Cosines

1. Given a triangle with $a = 80$, $b = 51$, and $c = 113$, find C.

   (a) 117.5°   (b) 27.5°   (c) 157.4°   (d) 62.5°   (e) None of these

   1—M—Answer: a

2. Given a triangle with $a = 17$, $b = 39$, and $c = 50$, find A.

   (a) 16.88°   (b) 73.12°   (c) 163.12°   (d) 106.88°   (e) None of these

   1—M—Answer: a

3. Given a triangle with $a = 117$, $b = 230$, and $c = 185$, find B.

   (a) 96.6°   (b) 6.6°   (c) 53.0°   (d) 37.0°   (e) None of these

   1—M—Answer: a

4. Given a triangle with $a = 78$, $b = 15$, and $c = 91$, find A, B, and C.

   1—O—Answer: $A = 27.5°$, $B = 5.1°$, $C = 147.4°$

5. Given a triangle with $a = 135$, $b = 71.6$, and $c = 69$, find B.

   1—O—Answer: 16.54°

6. Given a triangle with $a = 32$, $b = 47$, and $c = 25$, find C.

   (a) 110.5°   (b) 39.6°   (c) 60.1°   (d) 29.9°   (e) None of these

   1—M—Answer: d

7. Given a triangle with $a = 11$, $b = 12$, and $c = 13$, find A.

   (a) 38.0°   (b) 52.0°   (c) 68.7°   (d) 59.3°   (e) None of these

   1—M—Answer: b

8. Given a triangle with $a = 7$, $b = 9$, and $c = 15$, find B.

   (a) 23.2°   (b) 66.8°   (c) 113.2°   (d) 138.9°   (e) None of these

   1—M—Answer: a

9. Given a triangle with $a = 19$, $b = 4$, and $c = 22$, find C.

   (a) 117.4°   (b) 132.1°   (c) 87.2°   (d) 99.7°   (e) None of these

   1—M—Answer: e

10. Given a triangle with $a = 53$, $b = 94$, and $c = 87$, find A.

    (a) 80.3°   (b) 65.9°   (c) 33.8°   (d) 48.6°   (e) None of these

    1—M—Answer: c

11. Given a triangle with $a = 2178$, $B = 23°$, $c = 1719$, and find b.

    (a) 2184.9   (b) 805,937.8   (c) 2062.1

    (d) 897.7   (e) None of these

    1—M—Answer: d

12. Given triangle with $B = 81°$, $a = 15$, and $c = 72$, find b.

    (a) 57.2   (b) 3275.6   (c) 5071   (d) 71.2   (e) None of these

    1—M—Answer: d

13. Given a triangle with $A = 58°20'$, $b = 23$, and $c = 18$, find a.

    (a) 20.41   (b) 20.45   (c) 25.21   (d) 35.88   (e) None of these

    1—M—Answer: b

14. Given triangle with $A = 38°$, $b = 22$, and $c = 98$, find a.

    1—O—Answer: $a = 81.79$

15. Given the triangle to the right, find B.

    1—O—Answer: $B = 150.62°$

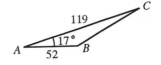

16. Given a triangle with $a = 12$, $c = 21$, and $B = 72°$, find C.

    (a) 69.2°   (b) 74.6°   (c) 81.0°   (d) 33.4°   (e) None of these

    2—M—Answer: b

17. Given a triangle with $b = 37$, $c = 96$, and $A = 23°$, find C.

    (a) 127.4°   (b) 13.1°   (c) 143.9°   (d) 36.1°   (e) None of these

    2—M—Answer: c

18. Given a triangle with $a = 32$, $c = 41$, and $B = 22°$, find C.

    (a) 98.2°   (b) 111.4°   (c) 46.6   (d) 68.6°   (e) None of these

    2—M—Answer: b

19. Given a triangle with $a = 15$, $b = 24$, and $C = 45°$, find B.

    (a) 38.4°   (b) 83.4°   (c) 79.2°   (d) 96.6°   (e) None of these

    2—M—Answer: d

20. Given a triangle with $a = 16$, $b = 19$, and $C = 63°$, find A.

    (a) 66.5°   (b) 50.5°   (c) 23.5°   (d) 94°   (e) None of these

    1—M—Answer: b

21. Given a triangle with $a = 80$, $b = 90$, and $c = 110$, find the area.

    (a) 12,600,000   (b) 69,135.8   (c) 262.9

    (d) 3549.6   (e) None of these

    1—M—Answer: d

22. Given a triangle with $a = 121$, $b = 82$, and $c = 90$, find the area.

    (a) 9922   (b) 4961   (c) 523.2

    (d) 3689.7   (e) None of these

    1—M—Answer: d

23. Given a triangle with $a = 78$, $b = 15$, and $c = 91$, find the area.

    1—O—Answer: 314.9 square units

24. Given a triangle with $a = 36$, $b = 91$, and $c = 72$, find the area.

    1—O—Answer: 1215.27 square units

25. Use Heron's Formula to find the area of the triangle with $a = 23$, $b = 17$, and $c = 28$.

    (a) 195.3   (b) 15.1   (c) 104.7   (d) 195.5   (e) None of these

    1—M—Answer: a

26. Use Heron's Formula to find the area of the triangle with $a = 16$, $b = 37$, and $c = 32$.

    (a) 255.0   (b) 256.0   (c) 252.7   (d) 258.0   (e) None of these

    1—M—Answer: a

27. Use Heron's Formula to find the area of the triangle with $a = 21$, $b = 22$, and $c = 23$.

    (a) 208.7   (b) 231.0   (c) 193.6   (d) 205.2   (e) None of these

    1—M—Answer: a

28. Use Heron's Formula to find the area of the triangle with $a = 42$, $b = 51$, and $c = 57$.

    (a) 1860   (b) 3136   (c) 1034   (d) 1071   (e) None of these

    1—M—Answer: c

29. Use Heron's Formula to find the area of the triangle with $a = 11$, $b = 27$, and $c = 19$.

    (a) 7107.2   (b) 84.3   (c) 1728.9

    (d) 4722.3   (e) None of these

    1—M—Answer: b

30. Use Heron's Formula to find the area of the triangle with $a = 41.6$, $b = 54.2$, and $c = 47.1$.

    (a) 946.5   (b) 1276.4   (c) 1006.5

    (d) 1127.1   (e) None of these

    1—M—Answer: a

31. Ship A is 72 miles from a lighthouse on the shore. Its bearing from the lighthouse is N 15° E. Ship B is 81 miles from the same lighthouse. Its bearing from the lighthouse is N 52° E. Find the number of miles between the two ships.

    (a) 84.57   (b) 44.44   (c) 49.29   (d) 90.75   (e) None of these

    2—M—Answer: c

32. Determine the number of acres in a triangular parcel of land if the lengths of the sides measure 1507 feet, 1750 feet, and 970 feet. There are 43,560 square feet in 1 acre.

    (a) 15.9A   (b) 21.7A   (c) 19.2A   (d) 16.8A   (e) None of these

    1—M—Answer: d

33. Determine the number of acres in a triangular parcel of land if the lengths of the sides measure 1702 feet, 4021 feet, and 4000 feet. There are 43,560 square feet in 1 acre.

    (a) 90.2A   (b) 76.6A   (c) 89.5A   (d) 46.2A   (e) None of these

    1—M—Answer: b

34. In order to determine the distance between two aircraft, a tracking station continuously determines the distance to each aircraft and the angle α between them. Determine the distance between the planes when $\alpha = 28°$, $b = 71$ miles and $c = 36$ miles.

    1—O—Answer: 42.7 miles

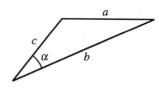

35. A trigonometry class wants to determine the length of a pond near the school. From a point, A, they measure the distance to each end of the pond and the angle between these two sides. What is the approximate length of the pond?

    (a) 352 feet   (b) 298 feet

    (c) 407 feet   (d) 331 feet

    (e) None of these

    2—M—Answer: d

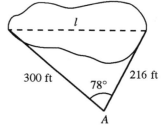

36. The airline distance from Curtis City to Clearfield is 350 miles. It is 620 miles from Curtis City to Spinville and 495 miles from Clearfield to Spinville. Find the angle between the routes from Clearfield.

    2—O—Answer: 92.8°

37. A group of scientist wants to measure the length of a crater caused by a meteorite crashing into the earth. From a point, O, they measure the distance to each end of the crater and the angle between these two sides. What is the approximate length of the crater?

    2—O—Answer: 1197 ft

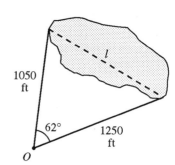

8.3 Vectors in the Plane

1. A vector **v** has initial point $(3, 7)$ and terminal point $(3, -2)$. Find its component form.

   (a) $\langle 0,\ 9 \rangle$ (b) $\langle 9,\ 0 \rangle$ (c) $\langle 0,\ -9 \rangle$

   (d) $\langle -9,\ 0 \rangle$ (e) None of these

   1—M—Answer: c

2. Find the component form of the vector at the right.

   (a) $\langle -2,\ 4 \rangle$ (b) $\langle 2,\ -4 \rangle$

   (c) $\langle -6,\ -6 \rangle$ (d) $\langle 6,\ 6 \rangle$

   (e) None of these

   1—M—Answer: b

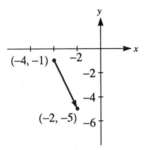

3. A vector **v** has initial point $(-2,\ 1)$ and terminal point $(7,\ 6)$. Find the component form of vector **v**.

   (a) $\langle 9,\ 5 \rangle$ (b) $\langle -9,\ -5 \rangle$ (c) $\langle 5,\ 7 \rangle$

   (d) $\langle -5,\ -7 \rangle$ (e) None of these

   1—M—Answer: a

4. Determine the magnitude of the vector with initial point $(4,\ 6)$ and terminal point $(7,\ 2)$.

   (a) $\sqrt{73}$ (b) 19 (c) $\sqrt{185}$ (d) 5 (e) None of these

   1—M—Answer: d

5. Determine the magnitude of **v**: $\mathbf{v} = 4\mathbf{i} - 7\mathbf{j}$

   (a) 65 (b) $\sqrt{65}$ (c) 11 (d) $\sqrt{11}$ (e) None of these

   1—M—Answer: b

6. Determine the magnitude of **v**: $\mathbf{v} = \langle 5,\ -6 \rangle$

   (a) 11 (b) $\sqrt{11}$ (c) 61 (d) $\sqrt{61}$ (e) None of these

   1—M—Answer: d

7. A vector **v** has initial point $(1,\ 8)$ and terminal point $(3,\ -7)$. Find its magnitude.

   (a) $\sqrt{229}$ (b) $\sqrt{5}$ (c) $4\sqrt{14}$ (d) $\sqrt{15}$ (e) None of these

   1—M—Answer: a

8. Find the direction of **v**: **v** = 7**i** − 2**j**

   (a) 344°   (b) 16°   (c) 164°   (d) 196°   (e) None of these

   1—M—Answer: a

9. Find the direction of **v**: **v** = $\langle -1, \ -4 \rangle$

   (a) 76°   (b) 14°   (c) 256°   (d) 194°   (e) None of these

   1—M—Answer: c

10. Find the direction of **v**: **v** = $\langle -2, \ 5 \rangle$

    (a) 112°   (b) 68°   (c) 167°   (d) 193°   (e) None of these

    1—M—Answer: a

11. A vector **v** has initial point (2, 5) and terminal point (−1, 9). Find its magnitude and direction.

    1—O—Answer: $\|\mathbf{v}\| = 5, \theta = 126.9°$

12. Given **u** = 3**i** + 2**j**, **w** = **i** − **j**, and **v** = 3**u** − 2**w**, find the component form of **v**.

    (a) $\langle 11, \ 4 \rangle$ (b) $\langle 7, \ 8 \rangle$ (c) $\langle \sqrt{77}, \ 4\sqrt{2} \rangle$

    (d) $\langle \sqrt{85}, \ 2\sqrt{10} \rangle$ (e) None of these

    1—M—Answer: b

13. Given **w** = **i** and **u** = 4**i** − 2**j**, find **v** = $\frac{2}{3}$**w** + $\frac{1}{2}$**u**.

    (a) $\frac{8}{3}$**i** − **j**   (b) $\frac{8}{3}$**i** − 2**j**   (c) $\frac{8}{3}$**i** + **j**

    (d) $\frac{8}{3}$**i** + 2**j**   (e) None of these

    1—M—Answer: a

14. Given **u** = 3**i** − 2**j** and **w** = 9**i** + 5**j**, find **v** = $\frac{1}{2}$**u** + 4**w**.

    1—O—Answer: $\frac{75}{2}$**i** + 19**j**

15. Given **u** = 4**i** − 3**j**, **w** = **i** − **j**, and **v** = 2**u** + 3**w**, find **v**.

    (a) $\langle 7, \ -4 \rangle$ (b) $\langle 7, \ -9 \rangle$ (c) $\langle 11, \ -9 \rangle$

    (d) $\langle 11, \ -4 \rangle$ (e) None of these

    1—M—Answer: c

16. A vector **v** has magnitude 8 and direction $\theta = 120°$. Find its component form.

    (a) $\left\langle \dfrac{8\sqrt{3}}{3}, \ -8\sqrt{3} \right\rangle$ (b) $\left\langle 8\sqrt{3}, \ \dfrac{8\sqrt{3}}{3} \right\rangle$ (c) $\langle 4\sqrt{3}, \ -4 \rangle$

    (d) $\langle -4, \ 4\sqrt{3} \rangle$ (e) None of these

    1—M—Answer: d

17. A unit vector has direction $\theta = 120°$. Find its component form.

 1—O—Answer: $\left\langle -\dfrac{1}{2}, \dfrac{\sqrt{3}}{2} \right\rangle$

18. A vector **v** has magnitude 27 and direction $\theta = 216°$. Find its component form.

 1—O—Answer: $\langle -21.84, \ -15.87 \rangle$

19. A vector **v** has magnitude 6 and direction $\theta = 210°$. Find **v**.

 (a) $\langle -3, \ \sqrt{3} \rangle$　　　(b) $\langle -3\sqrt{3}, \ 12 \rangle$　　　(c) $\left\langle 3, \ -\dfrac{\sqrt{3}}{2} \right\rangle$

 (d) $\langle -3\sqrt{3}, \ -3 \rangle$　　　(e) None of these

 1—M—Answer: d

20. Given **v** of magnitude 200 and direction 215°, and **w** of magnitude 150 and direction 162°, find **v** + **w**.

 (a) $-21.2\mathbf{i} - 161.1\mathbf{j}$　　　(b) $350\mathbf{i} + 350\mathbf{j}$　　　(c) $50\mathbf{i} - 50\mathbf{j}$

 (d) $-306.5\mathbf{i} - 68.4\mathbf{j}$　　　(e) None of these

 1—M—Answer: d

21. Given **v** of magnitude 150 and direction 30°, and **w** of magnitude 75 and direction 206°, find **v** + **w**.

 (a) $97.0\mathbf{i} + 7.6\mathbf{j}$　　　(b) $62.5\mathbf{i} + 42.1\mathbf{j}$　　　(c) $225\mathbf{i} + 225\mathbf{j}$

 (d) $-7.4\mathbf{i} + 13.9\mathbf{j}$　　　(e) None of these

 1—M—Answer: b

22. Given **v** of magnitude 50 and direction 315° and **w** of magnitude 20 and direction 210°, find **v** + **w**.

 (a) $18.0\mathbf{i} - 45.4\mathbf{j}$　　　(b) $52.7\mathbf{i} - 25.4\mathbf{j}$　　　(c) $18.0\mathbf{i} - 25.4\mathbf{j}$

 (d) $52.7\mathbf{i} - 45.4\mathbf{j}$　　　(e) None of these

 1—M—Answer: a

23. Given **v** of magnitude 100 and direction 172° and **w** of magnitude 300 and direction 310°, find **v** + **w**.

 (a) $-139.0\mathbf{i} - 250.7\mathbf{j}$　　　(b) $-291.9\mathbf{i} + 13.2\mathbf{j}$　　　(c) $93.8\mathbf{i} - 215.9\mathbf{j}$

 (d) $-212\mathbf{i} + 339.2\mathbf{j}$　　　(e) None of these

 1—M—Answer: c

24. Given **v** of magnitude 300 and direction 90° and **w** of magnitude 250 and direction 253°, find **v** + **w**.

 (a) $-98.7\mathbf{i} + 20.4\mathbf{j}$　　　(b) $-526\mathbf{i} + 160.8\mathbf{j}$　　　(c) $526.0\mathbf{i} - 160.8\mathbf{j}$

 (d) $-73.1\mathbf{i} + 60.9\mathbf{j}$　　　(e) None of these

 1—M—Answer: d

25. Find a unit vector in the direction of $\mathbf{v} = 3\mathbf{i} - 2\mathbf{j}$.

     (a) $\langle 3\sqrt{13}, -2\sqrt{13} \rangle$ (b) $\left\langle \dfrac{3\sqrt{13}}{13}, -\dfrac{2\sqrt{13}}{13} \right\rangle$ (c) $\langle \sqrt{13}, -\sqrt{13} \rangle$

     (d) $\langle 1, -1 \rangle$ (e) None of these

     1—M—Answer: b

26. Find a unit vector in the direction of $\mathbf{v}$: $\mathbf{v} = 4\mathbf{i} + 2\mathbf{j}$

     (a) $\dfrac{2\sqrt{5}}{5}\mathbf{i} + \dfrac{\sqrt{5}}{5}\mathbf{j}$ (b) $\mathbf{i} + \mathbf{j}$ (c) $\dfrac{4\sqrt{5}}{5}\mathbf{i} + \dfrac{2\sqrt{5}}{5}\mathbf{j}$

     (d) $8\sqrt{5}\mathbf{i} + 4\sqrt{5}\mathbf{j}$ (e) None of these

     1—M—Answer: a

27. Find a unit vector in the direction of $\mathbf{v}$: $\mathbf{v} = 4\mathbf{i} - 3\mathbf{j}$

     (a) $\dfrac{4\sqrt{5}}{5}\mathbf{i} - \dfrac{3\sqrt{5}}{5}\mathbf{j}$ (b) $\dfrac{4\sqrt{27}}{27}\mathbf{i} + \dfrac{3\sqrt{27}}{27}\mathbf{j}$ (c) $\dfrac{4}{5}\mathbf{i} - \dfrac{3}{5}\mathbf{j}$

     (d) $\dfrac{\sqrt{2}}{2}\mathbf{i} - \dfrac{\sqrt{2}}{2}\mathbf{j}$ (e) None of these

     1—M—Answer: c

28. Find a unit vector in the direction of $\mathbf{v}$: $\mathbf{v} = 3\mathbf{i} - 3\mathbf{j}$

     (a) $3\mathbf{i} - 3\mathbf{j}$ (b) $\mathbf{i} - \mathbf{j}$ (c) $\dfrac{\sqrt{2}}{2}\mathbf{i} - \dfrac{\sqrt{2}}{2}\mathbf{j}$

     (d) $\dfrac{3\sqrt{2}}{2}\mathbf{i} - \dfrac{3\sqrt{2}}{2}\mathbf{j}$ (e) None of these

     1—M—Answer: c

29. Find a unit vector in the direction of $\mathbf{v}$: $\mathbf{v} = -5\mathbf{i} + 2\mathbf{j}$

     (a) $\dfrac{-5\sqrt{21}}{21}\mathbf{i} + \dfrac{2\sqrt{21}}{21}\mathbf{j}$ (b) $-\mathbf{i} + \mathbf{j}$ (c) $-\sqrt{5}\mathbf{i} + \dfrac{\sqrt{5}}{5}\mathbf{j}$

     (d) $\dfrac{-5\sqrt{29}}{29}\mathbf{i} + \dfrac{2\sqrt{29}}{29}\mathbf{j}$ (e) None of these

     1—M—Answer: d

30. Given $\mathbf{v} = 3\mathbf{i} - 2\mathbf{j}$ and $\mathbf{w} = 6\mathbf{i} + \mathbf{j}$. Find the angle between $\mathbf{v}$ and $\mathbf{w}$.

     1—O—Answer: 43.15°

31. Given $\mathbf{v} = 3\mathbf{i} + 2\mathbf{j}$ and $\mathbf{w} = 7\mathbf{i} - 5\mathbf{j}$, find the angle between $\mathbf{v}$ and $\mathbf{w}$.

     (a) 16.7°   (b) 110.8°   (c) 50.4°   (d) 69.2°   (e) None of these

     1—M—Answer: d

32. Given **v** = ⟨5, −2⟩ and **w** = ⟨6, 1⟩, find the angle between **v** and **w**.

(a) 58.7°   (b) 148.7°   (c) 31.3°   (d) 121.3°   (e) None of these

1—M—Answer: c

33. Given **v** = ⟨4, 1⟩ and **w** = ⟨−2, −3⟩, find the angle between **v** and **w**.

(a) 47.7°   (b) 227.7°   (c) 42.3°   (d) 137.7°   (e) None of these

1—M—Answer: d

34. Two forces, one of 120 pounds and the other of 200 pounds, act on the same object at angles of 30° and −30° respectively, with the positive x-axis. Find the direction of the resultant of these two forces.

(a) 14°   (b) −8.2°   (c) 0°   (d) −18°   (e) None of these

2—M—Answer: b

35. Two forces, one of 45 pounds and the other 52 pounds, act upon the same object. The angle between these forces is 25°. Find the magnitude of the resultant force.

2—O—Answer: 94.71 pounds

36. What force is required to keep a 2000 pound vehicle from rolling down a ramp inclined at 30° from the horizontal?

1—O—Answer: 1000 pounds

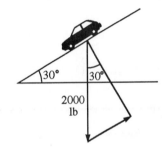

37. A storm front is moving east at 30.0 mph and north at 18.5 mph. Find the resultant velocity of the front.

2—O—Answer: 35.2 mph at 31.7° north of east

38. An airliner's navigator determines that the jet is flying 475 mph with a heading of 42.5° north of west, but the jet is actually moving at 465 mph in a direction 37.7° north of west. What is the velocity of the wind?

2—O—Answer: 40.6 mph at 73.4° south of east

8.4 | Trigonometric Form of a Complex Number

1. Represent the complex number graphically: $7 - 2i$

(a)

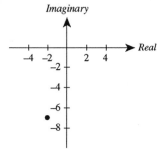

(b)

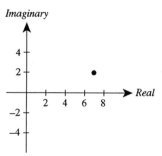

(c)

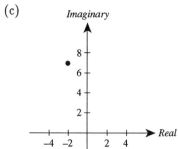

(d)

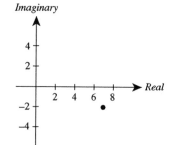

(e) None of these

1—M—Answer: d

2. Represent the complex number graphically: $6 - 2i$

1—O—Answer:

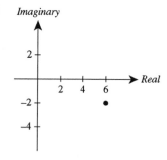

3. Represent the complex number graphically: $-5(3 - \sqrt{2}\,i)$

(a)
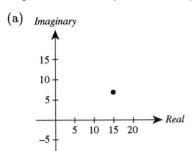

(b)
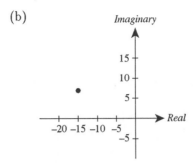

(c)
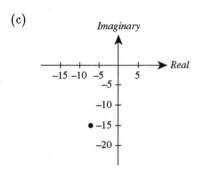

(d)
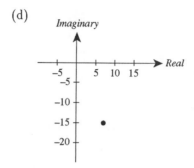

(e) None of these

1—M—Answer: b

4. Rewrite in standard form and represent graphically: $3(\cos 150° + i \sin 150°)$

1—O—Answer: $-\dfrac{3\sqrt{3}}{2} + \dfrac{3}{2}i$

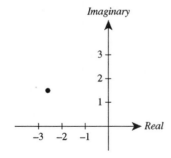

5. Represent the complex number graphically: $5(\cos 210 + i \sin 210)$

(a)

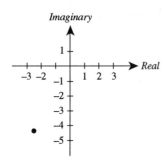

(b)

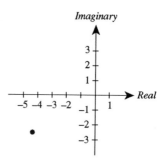

(c)

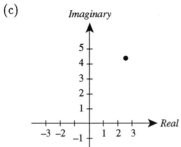

(d)

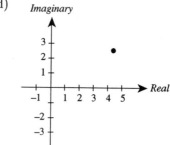

(e) None of these

1—M—Answer: b

6. Represent the complex number graphically: $-4(1 - 2i)$

(a)

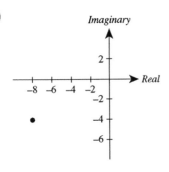

(b)

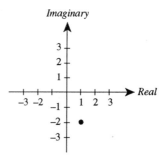

(c)

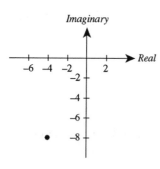

(d)

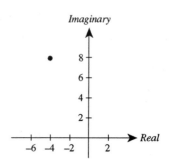

(e) None of these

1—M—Answer: d

7. Evaluate: $|3 - 2i|$

    (a) 1   (b) $\sqrt{5}$ (c) $\sqrt{13}$ (d) 5   (e) None of these

    1—M—Answer: c

8. Evaluate: $|5 + 4i|$

    (a) 9   (b) −9   (c) 41   (d) $\sqrt{41}$ (e) None of these

    1—M—Answer: d

9. Evaluate: $|7 - 3i|$

    (a) $\sqrt{58}$ (b) 4   (c) 2   (d) −58   (e) None of these

    1—M—Answer: a

10. Evaluate: $|3 - 4i|$

    (a) 1   (b) −1   (c) 7   (d) 5   (e) None of these

    1—M—Answer: d

11. Evaluate: $\left| 2 - \dfrac{\sqrt{3}}{2} i \right|$

    (a) $\dfrac{19}{4}$ (b) $\dfrac{4 - \sqrt{3}}{2}$ (c) $\dfrac{\sqrt{19}}{2}$

    (d) $\dfrac{1}{2}$ (e) None of these

    1—M—Answer: c

12. Evaluate: $|5 - 7i|$

    (a) $\sqrt{74}$ (b) 2   (c) $\sqrt{10}$ (d) $2\sqrt{3}$ (e) None of these

    1—M—Answer: a

13. Rewrite in trigonometric form: $16 - 4i$

    (a) $4\sqrt{15}(\cos 14° + i \sin 14°)$ (b) $4\sqrt{15}(\cos 346° + i \sin 346°)$ (c) $4\sqrt{17}(\cos 346° + i \sin 346°)$
    (d) $4\sqrt{17}(\cos 194° + i \sin 194°)$ (e) None of these

    1—M—Answer: c

14. Rewrite in trigonometric form: $-4i$

    (a) $4\left(\cos \dfrac{3\pi}{2} + i \sin \dfrac{3\pi}{2} \right)$ (b) $4(\cos \pi + i \sin \pi)$ (c) $4\left(\cos \dfrac{\pi}{2} + i \sin \dfrac{\pi}{2} \right)$

    (d) $4(\cos 0 + i \sin 0)$ (e) None of these

    1—M—Answer: a

15. Rewrite in trigonometric form: $-2 + 3i$
    - (a) $\sqrt{13}(\cos 56.3° + i \sin 56.3°)$
    - (b) $\sqrt{13}(\cos 123.7° + i \sin 123.7°)$
    - (c) $\sqrt{13}(\cos 236.3° + i \sin 236.3°)$
    - (d) $\sqrt{13}(\cos 303.7° + i \sin 303.7°)$
    - (e) None of these

    1—M—Answer: b

16. Rewrite in trigonometric form: $7 - 2i$
    - (a) $\sqrt{53}(\cos 344.1° + i \sin 344.1°)$
    - (b) $3\sqrt{5}(\cos 344.1° + i \sin 344.1°)$
    - (c) $3\sqrt{5}(\cos 15.9° + i \sin 15.9°)$
    - (d) $\sqrt{53}(\cos 15.9° + i \sin 15.9°)$
    - (e) None of these

    1—M—Answer: a

17. Rewrite in trigonometric form: $-2 + \sqrt{3}\, i$

    1—O—Answer: $\sqrt{7}(\cos 139.1° + i \sin 139.1°)$

18. Rewrite in trigonometric form: $-17 + 32i$

    1—O—Answer: $36.235(\cos 117.98° + i \sin 117.98°)$

19. Rewrite in standard form: $10\left(\cos \dfrac{2\pi}{3} + i \sin \dfrac{2\pi}{3}\right)$
    - (a) $5\sqrt{3} + 5i$
    - (b) $10\sqrt{3}\, i$
    - (c) $5 + 5\sqrt{3}\, i$
    - (d) $-5 + 5\sqrt{3}\, i$
    - (e) None of these

    1—M—Answer: d

20. Rewrite in standard form: $4\left(\cos \dfrac{7\pi}{6} + i \sin \dfrac{7\pi}{6}\right)$
    - (a) $\dfrac{\sqrt{3}}{2} - i$
    - (b) $-2\sqrt{3} - 2i$
    - (c) $-1 - 2\sqrt{3}i$
    - (d) $-2 + 2\sqrt{2}i$
    - (e) None of these

    1—M—Answer: b

21. Rewrite in standard form: $2(\cos 240° + i \sin 240°)$
    - (a) $-1 - \sqrt{3}i$
    - (b) $1 + \sqrt{3}i$
    - (c) $-\sqrt{3} - i$
    - (d) $-\sqrt{3} + i$
    - (e) None of these

    1—M—Answer: a

22. Rewrite in standard form: $3(\cos 300° + i \sin 300°)$

(a) $\dfrac{3}{2} + \dfrac{3\sqrt{3}}{2}i$ (b) $\dfrac{3}{2} - \dfrac{3\sqrt{3}}{2}i$ (c) $-\dfrac{3}{2} - \dfrac{3\sqrt{3}}{2}i$

(d) $\dfrac{3\sqrt{3}}{2} - \dfrac{3}{2}i$ (e) None of these

1—M—Answer: b

23. Rewrite in standard form: $5(\cos 120° + i \sin 120°)$

(a) $\dfrac{5}{2} + \dfrac{5\sqrt{3}}{2}i$ (b) $-\dfrac{5\sqrt{3}}{2} - \dfrac{5}{2}i$ (c) $-\dfrac{5}{2} + \dfrac{5\sqrt{3}}{2}i$

(d) $\dfrac{5\sqrt{3}}{2} - \dfrac{5}{2}i$ (e) None of these

1—M—Answer: c

24. Rewrite in standard form: $6\left(\cos \dfrac{11\pi}{6} + i \sin \dfrac{11\pi}{6}\right)$

(a) $-3 + 3\sqrt{3}i$ (b) $3\sqrt{3} - 3i$ (c) $3 - 3\sqrt{3}i$

(d) $3\sqrt{3} + 3i$ (e) None of these

1—M—Answer: b

25. Rewrite each number in standard form, then perform the addition.

$$\left[5\left(\cos \frac{7\pi}{6} + i \sin \frac{7\pi}{6}\right)\right] + \left[3\left(\cos \frac{5\pi}{6} + i \sin \frac{5\pi}{6}\right)\right]$$

(a) $-1 - 4\sqrt{3}i$ (b) $4\sqrt{3} - 4i$ (c) $-4\sqrt{3}i - 4$

(d) $-4\sqrt{3} - i$ (e) None of these

2—M—Answer: d

26. Rewrite each number in standard form, then perform the subtraction.

$$\left[6\left(\cos \frac{4\pi}{3} + i \sin \frac{4\pi}{3}\right)\right] - \left[2\left(\cos \frac{5\pi}{3} + i \sin \frac{5\pi}{3}\right)\right]$$

(a) $-4 - 4\sqrt{3}i$ (b) $-2 - 2\sqrt{3}i$ (c) $-4 - 2\sqrt{3}i$

(d) $4\left[\cos\left(-\dfrac{\pi}{3}\right) + i \sin\left(-\dfrac{\pi}{3}\right)\right]$ (e) None of these

2—M—Answer: c

27. Rewrite each number in standard form, then perform the addition.

$$\left[\frac{2}{5}\left(\cos \frac{7\pi}{4} + i \sin \frac{7\pi}{4}\right)\right] + \left[8\left(\cos \frac{\pi}{4} + i \sin \frac{\pi}{4}\right)\right]$$

2—O—Answer: $\dfrac{21\sqrt{2}}{5} + \dfrac{19\sqrt{2}}{5}i$

28. Rewrite each number in standard form, then perform the subtraction.

$$[10\,(\cos 180° + i\sin 180°)] - [16\,(\cos 270° + i\sin 270°)]$$

(a) $-10 + 16i$ (b) $10 - 16i$ (c) $-10 - 16i$

(d) $10 + 16i$ (e) None of these

1—M—Answer: a

29. Multiply: $[5(\cos 15° + i\sin 15°)][12(\cos 23° + i\sin 23°)]$

(a) $60(\cos 345° + i\sin 345°)$ (b) $60(\cos 38° + i\sin 38°)$ (c) $17(\cos 38° + i\sin 38°)$

(d) $17(\cos 345° + i\sin 345°)$ (e) None of these

1—M—Answer: b

30. Multiply: $[5(\cos 30° + i\sin 30°)][7(\cos 30° + i\sin 30°)]$

(a) $35(\cos 60° + i\sin 60°)$ (b) $35(\cos 30° + i\sin 30°)$ (c) $35(\cos 900° + i\sin 900°)$

(d) $12(\cos 30° + i\sin 30°)$ (e) None of these

1—M—Answer: a

31. Multiply: $[16(\cos 33° + i\sin 33°)][8(\cos 17° + i\sin 17°)]$

1—O—Answer: $128(\cos 50° + i\sin 50°)$

32. Multiply: $[3(\cos 85° + i\sin 85°)][12(\cos 10° + i\sin 10°)]$

(a) $4(\cos 75° + i\sin 75°)$ (b) $36(\cos 850° + i\sin 850°)$ (c) $36(\cos 95° + i\sin 95°)$

(d) $4(\sin 95° + i\cos 95°)$ (e) None of these

1—M—Answer: c

33. Multiply: $[6(\cos 52° + i\sin 52°)][15(\cos 8° + i\sin 8°)]$

(a) $45 + 45\sqrt{3}i$ (b) $45\sqrt{2} + 45\sqrt{2}i$ (c) $\dfrac{21}{2} + \dfrac{21\sqrt{3}}{2}i$

(d) $21(\cos 56° + i\sin 56°$ (e) None of these

1—M—Answer: a

34. Multiply: $[12(\cos 15° + i\sin 15°)]^2$

(a) $134.4 + 9.6i$ (b) $124.7 + 72i$ (c) $101.8 + 101.8i$

(d) $11.6 + 3.1i$ (e) None of these

1—M—Answer: b

35. Divide: $\dfrac{7(\cos 75° + i \sin 75°)}{2(\cos 25° + i \sin 25°)}$

(a) $\dfrac{7}{2}(\cos 50° - i \sin 50°)$ (b) $\dfrac{7}{2}(\cos 3° + i \sin 3°)$ (c) $\dfrac{7}{2}(\cos 50° + i \sin 50°)$

(d) $\dfrac{7}{2}(\cos 3° - i \sin 3°)$ (e) None of these

1—M—Answer: c

36. Divide: $\dfrac{16[\cos(3\pi/4) + i \sin(3\pi/4)]}{2[\cos(\pi/2) + i \sin(\pi/2)]}$

1—O—Answer: $8\left(\cos \dfrac{\pi}{4} + i \sin \dfrac{\pi}{4}\right) = 4\sqrt{2} + 4\sqrt{2}\,i$

37. Divide: $\dfrac{5(\cos 200° + i \sin 200°)}{10(\cos 20° + i \sin 20°)}$

(a) $\dfrac{1}{2}(\cos 10° + i \sin 10°)$ (b) $-\dfrac{1}{2}$ (c) $\dfrac{1}{2}$

(d) $\dfrac{1}{2}(\cos 10° - i \sin 10°)$ (e) None of these

1—M—Answer: b

38. Divide: $\dfrac{12(\cos 20° + i \sin 20°)}{4(\cos 50° + i \sin 50°)}$

(a) $\dfrac{3\sqrt{3}}{2} + \dfrac{3}{2}i$ (b) $-\dfrac{3\sqrt{3}}{2} - \dfrac{3}{2}i$ (c) $\dfrac{3\sqrt{3}}{2} - \dfrac{3}{2}i$

(d) $3(\cos 0.4° + i \sin 0.4)$ (e) None of these

1—M—Answer: c

39. Divide: $\dfrac{60(\cos 300 + i \sin 300)}{20(\cos 30 + i \sin 30)}$

(a) $-3i$ (b) $3 + 3i$ (c) $-3 - 3i$

(d) -3 (e) None of these

1—M—Answer: a

40. Divide: $\dfrac{12(\cos 50 + i \sin 50)}{6(\cos 20 + i \sin 20)}$

(a) $2 - \sqrt{3}i$ (b) $1 + \sqrt{3}i$ (c) $\sqrt{3} + i$

(d) $2(\cos 2.5° + \sin 2.5°)$ (e) None of these

1—M—Answer: c

8.5 │ DeMoivre's Theorem and nth Roots

1. Evaluate: $(3 + 3i)^8$

   (a) 104,976
   (b) 6561
   (c) 16
   (d) $6561 + 6561i$
   (e) None of these

   1—M—Answer: a

2. Evaluate: $(-2 + 2i)^8$

   (a) $-2896.3 + 2896.3i$
   (b) $-16i$
   (c) $4096i$
   (d) 4096
   (e) None of these

   1—M—Answer: d

3. Evaluate: $(\sqrt{3} - i)^7$

   1—O—Answer: $-64\sqrt{3} + 64i$

4. Evaluate: $\left(\dfrac{5}{2} - \dfrac{5\sqrt{3}}{2}i \right)^6$

   (a) $15625i$
   (b) 15625
   (c) $15625(1 + i)$
   (d) $\dfrac{15625}{64} - \dfrac{421,875}{64}i$
   (e) None of these

   1—M—Answer: b

5. Evaluate: $\left[4\left(-\dfrac{\sqrt{3}}{2} + \dfrac{1}{2}i \right) \right]^6$

   (a) $1728 + \dfrac{1}{64}i$
   (b) $4096i$
   (c) $4096(-1 + i)$
   (d) -4096
   (e) None of these

   1—M—Answer: d

6. Evaluate: $[3(\sqrt{2} - \sqrt{2}i)]^4$

   (a) -1296
   (b) $1296 - 1296i$
   (c) -81
   (d) $12 + 12i$
   (e) None of these

   1—M—Answer: a

7. Evaluate: $[3(-\sqrt{2} - \sqrt{2}i)]^3$

   (a) $-54\sqrt{2} - 54\sqrt{2}i$ (b) $\dfrac{216\sqrt{3}}{3} + 216i$ (c) $108\sqrt{2} - 108\sqrt{2}i$

   (d) $-108\sqrt{2} - 108\sqrt{2}i$ (e) None of these

   1—M—Answer: c

8. Evaluate: $[3(\cos 120° + i\sin 120°)]^5$

   (a) $\dfrac{-243}{2} - \dfrac{243\sqrt{3}}{2}i$ (b) $\dfrac{-243}{2} + \dfrac{243\sqrt{3}}{2}i$ (c) $\dfrac{243}{2} + \dfrac{243\sqrt{3}}{2}i$

   (d) $\dfrac{243}{2} - \dfrac{243\sqrt{3}}{2}i$ (e) None of these

   1—M—Answer: a

9. Evaluate: $[2(\cos 15° + i\sin 15°)]^{12}$

   (a) 4096   (b) $4096i$ (c) -4096

   (d) $-4096i$ (e) None of these

   1—M—Answer: c

10. Evaluate: $\left[2\left(\cos\dfrac{\pi}{4} + i\sin\dfrac{\pi}{4}\right)\right]^{12}$

    1—O—Answer: -4096

11. Evaluate: $\left[3\left(\cos\dfrac{\pi}{6} + i\sin\dfrac{\pi}{6}\right)\right]^{12}$

    (a) 531,441   (b) 22,436,771.7   (c) $531,441 - 531,441i$

    (d) $3^{12}\left(\dfrac{729}{4096} + \dfrac{1}{4096}i\right)$ (e) None of these

    1—M—Answer: a

12. Evaluate: $\left[4\left(\cos\dfrac{2\pi}{3} + i\sin\dfrac{2\pi}{3}\right)\right]^3$

    (a) $-8 + 3.5i$ (b) $64\left(\cos\dfrac{2\pi}{3} + i\sin\dfrac{2\pi}{3}\right)$ (c) 64

    (d) $64 - 64i$ (e) None of these

    1—M—Answer: c

13. Evaluate: $\left[4\left(\cos\dfrac{\pi}{3}+i\sin\dfrac{\pi}{3}\right)\right]^3$

   (a) $64(1-i)$ (b) $64i$ (c) $-64(1+i)$

   (d) -64 (e) None of these

   1—M—Answer: d

14. Evaluate: $\left[4\left(\cos\dfrac{\pi}{3}+i\sin\dfrac{\pi}{3}\right)\right]^5$

   (a) $512-512\sqrt{3}i$ (b) 1024 (c) $32+32\sqrt{3}i$

   (d) $-32+32\sqrt{3}i$ (e) None of these

   1—M—Answer: a

15. Find the square roots: $64\left(\cos\dfrac{\pi}{3}+i\sin\dfrac{\pi}{3}\right)$

   (a) $8\left(\cos\dfrac{\pi}{3}+i\sin\dfrac{\pi}{3}\right),\;\;8\left(\cos\dfrac{2\pi}{3}+i\sin\dfrac{2\pi}{3}\right)$ (b) $8\left(\cos\dfrac{\pi}{6}+i\sin\dfrac{\pi}{6}\right),\;\;8\left(\cos\dfrac{7\pi}{6}+i\sin\dfrac{7\pi}{6}\right)$

   (c) $8\left(\cos\dfrac{\pi}{3}+i\sin\dfrac{\pi}{3}\right),\;\;8\left(\cos\dfrac{\pi}{6}+i\sin\dfrac{\pi}{6}\right)$ (d) $4\sqrt{2}+4\sqrt{3}\,i,\;4\sqrt{2}-4\sqrt{3}\,i$

   (e) None of these

   1—M—Answer: b

16. Find the cube roots: $8\left(\cos\dfrac{\pi}{3}+i\sin\dfrac{\pi}{3}\right)$

   1—O—Answer: $2\left(\cos\dfrac{\pi}{9}+i\sin\dfrac{\pi}{9}\right),\;2\left(\cos\dfrac{7\pi}{9}+i\sin\dfrac{7\pi}{9}\right),\;2\left(\cos\dfrac{13\pi}{9}+i\sin\dfrac{13\pi}{9}\right)$

17. Find the square roots: $49\left(\cos\dfrac{\pi}{3}+i\sin\dfrac{\pi}{3}\right)$

   (a) $-\dfrac{7}{2}+\dfrac{7\sqrt{3}}{2}i,\;\dfrac{7}{2}-\dfrac{7\sqrt{3}}{2}i$ (b) $4.9+6.5i,\;4.9-6.5i$

   (c) $\dfrac{7\sqrt{3}}{2}+\dfrac{7}{2}i,\;-\dfrac{7\sqrt{3}}{2}-\dfrac{7}{2}i$ (d) $-\dfrac{7}{2}-\dfrac{7\sqrt{3}}{2}i,\;\dfrac{7}{2}+\dfrac{7\sqrt{3}}{2}i$

   (e) None of these

   1—M—Answer: c

18. Find the square roots: $81\left(\cos\dfrac{5\pi}{3}+i\sin\dfrac{5\pi}{3}\right)$

   (a) $6.4+8.4i,\;-6.4-8.4i$ (b) $\dfrac{9}{2}-\dfrac{9\sqrt{3}}{2}i,\;-\dfrac{9}{2}+\dfrac{9\sqrt{3}}{2}i$

   (c) $-\dfrac{9}{2}-\dfrac{9\sqrt{3}}{2}i,\;\dfrac{9}{2}+\dfrac{9\sqrt{3}}{2}i$ (d) $-\dfrac{9}{2}\sqrt{3}+\dfrac{9}{2}i,\;-\dfrac{9}{2}\sqrt{3}-\dfrac{9}{2}i$

   (e) None of these

   1—M—Answer: d

19. Find the cube roots: $8\left(\cos\dfrac{5\pi}{3} + i\sin\dfrac{5\pi}{3}\right)$

    1—O—Answer: $2\left(\cos\dfrac{5\pi}{9} + i\sin\dfrac{5\pi}{9}\right),\ 2\left(\cos\dfrac{11\pi}{9} + i\sin\dfrac{11\pi}{9}\right),\ 2\left(\cos\dfrac{17\pi}{9} + i\sin\dfrac{17\pi}{9}\right)$

20. Find the cube roots: $-64i$

    (a) $-4i,\ 4(\cos 330° + i\sin 330°),\ 4(\cos 330° - i\sin 330°)$

    (b) $4i,\ 4(\cos 90° - i\sin 90°),\ 4(\cos 270° + i\sin 270°)$

    (c) $-4i,\ 4(\cos 210° + i\sin 210°),\ 4(\cos 70° + i\sin 70°)$

    (d) $4i,\ 4(\cos 210° + i\sin 210°),\ 4(\cos 330° + i\sin 330°)$

    (e) None of these

    1—M—Answer: d

21. Find the cube roots: $8\left(\cos\dfrac{4\pi}{3} + i\sin\dfrac{4\pi}{3}\right)$

    (a) $2\left(\cos\dfrac{4\pi}{9} + i\sin\dfrac{4\pi}{9}\right),\ 2\left(\cos\dfrac{10\pi}{9} + i\sin\dfrac{10\pi}{9}\right),\ 2\left(\cos\dfrac{16\pi}{9} + i\sin\dfrac{16\pi}{9}\right)$

    (b) $2\left(\cos\dfrac{4\pi}{9} + i\sin\dfrac{4\pi}{9}\right),\ 2\left(\dfrac{13\pi}{9} + i\sin\dfrac{13\pi}{9}\right),\ 2\left(\dfrac{21\pi}{9} + i\sin\dfrac{21\pi}{9}\right)$

    (c) $2(\cos 4\pi + i\sin 4\pi),\ 2(\cos 6\pi + i\sin 6\pi),\ 2(\cos 18\pi + i\sin 18\pi)$

    (d) $2\left(\cos\dfrac{4\pi}{9} + i\sin\dfrac{4\pi}{9}\right),\ 2\left(\cos\dfrac{4\pi}{27} + i\sin\dfrac{4\pi}{27}\right),\ 2\left(\cos\dfrac{4\pi}{81} + i\sin\dfrac{4\pi}{81}\right)$

    (e) None of these

    1—M—Answer: a

22. Find the square roots: $-4i$

    (a) $2(\cos 135° - i\sin 135°),\ 2(-\cos 135° - i\sin 135°)$

    (b) $2(\cos 135° + i\sin 135°),\ 2(\cos 67.5° + i\sin 67.5°)$

    (c) $2(\cos 135° + i\sin 135°),\ 2(\cos 315° + i\sin 315°)$

    (d) $2i,\ -2i$

    (e) None of these

    1—M—Answer: c

23. Find the square roots: $81i$

  (a) $9(\cos 90° + i\sin 90°)$, $9(-\cos 90° - i\sin 90°)$

  (b) $9(\cos 45° + i\sin 45°)$, $9(\cos 225° + i\sin 225°)$

  (c) $9(\cos 45° - i\sin 45°)$, $9(-\cos 45° - i\sin 45°)$

  (d) $9(\cos 90° + i\sin 90°)$, $9(\cos 45° + i\sin 45°)$

  (e) None of these

  1—M—Answer: b

24. Find the cube roots: $-27i$

  (a) $3(\cos 90° + i\sin 90°)$, $-3(\cos 90° + i\sin 90°)$, $3(\cos 30° + i\sin 30°)$

  (b) $3(\cos 90° - i\sin 90°)$, $3(\cos 210° - i\sin 210°)$, $3(\cos 330° - i\sin 330°)$

  (c) $3(\cos 45° + i\sin 45°)$, $3(\cos 135° + i\sin 135°)$, $3(\cos 180° + i\sin 180°)$

  (d) $3(\cos 90° + i\sin 90°)$, $3(\cos 210° + i\sin 210°)$, $3(\cos 330° + i\sin 330°)$

  (e) None of these

  1—M—Answer: d

25. Find the fourth roots: $81i$

  (a) ± 3, $\pm 3i$

  (b) $3\left(\cos \dfrac{\pi}{8} + i\sin \dfrac{\pi}{8}\right)$, $3\left(\cos \dfrac{17\pi}{8} + i\sin \dfrac{17\pi}{8}\right)$, $3\left(\cos \dfrac{33\pi}{8} + i\sin \dfrac{33\pi}{8}\right)$, $3\left(\cos \dfrac{49\pi}{8} + i\sin \dfrac{49\pi}{8}\right)$

  (c) $3\left(\cos \dfrac{\pi}{2} + i\sin \dfrac{\pi}{2}\right)$, $-3\left(\cos \dfrac{\pi}{2} + i\sin \dfrac{\pi}{2}\right)$, $3\left(\cos \dfrac{3\pi}{2} + i\sin \dfrac{3\pi}{2}\right)$, $-3\left(\cos \dfrac{3\pi}{2} + i\sin \dfrac{3\pi}{2}\right)$

  (d) $3\left(\cos \dfrac{\pi}{8} + i\sin \dfrac{\pi}{8}\right)$, $3\left(\cos \dfrac{5\pi}{8} + i\sin \dfrac{5\pi}{8}\right)$, $3\left(\cos \dfrac{9\pi}{8} + i\sin \dfrac{9\pi}{8}\right)$, $3\left(\cos \dfrac{13\pi}{8} + i\sin \dfrac{13\pi}{8}\right)$

  (e) None of these

  1—M—Answer: d

26. Find the cube roots: -64

  1—O—Answer: $2 - 2\sqrt{3}\,i$, -4, $2 + 2\sqrt{3}\,i$

27. Find the square roots of $-64i$. Represent each of the roots in standard form graphically.

  2—O—Answer:

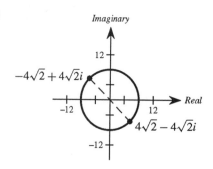

28. Find the cube roots of 27. Represent each of the roots in standard form graphically.

    2—O—Answer:

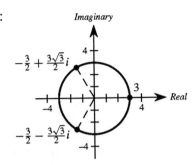

29. Find all solutions: $x^2 - 4i = 0$

    (a) $\sqrt{2} - \sqrt{2}\,i,\ -\sqrt{2} + \sqrt{2}\,i$ (b) $2 + i,\ -2 - i$ (c) $2 - i,\ 2 + i$

    (d) $\sqrt{2} + \sqrt{2}\,i,\ -\sqrt{2} - \sqrt{2}\,i$ (e) None of these

    1—M—Answer: d

30. Find all solutions: $x^2 + 4i = 0$

    1—O—Answer: $-\sqrt{2} + \sqrt{2}\,i,\ \sqrt{2} - \sqrt{2}\,i$

31. Which of the following is *not* a solution to $x^3 - 1 = 0$?

    (a) 1   (b) $\dfrac{1}{2} + \dfrac{\sqrt{3}}{2}\,i$ (c) $-\dfrac{1}{2} + \dfrac{\sqrt{3}}{2}\,i$

    (d) $-\dfrac{1}{2} - \dfrac{\sqrt{3}}{2}\,i$ (e) All are solutions

    1—M—Answer: b

32. Find all solutions: $x^2 - 4i = 0$

    (a) $-\sqrt{2} + \sqrt{2}i,\ \sqrt{2} - \sqrt{2}i$ (b) $-\sqrt{2} - \sqrt{2}i,\ -\sqrt{2} - \sqrt{2}i$ (c) $\sqrt{2} + \sqrt{2}i,\ \sqrt{2} - \sqrt{2}i$

    (d) $\sqrt{2} + \sqrt{2}i,\ -\sqrt{2} - \sqrt{2}i$ (e) None of these

    1—M—Answer: d

33. Find all solutions: $x^2 - 16i = 0$

    (a) $2\sqrt{2} + 2\sqrt{2}i,\ -2\sqrt{2} - 2\sqrt{2}i$ (b) $2\sqrt{2} - 2\sqrt{2}i,\ -2\sqrt{2} - 2\sqrt{2}i$

    (c) $-2\sqrt{2} + 2\sqrt{2}i,\ -2\sqrt{2} - 2\sqrt{2}i$ (d) $2\sqrt{2} + 2\sqrt{2}i,\ -2\sqrt{2} + 2\sqrt{2}i$

    (e) None of these

    1—M—Answer: a

34. Which of the following is *not* a solution to $x^3 + 27i = 0$?

    (a) $3i$ (b) $-\dfrac{3\sqrt{2}}{2} - \dfrac{3}{2}i$ (c) $-\dfrac{3\sqrt{3}}{2} - \dfrac{3}{2}i$

    (d) $\dfrac{3\sqrt{3}}{2} - \dfrac{3}{2}i$ (e) Neither **b** nor **c** is a solution.

    1—M—Answer: c

35. Which of the following is *not* a solution to $x^3 - 64 = 0$?

    (a) 4 (b) $2 - 2\sqrt{3}i$ (c) $-2 + 2\sqrt{3}i$

    (d) $-2 - 2\sqrt{3}i$ (e) Neither **a** nor **c** are solutions.

    1—M—Answer: b

36. Which of the following is *not* a solution to $x^4 - 16i = 0$?

    (a) $2(\cos 45° + i \sin 45°)$ (b) $2(\cos 112.5° + i \sin 112.5°)$ (c) $2(\cos 22.5° + i \sin 22.5°)$

    (d) $2(\cos 292.5° + i \sin 292.5°)$ (e) All of these are solutions.

    1—M—Answer: a

C H A P T E R   N I N E
Linear Models and Systems of Equations

9.1 **Linear Modeling and Scatter Plots**

1. Assume y is directly proportional to x. Find a linear model that relates y and x given $y = 25$ when $x = 10$.

    (a) $y = 0.4x$ (b) $y = 2.5x + 10$ (c) $y = 0.4x + 10$

    (d) $y = 2.5x$ (e) None of these

    1—M—Answer: d

2. Assume y is directly proportional to x. Find a linear model that relates y and x given $y = 36$ when $x = 144$.

    (a) $y = 4x + 36$ (b) $y = 0.25x$ (c) $y = 4x$

    (d) $y = 0.25x + 36$ (e) None of these

    1—M—Answer: b

3. Assume z is directly proportional to x. Find a linear model that relates z and x given $z = 150$ when $x = 50$.

    (a) $z = \dfrac{x}{3}$ (b) $z = x - 100$ (c) $z = 3x$

    (d) $z = 3z + 100$ (e) None of these

    1—M—Answer: c

4. Assume y varies directly to x. Find a linear model that relates y and x given $y = 225$ and $x = 45$.

    (a) $x = 5y$ (b) $y = 5x + 180$ (c) $x = 5y - 180$

    (d) $y = 5x$ (e) None of these

    1—M—Answer: d

5. Assume z varies directly to w. Find a linear model that relates z and w given $z = 40$ and $w = \frac{1}{8}$.

    (a) $z = \dfrac{w}{5}$ (b) $z = 5w$ (c) $z = 500w$

    (d) $z = \dfrac{w}{500}$ (e) None of these

    1—M—Answer: e

6. During the winter, as the temperature drops below 30°F, the more cups of hot chocolate are sold per hour at a local diner. This behavior is approximated by the model $C = 15t + 10$, where C is the number of cups sold per hour and t is the degrees Fahrenheit below 30° with $t = 0$ corresponding to 30°F. Using the model, fill in the table.

Temp (°F)	30°	25°	20°	15°	10°	5°	0°
Cups							

1—O—Answer:

Temp (°F)	30°	25°	20°	15°	10°	5°	0°
Cups	10	85	160	235	310	385	460

7. The average growth of a forest is proportional to the amount of monthly rainfall. A linear model that approximates the growth is $g = 0.25r + 1.5$ where g represents the growth in inches and r represents the monthly rainfall. Using the model, fill in the table.

Monthly Rainfall	0.10	0.20	0.70	1.20	0.35	0.75
Growth						

1—O—Answer:

Monthly Rainfall	0.10	0.20	0.70	1.20	0.35	0.75
Growth	1.525	1.55	1.675	1.8	1.5875	1.6875

8. The revenue of a certain product is proportional to the number of units sold. The linear model is $R = 3250x + 15,000$ where R represents the revenue and x represents the number of units sold in thousands. Using the model, fill in the table.

Units	10,000	22,500	34,000	50,000	75,000
Revenue					

1—O—Answer:

Units	10,000	22,500	34,000	50,000	75,000
Revenue	47,500	88,125	125,500	177,500	258,750

9. The total revenue, R (in dollars), obtained from selling x units of a given product is directly proportional to the number of units sold. When 15,000 units are sold, the total revenue is $191,250. Find a model that relates the total revenue, R, to the number of units sold, x.

(a) $R = 12.75x + 15,000$ (b) $R = 0.0784x$ (c) $R = x + 15,000$

(d) $R = 12.75x$ (e) None of these

1—M—Answer: d

10. On weekends a TV repairman has an initial service charge of $30 plus a charge of $2.00 per minute. Find a linear model representing the total charge, c, in terms of x, the number of minutes.

   (a) $c = 32x$ (b) $c = 30x + 2$ (c) $c = 30 + 2x$

   (d) $c = 32x + 2$ (e) None of these

   1—M—Answer: c

11. An appliance salesperson receives $200 per week plus 8% of their net sales. Write a linear model for the wages for this salesperson, where w equals the wages in terms of n, net sales.

   (a) $w = 200n + 908$ (b) $w = 16n$ (c) $w = 200 + 8n$

   (d) $w = 0.08n + 200$ (e) None of these

   1—M—Answer: d

12. The list price of a new automobile is $15,500. The dealership as a promotion is giving various percentage discounts. Find a linear model for the selling price of the new car where p is the selling price in terms of x, percentage discount.

   (a) $y = 155x$ (b) $y = 15,500 - 155x$ (c) $y = 15,500 - x$

   (d) $y = 15,500x$ (e) None of these

   1—M—Answer: b

13. The ground floor of the new building being constructed is 12 feet high. The plans call for each floor above the ground floor are to be 10 feet high. Find a linear model for the total height of the building h in terms of the number of floors, x.

   (a) $h = 12 + 10x$ (b) $h = 10 + 12x$ (c) $h = 120x$

   (d) $h = 120 + x$ (e) None of these

   1—M—Answer: a

14. The number of bees in a hive is 1750 and is increasing at a rate of 750 per week up to 12 weeks. Find a linear model for the number of bees, b, in terms of the number of weeks, w.

   (a) $b = \dfrac{1750w}{750}$ (b) $b = 1750 + 750w$ (c) $b = 2500w$

   (d) $b = 1750w + 750$ (e) None of these

   1—M—Answer: b

15. The trade-in value, V, of a certain model of automobile is $V = 25,000 - 0.25m$ where m is the mileage. Find the mileage when the trade-in value is $11,250.

   (a) 28,125   (b) 88,750   (c) 55,000

   (d) 45,000   (e) None of these

   1—M—Answer: c

16. The number of pounds, p, of dog food needed per week for a new puppy is directly proportional to the age of the puppy in months, m, up to 18 months. If a puppy 6 months old requires 7.5 pounds of dog food, find a linear model for the number of pounds, p, in terms of the age of puppy in months.

(a) $p = 7.5 + 6x$

(b) $p = 7.5 + x$

(c) $p = 0.8m$

(d) $p = 1.25m$

(e) None of these

1—M—Answer: d

17. A recent study shows that 55% of all American households regularly have their televisions turned on for at least six hours a day. Using this fact, find a linear model that will give the number of households, y, which have their televisions turned on for at least six hours a day from a group of x households.

(a) $y = 55x$

(b) $y = 0.55x$

(c) $y = x + 55$

(d) $y = \dfrac{x}{55}$

(e) None of these

1—M—Answer: b

18. In 1987, a small town had a population of 15,500. Since then there has been a decline of 175 residents each year. Find a linear model that will give the population, y, in terms of x, the number of years since 1987.

(a) $y = 15,500 - 175x$

(b) $y = 175x$

(c) $y = 15,325 - x$

(d) $y = 15,325 - 175x$

(e) None of these

1—M—Answer: a

19. The Curtis Sporting Goods Store has 250 dozen baseballs in stock on May 1 and sells them at a rate of 5 dozen per day. Find a linear model that gives the number of dozens of baseballs, d, in stock in terms of x, the number of days since May 1.

(a) $d = 50 - 5x$

(b) $d = 245x$

(c) $d = 250 - 5x$

(d) $d = 50x$

(e) None of these

1—M—Answer: c

20. The new car initially costs $20,000 and loses value at a rate of $1250 each year. Find a linear model that gives the value of the car, V, in terms of t, the number of years after its initial purchase.

(a) $V = 16t$

(b) $V = \dfrac{t}{16}$

(c) $V = 20,000 - 1250t$

(d) $V = 18,750 - t$

(e) None of these

1—M—Answer: c

21. The fixed costs to produce a certain sport shoe are $4000. If 200 pairs cost a total of $5050, find a linear model that relates total cost, c, and x, the number of pairs of shoes produced.

(a) $c = 200x + 4000$

(b) $c = 25.25x$

(c) $c = 1050x + 4000$

(d) $c = 5.25x + 4000$

(e) None of these

2—M—Answer: d

22. A chocolate factory has fixed costs of \$10,500 to produce boxes of candy. When 25,000 boxes are produced, the total cost is \$11,125. Find a linear model for the total cost, c, in terms of x, the number of boxes of candy produced.

    2—O—Answer: $c = 0.025x + 10,500$

23. Find a linear model that will give the total cost, c, of producing x units given that 200 graphing calculators cost \$1050 to produce and 525 calculators cost \$2350 to produce.

    2—O—Answer: $c = 4x + 250$

24. When a cinema charged \$6.00 per person, the box office sold 270 tickets. When the manager raised the ticket price to \$9.00, the box office only sold 255 tickets. Find a linear model that gives the number of tickets sold, t, in terms of the ticket price, p.

    2—O—Answer: $t = 300 - 5p$

25. A salesperson who gets paid a salary plus a commission of some percentage of gross sales received a gross pay of \$515 when gross sales are \$4000. The next month the salesperson receives \$727.50 when gross sales are \$6500. Find a linear model that gives the salesperson's gross pay, p, in terms of the gross sales, s.

    2—O—Answer: $p = 0.085s + 175$

26. During her vacation, Maureen found it necessary to rent a car from a car rental agency. The agency charges a fee per day plus a rate per mile. The first day Maureen rented the car, she drove a total of 125 miles and was charged a total of \$66.25. The second day of rental she drove 265 miles and was charged \$101.25. Find a linear model that related y, the total charge per day in terms of x, the number of miles driven.

    2—O—Answer: $y = 0.25x + 35$

27. In 1987, Jay's Pizza Shoppe sales were \$155,000, and in 1991, sales were \$325,000. Find a linear model that approximates the sales, s, in terms of t, the year with $t = 0$ for 1987. Using this model, approximate the sales for the year 2000.

    2—O—Answer: $s = 42,500t + 155,000$
    $t = 13$ for the year 2000. $s = 42,500(13) + 155,000 = 707,500$

28. A pediatrician prescribed 10 ml per day of a medication for a 30-pound child. The next patient was prescribed 20 ml per day. This child weighed 50 pounds. Find a linear model for prescribing the correct dosage of the medication, d, in terms of the child's body weight, w. Using this model, find the dosage for a 85-pound child.

    2—O—Answer: $d = 0.5w - 5$
    $w = 85$
    $d = 0.5(85) - 5 = 37.5$ ml

29. For a certain mathematics exam, one student studied for 7 hours and 30 minutes over a three day period and received a score of 98. Another student studied only 5 hours over the same three days and received a score of 85. Find a linear model that related the score, s, in terms of h, the hours spent studying.

    2—O—Answer: $s = 5.2h + 59$

30. An elevator in a new 39-story office building takes 10.2 seconds to reach the sixth floor. It takes 16.2 seconds to reach the fifteenth floor. Find a linear model that related the floor, f, in terms of the time the elevator has traveled, t. Use this model to find the time it takes for the elevator to reach the thirty-sixth floor.

    2—O—Answer: $f = 1.5t - 9.3$

    It takes 30.2 seconds to reach the 36th floor.

31. The price per ton for wheat from April to October is shown in the scatter plot at the right. Find the equation of the line that you think bests fits these data. Let p represent the price per ton and let t represent the month with $t = 0$ corresponding to April.

    2—O—Answer: $p = -\frac{25}{6}t + 200$

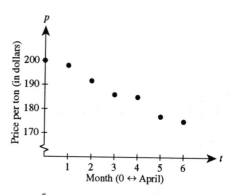

32. The sales for a company from 1980 to 1992 are shown in the scatter plot at the right. Find the equation of the line that you think best fits these data. Let s represent the sales. Let t represent the year with $t = 0$ corresponding to 1980.

    2—O—Answer: $s = \frac{125}{6}t + 550$

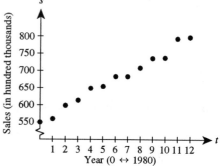

33. The bee population in a hive from May to December is shown in the scatter plot at the right. Find the equation of the line that you think best fits these data. Let b represent the bee population. Let t represent the month with $t = 0$ corresponding to May.

    2—O—Answer: $b = -\frac{1500}{7}t + 5500$

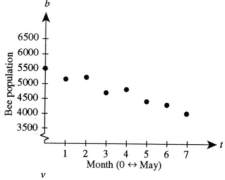

34. The number of passenger vehicles passing through a toll booth per week on a major interstate highway from May 30 to July 4 is shown in the scatter plot shown at the right. Find the equation of the line that you think best fits these data. Let v represent the number of vehicles. Let t represent the week with $t = 0$ corresponding to May 30.

    2—O—Answer: $v = 410t + 7700$

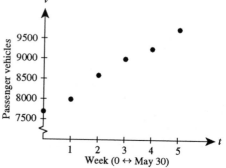

35. The average height of trees for twelve years at a tree farm is shown in the scatter plot at the right. Find the equation of the line that you think best fits these data. Let h represent the height. Let t represent the year.

2—O—Answer: $h = \frac{7}{12}t + 3$

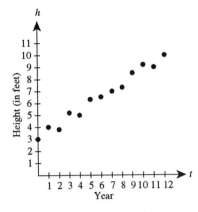

9.2 Solving Systems of Equations Algebraically and Graphically

1. Solve the system by the method of substitution:

$$x + y = 1$$
$$x^2 + 3y^2 = 21$$

(a) $\left(\frac{3}{2}, -3\right)$

(b) $\left(3, -\frac{3}{2}\right)$

(c) $\left(-\frac{3}{2}, \frac{5}{2}\right), (3, -2)$

(d) $\left(\frac{3}{2}, -\frac{1}{2}\right), (-3, 4)$

(e) No solution

1—M—Answer: c

2. Solve the system by the method of substitution:

$$2x^2 + 2y^2 = 7$$
$$x + y^2 = 7$$

(a) $(2.8, 2.0), (-0.5, 7.3)$

(b) $(4.6, 1.5), (-2.6, 3.1)$

(c) $(2.8, -0.5)$

(d) $(4.6), (-2.6)$

(e) No solution

2—M—Answer: e

3. Solve the system graphically:

$$x^2 + y^2 = 25$$
$$x - y = 1$$

1—O—Answer:

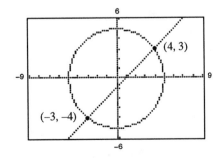

4. Solve the system graphically:

$$x^2 + 2y - 5 = 0$$
$$3x^2 - y - 1 = 0$$

1—O—Answer:

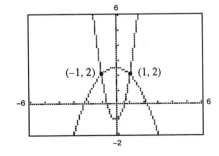

5. Solve the system by the method of substitution:

$$y = \frac{1}{x}$$
$$x + 5y = 6$$

1—O—Answer: $(1,\ 1),\ \left(5,\ \frac{1}{5}\right)$

6. Solve the system graphically:

$$x^2 - 4y = 17$$
$$x - 2y = 1$$

1—O—Answer:

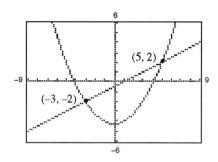

7. Solve the system graphically:

$$2x + y = 1$$
$$-x + 2y = 7$$

1—O—Answer:

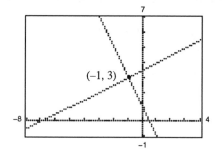

8. Solve the system by the method of substitution:

$$5x + y = 11$$
$$3x - 2y = 4$$

(a) $\left(\frac{15}{13},\ \frac{68}{13}\right)$ (b) $(2,\ 21)$ (c) $(2,\ 1)$

(d) $\left(\frac{15}{8},\ -15\right)$ (e) None of these

1—M—Answer: c

9. Solve the system graphically:

$$3x + 4y = 2$$
$$2x + y = 3$$

1—O—Answer:

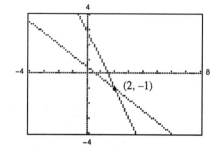

10. Solve the system by the method of substitution:

$$0.1x - 0.3y = 1.2$$
$$3x - 2y = 71$$

(a) $(5, 27)$ (b) $(a, 5a)$ (c) $(27, 5)$

(d) $\left(\frac{61}{3}, 5\right)$ (e) None of these

1—M—Answer: c

11. Solve the system by the method of substitution:

$$\tfrac{1}{3}x - \tfrac{3}{5}y = -2$$
$$2x - y = 14$$

(a) $\left(\frac{136}{23}, \frac{50}{23}\right)$ (b) $(12, 10)$ (c) $(12, -38)$

(d) No solution   (e) None of these

1—M—Answer: b

12. Solve the system by the method of substitution:

$$x^2 + 2y = 6$$
$$2x + y = 3$$

(a) $(4, -5)$ (b) $(2, 1)$ (c) $(0, 3)$

(d) $(0, 3)$ and $(4, -5)$ (e) None of these

1—M—Answer: d

13. Solve the system graphically:

$$x^2 + 2y = -6$$
$$x - y = 3$$

1—O—Answer:

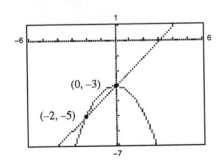

14. Solve the system by the method of substitution:

$$2x^2 - y = -2$$
$$x - y = -2$$

1—O—Answer: $(0, 2)$ and $\left(\frac{1}{2}, \frac{5}{2}\right)$

15. Solve the system by the method of substitution:

$$3x + 2y = 12$$
$$5x - y = 23$$

(a) $\left(-\frac{14}{13}, -\frac{344}{13}\right)$ (b) $\left(\frac{58}{13}, -\frac{9}{13}\right)$ (c) $\left(\frac{35}{13}, -\frac{124}{13}\right)$

(d) $(-17, \ 108)$ (e) None of these

1—M—Answer: b

16. Solve the system by the method of substitution:

$$6x + 2y = \quad 7$$
$$4x - 7y = -37$$

(a) $\left(4, -\frac{53}{7}\right)$ (b) $\left(6, \frac{61}{7}\right)$ (c) $\left(6, -\frac{29}{2}\right)$ (d) $\left(-\frac{1}{2}, 5\right)$ (e) None of these

1—M—Answer: d

17. Solve the system by the method of substitution:

$$x - 2y = \quad 0$$
$$4y - 3x = 10$$

(a) $(-10, -5)$ (b) $(6, \ 3)$ (c) $\left(\frac{1}{2}, \frac{1}{4}\right)$ (d) $\left(1, \frac{1}{2}\right)$ (e) None of these

1—M—Answer: a

18. Solve the system graphically:

$$x - y = \quad 4$$
$$3x - 2y = 14$$

1—O—Answer:

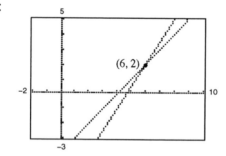

19. Solve the system:

$$x + y = 16$$
$$\frac{1}{2}x + \frac{1}{6}y = \quad 2$$

(a) $(4, \ 12)$ (b) $(-2, \ 18)$ (c) $(-4, \ 20)$ (d) $(2, \ 14)$ (e) None of these

1—M—Answer: b

20. Find all points of intersection of the graphs:

$$x^2 + y^2 = 3$$
$$2x^2 - y = 0$$

(a) $\left(\dfrac{3}{2}, -2\right)$

(b) $\left(\pm\dfrac{\sqrt{3}}{2}, \dfrac{3}{2}\right)$

(c) $\left(\pm\dfrac{\sqrt{3}}{2}, \dfrac{3}{2}\right)$, $(\pm 1, -2)$

(d) No points of intersection

(e) None of these

2—M—Answer: b

21. Use a graphing utility to find all points of intersection of the graphs.

$$(x - 3)^2 + y^2 = 4$$
$$-2x + y^2 = 0$$

2—O—Answer:

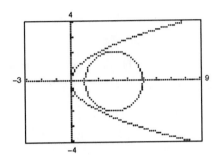

No points of intersection.

22. Use a graphing utility to find all the points of intersection of the graphs.

$$x^2 - 4x + y = 0$$
$$x - y = 0$$

1—O—Answer:

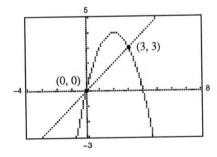

23. Use a graphing utility to find all the points of intersection of the graphs.

    $$2x^2 - y - 1 = 0$$
    $$2x^2 + y - 3 = 0$$

    1—O—Answer:

    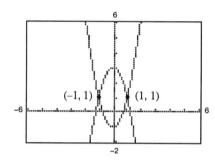

24. Find all points of intersection of the graphs:

    $$3x - y = -2$$
    $$x^3 - y = 0$$

    (a) $(2,\ 8)(1,\ 1)$ (b) $(-2,\ -8)(-1,\ -1)$ (c) $(-2,\ -8)(1,\ 1)$

    (d) $(2,\ 8)(-1,\ -1)$ (e) None of these

    1—M—Answer: d

25. Find the number of points of intersection of the graphs:

    $$x^2 + y = 3$$
    $$x^2 + y^2 = 1$$

    (a) 4   (b) 3   (c) 2   (d) 1   (e) 0

    1—M—Answer: e

26. Find the number of points of intersection of the graphs:

    $$x^2 + y^2 = 2$$
    $$2x + y = 10$$

    (a) 4   (b) 3   (c) 2   (d) 1   (e) 0

    1—M—Answer: e

27. Find the number of points of intersection of the graphs:

    $$x^2 + y = 1$$
    $$x^2 - y = 3$$

    (a) 4   (b) 3   (c) 2   (d) 1   (e) 0

    1—M—Answer: c

28. Find the number of points of intersection:

$$x^2 + y^2 = 5$$
$$x + 2y - 5 = 0$$

(a) 4   (b) 3   (c) 2   (d) 1   (e) 0

1—M—Answer: d

29. A total of $11,000 is invested in two funds paying 7% and 8% simple interest. If the yearly interest for both funds totals $865, determine the amount invested at 8%.

(a) $9,500   (b) $6,500   (c) $1,500   (d) $4,500   (e) None of these

1—M—Answer: a

30. A total of $50,000 is invested in two funds paying 8% and 10% simple interest. If the yearly interest for both funds totals $4,660, determine the amount invested at 8%.

(a) $33,000   (b) $24,000   (c) $26,000   (d) $17,000   (e) None of these

1—M—Answer: d

31. A total of $12,000 is invested in two funds paying 7% and $9\frac{1}{2}$% simple interest. If the annual interest totals $913.75, determine the amount invested at 7%.

(a) $7325   (b) $840   (c) $9050   (d) $10,000   (e) None of these

1—M—Answer: c

32. A total of $6000 is invested in two funds paying $5\frac{1}{4}$% and 6% simple interest. If the annual interest totals $327, determine the amount invested at 6%.

(a) $1600   (b) $3750   (c) $6000   (d) $270   (e) None of these

1—M—Answer: a

33. If the total cost of running a business is given by the equation $C = 450x + 1,000$ and the revenue is given by the equation $R = 500x$, find the sales necessary to break even.

(a) 220   (b) 11   (c) 20   (d) 2,000   (e) None of these

1—M—Answer: c

34. If the total cost of running a business is given by the equation $C = 4.16x + 75,000$ and the revenue is given by the equation $R = 7.91x$, find the sales necessary to break even.

(a) 6,214   (b) 20,000   (c) 200   (d) 9,482   (e) None of these

1—M—Answer: b

35. Suppose you are setting up for a small business and have invested $5,000 to produce an item that will sell for $9. If each unit can be produced for $7, how many units must you sell to break even?

(a) 25   (b) 2,500   (c) 556   (d) 714   (e) None of these

1—M—Answer: b

36. Suppose you are setting up a small business and have invested $18,000 to produce an item that will sell for $20.65. If each unit can be produced for $13.45, determine the number of units that you must sell in order to break even.

(a) 2,500   (b) 872   (c) 1,338   (d) 250   (e) None of these

1—M—Answer: a

9.3 Systems of Linear Equations in Two Variables

1. Solve the linear system by the method of elimination:

$$7x - 3y = 26$$
$$2x + 5y = 25$$

(a) $\left(-5, -\frac{61}{3}\right)$ (b) $(5, 3)$ (c) Infinitely many solutions

(d) No solution   (e) None of these

1—M—Answer: b

2. Solve the linear system by the method of elimination:

$$2x + 4y = 7$$
$$3x + 6y = 5$$

(a) $\left(1, \frac{5}{4}\right)$ (b) $(0, 0)$ (c) Infinitely many solutions

(d) No solution   (e) None of these

1—M—Answer: d

3. Solve the linear system by the method of elimination:

$$6x - 5y = 4$$
$$3x + 2y = 1$$

(a) $\left(\frac{13}{27}, -\frac{2}{9}\right)$ (b) $\left(-\frac{2}{9}, -\frac{8}{5}\right)$ (c) $\left(-\frac{8}{5}, -\frac{68}{25}\right)$

(d) $\left(2, \frac{8}{5}\right)$ (e) None of these

1—M—Answer: a

4. Solve the linear system by the method of elimination:

$$7x + y = 3$$
$$21x + 5y = 11$$

1—O—Answer: $\left(\frac{2}{7}, 1\right)$

5. Use the method of elimination to find the value of y in the solution of the system of equations:

$$2x - 3y = 5$$
$$2x + 3y = -3$$

(a) $\frac{1}{2}$ (b) $-\frac{3}{4}$ (c) $-\frac{4}{3}$

(d) $\frac{4}{3}$ (e) None of these

1—M—Answer: c

6. Use the method of elimination to find the value of x in the solution of the system of equations:

$$2x - y = 6$$
$$2x + 2y = -9$$

(a) 2   (b) $\frac{1}{2}$ (c) -5

(d) $\frac{21}{2}$ (e) None of these

1—M—Answer: b

7. Use the method of elimination to find the value of y in the solution of the system of equations:

$$5x + 2y = -1$$
$$-15x + 8y = 10$$

(a) $\frac{1}{2}$ (b) $\frac{9}{10}$ (c) $\frac{9}{14}$

(d) 0   (e) None of these

1—M—Answer: a

8. Find the value of y in the solution of the system of equations:

$$-2x + 3y = 5$$
$$3x - 2y = 0$$

(a) 0   (b) 1   (c) 3

(d) -1 (e) None of these

1—M—Answer: c

9. Find the value of y in the solution of the system of equations:

$$3x + 7y = 15$$
$$-5x + 2y = 16$$

(a) 3   (b) -2 (c) 2

(d) $\frac{6}{7}$ (e) None of these

1—M—Answer: a

10. Solve this system by method of elimination and verify the solution with a graphing utility:

$$2x - 5y = -4$$
$$4x + 3y = 5$$

2—O—Answer: $\left(\frac{1}{2},\ 1\right)$

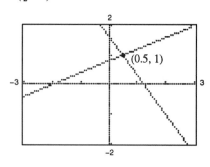

11. Solve the system by method of elimination and verify the solution with a graphing utility:

$$6x + y = -2$$
$$4x - 3y = 17$$

2—O—Answer: $\left(\frac{1}{2},\ -5\right)$

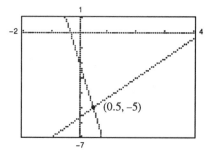

12. Solve the system by the method of elimination and verify the solution using a graphing utility.

$$\frac{6}{x} - \frac{8}{y} = 2$$

$$\frac{9}{2x} - \frac{6}{y} = \frac{3}{2}$$

2—O—Answer: Infinitely many solutions

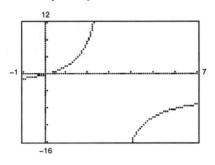

13. Solve the system by the method of elimination:

$$\frac{2}{x} - \frac{3}{y} = 8$$

$$\frac{3}{x} + \frac{3}{y} = 2$$

(a) $(2, -\frac{4}{3})$ (b) $(\frac{1}{2}, -\frac{3}{4})$ (c) Infinitely many solutions

(d) No solution   (e) None of these

1—M—Answer: b

14. Solve the system by the method of elimination:

$$\frac{6}{x} + \frac{2}{y} = 8$$

$$\frac{9}{x} + \frac{5}{y} = 16$$

(a) $(\frac{2}{3}, 2)$ (b) $(\frac{3}{2}, \frac{1}{2})$ (c) $(2, \frac{3}{2})$

(d) $(\frac{1}{2}, \frac{2}{3})$ (e) None of these

2—M—Answer: b

15. Solve the system of equations:

$$\frac{6}{x} + \frac{1}{y} = -2$$

$$\frac{4}{x} - \frac{3}{y} = 17$$

1—O—Answer: $\left(2, -\frac{1}{5}\right)$

16. Solve the following system of equations for x:

$$\frac{3}{x} - \frac{2}{y} = 5$$

$$\frac{1}{x} + \frac{4}{y} = 4$$

(a) $\frac{1}{2}$ (b) 2   (c) 5   (d) $\frac{1}{5}$ (e) None of these

1—M—Answer: a

17. Solve the following system of equations for x:

$$\frac{5}{2x} - \frac{3}{y} = \frac{1}{3}$$

$$\frac{1}{x} + \frac{2}{y} = \frac{2}{3}$$

(a) $\frac{1}{2}$ (b) 6   (c) $\frac{1}{3}$ (d) 3   (e) None of these

1—M—Answer: d

18. Solve the following system of equations for y:

$$\frac{2}{x} + \frac{3}{y} = 7$$

$$\frac{3}{x} - \frac{1}{y} = 16$$

(a) 5   (b) −1   (c) $\frac{1}{5}$ (d) 2   (e) None of these

1—M—Answer: b

19. Solve the following system of equations for x:

$$\frac{5}{x} - \frac{3}{y} = 2$$

$$\frac{2}{x} + \frac{5}{y} = -24$$

(a) $-\frac{1}{2}$ (b) $-\frac{1}{4}$ (c) 5   (d) $-\frac{1}{3}$ (e) None of these

1—M—Answer: a

20. Solve the following system of equations for x:

$$\frac{5}{x} - \frac{7}{y} = 11$$

$$\frac{3}{x} + \frac{2}{y} = -12$$

(a) $-\frac{1}{2}$ (b) −2   (c) −1   (d) 1   (e) None of these

1—M—Answer: e

21. Solve the system of linear equations graphically:

$$\tfrac{1}{3}x - \tfrac{3}{5}y = -2$$
$$2x - y = 14$$

2—O—Answer:

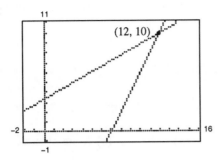

22. Solve the system of linear equations graphically.

$$3x + 2y = 8$$
$$6x + 4y = 10$$

1—O—Answer: No solutions

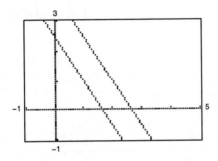

23. Solve the system of linear equations:

$$6x - 8y = 2$$
$$\tfrac{9}{2}x - 6y = \tfrac{3}{2}$$

(a) $(\tfrac{3}{2}, 4)$ (b) $(\tfrac{2}{3}, \tfrac{1}{4})$ (c) Infinitely many solutions

(d) No solutions (e) None of these

2—M—Answer: c

24. Solve the system of linear equations:

$$0.06x + 0.02y = 0.08$$
$$0.09x + 0.05y = 0.16$$

(a) $(\tfrac{3}{2}, \tfrac{1}{2})$ (b) $(\tfrac{2}{3}, 2)$ (c) $(\tfrac{1}{2}, \tfrac{2}{3})$

(d) $(2, \tfrac{3}{2})$ (e) None of these

2—M—Answer: b

25. Solve the following system of linear equations for x:

$$x + \quad y = 1000$$
$$0.03x + 0.04y = 31.50$$

(a) 325   (b) 540   (c) 675   (d) 850   (e) None of these

1—M—Answer: d

26. Solve the following system of linear equations for x:

$$x + 2.5y = 900$$
$$5x - \quad 2y = 150$$

(a) 300   (b) 150   (c) 900   (d) 0   (e) None of these

1—M—Answer: b

27. Solve the following system of linear equations for y:

$$3x + 4.5y = 825$$
$$0.2x + 0.5y = \quad 89$$

(a) 100   (b) 150   (c) 170   (d) 190   (e) None of these

1—M—Answer: c

28. A twenty pound mixture of two kinds of candy sells for \$30.52. One kind of candy in the mixture sells for \$1.35 per pound. The other kind sells for \$1.79 per pound. How much of the cheaper priced candy is in the mixture?

(a) 8 pounds   (b) 10 pounds   (c) 12 pounds

(d) 14 pounds   (e) None of these

2—M—Answer: c

29. How many liters of a 40% solution of acid must be combined with a 15% solution to obtain 30 liters of a 20% solution?

2—O—Answer: 6

30. The perimeter of a rectangle is 91 feet and the length is 8 feet more than twice the width. Find the dimensions of the rectangle.

2—O—Answer: $L = 33$ feet, $W = 12.5$ feet

31. A total of \$15,000 is invested in two corporate bonds that pay $7\frac{1}{4}\%$ and 9% simple interest. The annual income from both bonds is \$1,280. Determine how much is invested at 9%.

(a) \$9000   (b) \$4000   (c) \$11,000

(d) \$6000   (e) None of these

1—M—Answer: c

32. Suppose the demand and supply equations for a certain product are given by

$$p = 220 - 0.0002x \qquad \text{Demand equation}$$
$$p = 90 + 0.0003x \qquad \text{Supply equation}$$

where p is the price in dollars and x represents the number of units. Find the point of equilibrium.

1—O—Answer: $x = 260{,}000$ and $p = \$168$

33. Suppose the demand and supply equations for a certain product are given by:

$$p = 860 - 0.05x \qquad \text{Demand equation}$$
$$p = 420 + 0.15x \qquad \text{Supply equation}$$

Find the point $(x,\ p)$ of equilibrium.

(a) (12,800, 220)   (b) (1700, 775)   (c) (420, 839)

(d) (2200, 750)   (e) None of these

1—M—Answer: d

34. Find the least squares regression line $y = ax + b$ for the points $(0.6,\ 9.3)(1.2,\ 12.0)$ and $(1.8,\ 15.2)$ if

$$nb + \left(\sum_{i=1}^{n} x_i \right) a = \sum_{i=1}^{n} y_i \text{ and } \left(\sum_{i=1}^{n} x_i \right) b + \left(\sum_{i=1}^{n} x_i^2 \right) a = \sum_{i=1}^{n} x_i y_i .$$

2—O—Answer: $y = 5.1x + 6.8$

35. Find the least squares regression line $y = ax + b$ for the points $(1, 2)$, $(2, 4)$, $(3, 5)$ and $(4, 7)$ if

$$nb + \left(\sum_{i=1}^{n} x_i \right) a = \sum_{i=1}^{n} y_i \text{ and } \left(\sum_{i=1}^{n} x_i \right) b + \left(\sum_{i=1}^{n} x_i^2 \right) a = \sum_{i=1}^{n} x_i y_i .$$

2—O—Answer: $y = 1.4x + 1$

36. Find the least squares regression line $y = ax + b$ by solving the following system for a and b.

$$5b + 10a = 12.3$$
$$10b + 30a = 29.1$$

(a) $y = 0.45x + 1.56$ (b) $y = 0.26x + 1.94$ (c) $y = 0.6x + 1.26$

(d) $y = 3.2x - 3.94$ (e) None of these

1—M—Answer: a

37. Find the least squares regression line $y = ax + b$ by solving the following system for a and b.

$$5b + 10a = 9.2$$
$$10b + 30a = 21.1$$

1—O—Answer: $y = 0.27x + 1.3$

9.4 Systems of Linear Equations in More Than Two Variables

1. Use the method of back substitution to find the value of x for the solution of the system of equations:

$$x + 2y + z = 15$$
$$5y - 2z = -16$$
$$z = 3$$

(a) 22   (b) 16   (c) $\frac{15}{7}$ (d) 8   (e) None of these

1—M—Answer: b

2. Use the method of back substitution to find the value of x for the solution of the system of equations:

$$x + 2y - z = 26$$
$$y + 3z = 5$$
$$z = -2$$

(a) 4   (b) 26   (c) 6   (d) 2   (e) None of these

1—M—Answer: d

3. Use the method of back substitution to find the solution of the system of equations:

$$x + y + z = 2$$
$$y - z = 5$$
$$z = -2$$

1—O—Answer: $(1, \ 3, \ -2)$

4. Use Gaussian elimination to solve the system of equations:

$$x - 6y + z = 1$$
$$-x + 2y - 4z = 3$$
$$7x - 10y + 3z = -25$$

(a) $(5, \ 1, \ 2)$ (b) $(-5, \ -1, \ 0)$ (c) $(-1, \ 3, \ 1)$
(d) No solution   (e) None of these

1—M—Answer: b

5. Use Gaussian elimination to solve the system of equations:

$$x + 2y + z = 6$$
$$2x - y + 3z = -2$$
$$x + y - 2z = 0$$

1—O—Answer: $(-1, \ 3, \ 1)$

6. Solve the system of linear equations:

$$x + 3y + z \qquad = 0$$
$$5x - y + z + w = 0$$
$$2x \qquad + 2z + w = 2$$
$$3x \qquad + 2z - w = 10$$

2—O—Answer: $x = 0$, $y = -1$, $z = 3$, $w = -4$

7. Solve the system of linear equations:

$$x - y + z = 5$$
$$3x + 2y - z = -2$$
$$2x + y + 3z = 10$$

(a) $(1, -1, 3)$ (b) $(2, -5, -2)$ (c) $(-1, 7, 13)$

(d) $(3, -9, -7)$ (e) No solution

1—M—Answer: a

8. Solve the system of linear equations:

$$x + y + 3z = 0$$
$$2x - y - 3z = -9$$
$$x + 2y + 3z = 1$$

(a) $\left(-3a, a, \dfrac{2a}{3}\right)$ (b) $\left(-1, 2, -\dfrac{1}{3}\right)$ (c) $\left(-3, 1, \dfrac{2}{3}\right)$

(d) No solution   (e) None of these

1—M—Answer: c

9. Solve the system of linear equations:

$$6x - 9y + 4z = -7$$
$$2x + 6y - z = 6$$
$$4x - 3y + 2z = -2$$

(a) $\left(\dfrac{1}{2}, \dfrac{2}{3}, -1\right)$ (b) $\left(\dfrac{11}{21}, 1, -\dfrac{2}{7}\right)$ (c) $\left(a, \dfrac{31a}{15}, \dfrac{44a}{5}\right)$

(d) No solution   (e) None of these

2—M—Answer: a

10. Solve the system of linear equations:

$$x + y - z = -1$$
$$2x + 3y - z = -2$$
$$-3x - 2y + 2z = -3$$

1—O—Answer: $(5, -3, 3)$

11. Solve the system of linear equations:

$$x - 3y + 2z = -11$$
$$x + 4y - 5z = 17$$
$$-2x + y - z = 6$$

1—O—Answer: $(-1, 2, -2)$

12. Solve the system of linear equations:

$$2x + y - z = 3$$
$$x - 3y + z = 7$$
$$3x + 5y - 3z = 0$$

(a) $\left(a, \dfrac{3a - 10}{2}, \dfrac{7a - 16}{2}\right)$

(b) $\left(\dfrac{3a + 10}{3}, a, 6a - 21\right)$

(c) $(2, -2, -1)$

(d) No solution

(e) None of these

2—M—Answer: d

13. Solve the system of linear equations:

$$x + y - 2z = 1$$
$$3x + y + z = 4$$
$$-x - 3y + 9z = 10$$

1—O—Answer: No solution

14. Solve the system of linear equations:

$$2x - 4y + z = 7$$
$$x + 3y - z = 2$$
$$-5x + 15y - 4z = 10$$

2—O—Answer: No solution

15. Solve the system of linear equations:

$$x - y + z = 2$$
$$2x + 3y + z = 7$$
$$3x + 2y + 2z = -8$$

(a) $(1, 0, 1)$

(b) $(6, 4, 4)$

(c) $(1, 2, 3)$

(d) No solution

(e) None of these

1—M—Answer: d

16. Solve the system of linear equations:

$$x - 2y - z = 7$$
$$-3x + 6y + 3z = 0$$

(a) $(7 + 5a, 2a, a)$

(b) $(1, 1, -8)$

(c) $(1, 0, 1)$

(d) No solution

(e) None of these

2—M—Answer: d

17. Solve the system of linear equations:

$$x + y + z = 4$$
$$x - 3y - z = 1$$
$$2x - 2y = 9$$

(a) $\left(-1, \dfrac{4}{7}, \dfrac{31}{7}\right)$

(b) $\left(a, \dfrac{2a - 9}{2}, 17 - 4a\right)$

(c) $\left(\dfrac{9 + 2a}{2}, a, -\dfrac{4a + 1}{2}\right)$

(d) No solution

(e) None of these

1—M—Answer: d

18. Solve the system of linear equations:

$$2x - 4y + z = 5$$
$$x + y + z = 3$$
$$6x + 5z = 17$$

(a) $\left(\dfrac{5}{6}, \dfrac{1}{6}, 0\right)$

(b) $\left(a, \dfrac{a - 2}{5}, \dfrac{17 - 6a}{5}\right)$

(c) $\left(a, \dfrac{2a - 3}{5}, \dfrac{a + 7}{5}\right)$

(d) No solution

(e) None of these

1—M—Answer: b

19. Solve the system of linear equations:

$$3x + 4y - 2z = 6$$
$$x + y + z = 2$$
$$x + 2y - 4z = 2$$

(a) $(20, -15, -3)$

(b) $\left(\dfrac{a}{2}, \dfrac{5a}{4}, \dfrac{a}{4}\right)$

(c) $(2 - 6a, 5a, a)$

(d) No solution

(e) None of these

2—M—Answer: c

20. Solve the system of linear equations:

$$x + y + z = 2$$
$$3x - 2y + z = 7$$
$$5y + 2z = -1$$

(a) $\left(\dfrac{2}{5}, -\dfrac{7}{5}, 3\right)$ (b) $\left(a, \dfrac{2a}{3}, \dfrac{a}{3}\right)$

(c) $\left(\dfrac{11 - 3a}{5}, \dfrac{-1 - 2a}{5}, a\right)$ (d) No solution

(e) None of these

2—M—Answer: c

21. Solve the system of linear equations:

$$2x + y - z = 1$$
$$x + 4y + 2z = 7$$
$$-5x + y + 5z = 4$$

2—O—Answer: $\left(\dfrac{-3 + 6a}{7}, \dfrac{13 - 5a}{7}, a\right)$

22. Solve the system of linear equations:

$$x - y - z = 0$$
$$2x + 4y + z = 0$$
$$3x + y - z = 0$$

1—O—Answer: $(a, -a, 2a)$ where a is any real number.

23. Solve the system of linear equations:

$$2x + 3y + 3z = 6$$
$$-x + y + z = 2$$

(a) $(2a - 4, 2 - a, a)$ (b) $(0, 2 - a, a)$ (c) $(2a, 2 + a, a)$

(d) No solutions   (e) None of these

2—M—Answer: b

24. Solve the system of linear equations:

$$2x + 3y - z = 6$$
$$x - y + 2z = 1$$

(a) $\left(a, \dfrac{13 - 5a}{5}, \dfrac{9 - 5a}{5}\right)$ (b) $\left(\dfrac{10 - 2a}{3}, a, \dfrac{5 - 2a}{3}\right)$ (c) $\left(3, -\dfrac{2}{5}, -\dfrac{6}{5}\right)$

(d) No solution   (e) None of these

1—M—Answer: a

25. Solve the system of linear equations:

$$2x + 3y - 3z = 7$$
$$-3x + y + z = 2$$

1—O—Answer: $\left(\dfrac{1 + 6a}{11}, \dfrac{25 + 7a}{11}, a \right)$

26. Find the value of b that makes the system inconsistent:

$$6x + by = 14$$
$$-2x + 3y = 2$$

(a) -9 (b) -3 (c) $\frac{1}{7}$ (d) $\frac{1}{3}$ (e) None of these

1—M—Answer: a

27. Find the value of a that makes the system inconsistent:

$$-3x + 5y = 2$$
$$ax - 10y = 0$$

(a) 3   (b) 6   (c) 2   (d) -6 (e) None of these

1—M—Answer: b

28. Find an equation of the parabola, $y = ax^2 + bx + c$, that passes through $(1, 4)$, $(-1, 0)$, and $(2, -3)$. Verify your result with a graphing utility.

(a) $y = 4x^2 + 2x - 2$ (b) $y = 3x^2 + 2x - 7$ (c) $y = -3x^2 + 2x + 5$

(d) $y = 4x^2$ (e) None of these

2—M—Answer: c

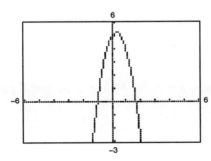

29. Find an equation of the parabola, $y = ax^2 + bx + c$, that passes through $(0, 5)$, $(2, -5)$, and $(-3, -40)$.

(a) $y = 3x^2 - 2x - 7$ (b) $y = -4x^2 + 3x + 5$ (c) $y = 4x^2 + 3x + 5$

(d) $y = 9x^2 - 121$ (e) None of these

2—M—Answer: b

30. Find an equation of the parabola, $y = ax^2 + bx + c$, that passes through $(0, -5)$, $(2, 1)$, and $(-1, -14)$. Verify your result with a graphing utility.

    2—O—Answer: $y = -2x^2 + 7x - 5$

    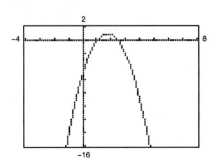

31. Find an equation of the parabola, $y = ax^2 + bx + c$, that passes through $(1, 1)$, $(-1, 11)$, and $(3, 23)$. Verify your result with a graphing utility.

    2—O—Answer: $y = 4x^2 - 5x + 2$

    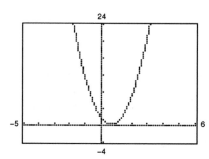

32. Find the value of c in the quadratic equation, $y = ax^2 + bx + c$, if its graph passes through the points $(1, 0)$, $(-1, -6)$, and $(2, 9)$.

    (a) -5 (b) -4 (c) 3   (d) 11   (e) None of these

    2—M—Answer: a

33. Find the value of b in the quadratic equation, $y = ax^2 + bx + c$, if its graph passes through the points $(-1, 4)$, $(1, -2)$, and $(2, -2)$.

    (a) -3 (b) 2   (c) -2 (d) -1 (e) None of these

    2—M—Answer: a

34. Find an equation of the parabola, $y = ax^2 + bx + c$, that passes through the points $(1, -2)$, $(-2, 19)$, and $(3, 4)$.

    2—O—Answer: $y = 2x^2 - 5x + 1$

35. Find an equation of the circle, $x^2 + y^2 + Dx + Ey + F = 0$, that passes through $(9, -3)$, $(2, 4)$, and $(-5, -3)$.

    (a) $x^2 + y^2 + 3x - 2y + 10 = 0$ (b) $x^2 + y^2 - 4x + 6y - 36 = 0$

    (c) $x^2 + y^2 - 8x + 2y - 12 = 0$ (d) $x^2 + y^2 + 2x - 7y + 1 = 0$

    (e) None of these

    2—M—Answer: b

36. The sum of three positive numbers is 19. Find the second number if the third is three times the first and the second is one more than twice the first.

    (a) 7   (b) 13   (c) 1   (d) 9   (e) None of these

    1—M—Answer: a

37. The sum of three positive numbers is 180. Find the first number if the third is four times the first and the second is thirty-six less than the third.

    (a) 12   (b) 36   (c) 24   (d) 60   (e) None of these

    2—M—Answer: c

38. A total of $7000 is invested in three separate accounts. Some of the money was invested at 6%, some at 8%, and the remaining at 9%. Find the amount invested at each rate if the total interest for one year was $555 and the amount invested at 8% was three times the amount invested at 9%. (Assume simple interest.)

    2—O—Answer: $1000 at 6%, $4500 at 8%, and $1500 at 9%

39. Write the partial fraction decomposition: $\dfrac{8x + 6}{x(x + 1)(x + 2)}$

    (a) $\dfrac{2}{x + 1} - \dfrac{5}{x + 2} + \dfrac{3}{x}$ (b) $\dfrac{7}{x + 1} + \dfrac{1}{x + 2} - \dfrac{6}{x}$

    (c) $\dfrac{1}{x + 1} + \dfrac{3}{x + 2} - \dfrac{1}{x}$ (d) $\dfrac{6}{x + 1} - \dfrac{1}{x + 2} - \dfrac{1}{x}$

    (e) None of these

    1—M—Answer: a

40. Write the partial fraction decomposition: $\dfrac{5}{x^2 - 7x + 12}$

    1—O—Answer: $\dfrac{5}{x - 4} - \dfrac{5}{x - 3}$

9.5 Matrices and Systems of Linear Equations

1. Determine the order of the matrix: $\begin{bmatrix} 2 & 7 & 9 \\ 3 & 5 & -1 \end{bmatrix}$

(a) 2×3 (b) 3×2 (c) 3

(d) 2 (e) None of these

1—M—Answer: a

2. Determine the order of the matrix: $\begin{bmatrix} 1 & 3 \\ 0 & 6 \\ 2 & 1 \\ 4 & 7 \end{bmatrix}$

(a) 2×4 (b) 4×2 (c) 4

(d) 2 (e) None of these

1—M—Answer: b

3. Determine the order of the matrix: $\begin{bmatrix} 2 & 1 \\ -1 & 5 \\ 4 & -3 \end{bmatrix}$

(a) 6 (b) 2×3 (c) 5

(d) 3×2 (e) None of these

1—M—Answer: d

4. Determine which of the following matrices is in row-echelon form.

(a) $\begin{bmatrix} 1 & 3 & -1 & 4 \\ 0 & 2 & 1 & 1 \\ 0 & 0 & 1 & 4 \end{bmatrix}$ (b) $\begin{bmatrix} 1 & 2 & 3 & 4 \\ 0 & 1 & 4 & 5 \\ 0 & 0 & 0 & 0 \end{bmatrix}$ (c) $\begin{bmatrix} 2 & -1 & 6 & 3 \\ 4 & 1 & 2 & 0 \\ 0 & 1 & 2 & 0 \end{bmatrix}$

(d) All of these (e) None of these

1—M—Answer: b

5. Determine which of the following matrices is in row-echelon form.

(a) $\begin{bmatrix} 0 & 3 & 2 & -1 \\ 4 & 0 & 1 & 0 \\ 0 & 0 & 2 & 5 \end{bmatrix}$ (b) $\begin{bmatrix} 3 & 1 & 2 & 5 \\ 0 & 2 & 0 & 4 \\ 0 & 0 & 3 & 7 \end{bmatrix}$ (c) $\begin{bmatrix} 1 & 2 & 3 & 4 \\ 0 & 2 & 4 & 7 \\ 0 & 0 & 1 & 0 \end{bmatrix}$

(d) All of these (e) None of these

1—M—Answer: e

6. Determine which of the following matrices is in row-echelon form.

(a) $\begin{bmatrix} 1 & 2 & 4 & 6 \\ 0 & 1 & 3 & 2 \\ 0 & 0 & 1 & 0 \end{bmatrix}$
(b) $\begin{bmatrix} 3 & 4 & 7 & 0 \\ 6 & 2 & 1 & 4 \\ 3 & 2 & 1 & 3 \end{bmatrix}$
(c) $\begin{bmatrix} 1 & 6 & 4 & 2 \\ 0 & 2 & 3 & 1 \\ 0 & 0 & 1 & 0 \end{bmatrix}$

(d) All of these
(e) None of these

1—M—Answer: a

7. Determine which of the following matrices is in row-echelon form.

(a) $\begin{bmatrix} 1 & 2 & 3 & 4 \\ 0 & 1 & 7 & 2 \\ 0 & 0 & 1 & 5 \end{bmatrix}$
(b) $\begin{bmatrix} 1 & 0 & 0 & 3 \\ 0 & 1 & 0 & 2 \\ 0 & 0 & 1 & 5 \end{bmatrix}$
(c) $\begin{bmatrix} 1 & 0 & 4 & 7 \\ 0 & 1 & 0 & 2 \\ 0 & 0 & 1 & 2 \end{bmatrix}$

(d) All of these
(e) None of these

1—M—Answer: d

8. Determine which matrix is in row-echelon form.

(a) $\begin{bmatrix} 1 & 5 \\ 0 & 1 \\ 0 & 0 \end{bmatrix}$
(b) $\begin{bmatrix} 0 & 0 & 0 \\ 0 & 1 & 2 \end{bmatrix}$
(c) $\begin{bmatrix} 1 & -4 & 3 & 7 \\ 0 & 1 & 2 & -1 \\ 0 & 0 & 3 & 5 \end{bmatrix}$

(d) $[3]$
(e) None of these

1—M—Answer: a

9. Determine which matrix is in reduced row-echelon form.

(a) $\begin{bmatrix} 1 & -2 \\ 0 & 1 \\ 0 & 0 \end{bmatrix}$
(b) $\begin{bmatrix} 1 & 0 & 4 & -2 \\ 0 & 1 & 7 & 5 \\ 0 & 0 & 0 & 0 \end{bmatrix}$
(c) $\begin{bmatrix} 1 & -6 & 2 \\ 0 & 1 & 4 \end{bmatrix}$

(d) $\begin{bmatrix} 1 & 1 \\ 0 & 1 \end{bmatrix}$
(e) None of these

1—M—Answer: b

10. Write the matrix in reduced row-echelon form: $\begin{bmatrix} 3 & 1 & 1 & 7 \\ 1 & -2 & 0 & 5 \\ 1 & 1 & 2 & 6 \end{bmatrix}$

(a) $\begin{bmatrix} 1 & 1 & 2 & 6 \\ 0 & 3 & 2 & 1 \\ 0 & 0 & 11 & 31 \end{bmatrix}$
(b) $\begin{bmatrix} 1 & 0 & 0 & \frac{21}{11} \\ 0 & 1 & 0 & -\frac{17}{11} \\ 0 & 0 & 1 & \frac{31}{11} \end{bmatrix}$

(c) $\begin{bmatrix} 1 & -2 & 0 & 5 \\ 0 & 1 & \frac{1}{7} & -\frac{8}{7} \\ 0 & 0 & 11 & 31 \end{bmatrix}$
(d) $\begin{bmatrix} 1 & 0 & 0 & \frac{3}{11} \\ 0 & 1 & 0 & \frac{7}{11} \\ 0 & 0 & 1 & -\frac{14}{11} \end{bmatrix}$

(e) None of these

1—M—Answer: b

11. Write the matrix in reduced row-echelon form: $\begin{bmatrix} 3 & 6 & -2 & 28 \\ -2 & -4 & 5 & -37 \\ 1 & 2 & 9 & -39 \end{bmatrix}$

(a) $\begin{bmatrix} 1 & 2 & 1 & 1 \\ 0 & 0 & 1 & -5 \\ 0 & 0 & 0 & 0 \end{bmatrix}$ (b) $\begin{bmatrix} 0 & 0 & 0 & 0 \\ 1 & 2 & 0 & 6 \\ 0 & 0 & 1 & -5 \end{bmatrix}$ (c) $\begin{bmatrix} 1 & 2 & 0 & 6 \\ 0 & 0 & 1 & -5 \\ 0 & 0 & 0 & 0 \end{bmatrix}$

(d) $\begin{bmatrix} 1 & 2 & 1 & 1 \\ 0 & 0 & 1 & -5 \\ 0 & 0 & 0 & 3 \end{bmatrix}$ (e) None of these

1—M—Answer: c

12. Write the matrix in reduced row-echelon form: $\begin{bmatrix} 1 & 3 & -8 & 13 \\ 2 & -1 & 6 & -19 \\ -5 & 1 & 2 & 44 \end{bmatrix}$

(a) $\begin{bmatrix} 1 & 0 & 0 & -7 \\ 0 & 1 & 0 & 8 \\ 0 & 0 & 1 & \frac{1}{2} \end{bmatrix}$ (b) $\begin{bmatrix} 1 & 0 & 6 & -4 \\ 0 & 1 & 2 & 9 \\ 0 & 0 & 2 & 1 \end{bmatrix}$ (c) $\begin{bmatrix} 1 & 0 & 6 & -4 \\ 0 & 1 & -4 & 6 \\ 0 & 0 & 0 & 0 \end{bmatrix}$

(d) $\begin{bmatrix} 1 & 1 & 8 & 5 \\ 0 & 1 & 2 & 9 \\ 0 & 0 & 2 & 1 \end{bmatrix}$ (e) None of these

1—M—Answer: a

13. Write the matrix in reduced row-echelon form: $\begin{bmatrix} 1 & 2 & -1 & 3 \\ 7 & -1 & 0 & 2 \\ 3 & 2 & 1 & -1 \end{bmatrix}$

1—O—Answer: $\begin{bmatrix} 1 & 0 & 0 & \frac{5}{16} \\ 0 & 1 & 0 & \frac{3}{16} \\ 0 & 0 & 1 & -\frac{37}{16} \end{bmatrix}$

14. Write the matrix in reduced row-echelon form: $\begin{bmatrix} 21 & 14 & -7 & 10 \\ 7 & 7 & 7 & -1 \\ 7 & -14 & 28 & 23 \end{bmatrix}$

(a) $\begin{bmatrix} 1 & 0 & 0 & \frac{2}{7} \\ 0 & 0 & 1 & -\frac{5}{7} \\ 0 & 1 & 4 & \frac{1}{7} \end{bmatrix}$ (b) $\begin{bmatrix} 0 & 1 & 4 & -\frac{13}{7} \\ 1 & 0 & -3 & \frac{12}{7} \\ 5 & 0 & 0 & \frac{45}{7} \end{bmatrix}$ (c) $\begin{bmatrix} 1 & 0 & 0 & \frac{9}{7} \\ 0 & 1 & 0 & -\frac{9}{7} \\ 0 & 0 & 1 & -\frac{1}{7} \end{bmatrix}$

(d) $\begin{bmatrix} 1 & 0 & 0 & \frac{2}{7} \\ 0 & 1 & 0 & \frac{5}{7} \\ 0 & 0 & 1 & -\frac{2}{7} \end{bmatrix}$ (e) None of these

1—M—Answer: c

15. Use variables x, y and z to write the system of linear equations represented by the augmented matrix:

$$\begin{bmatrix} 2 & -1 & 0 & \vdots & 4 \\ 0 & 3 & 1 & \vdots & -2 \\ 1 & -3 & 1 & \vdots & 1 \end{bmatrix}$$

1—O—Answer:

$$2x - y = 4$$
$$3y + z = -2$$
$$x - 3y + z = 1$$

16. Find the solution to the system of linear equations with the augmented matrix: $\begin{bmatrix} 2 & -1 & \vdots & 3 \\ 0 & 1 & \vdots & 2 \end{bmatrix}$

(a) $(3, 2)$ (b) $(2, 3)$ (c) $(-1, 3)$

(d) $\left(\frac{5}{2}, 2\right)$ (e) None of these

1—M—Answer: d

17. Find the solution to the system of linear equations with the augmented matrix: $\begin{bmatrix} 1 & 2 & -1 & \vdots & 4 \\ 0 & 2 & 1 & \vdots & -3 \\ 0 & 0 & 2 & \vdots & -4 \end{bmatrix}$

(a) $\left(3, -\frac{1}{2}, -2\right)$ (b) $(4, -3, -4)$ (c) $(1, 2, -1)$

(d) $\left(10, -\frac{5}{2}, -2\right)$ (e) None of these

1—M—Answer: a

18. Find the solution to the system of linear equations with the augmented matrix: $\begin{bmatrix} 1 & 0 & 1 & \vdots & 0 \\ 0 & 1 & -2 & \vdots & 1 \end{bmatrix}$

(a) $(a, 1 + 2a, -a)$ (b) $(-a, 2a + 1, a)$ (c) $(a, 1 - 2a, a)$

(d) $(-a, 1 - 2a, a)$ (e) None of these

1—M—Answer: b

19. Find the solution to the system of linear equations with the augmented matrix: $\begin{bmatrix} 2 & 1 & \vdots & 7 \\ 5 & -3 & \vdots & 1 \end{bmatrix}$

(a) $(3, 1)$ (b) $(1, 1)$ (c) $(4, -1)$

(d) $(2, 3)$ (e) None of these

1—M—Answer: d

20. Find the solution to the system of linear equations with the augmented matrix: $\begin{bmatrix} 1 & 0 & 1 & \vdots & 1 \\ 2 & 1 & -1 & \vdots & 2 \end{bmatrix}$

(a) $(2a, -3a, a)$ (b) $(1 - a, 3a, a)$ (c) $(a + 2, 4a, -a)$

(d) $(3a, 0, 2a)$ (e) None of these

1—M—Answer: b

21. Find the solution to the system of linear equations with the augmented matrix: $\begin{bmatrix} 3 & 2 & 1 & \vdots & 3 \\ 2 & -1 & 3 & \vdots & 2 \end{bmatrix}$

(a) $(a,\ 3a,\ -7a)$ (b) $(3+a,\ 2a,\ a)$ (c) $(2a,\ 1+a,\ a)$

(d) $(1-a,\ a,\ a)$ (e) None of these

1—M—Answer: d

22. Write the augmented matrix for the given system of linear equations.

$$2x - 3y = 12$$
$$x + y = 16$$

1—O—Answer: $\begin{bmatrix} 2 & -3 & \vdots & 12 \\ 1 & 1 & \vdots & 16 \end{bmatrix}$

23. Write the augmented matrix for the given system of linear equations.

$$3x - y = 2$$
$$x + 2y = 7$$

(a) $\begin{bmatrix} 3 & 1 & \vdots & -2 \\ 1 & 2 & \vdots & -7 \end{bmatrix}$ (b) $\begin{bmatrix} 3 & 1 & \vdots & 2 \\ -1 & 2 & \vdots & 7 \end{bmatrix}$ (c) $\begin{bmatrix} 3 & -1 & \vdots & 2 \\ 1 & 2 & \vdots & 7 \end{bmatrix}$

(d) $\begin{bmatrix} -3 & 1 & \vdots & -2 \\ 1 & 2 & \vdots & -7 \end{bmatrix}$ (e) None of these

1—M—Answer: c

24. Write the augmented matrix for the given system of linear equations.

$$7x + 2y = 12$$
$$x - y = 16$$

(a) $\begin{bmatrix} 7 & 2 & \vdots & 12 \\ 1 & 1 & \vdots & 16 \end{bmatrix}$ (b) $\begin{bmatrix} 7 & 2 & \vdots & -12 \\ 1 & 1 & \vdots & -16 \end{bmatrix}$ (c) $\begin{bmatrix} 7 & 2 & \vdots & 12 \\ 1 & -1 & \vdots & 16 \end{bmatrix}$

(d) $\begin{bmatrix} 7 & 1 & \vdots & 12 \\ 2 & -1 & \vdots & 16 \end{bmatrix}$ (e) None of these

1—M—Answer: c

25. Write the augmented matrix for the given system of linear equations.

$$3x + 2y = 5$$
$$7x - 6y = 12$$

(a) $\begin{bmatrix} 3 & 2 & \vdots & 5 \\ 7 & -6 & \vdots & 12 \end{bmatrix}$ (b) $\begin{bmatrix} 3 & 2 & \vdots & -5 \\ 7 & 6 & \vdots & -12 \end{bmatrix}$ (c) $\begin{bmatrix} 3 & 2 & \vdots & 5 \\ 7 & 6 & \vdots & 12 \end{bmatrix}$

(d) $\begin{bmatrix} 3 & 7 & \vdots & 5 \\ 2 & -6 & \vdots & 12 \end{bmatrix}$ (e) None of these

1—M—Answer: a

26. Form the augmented matrix of the system of equations.

$$y - 3z = 5$$
$$2x + z = -1$$
$$4x - y = 0$$

(a) $\begin{bmatrix} 1 & -3 \\ 2 & 1 \\ 4 & -1 \end{bmatrix}$

(b) $\begin{bmatrix} 1 & -3 & \vdots & 5 \\ 2 & 1 & \vdots & -1 \\ 4 & -1 & \vdots & 0 \end{bmatrix}$

(c) $\begin{bmatrix} 0 & 1 & -3 \\ 2 & 0 & 1 \\ 4 & -1 & 0 \end{bmatrix}$

(d) $\begin{bmatrix} 0 & 1 & -3 & \vdots & 5 \\ 2 & 0 & 1 & \vdots & -1 \\ 4 & -1 & 0 & \vdots & 0 \end{bmatrix}$

(e) None of these

1—M—Answer: d

27. Use Gauss-Jordan elimination to solve the system of linear equations.

$$x + 2y + z = 7$$
$$3x \quad\quad + z = 2$$
$$x - y - z = 1$$

(a) $\left(\frac{2}{3}, \frac{20}{3}, -7\right)$

(b) $\left(-\frac{7}{3}, \frac{1}{6}, 9\right)$

(c) $\left(\frac{11}{6}, \frac{13}{3}, -\frac{7}{2}\right)$

(d) $\left(-\frac{19}{3}, -\frac{2}{3}, \frac{44}{3}\right)$

(e) None of these

1—M—Answer: c

28. Use Gauss-Jordan elimination to solve the system of linear equations.

$$x + 2y + z = 5$$
$$2x - y - 3z = 5$$
$$-2x + 3y + z = -11$$

1—O—Answer: $(5, -1, 2)$

29. Use Gauss-Jordan elimination to solve the system of linear equations.

$$3x + 2y - 5z = -10$$
$$2x + 4y + z = 0$$
$$x - 6y - 4z = -3$$

1—O—Answer: $\left(\frac{1}{2}, -\frac{3}{4}, 2\right)$

30. Use Gaussian elimination with back-substitution or Gauss-Jordan elimination to solve the following system of linear equations.

$$3x + 2y + z = 7$$
$$x - y + z = 6$$
$$x \quad\;\; + z = 5$$

(a) $(2, -1, 3)$ (b) $\left(1, -\frac{1}{2}, 5\right)$ (c) $(-1, 1, 2)$

(d) $(0, 4, -1)$ (e) None of these

1—M—Answer: a

31. Use Gaussian elimination with back-substitution or Gauss-Jordan elimination to solve the following system of linear equations.

$$2x + y - z = -3$$
$$4x - y + z = 6$$
$$2x + 3y + 2z = 9$$

(a) $(1, -1, 4)$ (b) $\left(\frac{1}{2}, 0, 4\right)$ (c) $\left(\frac{1}{2}, 2, 0\right)$

(d) $\left(\frac{3}{2}, -9, 0\right)$ (e) None of these

1—M—Answer: b

32. Use Gaussian elimination with back-substitution or Gauss-Jordan elimination to solve the following system of linear equations.

$$2x + 3y - 4z = 4$$
$$x - y - 5z = 0$$
$$-2x + 4y + 5z = 9$$

(a) $(-3, 2, -1)$ (b) $(3, -2, -1)$ (c) $(2, 1, 1)$

(d) $(0, 4, 2)$ (e) None of these

1—M—Answer: a

33. Find an equation of the parabola that passes through the points $(1, 4)$, $(2, 5)$, and $(-1, -4)$.

(a) $y = -3x^2 + 10x + 5$ (b) $y = x^2 - 2x + 5$ (c) $y = -x^2 + 4x + 1$

(d) $y = -x^2 - 2x + 3$ (e) None of these

1—M—Answer: c

34. Find an equation of the parabola that passes through the points $(1, -1)$, $(2, 1)$, and $(3, 7)$.

(a) $y = -x^2 + 5x - 5$ (b) $y = x^2 - x - 1$ (c) $y = -2x^2 + 12x - 11$

(d) $y = 2x^2 - 4x + 1$ (e) None of these

1—M—Answer: d

35. Find an equation of the parabola that passes through the points $(-1, 0)$, $(1, 4)$, and $(2, 15)$.

(a) $y = x^2 + 2x + 1$ (b) $y = -x^2 + 2x + 3$ (c) $y = -2x^2 + 2x + 4$

(d) $y = 2x^2 + 3x + 1$ (e) None of these

1—M—Answer: e

36. Find the equation of the parabola that passes through the given points. Use a graphing utility to verify your result.

1—O—Answer: $y = 2x^2 + 5x - 3$

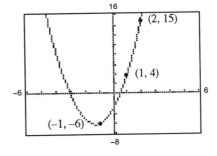

37. Find an equation of the parabola that passes through the given points. Use a graphing utility to verify your result.

1—O—Answer: $y = x^2 - x + 4$

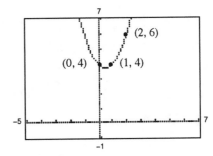

38. A small corporation borrowed $900,000; some at 7%, some at 8%, and some at 11%. How much was borrowed at 8% if the annual interest was $72,250 and the amount borrowed at 8% was $50,000 more than the amount borrowed at 11%?

(a) $225,000   (b) $175,000   (c) $650,000

(d) $450,000   (e) None of these

2—M—Answer: a

39. A small corporation borrowed $900,000; some at 7%, some at 8%, and some at 11%. How much was borrowed at 11% if the annual interest was $71,500 and the amount borrowed at 7% was twice the amount borrowed at 8%?

(a) $400,000   (b) $800,000   (c) $150,000

(d) $300,000   (e) None of these

2—M—Answer: c

9.6 Operations with Matrices

1. Find x: $\begin{bmatrix} 3x+2 & 5 & 2 \\ 7 & 2y & x \\ 4 & -1 & y+1 \end{bmatrix} = \begin{bmatrix} x-4 & 5 & \frac{y}{2} \\ 7 & 8 & -3 \\ 4 & -1 & 5 \end{bmatrix}$

(a) 4   (b) -3 (c) -1 (d) 6   (e) None of these

1—M—Answer: b

2. Find x: $\begin{bmatrix} 9-2x & y & 0 \\ 4 & 2-y & 3 \\ 6 & \frac{2}{5}x & 5 \end{bmatrix} = \begin{bmatrix} -1 & 3 & 0 \\ 4 & -1 & x-2 \\ 6 & 2 & x \end{bmatrix}$

(a) -2 (b) -3 (c) 4   (d) 5   (e) None of these

1—M—Answer: d

3. Find x: $\begin{bmatrix} x-1 & 4 & 5 \\ 2 & -1 & 5 \\ -6 & x & 7 \end{bmatrix} = \begin{bmatrix} -3 & 4 & 5 \\ 2 & \frac{-y}{2} & y+3 \\ -6 & -2 & -4x-1 \end{bmatrix}$

(a) -2 (b) -3 (c) 4   (d) 5   (e) None of these

1—M—Answer: a

4. Evaluate: $2\begin{bmatrix} 4 & 7 \\ 2 & 0 \end{bmatrix} - 3\begin{bmatrix} 1 & 2 \\ -1 & 5 \end{bmatrix}$

(a) $\begin{bmatrix} 5 & 8 \\ 7 & -15 \end{bmatrix}$ (b) $\begin{bmatrix} 5 & 9 \\ 1 & -15 \end{bmatrix}$ (c) $-1\begin{bmatrix} 3 & 5 \\ 3 & 5 \end{bmatrix}$

(d) $-1\begin{bmatrix} 5 & 9 \\ 1 & 5 \end{bmatrix}$ (e) None of these

1—M—Answer: a

5. Evaluate: $3\begin{bmatrix} 2 & 7 \\ 9 & -1 \end{bmatrix} + 3\begin{bmatrix} 4 & 1 \\ 6 & 2 \end{bmatrix}$

1—O—Answer: $\begin{bmatrix} 18 & 24 \\ 45 & 3 \end{bmatrix}$

6. Evaluate: $3\begin{bmatrix} 7 & 5 & 2 \\ -1 & 1 & 0 \\ 0 & 3 & 6 \end{bmatrix} + 2\begin{bmatrix} 1 & 0 & 0 \\ 0 & 1 & 0 \\ 0 & 0 & 1 \end{bmatrix} - 4\begin{bmatrix} 1 & -1 & 2 \\ 7 & 1 & -1 \\ 2 & 5 & 1 \end{bmatrix}$

1—O—Answer: $\begin{bmatrix} 19 & 19 & -2 \\ -31 & 1 & 4 \\ -8 & -11 & 16 \end{bmatrix}$

7. Given $A = \begin{bmatrix} 3 & 6 & -1 \\ 0 & 5 & 2 \end{bmatrix}$ and $B = \begin{bmatrix} 1 & 0 & 5 \\ -1 & 2 & 7 \end{bmatrix}$, find $3A - 2B$.

(a) $\begin{bmatrix} 7 & 18 & -13 \\ 2 & 11 & -8 \end{bmatrix}$ 　　(b) $\begin{bmatrix} 7 & 18 & 2 \\ 0 & 11 & -8 \end{bmatrix}$ 　　(c) $\begin{bmatrix} 11 & 18 & 7 \\ -2 & 19 & 20 \end{bmatrix}$

(d) $\begin{bmatrix} 7 & 18 & -13 \\ -2 & 9 & 20 \end{bmatrix}$ 　　(e) None of these

1—M—Answer: a

8. Given $A = \begin{bmatrix} 1 & 2 & 3 \\ 4 & 7 & 1 \\ 0 & 3 & 2 \end{bmatrix}$ and $B = \begin{bmatrix} 0 & 0 & 1 \\ 1 & 4 & 0 \\ 2 & 3 & 7 \end{bmatrix}$, find $6A - 2B$.

(a) $\begin{bmatrix} 30 & 72 & 52 \\ 32 & 10 & 6 \\ 1 & 6 & -8 \end{bmatrix}$ 　　(b) $\begin{bmatrix} 30 & 12 & 4 \\ 3 & 10 & 6 \\ 1 & 6 & -8 \end{bmatrix}$ 　　(c) $\begin{bmatrix} 6 & 12 & 16 \\ 22 & 34 & 6 \\ -4 & 12 & -2 \end{bmatrix}$

(d) $\begin{bmatrix} 30 & 22 & 20 \\ 66 & 28 & 26 \\ 24 & 16 & 14 \end{bmatrix}$ 　　(e) None of these

1—M—Answer: c

9. Given $A = \begin{bmatrix} 2 & 4 & -1 \\ 1 & 0 & 4 \\ 8 & 1 & 2 \end{bmatrix}$ and $B = \begin{bmatrix} 1 & 1 & 1 \\ -1 & 0 & 0 \\ 4 & 10 & -2 \end{bmatrix}$, find $2A - 2B$.

(a) $\begin{bmatrix} 2 & 6 & 4 \\ 4 & 0 & -8 \\ -8 & 18 & 1 \end{bmatrix}$ 　　(b) $\begin{bmatrix} 2 & 6 & -4 \\ 4 & 0 & 8 \\ 8 & -18 & 8 \end{bmatrix}$ 　　(c) $\begin{bmatrix} 0 & 6 & -4 \\ -4 & 0 & 4 \\ 4 & -9 & 0 \end{bmatrix}$

(d) $\begin{bmatrix} 1 & 3 & -2 \\ 0 & 0 & 4 \\ 4 & -9 & 4 \end{bmatrix}$ 　　(e) None of these

1—M—Answer: b

10. Given $A = \begin{bmatrix} 3 & -2 & 4 \\ 0 & 0 & -1 \\ 3 & 2 & -1 \end{bmatrix}$ and $B = \begin{bmatrix} 3 & 1 & -1 \\ -1 & 0 & 0 \\ 2 & 4 & -2 \end{bmatrix}$, find $3A - 2B$.

(a) $\begin{bmatrix} 3 & -8 & 14 \\ 2 & 0 & -3 \\ 5 & -2 & 1 \end{bmatrix}$ 　　(b) $\begin{bmatrix} 3 & -8 & 10 \\ 2 & 0 & -3 \\ 7 & -2 & -7 \end{bmatrix}$ 　　(c) $\begin{bmatrix} 6 & -1 & 3 \\ -1 & 0 & -1 \\ 5 & 6 & -3 \end{bmatrix}$

(d) $\begin{bmatrix} 15 & -4 & 10 \\ -2 & 0 & -3 \\ 13 & 14 & 1 \end{bmatrix}$ 　　(e) None of these

1—M—Answer: a

11. Given $A = \begin{bmatrix} 3 & 2 & 2 \\ -1 & 0 & -1 \\ 0 & 1 & 0 \end{bmatrix}$ and $B = \begin{bmatrix} 1 & 1 & 0 \\ 0 & 1 & 1 \\ 2 & -1 & 2 \end{bmatrix}$, find $2A - 3B$.

(a) $\begin{bmatrix} 8 & 7 & 4 \\ -2 & 3 & 1 \\ 6 & -1 & 6 \end{bmatrix}$

(b) $\begin{bmatrix} 8 & 7 & 4 \\ -2 & -3 & -5 \\ -6 & -1 & -6 \end{bmatrix}$

(c) $\begin{bmatrix} 3 & 1 & 4 \\ 2 & 3 & 5 \\ -6 & 5 & 6 \end{bmatrix}$

(d) $\begin{bmatrix} 3 & 1 & 4 \\ -2 & -3 & -5 \\ -6 & 5 & -6 \end{bmatrix}$

(e) None of these

1—M—Answer: d

12. Given $A = \begin{bmatrix} 1 & 0 & 3 \\ -1 & 2 & -2 \\ 1 & 1 & 2 \end{bmatrix}$ and $B = \begin{bmatrix} 1 & 1 & 0 \\ 3 & 1 & 2 \\ -1 & 1 & -1 \end{bmatrix}$, find $-2A + 5B$.

(a) $\begin{bmatrix} 3 & 5 & -6 \\ 17 & 1 & 14 \\ -7 & 3 & -9 \end{bmatrix}$

(b) $\begin{bmatrix} 3 & 5 & 6 \\ 13 & 9 & 6 \\ -3 & 8 & -1 \end{bmatrix}$

(c) $\begin{bmatrix} 7 & 5 & 6 \\ 13 & 9 & 6 \\ -3 & 8 & -1 \end{bmatrix}$

(d) $\begin{bmatrix} 3 & 5 & -6 \\ -17 & 0 & 14 \\ 7 & -3 & -9 \end{bmatrix}$

(e) None of these

1—M—Answer: a

13. If $A = \begin{bmatrix} 2 & -1 \\ 3 & 1 \end{bmatrix}$ and $B = \begin{bmatrix} 4 & 0 \\ -1 & -1 \end{bmatrix}$, find $A - 2B$.

(a) $\begin{bmatrix} -6 & -1 \\ 5 & -1 \end{bmatrix}$

(b) 13

(c) $\begin{bmatrix} -6 & -1 \\ 1 & 3 \end{bmatrix}$

(d) $\begin{bmatrix} -2 & -1 \\ 5 & 3 \end{bmatrix}$

(e) None of these

1—M—Answer: e

14. If $A = \begin{bmatrix} 2 & -1 \\ 3 & 1 \end{bmatrix}$ and $B = \begin{bmatrix} 4 & 0 \\ -1 & -1 \end{bmatrix}$, find $B - 2A$.

(a) -14

(b) $\begin{bmatrix} -6 & -1 \\ 5 & 3 \end{bmatrix}$

(c) $\begin{bmatrix} 0 & -2 \\ -7 & -3 \end{bmatrix}$

(d) $\begin{bmatrix} 0 & 2 \\ -7 & -3 \end{bmatrix}$

(e) None of these

1—M—Answer: d

15. Let $A = \begin{bmatrix} 2 & -1 \\ -3 & 4 \end{bmatrix}$ and $B = \begin{bmatrix} -2 & 0 \\ -1 & 3 \end{bmatrix}$. Find C if $A + C = 2B$.

1—O—Answer: $\begin{bmatrix} -6 & 1 \\ 1 & 2 \end{bmatrix}$

16. Use a graphing utility to find AB, given $A = \begin{bmatrix} 1 & 3 & 6 \\ 4 & 1 & 3 \end{bmatrix}$ and $B = \begin{bmatrix} 0 & 1 & 6 \\ 3 & -1 & 1 \\ 5 & 2 & 3 \end{bmatrix}$

1—O—Answer: $\begin{bmatrix} 39 & 10 & 27 \\ 18 & 9 & 34 \end{bmatrix}$

17. Use a graphing utility to find AB, given $A = \begin{bmatrix} 2 & 1 \\ 3 & -2 \end{bmatrix}$ and $B = \begin{bmatrix} -1 & 5 \\ 6 & 2 \end{bmatrix}$

(a) $\begin{bmatrix} 4 & 12 \\ -15 & 11 \end{bmatrix}$ (b) $\begin{bmatrix} 13 & -11 \\ 18 & 2 \end{bmatrix}$ (c) $\begin{bmatrix} 16 & 16 \\ -13 & 1 \end{bmatrix}$

(d) $\begin{bmatrix} -2 & 5 \\ 18 & -4 \end{bmatrix}$ (e) None of these

1—M—Answer: a

18. Use a graphing utility to multiply: $\begin{bmatrix} 2 & 3 & 4 \\ -1 & 0 & 2 \end{bmatrix} \begin{bmatrix} -1 & 4 \\ 0 & 1 \\ 5 & 2 \end{bmatrix}$

(a) $\begin{bmatrix} 18 & 19 \\ 11 & 0 \end{bmatrix}$ (b) $\begin{bmatrix} -2 & 0 & 20 \\ -4 & 0 & 4 \end{bmatrix}$ (c) $\begin{bmatrix} -6 & -3 & 4 \\ -2 & 0 & 6 \\ -1 & 2 & 4 \end{bmatrix}$

(d) $\begin{bmatrix} -6 \\ 0 \\ 24 \end{bmatrix}$ (e) None of these

1—M—Answer: a

19. Use a graphing utility to find AB, given $A = \begin{bmatrix} 1 & -1 & 2 \\ 0 & 5 & 1 \\ -2 & 0 & -1 \end{bmatrix}$ and $B = \begin{bmatrix} -1 & 2 & 0 \\ 5 & -7 & 1 \\ 2 & 3 & -2 \end{bmatrix}$

(a) $\begin{bmatrix} -1 & -2 & 0 \\ 0 & -35 & 1 \\ -4 & 0 & 2 \end{bmatrix}$ (b) $\begin{bmatrix} -1 & 11 & 0 \\ 3 & -40 & 2 \\ 6 & 13 & 9 \end{bmatrix}$ (c) $\begin{bmatrix} 6 & 3 & -2 \\ 0 & -10 & -1 \\ -12 & 0 & 1 \end{bmatrix}$

(d) $\begin{bmatrix} -2 & 15 & -5 \\ 27 & -32 & 3 \\ 0 & -7 & 2 \end{bmatrix}$ (e) None of these

1—M—Answer: d

20. Use a graphing utility to find AB, given $A = \begin{bmatrix} 1 & 3 & 5 & 2 \\ -1 & 6 & 4 & 8 \end{bmatrix}$ and $B = \begin{bmatrix} 3 & 2 & 0 \\ 0 & 0 & 1 \\ 1 & 2 & -1 \\ 0 & 0 & 3 \end{bmatrix}$

1—O—Answer: $AB = \begin{bmatrix} 8 & 12 & 4 \\ 1 & 6 & 26 \end{bmatrix}$

21. Given $A = \begin{bmatrix} 3 & -2 & 4 & 0 \\ 0 & 0 & -1 & 4 \\ 3 & 2 & -1 & -1 \end{bmatrix}$ and $B = \begin{bmatrix} 1 & 1 & 1 \\ -1 & 0 & 0 \\ 4 & 10 & -2 \end{bmatrix}$, find BA.

(a) $\begin{bmatrix} 21 & 14 & 10 & -4 \\ -3 & -2 & 1 & -1 \\ 6 & 4 & 11 & 7 \end{bmatrix}$ (b) $\begin{bmatrix} 21 & 43 & -5 \\ -4 & -10 & 2 \\ -3 & -7 & 5 \end{bmatrix}$ (c) $\begin{bmatrix} 6 & 0 & 2 & 3 \\ -3 & 2 & -4 & 0 \\ 6 & -12 & 8 & 42 \end{bmatrix}$

(d) Impossible (e) None of these

1—M—Answer: c

22. Given $A = \begin{bmatrix} 3 & -2 & 4 & 0 \\ 0 & 0 & -1 & 4 \\ 3 & 2 & -1 & -1 \end{bmatrix}$ and $B = \begin{bmatrix} 1 & 1 & 1 \\ -1 & 0 & 0 \\ 4 & 10 & -2 \end{bmatrix}$, find AB.

(a) $\begin{bmatrix} 21 & 14 & 10 & -4 \\ -3 & -2 & 1 & -1 \\ 6 & 4 & 11 & 7 \end{bmatrix}$ (b) $\begin{bmatrix} 21 & 43 & -5 \\ -4 & -10 & 2 \\ -3 & -7 & 5 \\ 0 & 0 & 0 \end{bmatrix}$ (c) $\begin{bmatrix} 6 & 0 & 2 & 3 \\ -3 & 2 & -4 & 0 \\ 6 & -12 & 8 & 42 \end{bmatrix}$

(d) Impossible (e) None of these

1—M—Answer: d

23. Given $A = \begin{bmatrix} 2 & 4 & -1 \\ 1 & 0 & 4 \\ 8 & 1 & 2 \end{bmatrix}$ and $B = \begin{bmatrix} 1 & 1 & 1 \\ -1 & 0 & 0 \\ 4 & 10 & -2 \end{bmatrix}$, find AB.

(a) $\begin{bmatrix} 11 & 5 & 5 \\ -2 & -4 & 1 \\ 2 & 14 & 32 \end{bmatrix}$ (b) $\begin{bmatrix} -6 & -8 & 4 \\ 17 & 41 & -7 \\ 15 & 28 & 4 \end{bmatrix}$ (c) $\begin{bmatrix} -5 & -8 & 4 \\ 17 & 41 & -7 \\ 15 & 28 & 4 \end{bmatrix}$

(d) Impossible (e) None of these

1—M—Answer: b

24. Given $A = \begin{bmatrix} 2 & 4 & -1 & 3 \\ 1 & 0 & 4 & 0 \\ 8 & 1 & 2 & 1 \end{bmatrix}$ and $B = \begin{bmatrix} 3 & 1 & -1 \\ -1 & 0 & 0 \\ 2 & 4 & -2 \end{bmatrix}$, find BA.

(a) $\begin{bmatrix} -1 & 11 & -1 & 8 \\ -2 & -4 & 1 & -3 \\ -8 & 6 & 10 & 4 \end{bmatrix}$ (b) $\begin{bmatrix} 0 & -2 & 0 \\ 11 & 17 & -9 \\ 27 & 16 & -12 \end{bmatrix}$ (c) $\begin{bmatrix} -1 & -11 & 1 & 0 \\ -2 & 4 & -1 & -3 \\ 8 & -6 & 10 & -12 \end{bmatrix}$

(d) Impossible (e) None of these

1—M—Answer: a

25. Given $A = \begin{bmatrix} 2 & 4 & -1 & 3 \\ 1 & 0 & 4 & 0 \\ 8 & 1 & 2 & 1 \end{bmatrix}$ and $B = \begin{bmatrix} 3 & 1 & -1 \\ -1 & 0 & 0 \\ 2 & 4 & -2 \end{bmatrix}$, find AB.

(a) $\begin{bmatrix} -1 & 11 & -1 & 8 \\ -2 & -4 & 1 & -3 \\ -8 & 6 & 10 & 4 \end{bmatrix}$ (b) $\begin{bmatrix} 0 & -2 & 0 \\ 11 & 17 & -9 \\ 27 & 16 & -12 \end{bmatrix}$ (c) $\begin{bmatrix} 6 & 4 & 1 & 3 \\ -1 & 0 & 0 & 0 \\ 16 & 4 & -4 & 0 \end{bmatrix}$

(d) Impossible   (e) None of these

1—M—Answer: d

26. Use a graphing utility to find AB, given $A = \begin{bmatrix} 3 & -2 & 4 \\ 0 & 0 & -1 \\ 3 & 2 & -1 \end{bmatrix}$ and $B = \begin{bmatrix} 3 & 1 & -1 \\ -1 & 0 & 0 \\ 2 & 4 & -2 \end{bmatrix}$

(a) $\begin{bmatrix} 6 & -8 & 12 \\ -3 & 2 & -4 \\ 0 & -8 & 6 \end{bmatrix}$ (b) $\begin{bmatrix} 19 & 19 & -11 \\ -2 & -4 & 2 \\ 5 & -1 & -1 \end{bmatrix}$ (c) $\begin{bmatrix} 9 & -2 & -4 \\ 0 & 0 & 0 \\ 6 & 8 & 2 \end{bmatrix}$

(d) Impossible   (e) None of these

1—M—Answer: b

27. Use a graphing utility to find AB, given $A = \begin{bmatrix} 2 & 0 & 1 & 2 \\ 0 & 1 & 0 & 1 \\ -1 & -2 & 0 & 0 \end{bmatrix}$ and $B = \begin{bmatrix} 1 & 1 & 0 \\ 0 & 1 & 1 \\ 2 & -1 & 2 \end{bmatrix}$

(a) $\begin{bmatrix} 2 & 0 & 1 & 2 \\ 0 & 1 & 0 & 0 \\ -2 & 2 & 0 & 0 \end{bmatrix}$ (b) $\begin{bmatrix} 4 & 2 & 3 \\ -1 & -2 & -1 \\ 6 & -5 & -1 \end{bmatrix}$ (c) $\begin{bmatrix} 2 & 1 & 1 & 3 \\ -1 & -1 & 0 & 1 \\ 2 & -5 & 2 & 3 \end{bmatrix}$

(d) Impossible   (e) None of these

1—M—Answer: d

28. Use a graphing utility to find BA, given $A = \begin{bmatrix} 2 & 0 & 1 & 2 \\ 0 & 1 & 0 & 1 \\ -1 & -2 & 0 & 0 \end{bmatrix}$ and $B = \begin{bmatrix} 1 & 1 & 0 \\ 0 & 1 & 1 \\ 2 & -1 & 2 \end{bmatrix}$

(a) $\begin{bmatrix} 2 & 1 & 1 & 3 \\ -1 & -1 & 0 & 1 \\ 2 & -5 & 2 & 3 \end{bmatrix}$ (b) $\begin{bmatrix} 4 & 1 & 2 \\ 0 & 1 & 1 \\ -1 & -3 & -2 \end{bmatrix}$ (c) $\begin{bmatrix} 6 & -4 & 0 \\ 0 & 1 & 1 \\ -4 & -3 & -4 \end{bmatrix}$

(d) Impossible   (e) None of these

1—M—Answer: a

29. Use a graphing utility to find BA, given $A = \begin{bmatrix} 3 & 2 & 2 \\ -1 & 0 & -1 \\ 0 & 1 & 0 \end{bmatrix}$ and $B = \begin{bmatrix} 1 & 1 & 0 \\ 0 & 1 & 1 \\ 2 & -1 & 2 \end{bmatrix}$

(a) $\begin{bmatrix} 3 & 2 & 0 \\ 0 & 0 & -1 \\ 0 & -1 & 0 \end{bmatrix}$
(b) $\begin{bmatrix} 7 & 3 & 6 \\ -3 & 0 & -2 \\ 0 & 1 & 1 \end{bmatrix}$
(c) $\begin{bmatrix} 2 & 2 & 1 \\ -1 & 1 & -1 \\ 7 & 6 & 5 \end{bmatrix}$

(d) Impossible
(e) None of these

1—M—Answer: c

30. Use a graphing utility to find AB, given $A = \begin{bmatrix} 3 & 1 & 2 & 1 \\ 0 & 1 & 0 & 0 \\ 2 & 1 & 3 & -1 \end{bmatrix}$ and $B = \begin{bmatrix} 1 & 1 & 0 \\ 3 & 1 & 2 \\ -1 & 1 & -1 \end{bmatrix}$

(a) $\begin{bmatrix} 3 & 2 & 2 & 1 \\ 13 & 6 & 12 & 1 \\ -5 & -1 & -5 & 0 \end{bmatrix}$
(b) $\begin{bmatrix} 4 & 6 & 0 \\ 3 & 1 & 2 \\ 2 & 6 & -1 \end{bmatrix}$
(c) $\begin{bmatrix} 3 & 1 & 0 \\ 0 & 1 & 2 \\ -2 & 1 & -3 \end{bmatrix}$

(d) Impossible
(e) None of these

1—M—Answer: d

31. Given $A = \begin{bmatrix} 3 & 1 & 2 & 1 \\ 0 & 1 & 0 & 0 \\ 2 & 1 & 3 & -1 \end{bmatrix}$ and $B = \begin{bmatrix} 1 & 1 & 0 \\ 3 & 1 & 2 \\ -1 & 1 & -1 \end{bmatrix}$, find BA.

1—O—Answer: $\begin{bmatrix} 3 & 2 & 2 & 1 \\ 13 & 6 & 12 & 1 \\ -5 & -1 & -5 & 0 \end{bmatrix}$

32. Given $A = \begin{bmatrix} 1 & 0 & 3 \\ -1 & 2 & -2 \\ 1 & 1 & 2 \end{bmatrix}$ and $B = \begin{bmatrix} 1 & 1 & 0 \\ 3 & 1 & 2 \\ -1 & 1 & -1 \end{bmatrix}$, find BA.

1—O—Answer: $\begin{bmatrix} 0 & 2 & 1 \\ 4 & 4 & 11 \\ -3 & 1 & -7 \end{bmatrix}$

33. Solve for X given $A = \begin{bmatrix} 3 & 1 \\ -2 & 5 \end{bmatrix}$ and $B = \begin{bmatrix} 1 & 1 \\ 1 & 9 \end{bmatrix}$: $2X - A = B$

(a) 17
(b) $\begin{bmatrix} 5 & 1 \\ -5 & 1 \end{bmatrix}$
(c) $\begin{bmatrix} 4 & 2 \\ -1 & 14 \end{bmatrix}$

(d) $\begin{bmatrix} 2 & 1 \\ -\frac{1}{2} & 7 \end{bmatrix}$
(e) None of these

1—M—Answer: d

34. Find AB if $A = \begin{bmatrix} 2 & -1 & 0 \\ 3 & 4 & 1 \end{bmatrix}$ and $B = \begin{bmatrix} 0 & 1 \\ 4 & 3 \\ 5 & -1 \end{bmatrix}$.

(a) $\begin{bmatrix} -4 & -1 \\ 21 & 14 \end{bmatrix}$

(b) $\begin{bmatrix} 3 & 4 & 1 \\ 17 & 8 & 3 \\ 7 & -9 & -1 \end{bmatrix}$

(c) $\begin{bmatrix} -2 & -1 \\ 21 & 14 \end{bmatrix}$

(d) Cannot be done

(e) None of these

1—M—Answer: a

35. Let $A = \begin{bmatrix} 2 & -1 & 0 \\ 0 & 5 & 3 \\ 1 & -2 & -1 \end{bmatrix}$ and $B = \begin{bmatrix} 1 & 0 & -1 \\ 2 & 3 & 0 \end{bmatrix}$. Find BA.

1—O—Answer: $\begin{bmatrix} 1 & 1 & 1 \\ 4 & 13 & 9 \end{bmatrix}$

36. Solve for X given $A = \begin{bmatrix} 2 & 3 \\ 5 & -2 \end{bmatrix}$ and $B = \begin{bmatrix} 2 & 5 \\ -1 & 6 \end{bmatrix}$: $2X + A = B$

(a) $\begin{bmatrix} 2 & 4 \\ 2 & 2 \end{bmatrix}$

(b) $\begin{bmatrix} 0 & 1 \\ -3 & 4 \end{bmatrix}$

(c) $\begin{bmatrix} 4 & 8 \\ 4 & 4 \end{bmatrix}$

(d) $\begin{bmatrix} 0 & 2 \\ -6 & 8 \end{bmatrix}$

(e) None of these

1—M—Answer: b

37. Solve for X given $A = \begin{bmatrix} -3 & 4 \\ 2 & 6 \end{bmatrix}$ and $B = \begin{bmatrix} 6 & 2 \\ 7 & 0 \end{bmatrix}$: $3X - A = B$

(a) $\frac{-44}{9}$

(b) $\begin{bmatrix} -3 & \frac{2}{3} \\ -\frac{5}{3} & 2 \end{bmatrix}$

(c) -4

(d) $\begin{bmatrix} 1 & 2 \\ 3 & 2 \end{bmatrix}$

(e) None of these

1—M—Answer: d

38. Write the matrix equation for the system of linear equations:

$$3x + 2y = 5$$
$$7x - 6y = 1$$

(a) $\begin{bmatrix} x & y \end{bmatrix} = \begin{bmatrix} 3 & 7 \\ 2 & -6 \end{bmatrix} \begin{bmatrix} 5 \\ 1 \end{bmatrix}$

(b) $\begin{bmatrix} x \\ y \end{bmatrix} = \begin{bmatrix} 3 & 2 \\ 7 & -6 \end{bmatrix} \begin{bmatrix} 5 \\ 1 \end{bmatrix}$

(c) $\begin{bmatrix} 3 & 2 \\ 7 & -6 \end{bmatrix} \begin{bmatrix} x \\ y \end{bmatrix} = \begin{bmatrix} 5 \\ 1 \end{bmatrix}$

(d) $\begin{bmatrix} x & y \end{bmatrix} \begin{bmatrix} 5 \\ 1 \end{bmatrix} = \begin{bmatrix} 3 & 7 \\ 2 & -6 \end{bmatrix}$

(e) None of these

1—M—Answer: c

39. Write the matrix equation for the system of linear equations:

$$
\begin{aligned}
2x_1 + \ x_2 \qquad\qquad\ &= \ 0 \\
3x_1 + \ x_2 + \ x_3 \qquad\ &= -1 \\
2x_2 - \ x_3 + 3x_4 &= \ 1 \\
2x_3 - 3x_4 &= \ 4
\end{aligned}
$$

(a) $\begin{bmatrix} 2 & 1 & 0 & 0 \\ 3 & 1 & 1 & 0 \\ 0 & 2 & -1 & 3 \\ 0 & 0 & 2 & -3 \end{bmatrix} \begin{bmatrix} x_1 \\ x_2 \\ x_3 \\ x_4 \end{bmatrix} = \begin{bmatrix} 0 \\ -1 \\ 1 \\ 4 \end{bmatrix}$
(b) $\begin{bmatrix} 2 & 3 & 0 & 0 \\ 1 & 1 & 2 & 0 \\ 0 & 1 & -1 & 2 \\ 0 & 0 & 3 & -3 \end{bmatrix} \begin{bmatrix} x_1 \\ x_2 \\ x_3 \\ x_4 \end{bmatrix} = \begin{bmatrix} 0 \\ -1 \\ 1 \\ 4 \end{bmatrix}$

(c) $\begin{bmatrix} 2 & 1 & 0 & 0 \\ 3 & 1 & 1 & 0 \\ 0 & 2 & -1 & 3 \\ 0 & 0 & 2 & -3 \end{bmatrix} \begin{bmatrix} 0 \\ -1 \\ 1 \\ 4 \end{bmatrix} = \begin{bmatrix} x_1 \\ x_2 \\ x_3 \\ x_4 \end{bmatrix}$
(d) $\begin{bmatrix} 2 & 3 & 0 & 0 \\ 1 & 1 & 2 & 0 \\ 0 & 1 & -1 & 2 \\ 0 & 0 & 3 & -3 \end{bmatrix} \begin{bmatrix} 0 \\ -1 \\ 1 \\ 4 \end{bmatrix} = \begin{bmatrix} x_1 \\ x_2 \\ x_3 \\ x_4 \end{bmatrix}$

(e) None of these

1—M—Answer: a

40. Write the matrix equation for the system of linear equations:

$$
\begin{aligned}
2x - 4y &= 12 \\
x + 5y &= 16
\end{aligned}
$$

(a) $\begin{bmatrix} x & y \end{bmatrix} = \begin{bmatrix} 2 & -4 \\ 1 & 5 \end{bmatrix} \begin{bmatrix} 12 \\ 16 \end{bmatrix}$
(b) $\begin{bmatrix} 2 & -4 \\ 1 & 5 \end{bmatrix} \begin{bmatrix} x \\ y \end{bmatrix} = \begin{bmatrix} 12 \\ 16 \end{bmatrix}$

(c) $\begin{bmatrix} x \\ y \end{bmatrix} = \begin{bmatrix} 2 & -4 \\ 1 & 5 \end{bmatrix} \begin{bmatrix} 12 \\ 16 \end{bmatrix}$
(d) $\begin{bmatrix} x & y \end{bmatrix} \begin{bmatrix} 12 \\ 16 \end{bmatrix} = \begin{bmatrix} 3 & 7 \\ 2 & -6 \end{bmatrix}$

(e) None of these

1—M—Answer: b

9.7 Inverse Matrices and Systems of Linear Equations

1. Determine which of the following matrices have inverses.

(a) $\begin{bmatrix} 1 & -2 \\ -3 & 6 \end{bmatrix}$ (b) $\begin{bmatrix} 3 \\ 2 \end{bmatrix}$ (c) $\begin{bmatrix} 3 & 4 & -1 \\ 2 & 1 & 0 \end{bmatrix}$

(d) $\begin{bmatrix} 6 & 1 \\ -2 & 4 \end{bmatrix}$ (e) None of these

1—M—Answer: d

2. Determine which of the following matrices have inverses.

(a) $\begin{bmatrix} 2 & -5 \\ -4 & 10 \end{bmatrix}$ (b) $\begin{bmatrix} 2 & 6 \\ -4 & 12 \end{bmatrix}$ (c) $\begin{bmatrix} 0 \\ 2 \\ 5 \end{bmatrix}$

(d) $\begin{bmatrix} 4 & 2 \\ 1 & 7 \\ 0 & -1 \end{bmatrix}$ (e) None of these

1—M—Answer: b

3. Determine which of the following matrices have inverses.

(a) $\begin{bmatrix} -1 \\ 5 \\ 2 \end{bmatrix}$ (b) $\begin{bmatrix} 4 & -2 \\ -2 & 1 \end{bmatrix}$ (c) $\begin{bmatrix} -3 & 5 \\ 6 & -10 \end{bmatrix}$

(d) $\begin{bmatrix} -3 & 5 \\ -4 & 2 \end{bmatrix}$ (e) None of these

1—M—Answer: d

4. Determine which of the following matrices have inverses.

(a) $\begin{bmatrix} 1 & -7 \\ 2 & 14 \end{bmatrix}$ (b) $\begin{bmatrix} 2 & -7 \\ -4 & 14 \end{bmatrix}$ (c) $\begin{bmatrix} -6 & 9 \\ 4 & -6 \end{bmatrix}$

(d) $\begin{bmatrix} 4 \\ 1 \\ 3 \end{bmatrix}$ (e) None of these

1—M—Answer: a

5. Determine which of the following matrices have inverses.

(a) $\begin{bmatrix} -4 & -3 \\ 8 & 6 \end{bmatrix}$ (b) $\begin{bmatrix} 6 & 1 \\ -12 & -2 \end{bmatrix}$ (c) $\begin{bmatrix} -2 & -1 \\ 3 & 2 \end{bmatrix}$

(d) $\begin{bmatrix} 3 & 4 & 1 \end{bmatrix}$ (e) None of these

1—M—Answer: c

6. Determine the matrix that has an inverse.

(a) $\begin{bmatrix} 3 & 2 & 1 \\ 2 & -1 & -1 \\ 1 & 4 & 0 \end{bmatrix}$

(b) $\begin{bmatrix} 4 & 2 \\ 2 & 1 \end{bmatrix}$

(c) $\begin{bmatrix} 2 & 3 \\ 5 & -1 \\ 1 & 0 \end{bmatrix}$

(d) $\begin{bmatrix} 1 \\ 2 \\ 3 \end{bmatrix}$

(e) None of these

1—M—Answer: a

7. Given $A = \begin{bmatrix} 1 & 2 \\ -3 & 5 \end{bmatrix}$, find A^{-1}.

(a) $\begin{bmatrix} -1 & -2 \\ 3 & -5 \end{bmatrix}$

(b) $\begin{bmatrix} 1 & \frac{1}{2} \\ -\frac{1}{3} & \frac{1}{5} \end{bmatrix}$

(c) $\begin{bmatrix} -\frac{4}{15} & \frac{1}{3} \\ -\frac{2}{3} & \frac{11}{15} \end{bmatrix}$

(d) $\begin{bmatrix} \frac{5}{11} & -\frac{2}{11} \\ \frac{3}{11} & \frac{1}{11} \end{bmatrix}$

(e) None of these

1—M—Answer: d

8. Given $A = \begin{bmatrix} 5 & 1 \\ -2 & 3 \end{bmatrix}$, find A^{-1}.

(a) $\begin{bmatrix} \frac{5}{17} & \frac{1}{17} \\ -\frac{2}{17} & \frac{3}{17} \end{bmatrix}$

(b) $\begin{bmatrix} \frac{3}{17} & -\frac{1}{17} \\ \frac{2}{17} & \frac{5}{17} \end{bmatrix}$

(c) $\begin{bmatrix} 85 & 17 \\ 34 & 51 \end{bmatrix}$

(d) $\begin{bmatrix} -\frac{2}{5} & \frac{1}{3} \\ \frac{3}{2} & -\frac{1}{2} \end{bmatrix}$

(e) None of these

1—M—Answer: b

9. Given $A = \begin{bmatrix} 1 & 2 & 2 \\ 4 & 1 & 3 \\ -1 & 5 & 0 \end{bmatrix}$, find A^{-1}.

(a) $\frac{1}{21} \begin{bmatrix} -15 & 10 & 4 \\ -3 & 2 & 5 \\ 21 & -7 & -7 \end{bmatrix}$

(b) $\frac{1}{21} \begin{bmatrix} -15 & -22 & 28 \\ -3 & 27 & 25 \\ 21 & -7 & -7 \end{bmatrix}$

(c) $\begin{bmatrix} 1 & 0 & 0 \\ 0 & 1 & 0 \\ 0 & 0 & 1 \end{bmatrix}$

(d) $\begin{bmatrix} 1 & \frac{1}{2} & \frac{1}{2} \\ \frac{1}{4} & 1 & \frac{1}{3} \\ -1 & \frac{1}{5} & 0 \end{bmatrix}$

(e) None of these

1—M—Answer: a

10. Given $A = \begin{bmatrix} 1 & 3 & -1 \\ 0 & 2 & 1 \\ -1 & 1 & -2 \end{bmatrix}$, find A^{-1}.

1—O—Answer: $\begin{bmatrix} \frac{1}{2} & -\frac{1}{2} & -\frac{1}{2} \\ \frac{1}{10} & \frac{3}{10} & \frac{1}{10} \\ -\frac{1}{5} & \frac{2}{5} & -\frac{1}{5} \end{bmatrix}$

11. Given $A = \begin{bmatrix} 1 & 5 & -1 \\ 2 & 3 & -2 \\ -1 & -4 & 3 \end{bmatrix}$, find A^{-1}.

1—O—Answer: $A^{-1} = \begin{bmatrix} -\frac{1}{14} & \frac{11}{14} & \frac{1}{2} \\ \frac{2}{7} & -\frac{1}{7} & 0 \\ \frac{5}{14} & \frac{1}{14} & \frac{1}{2} \end{bmatrix}$

12. Given $A = \begin{bmatrix} 1 & 1 & 1 \\ -1 & 0 & 0 \\ 4 & 10 & -2 \end{bmatrix}$, find A^{-1}.

1—O—Answer: $\begin{bmatrix} 0 & -1 & 0 \\ \frac{1}{6} & \frac{1}{2} & \frac{1}{12} \\ \frac{5}{6} & \frac{1}{2} & -\frac{1}{12} \end{bmatrix}$

13. Given $C = \begin{bmatrix} 1 & 1 & 0 \\ 3 & 1 & 2 \\ -1 & 1 & -1 \end{bmatrix}$, find C^{-1}.

(a) $\begin{bmatrix} 1 & 1 & 0 \\ \frac{1}{3} & 1 & \frac{1}{2} \\ -1 & 1 & -1 \end{bmatrix}$

(b) $\begin{bmatrix} -1 & -1 & 0 \\ -3 & -1 & -2 \\ 1 & -1 & 1 \end{bmatrix}$

(c) $\begin{bmatrix} \frac{3}{2} & -\frac{1}{2} & -1 \\ -\frac{1}{2} & \frac{1}{2} & 1 \\ -2 & 1 & 1 \end{bmatrix}$

(d) $\begin{bmatrix} -\frac{3}{2} & 1 & -1 \\ \frac{1}{2} & 2 & 1 \\ -2 & 1 & 1 \end{bmatrix}$

(e) None of these

1—M—Answer: c

14. Given $A = \begin{bmatrix} 1 & 3 \\ 2 & 1 \end{bmatrix}$, find A^{-1}.

(a) $\begin{bmatrix} 1 & \frac{1}{3} \\ \frac{1}{2} & 1 \end{bmatrix}$

(b) $\begin{bmatrix} 1 & -3 \\ -2 & 1 \end{bmatrix}$

(c) $\begin{bmatrix} \frac{1}{5} & \frac{3}{5} \\ \frac{2}{5} & \frac{1}{5} \end{bmatrix}$

(d) $\begin{bmatrix} -\frac{1}{5} & \frac{3}{5} \\ \frac{2}{5} & -\frac{1}{5} \end{bmatrix}$

(e) None of these

1—M—Answer: d

15. Find the inverse of $A = \begin{bmatrix} 3 & 2 \\ 1 & 4 \end{bmatrix}$.

(a) $\begin{bmatrix} \frac{2}{5} & -\frac{1}{5} \\ -\frac{1}{10} & \frac{3}{10} \end{bmatrix}$

(b) $\begin{bmatrix} \frac{1}{3} & \frac{1}{2} \\ 1 & \frac{1}{4} \end{bmatrix}$

(c) $\begin{bmatrix} 4 & -2 \\ -1 & 3 \end{bmatrix}$

(d) $\begin{bmatrix} -3 & 1 \\ 2 & -4 \end{bmatrix}$

(e) None of these

1—M—Answer: a

16. Find the inverse of $A = \begin{bmatrix} 2 & 3 \\ 1 & 2 \end{bmatrix}$.

(a) $\begin{bmatrix} \frac{1}{2} & \frac{1}{3} \\ 1 & \frac{1}{2} \end{bmatrix}$

(b) $\begin{bmatrix} 2 & -3 \\ -1 & 2 \end{bmatrix}$

(c) $\begin{bmatrix} -2 & 1 \\ 3 & -2 \end{bmatrix}$

(d) $\begin{bmatrix} \frac{2}{7} & -\frac{3}{7} \\ -\frac{1}{7} & \frac{2}{7} \end{bmatrix}$

(e) None of these

1—M—Answer: b

17. Find the inverse of $A = \begin{bmatrix} 2 & 3 \\ -3 & -3 \end{bmatrix}$

(a) $\begin{bmatrix} -3 & -3 \\ 3 & 2 \end{bmatrix}$

(b) $\begin{bmatrix} \frac{1}{2} & \frac{1}{3} \\ -\frac{1}{3} & -\frac{1}{3} \end{bmatrix}$

(c) $\begin{bmatrix} \frac{1}{4} & \frac{1}{4} \\ -\frac{1}{4} & -\frac{1}{3} \end{bmatrix}$

(d) $\begin{bmatrix} -1 & -1 \\ 1 & \frac{2}{3} \end{bmatrix}$

(e) None of these

1—M—Answer: d

18. Find A^{-1} if $A = \begin{bmatrix} 2 & 0 & 3 \\ -1 & 0 & 2 \\ 0 & 1 & 1 \end{bmatrix}$

(a) $\begin{bmatrix} 2 & -3 & 0 \\ -1 & -2 & 7 \\ 1 & 2 & 0 \end{bmatrix}$

(b) $\frac{1}{7} \begin{bmatrix} 2 & -3 & 0 \\ -1 & -2 & 7 \\ 1 & 2 & 0 \end{bmatrix}$

(c) $\begin{bmatrix} \frac{1}{2} & 0 & \frac{1}{3} \\ -1 & 0 & \frac{1}{2} \\ 0 & 1 & 1 \end{bmatrix}$

(d) $\begin{bmatrix} 2 & -1 & 0 \\ 0 & 0 & 1 \\ 3 & 2 & 1 \end{bmatrix}$

(e) None of these

1—M—Answer: b

19. Find A^{-1} if $A = \begin{bmatrix} 1 & -1 & -1 \\ 5 & 0 & 20 \\ 0 & 10 & -20 \end{bmatrix}$

1—O—Answer: $\begin{bmatrix} \frac{4}{7} & \frac{3}{35} & \frac{2}{35} \\ -\frac{2}{7} & \frac{2}{35} & \frac{1}{14} \\ -\frac{1}{7} & \frac{1}{35} & -\frac{1}{70} \end{bmatrix}$

20. Use a graphing utility to find A^{-1} if it exists, given $A = \begin{bmatrix} 1 & 2 \\ 3 & 4 \end{bmatrix}$

1—O—Answer: $\begin{bmatrix} -2 & 1 \\ 1.5 & -0.5 \end{bmatrix}$

21. Use a graphing utility to find B^{-1} if it exists given

$$B = \begin{bmatrix} 2 & -1 & 1 \\ 1 & 2 & -1 \\ 3 & -4 & 2 \end{bmatrix}.$$

1—O—Answer: $\begin{bmatrix} 0 & 0.4 & 0.2 \\ 1 & -0.2 & -0.6 \\ 2 & -1 & -1 \end{bmatrix}$

22. Use a graphing utility to find C^{-1} if it exists, given

$$C = \begin{bmatrix} 1 & 0 & -2 & 3 \\ 1 & 1 & -3 & 2 \\ 2 & 1 & 0 & 3 \\ 0 & 1 & 0 & -3 \end{bmatrix}.$$

1—O—Answer: $\begin{bmatrix} 2.25 & -1.5 & 0.125 & 1.375 \\ -2.25 & 1.5 & 0.375 & -0.875 \\ -0.5 & 0 & 0.25 & -0.25 \\ -0.75 & 0.5 & 0.125 & -0.625 \end{bmatrix}$

23. Use a graphing utility to find A^{-1} if it exists, given

$$A = \begin{bmatrix} 1 & 1 & 1 \\ 0 & 1 & 0 \\ 2 & -1 & 3 \end{bmatrix}.$$

1—O—Answer: $\begin{bmatrix} 3 & -4 & -1 \\ 0 & 1 & 0 \\ -2 & 3 & 1 \end{bmatrix}$

24. Use a graphing utility to find A^{-1} if it exists, given

$$A = \begin{bmatrix} 1 & 4 & 3 \\ 2 & 6 & 1 \\ 1 & 0 & 3 \end{bmatrix}.$$

1—O—Answer: $\begin{bmatrix} -0.9 & 0.6 & 0.7 \\ 0.25 & 0 & -0.25 \\ 0.3 & -0.2 & 0.1 \end{bmatrix}$

25. Use a graphing utility to find B^{-1} if it exists, given

$$B = \begin{bmatrix} 1 & 0 & 0 \\ 0 & -1 & 0 \\ 1 & 0 & 1 \end{bmatrix}.$$

1—O—Answer: $\begin{bmatrix} 1 & 0 & 0 \\ 0 & -1 & 0 \\ -1 & 0 & 1 \end{bmatrix}$

26. Given the system of linear equations with coefficient matrix A, use A^{-1} to find (x, y, z, w).

$$
\begin{aligned}
x + y + z + w &= 0 \\
2x - y &= -2 \\
3z - 2w &= 0 \\
y - 3z &= 6
\end{aligned}
\qquad
A^{-1} = \begin{bmatrix}
\frac{3}{14} & \frac{11}{28} & \frac{3}{28} & \frac{5}{28} \\
\frac{3}{7} & -\frac{3}{14} & \frac{3}{14} & \frac{5}{14} \\
\frac{1}{7} & -\frac{1}{14} & \frac{1}{14} & -\frac{3}{14} \\
\frac{3}{14} & -\frac{3}{28} & -\frac{11}{28} & -\frac{9}{28}
\end{bmatrix}
$$

(a) $(10, -15, -5, 0)$ (b) $\left(\frac{2}{7}, \frac{18}{7}, -\frac{8}{7}, -\frac{12}{7}\right)$ (c) $\left(\frac{3}{11}, \frac{18}{11}, -\frac{7}{11}, \frac{16}{11}\right)$

(d) $(0, 1, -1, 0)$ (e) None of these

1—M—Answer: b

27. Given the system of linear equations with coefficient matrix A, use A^{-1} to find (x, y, z, w).

$$
\begin{aligned}
x + 2y &= 1 \\
3x + 8y + 5w &= 0 \\
x + 4y + 3z + 10w &= -1 \\
x - 3z &= -1
\end{aligned}
\qquad
A^{-1} = \begin{bmatrix}
3 & -1 & \frac{1}{2} & \frac{1}{2} \\
-1 & \frac{1}{2} & -\frac{1}{4} & -\frac{1}{4} \\
1 & -\frac{1}{3} & \frac{1}{6} & -\frac{1}{6} \\
-\frac{1}{5} & 0 & \frac{1}{10} & \frac{1}{10}
\end{bmatrix}
$$

(a) $\left(2, -\frac{1}{2}, 1, -\frac{2}{5}\right)$ (b) $(3, -1, -1, 0)$ (c) $\left(\frac{2}{3}, \frac{1}{6}, -\frac{5}{9}, \frac{2}{3}\right)$

(d) $\left(1, 0, \frac{2}{3}, -\frac{5}{3}\right)$ (e) None of these

1—M—Answer: a

28. Given the system of linear equations with coefficient matrix A, use A^{-1} to find (x, y, z).

$$
\begin{aligned}
3x + 2y + z &= 5 \\
x - 4y &= 6 \\
x - y + 3z &= 6
\end{aligned}
\qquad
A^{-1} = \frac{1}{39} \begin{bmatrix}
12 & 7 & -4 \\
3 & -8 & -1 \\
-3 & -5 & 14
\end{bmatrix}
$$

(a) $(-2, -1, 1)$ (b) $(-1, 6, -2)$ (c) $(2, -1, 1)$

(d) $(6, -1, 3)$ (e) None of these

1—M—Answer: c

29. Given the system of linear equations with coefficient matrix A, use A^{-1} to find (x, y, z).

$$
\begin{aligned}
3x + y - z &= -11 \\
x - y - z &= -5 \\
x + 2y + 3z &= 3
\end{aligned}
\qquad
A^{-1} = \frac{1}{10} \begin{bmatrix}
1 & 5 & 2 \\
4 & -10 & -2 \\
-3 & 5 & 4
\end{bmatrix}
$$

(a) $(3, -2, 0)$ (b) $(2, -2, 3)$ (c) $(-1, 5, 1)$

(d) $(-3, 0, 2)$ (e) None of these

1—M—Answer: d

30. Given the system of linear equations with coefficient matrix A, use A^{-1} to find (x, y, z).

$$4x - y + z = 5$$
$$x - 4y + z = 8$$
$$2x + 2y - 3z = -12$$

$$A^{-1} = \frac{1}{45} \begin{bmatrix} 10 & -1 & 3 \\ 5 & -14 & -3 \\ 10 & -10 & -15 \end{bmatrix}$$

(a) $(0, -1, 4)$ (b) $(0, 4, -2)$ (c) $(1, -1, 2)$

(d) $(3, 0, 2)$ (e) None of these

1—M—Answer: e

31. Given $A = \begin{bmatrix} 1 & 2 \\ -3 & 5 \end{bmatrix}$, find A^{-1}.

(a) $\begin{bmatrix} -1 & -2 \\ 3 & -5 \end{bmatrix}$ (b) $\begin{bmatrix} 1 & \frac{1}{2} \\ -\frac{1}{3} & \frac{1}{5} \end{bmatrix}$ (c) $\begin{bmatrix} -\frac{4}{15} & \frac{1}{3} \\ -\frac{2}{3} & \frac{11}{15} \end{bmatrix}$

(d) $\begin{bmatrix} \frac{5}{11} & -\frac{2}{11} \\ \frac{3}{11} & \frac{1}{11} \end{bmatrix}$ (e) None of these

1—M—Answer: d

32. Use the inverse matrix to solve the system of linear equations.

$$2x + 2y = 12$$
$$x + 3y = 16$$

1—O—Answer: $(1, 5)$

33. Use an inverse matrix to solve the system of linear equations.

$$x + y + z = 5$$
$$2x - y + z = 1$$
$$-x + y + 3z = 1$$

(a) $(2, 3, 0)$ (b) $(-3, 0, 8)$ (c) $(2, 2, 1)$

(d) $(-3, 6, 2)$ (e) None of these

1—M—Answer: a

34. Use a graphing utility to solve (if possible) the system of linear equations.

$$x + y + z = 0$$
$$x + 2y + z = 1$$
$$2x + y + z = -1$$

(a) $(2, -3, 1)$ (b) $(-3, -5, 8)$ (c) $(-1, 1, 0)$

(d) $(-2, 1, 1)$ (e) None of these

1—M—Answer: c

35. Use an inverse matrix to solve the system of linear equations.

$$2x + 3y + 2z = 0$$
$$x \qquad - 6z = 4$$
$$x + \ y - 2z = 1$$

1—O—Answer: $\left(7, \ -5, \ \frac{1}{2}\right)$

36. Use a graphing utility to solve (if possible) the system of linear equations.

$$5x + y + 2z = \ \ 0$$
$$x \qquad - 3z = -2$$
$$2x + y + \ \ z = \ \ 6$$

1—O—Answer: $(-2, \ 10, \ 0)$

37. Use a graphing utility to solve the system of linear equations.

$$x - y + z = \ \ 6$$
$$2x \qquad - z = \ \ 4$$
$$-x - y - z = -4$$

(a) $(4, \ 2, \ 4)$ \qquad\qquad (b) $(3, \ -1, \ 2)$ \qquad\qquad (c) $(1, \ -7, \ -2)$

(d) $(2, \ -4, \ 0)$ \qquad\qquad (e) None of these

1—M—Answer: b

38. Use a graphing utility to solve (if possible) the system of linear equations.

$$x + y + \ \ z = 4$$
$$2x + y + \ \ z = 6$$
$$x + y + 2z = 9$$

(a) $(2, \ 2, \ 0)$ \qquad\qquad (b) $(-2, \ 3, \ 3)$ \qquad\qquad (c) $(2, \ -3, \ 5)$

(d) $(1, \ -1, \ 4)$ \qquad\qquad (e) None of these

1—M—Answer: c

39. Use an inverse matrix to solve the system of linear equations.

$$3x + 2y + \ \ z = \ \ 1$$
$$x - \ y \qquad = 10$$
$$-x \qquad + 2z = \ \ 5$$

2—O—Answer: $\left(\frac{37}{11}, \ -\frac{73}{11}, \ \frac{46}{11}\right)$

40. Use the inverse matrix method to solve the system of linear equations.

$$6x + 6y - 5z = 11$$
$$3x + 6y - z = 6$$
$$9x - 3y + z = 0$$

2—O—Answer: $\left(\frac{1}{3}, \frac{2}{3}, -1\right)$

41. A small business borrows \$90,000; some at 7%, some at 9%, and the rest at 10% simple interest. The annual interest is \$7110, and twice as much is borrowed at 7% as at 9%. Set up a system where x, y, and z represent the amounts borrowed at 7%, 9% and 10%, respectively, then use the inverse of the coefficient matrix to find (x, y, z).

(a) (\$46,000, \$23,000, \$21,000)   (b) (\$54,000, \$27,000, \$9000)

(c) (\$18,000, \$36,000, \$36,000)   (d) (\$41,000, \$20,500, \$28,500)

(e) None of these

2—M—Answer: b

42. A small business borrows \$550,000; some at 7%, some at 8%, and the rest at 11% simple interest. The annual interest is \$53,600, and one-third of the amount borrowed at 11% is borrowed at 7%. Set up a system where x, y, and z represent the amounts borrowed at 7%, 8% and 11%, respectively, then use the inverse of the coefficient matrix to find y.

(a) \$70,000   (b) \$90,000   (c) \$120,000

(d) \$130,000   (e) None of these

2—M—Answer: a

43. A small business borrows \$175,000; some at 7%, some at 10%, and the rest at 11% simple interest. The annual interest is \$15,800, and the amount borrowed at 7% exceeds the amount borrowed at 10% by \$20,000. Set up a system where x, y, and z represent the amounts borrowed at 7%, 10% and 11%, respectively, then use the inverse of the coefficient matrix to find x.

(a) \$90,000   (b) \$40,000   (c) \$75,000

(d) \$60,000   (e) None of these

2—M—Answer: c

9.8 Systems of Inequalities

1. Match the graph with the the correct inequality.

   (a) $y < x^2 + 3x - 1$ (b) $y > x^2 + 3x - 1$

   (c) $y \leq x^2 + 3x - 1$ (d) $y \geq x^2 + 3x - 1$

   (e) None of these

   1—M—Answer: c

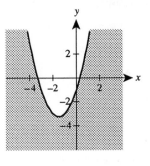

2. Match the graph with the correct inequality.

   (a) $y > -2$ (b) $y < -2$

   (c) $x > -2$ (d) $x \geq -2$

   (e) None of these

   1—M—Answer: c

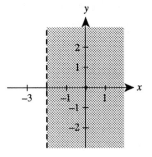

3. Match the graph with the correct inequality.

   (a) $3x - 4y < 12$ (b) $3x - 4y \leq 12$

   (c) $3x - 4y > 12$ (d) $3x - 4y \geq 12$

   (e) None of these

   1—M—Answer: b

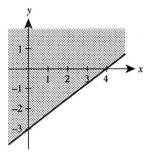

4. Match the graph with the correct inequality.

   (a) $4x^2 - y \leq 0$ (b) $4x^2 - y > 0$

   (c) $4x^2 - y < 0$ (d) $4x^2 - y^2 \geq 0$

   (e) None of these

   1—M—Answer: b

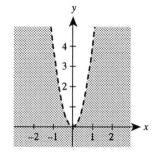

5. Using a graphing utility, sketch the graph of the inequality: $x^2 + (y-1)^2 \leq 25$

1—O—Answer:

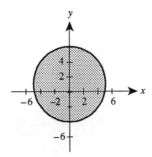

6. Using a graphing utility, sketch the graph of the inequality: $3x^2 + y \geq 6$

1—O—Answer:

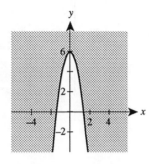

7. Using a graphing utility, sketch the graph of the inequality: $y > e^x$

1—O—Answer:

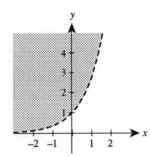

8. Using a graphing utility, sketch the graph of the inequality: $x + y \leq 2$

(a)
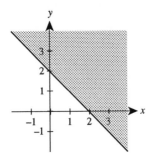

(b)
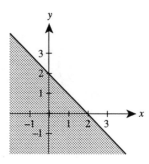

(c)
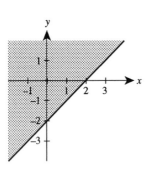

(d)
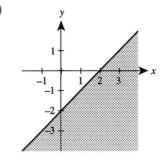

(e) None of these

1—M—Answer: b

9. Using a graphing utility, sketch the graph of the inequality: $x - y > 1$

(a)
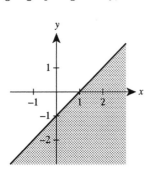

(b)
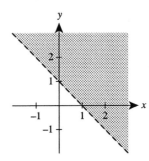

(c)
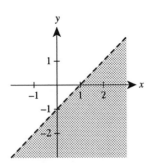

(d)
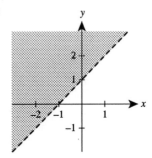

(e) None of these

1—M—Answer: c

10. Using a graphing utility, sketch the graph of the inequality: $3x^2 + y > 6$

    1—O—Answer:

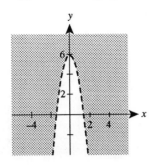

11. Identify the sketch of the inequality: $\dfrac{x^2}{9} - \dfrac{y^2}{16} \le 1$

(a)

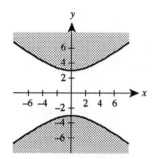

(b)

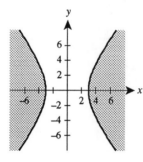

(c)

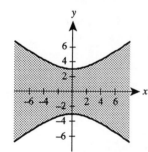

(d)

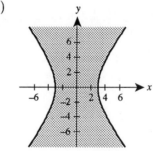

(e) None of these

    1—M—Answer: d

12. Identify the sketch of the inequality: $(x-1)^2 + (y+2)^2 > 4$

(a)

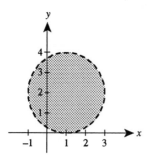

(b)

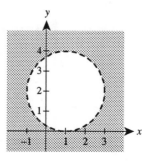

(c)

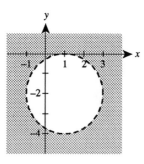

(d)

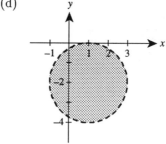

(e) None of these

1—M—Answer: c

13. Use a graphing utility to sketch the graph of the system of inequalities:

$$y \geq -|x+2|$$
$$x \leq 0$$
$$y \leq 0$$

2—O—Answer:

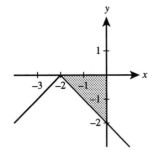

14. Use a graphing utility to sketch the graph of the system of inequalities:

$$x + y \geq 2$$
$$y \leq x$$
$$y > 0$$

1—O—Answer:

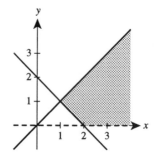

15. Use a graphing utility to sketch the graph of the system of inequalities:

$$2x + 3y \leq 6$$
$$x - 2y \geq -2$$

1—O—Answer:

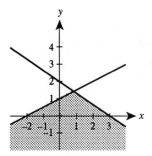

16. Use a graphing utility to sketch the graph of the system of inequalities:

$$2y - 3x \leq 10$$
$$2y \geq x^2$$

2—O—Answer:

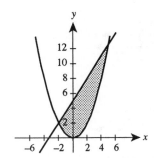

17. Identify the sketch of the graph of the solution for the system:

$$x + y \geq 2$$
$$y \leq 2$$
$$x \leq 2$$

(a)

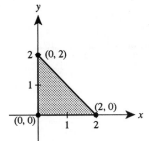

(b)

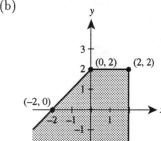

17. – CONTINUED–

(c)

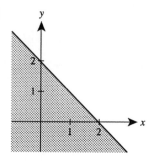

(d)

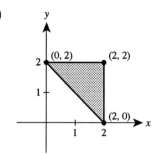

(e) None of these

1—M—Answer: d

18. Identify the sketch of the graph of the solution for the system:

$$x - y > 1$$

$$x < 2$$

$$y \geq 0$$

(a)

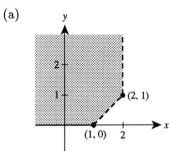

(b)

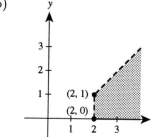

(c)

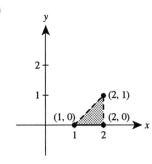

(d)

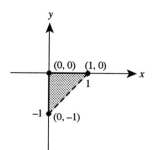

(e) None of these

1—M—Answer: c

19. Match the graph with the correct system of inequalities.

(a) $3x + y \leq 5$ (b) $3x + y \leq 5$

     $y \geq 1$ $y \leq 1$

     $x \geq 1$ $x \geq 1$

(c) $y \geq 5 + 3x$ (d) $3x + y \leq 5$

     $y \leq 1$ $y \geq 1$

     $x \leq 1$ $x \leq 1$

(e) None of these

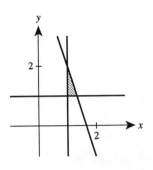

2—M—Answer: a

20. Match the graph with the correct system of inequalities.

(a) $x + 2y \leq 6$ (b) $x + 2y \geq 6$

    $x - y \leq 2$ $x - y \geq 2$

     $y \geq 0$ $x \geq 0$

(c) $x + 2y \leq 6$ (d) $x + 2y \geq 6$

    $x - y \geq 2$ $x - y \geq 2$

     $x \geq 0$ $y \geq 0$

(e) None of these

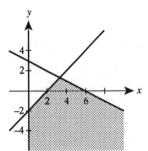

1—M—Answer: c

21. Match the graph with the correct system of inequalities.

(a) $x + 2y \leq 4$ (b) $x + 2y \geq 4$

     $x \leq y$ $x \leq y$

     $x \geq 0$ $y \geq 0$

(c) $x + 2y \leq 4$ (d) $x + 2y \leq 4$

     $x \leq y$ $y \leq x$

     $y \geq 0$ $y \geq 0$

(e) None of these

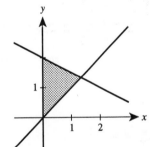

1—M—Answer: a

22. Match the graph with the correct system of inequalities.

(a) $x + 2y \leq 4$ (b) $x + 2y \leq 4$

     $x \leq y$ $y \leq x$

     $x \geq 0$ $y \geq 0$

(c) $x + 2y \geq 4$ (d) $x + 2y \geq 4$

     $y \leq x$ $x \leq y$

     $y \geq 0$ $y \geq 0$

(e) None of these

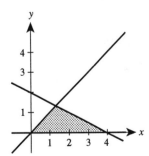

2—M—Answer: b

23. Match the graph with the correct system of inequalities.

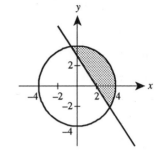

   (a) $x^2 + y^2 \geq 16$ (b) $x^2 + y^2 \leq 16$

        $3x + 2y \leq 6$ $3x + 2y \leq 6$

   (c) $x^2 + y^2 \geq 16$ (d) $x^2 + y^2 \leq 16$

        $3x + 2y \geq 6$ $3x + 2y \geq 6$

   (e) None of these

   2—M—Answer: d

24. Match the graph with the correct system of inequalities.

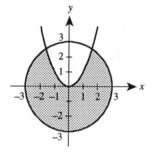

   (a) $x^2 + y^2 \geq 9$ (b) $x^2 + y^2 \geq 9$

        $y \geq x^2$ $y \leq x^2$

   (c) $x^2 + y^2 \leq 9$ (d) $x^2 + y^2 \leq 9$

        $y \leq x^2$ $y \geq x^2$

   (e) None of these

   2—M—Answer: c

25. Find a set of inequalities that describe the triangular region with vertices at $(0, 0)$, $(3, 3)$, and $(5, 0)$.

   2—O—Answer: $y \geq 0$, $y \leq x$, and $3x + 2y \leq 15$

26. For a circle of radius 3 and center at the origin, find a set of inequalities that describe the first quadrant sector bounded by radial lines that pass through $(3/\sqrt{2}, 3/\sqrt{2})$ and $(0, 3)$.

   2—O—Answer: $x \geq 0$, $y \geq x$, and $x^2 + y^2 \leq 9$

27. Find the vertices of the region described by the system of inequalities:

$$3x + y \leq 4$$
$$2x - y \geq 1$$
$$x + 2y \geq -2$$

   1—O—Answer: $(0, -1)$, $(1, 1)$, and $(2, -2)$

28. Find a set of inequalities that describe the triangular region with vertices $(0, 0)$, $(5, 5)$ and $(3, 0)$.

   (a) $5x - 2y \geq 15$ (b) $5x - 2y \geq 15$ (c) $5x - 2y \leq 15$

            $y \leq x$ $y \geq x$ $y \leq x$

            $y \geq 0$ $y \geq 0$ $y \geq 0$

   (d) $5x - 2y \leq 15$ (e) None of these

            $y \geq x$

            $y \geq 0$

   2—M—Answer: c

29. Find a set of inequalities that describe the triangular region with vertices $(0, 0)$, $(8, 8)$ and $(10, 0)$.

(a) $4x + y \leq 40$

$\ \ y \leq x$

$\ \ y \geq 0$

(b) $4x + y \leq 40$

$\ \ y \leq x$

(c) $4x + y \geq 40$

$\ \ y \leq x$

(d) $4x + y \geq 40$

$\ \ y \leq x$

$\ \ y \geq 0$

(e) None of these

2—M—Answer: a

30. Find the vertices of the region described by the system of inequalities.

$2x - y \leq 5$

$3x + y \geq 0$

$y \leq 0$

(a) $(1, -3)$, $(0, 0)$, $(0, -5)$

(b) $(2, -1)$, $(0, 0)$, $\left(\frac{5}{2}, 0\right)$

(c) $(1, -3)$, $(0, 0)$, $\left(\frac{5}{2}, 0\right)$

(d) $(2, -1)$, $(0, 0)$, $(0, -5)$

(e) None of these

2—M—Answer: c

31. Find the consumer surplus if the demand equation is $p = 110 - 20x$ and the supply equation is $p = 50 + 10x$.

(a) \$20   (b) \$30   (c) \$40   (d) \$50   (e) None of these

2—M—Answer: c

32. Find the producer surplus if the demand equation is $p = 110 - 20x$ and the supply equation is $p = 50 + 10x$.

(a) \$20   (b) \$30   (c) \$40   (d) \$50   (e) None of these

2—M—Answer: a

33. Find the producer surplus if the demand equation is $p = 90 - 10x$ and the supply equation is $p = 30 + 20x$.

(a) \$20   (b) \$30   (c) \$40   (d) \$50   (e) None of these

2—M—Answer: c

34. Find the consumer surplus if the demand equation is $p = 100 - 0.1x$ and the supply equation is $p = 10 + 0.4x$.

(a) \$1250

(b) \$1590

(c) \$1620

(d) \$6480

(e) None of these

2—M—Answer: c

35. Find the producer surplus if the demand equation is $p = 50 - 0.1x$ and the supply equation is $p = 10 + 0.4x$.

   (a) $1280   (b) $1200   (c) $560

   (d) $320   (e) None of these

   2—M—Answer: a

36. Find the consumer surplus if the demand equation is $p = 80 - \frac{1}{2}x$ and the supply equation is $p = 20 + \frac{5}{2}x$.

   (a) $500   (b) $300   (c) $100

   (d) $60   (e) None of these

   2—M—Answer: c

CHAPTER TEN
Sequences, Mathematical Induction, and Probability

10.1 Sequences and Summation Notation

1. Find the first 5 terms of the sequence whose nth term is $a_n = (-1)^n(2n+9)$. (Assume that n begins with 1.)

   (a) $-11, -13, -15, -17, -19, \ldots$ (b) $-11, 13, -15, 17, -19, \ldots$

   (c) $-11, 2, -13, 4, -15, \ldots$ (d) $-11, -24, -39, -56, -75, \ldots$

   (e) None of these

   1—M—Answer: b

2. Find the first 5 terms of the sequence whose nth term is $a_n = n!$. (Assume that n begins with 0.)

   (a) $0, 1, 2, 6, 24$ (b) $0, 1, 2, 6, 12$ (c) $1, 1, 2, 6, 12$

   (d) $1, 1, 2, 6, 24$ (e) None of these

   1—M—Answer: d

3. Find the first 5 terms of the sequence whose nth term is $a_n = 1 - \dfrac{1}{n}$. (Assume that n begins with 1.)

   (a) $\dfrac{1}{2}, \dfrac{1}{4}, \dfrac{1}{8}, \dfrac{1}{16}, \dfrac{1}{32}$ (b) $0, \dfrac{1}{2}, \dfrac{2}{3}, \dfrac{3}{4}, \dfrac{4}{5}$ (c) $0, \dfrac{1}{2}, \dfrac{1}{3}, \dfrac{1}{4}, \dfrac{1}{5}$

   (d) $1, \dfrac{1}{2}, \dfrac{2}{3}, \dfrac{3}{4}, \dfrac{4}{5}$ (e) None of these

   1—M—Answer: b

4. Write the first 5 terms of the sequence whose nth term is $a_n = \dfrac{n!}{(n+2)!}$. (Assume that n begins with 0.)

   1—O—Answer: $\dfrac{1}{2}, \dfrac{1}{6}, \dfrac{1}{12}, \dfrac{1}{20}, \dfrac{1}{30}$

5. Write the first five terms of the sequence whose nth term is $a_n = \dfrac{n-2}{n^2+1}$. (Assume that n begins with 1.)

   1—O—Answer: $-\dfrac{1}{2}, 0, \dfrac{1}{10}, \dfrac{2}{17}, \dfrac{3}{26}$

6. Write the first five terms of the sequence whose nth term is $a_n = \dfrac{n-2}{n^2+1}$. (Assume that n begins with 1.)

    1—O—Answer: $-\dfrac{1}{2}, \ 0, \ \dfrac{1}{10}, \ \dfrac{2}{17}, \ \dfrac{3}{26}$

7. Write the first five terms of the sequence whose nth term is $a_n = \dfrac{(-1)^n}{n!}$. (Assume that n begins with 1.)

    1—O—Answer: $-1, \ \dfrac{1}{2}, \ -\dfrac{1}{6}, \ \dfrac{1}{24}, \ -\dfrac{1}{120}$

8. Write the first five terms of the sequence whose nth term is $a_n = \dfrac{n!}{(n+2)!}$. (Assume that n begins with 0.)

    1—O—Answer: $\dfrac{1}{2}, \ \dfrac{1}{6}, \ \dfrac{1}{12}, \ \dfrac{1}{20}, \ \dfrac{1}{30}$

9. Simplify: $\dfrac{8!}{5!}$

  (a) $\dfrac{8}{5}$ (b) 336   (c) 56   (d) 48   (e) None of these

  1—M—Answer: b

10. Simplify: $\dfrac{6!}{4!2!}$

  (a) $\dfrac{3}{4}$ (b) $\dfrac{1}{8}$ (c) 15   (d) 30   (e) None of these

  1—M—Answer: c

11. Simplify: $\dfrac{(2n)!}{(2n-2)!}$

  2—O—Answer: $4n^2 + 2n$

12. Simplify: $\dfrac{3(4!)}{7!}$

  (a) 95,040   (b) $\dfrac{15}{14}$ (c) $\dfrac{1}{70}$

  (d) $\dfrac{1}{7}$ (e) None of these

  1—M—Answer: c

13. Simplify: $\dfrac{(2n)!}{(2n-3)!}$

(a) $\dfrac{2n}{2n-3}$ (b) $2n(2n-1)(2n-2)$ (c) $2n(n-1)(n-2)$

(d) $\dfrac{2}{(n-1)(n-2)}$ (e) None of these

1—M—Answer: b

14. Simplify: $\dfrac{(n+1)!}{(n-1)!}$

(a) $n+1$ (b) $n-1$ (c) $\dfrac{n+1}{n-1}$

(d) n^2+n (e) None of these

1—M—Answer: d

15. Find a formula for the nth term of the sequence. (Assume that n begins with 1.)

$$\dfrac{3}{2}, \dfrac{6}{4}, \dfrac{9}{12}, \dfrac{12}{48}, \dfrac{15}{240}, \cdots$$

(a) $\dfrac{3n}{2n!}$ (b) $\dfrac{3n}{n(n+1)}$ (c) $\dfrac{3n}{n!(n+1)!}$

(d) $\dfrac{3n}{2(n-1)!}$ (e) None of these

1—M—Answer: a

16. Find a formula for the nth term of the sequence. (Assume that n begins with 1.)

$$\dfrac{1}{4}, \dfrac{2}{9}, \dfrac{3}{16}, \dfrac{4}{25}, \cdots$$

(a) $a_n = 1 - \dfrac{3n}{n^2}$ (b) $a_n = \dfrac{n}{(n+1)!}$ (c) $a_n = \dfrac{1}{2} + \dfrac{n}{(n+1)^3}$

(d) $a_n = \dfrac{n}{(n+1)^2}$ (e) None of these

1—M—Answer: d

17. Find a formula for the nth term of the sequence. (Assume that n begins with 1.)

$$\dfrac{2}{1}, \dfrac{4}{1}, \dfrac{6}{2}, \dfrac{8}{6}, \dfrac{10}{24}, \cdots$$

(a) $\dfrac{2^n}{(n+1)!}$ (b) $\dfrac{3-2^n}{n(2^n)}$ (c) $\dfrac{2n}{2n-1}$

(d) $\dfrac{2n}{(n-1)!}$ (e) None of these

1—M—Answer: d

18. Find a formula for the nth term of the sequence. (Assume that n begins with 1.)

$$\frac{2}{1}, \frac{3}{2}, \frac{4}{3}, \frac{5}{4}, \frac{6}{5}, \cdots$$

(a) $\dfrac{n+1}{n-1}$ (b) $2 - \dfrac{1}{n}$ (c) $1 + \dfrac{1}{n}$

(d) $\dfrac{2n-1}{n}$ (e) None of these

1—M—Answer: c

19. Find a formula for the nth term of the sequence. (Assume that n begins with 1.)

$$1, 1, \frac{1}{2}, \frac{1}{6}, \frac{1}{24}, \cdots$$

(a) $\dfrac{n+1}{n!}$ (b) $\dfrac{n}{n!}$ (c) $\dfrac{n}{2n!}$

(d) $\dfrac{1}{2^n}$ (e) None of these

1—M—Answer: b

20. Find the sum: $\displaystyle\sum_{n=3}^{6} \frac{3}{n-2}$

(a) $\dfrac{12}{9}$ (b) $\dfrac{25}{4}$ (c) $\dfrac{3}{16}$

(d) $\dfrac{1}{2}$ (e) None of these

1—M—Answer: b

21. Find the sum: $\displaystyle\sum_{n=1}^{4} \frac{n+1}{n+2}$

(a) $\dfrac{61}{20}$ (b) $\dfrac{31}{20}$ (c) $\dfrac{143}{60}$

(d) $\dfrac{131}{60}$ (e) None of these

1—M—Answer: a

22. Find the sum: $\displaystyle\sum_{i=1}^{4} (1-i)$

(a) -3 (b) -6 (c) 6   (d) -5 (e) None of these

1—M—Answer: b

23. Find the sum: $\displaystyle\sum_{k=2}^{6} (-1)^k (2k)$

(a) 40   (b) −4   (c) 6   (d) 8   (e) None of these

1—M—Answer: d

24. Find the sum: $\displaystyle\sum_{i=0}^{3} i!$

(a) 9   (b) 6   (c) 10   (d) 7   (e) None of these

1—M—Answer: c

25. Use sigma notation to write the sum: $\dfrac{2}{1} + \dfrac{3}{2} + \dfrac{4}{3} + \cdots + \dfrac{7}{6}$

(a) $\displaystyle\sum_{n=1}^{7} \dfrac{n}{n-1}$ (b) $\displaystyle\sum_{n=1}^{6} \dfrac{n+1}{n}$ (c) $\displaystyle\sum_{n=1}^{7} \dfrac{n}{n+1}$

(d) $\displaystyle\sum_{n=2}^{n} \dfrac{n}{n-1}$ (e) None of these

1—M—Answer: b

26. Use sigma notation to write the sum: $\dfrac{3}{1} + \dfrac{3}{4} + \dfrac{3}{9} + \dfrac{3}{16} + \dfrac{3}{25}$

(a) $\displaystyle\sum_{i=1}^{5} \dfrac{1}{i^2}$ (b) $\displaystyle\sum_{i=1}^{5} \dfrac{3}{4i}$ (c) $\displaystyle\sum_{i=1}^{6} \dfrac{3}{i^2}$

(d) $\displaystyle\sum_{i=1}^{5} \dfrac{3}{i^2}$ (e) None of these

1—M—Answer: d

27. Use sigma notation to write the sum: $\dfrac{2}{3} + \dfrac{4}{4} + \dfrac{6}{5} + \dfrac{8}{6} + \cdots + \dfrac{14}{9}$

(a) $\displaystyle\sum_{n=1}^{7} \dfrac{2n}{n+2}$ (b) $\displaystyle\sum_{n=2}^{8} \dfrac{n+2}{n+1}$ (c) $\displaystyle\sum_{n=0}^{6} \dfrac{n+2}{n+3}$

(d) $\displaystyle\sum_{n=3}^{9} \dfrac{n-1}{n}$ (e) None of these

1—M—Answer: a

28. Use sigma notation to write the sum: $\dfrac{1}{2} + \dfrac{2}{6} + \dfrac{3}{24} + \dfrac{4}{120} + \dfrac{5}{720}$

1—O—Answer: $\displaystyle\sum_{n=1}^{5} \dfrac{n}{(n+1)!}$

29. Use sigma notation to write the sum: $\dfrac{4}{2} + \dfrac{5}{4} + \dfrac{6}{6} + \dfrac{7}{8}$

    (a) $\displaystyle\sum_{n=1}^{4} \dfrac{n+3}{2n}$ 　　　　　(b) $\displaystyle\sum_{n=1}^{4} \dfrac{4n-1}{2n}$ 　　　　　(c) $\displaystyle\sum_{n=1}^{4} \dfrac{2n+2}{2n}$

    (d) $\displaystyle\sum_{n=1}^{4} \dfrac{2^{n+1}+1}{n+2}$ 　　　　　(e) None of these

    1—M—Answer: a

30. Find the 10th term of the sequence: $\dfrac{3^1}{2^0}, \dfrac{3^2}{2^1}, \dfrac{3^3}{2^2}, \dfrac{3^4}{2^3}, \dfrac{3^5}{2^4}, \cdots$

    (a) $\dfrac{3^{10}}{2^{10}}$ 　　　　　(b) $\dfrac{3^{11}}{2^{10}}$ 　　　　　(c) $\dfrac{3^{10}}{2^9}$

    (d) $\dfrac{3^{11}}{2^{11}}$ 　　　　　(e) None of these

    1—M—Answer: c

31. Find the 40th term of the sequence whose nth term is $a_n = 500\left(1 + \dfrac{0.095}{12}\right)^n$.

    (a) 363.83 　　　　　(b) 752.19 　　　　　(c) 690.84
    (d) 685.42 　　　　　(e) None of these

    1—M—Answer: d

32. Find the fifth term of the sequence whose nth term is $a_n = 2(3^{n-1})$. (Assume that n begins with 1.)
    (a) 486 　　　(b) -486 　　　(c) $\frac{1}{162}$ 　　　(d) 162 　　　(e) None of these

    1—M—Answer: d

33. Find the third term of the sequence whose nth term is $a_n = \dfrac{(-1)^{n+1}}{n}$. (Assume that n begins with 1.)

    (a) $\dfrac{1}{3}$ 　　　(b) $\dfrac{1}{81}$ 　　　(c) $-\dfrac{1}{3}$ 　　　(d) $\dfrac{1}{27}$ 　　　(e) None of these

    1—M—Answer: a

34. Find the tenth term of the sequence whose nth term is $a_n = \dfrac{2n+1}{5+3(n-1)}$.
    (Assume that n begins with 1.)

    (a) $\dfrac{21}{32}$ 　　　(b) $\dfrac{21}{72}$ 　　　(c) $\dfrac{22}{32}$ 　　　(d) $\dfrac{19}{29}$ 　　　(e) None of these

    1—M—Answer: a

35. Find the fifth term of the sequence whose nth term is $a_n = \dfrac{(-1)^{n+1}}{(n+1)^2}$. (Assume that n begins with 1.)

(a) $-\dfrac{1}{25}$　　(b) $\dfrac{1}{5}$　　(c) $\dfrac{1}{36}$　　(d) $\dfrac{1}{6}$　　(e) None of these

1—M—Answer: c

36. A deposit of \$2000 is made in an account that earns 6% interest compounded monthly. The balance in the account after n months is given by $A_n = 2000\left(1 + \dfrac{0.06}{12}\right)^n$, $n = 1, 2, 3, \ldots$ Find the balance in this account after 8 years ($n = 96$).

(a) \$3552.17　　　　(b) \$2793.52　　　　　(c) \$2163.73

(d) \$3228.29　　　　(e) None of these

1—M—Answer: d

37. A deposit of \$4000 is made in an account that earns 7% interest compounded quarterly. The balance in the account after n months is given by $A_n = 4000\left(1 + \dfrac{0.07}{4}\right)^n$, $n = 1, 2, 3, \ldots$ Find the balance in this account after 8 years ($n = 32$).

(a) \$6968.85　　　　(b) \$4595.53　　　　　(c) \$27,439.59

(d) \$9874.31　　　　(e) None of these

1—M—Answer: a

10.2 Arithmetic Sequences

1. Which of the following is an arithmetic sequence?

(a) $1, 3, 9, 27, 81, \ldots$　　(b) $1, 16, 36, 64, 100, \ldots$　　(c) $2, 11, 20, 29, 38, \ldots$
(d) $3, -5, 7, -9, 11, \ldots$　　(e) None of these

1—M—Answer: c

2. Which of the following is an arithmetic sequence?

(a) $2, 4, 8, 16, 32, \ldots$　　(b) $-2, 4, -8, 16, -32, \ldots$　　(c) $3, 6, 9, 12, 15, \ldots$
(d) All of these　　(e) None of these

1—M—Answer: c

3. Which of the following is an arithmetic sequence?

(a) $1, 3, 5, 7, 9, \ldots$　　(b) $4, 7, 10, 13, 16, \ldots$　　(c) $-10, -6, -2, 2, 6, \ldots$
(d) All of these　　(e) None of these

1—M—Answer: d

4. Which of the following is an arithmetic sequence?

   (a) 2, 3, 5, 7, 11, ...   (b) $\frac{1}{2}$, $\frac{1}{3}$, $\frac{1}{4}$, $\frac{1}{5}$, $\frac{1}{6}$, ...   (c) $\frac{1}{2}$, $\frac{1}{4}$, $\frac{1}{6}$, $\frac{1}{8}$, $\frac{1}{10}$, ...

   (d) All of these   (e) None of these

   1—M—Answer: e

5. Which of the following is an arithmetic sequence?

   (a) $-\frac{1}{2}$, -1, $-\frac{3}{2}$, -2, $-\frac{5}{2}$, ...   (b) $\frac{2}{5}$, $\frac{2}{25}$, $\frac{2}{125}$, $\frac{2}{625}$, $\frac{2}{3125}$, ...   (c) -2, 2, -2, 2, -2, ...

   (d) All of these   (e) None of these

   1—M—Answer: a

6. Find the first 5 terms of the arithmetic sequence with $a_1 = 23$ and $d = -\frac{1}{2}$.

   (a) 23, $22\frac{1}{2}$, 22, $21\frac{1}{2}$, 21   (b) 23, $23\frac{1}{2}$, 24, $24\frac{1}{2}$, 25   (c) 23, $-\frac{23}{2}$, $\frac{23}{4}$, $-\frac{23}{8}$, $\frac{23}{16}$

   (d) 23, -46, 92, -184, 368   (e) None of these

   1—M—Answer: a

7. Find the first 4 terms of the arithmetic sequence with $a_1 = 4$ and $d = -3$.

   (a) 4, $-\frac{4}{3}$, $\frac{4}{9}$, $-\frac{4}{27}$, ...   (b) 4, 1, -2, -5, ...   (c) 4, 7, 10, 13, ...

   (d) 4, -12, 36, -108, ...   (e) None of these

   1—M—Answer: b

8. Find the first 4 terms of the arithmetic sequence with $a_1 = 4$ and $d = \frac{1}{2}$.

   (a) 4, 2, 1, $\frac{1}{2}$, ...   (b) 4, 8, 16, 32, ...   (c) 4, -2, 1, $-\frac{1}{2}$, ...

   (d) 4, 0, -4, -8 (e) None of these

   1—M—Answer: e

9. Find the first 4 terms of the arithmetic sequence with $a_1 = 4$ and $d = -2$.

   (a) 4, 2, 0, -2, ...   (b) 4, 6, 8, 10, ...   (c) 4, -2, 1, $-\frac{1}{2}$, ...

   (d) 4, -8, 16, -32, ...   (e) None of these

   1—M—Answer: a

10. Find the first 4 terms of the arithmetic sequence with $a_1 = 3$ and $d = -3$.

    (a) 3, 0, -3, -6, ...   (b) 3, 6, 9, 12, ...   (c) 3, -1, $\frac{1}{3}$, $-\frac{1}{9}$, ...

    (d) 3, -9, 27, -81, ...   (e) None of these

    1—M—Answer: a

11. Find a_n for the arithmetic sequence with $a_1 = 5$, $d = -4$, and $n = 98$.

    (a) -392 (b) -387 (c) -383

    (d) 393 (e) None of these

    1—M—Answer: c

12. Find a_n for the arithmetic sequence with $a_1 = 12$, $d = \frac{1}{3}$, and $n = 52$.

    1—O—Answer: 29

13. Find the 99th term of the arithmetic sequence with $a_1 = 7$ and $d = -3$. (Assume that n begins with 1.)

    (a) -287 (b) -290 (c) -293

    (d) -297 (e) None of these

    1—M—Answer: a

14. Find the 30th term of the arithmetic sequence with $a_1 = -5$ and $d = \frac{1}{3}$. (Assume that n begins with 1.)

    1—O—Answer: $\frac{14}{3}$

15. Find the ninth term of the arithmetic sequence with $a_1 = 4$ and $d = 10$. (Assume that n begins with 1.)

    (a) 94   (b) 84   (c) 46   (d) 49   (e) None of these

    1—M—Answer: b

16. Find the eighth term of the arithmetic sequence with $a_1 = 5$ and $d = 8$. (Assume that n begins with 1.)

    (a) 69   (b) 48   (c) 61   (d) 104   (e) None of these

    1—M—Answer: c

17. Find the seventeenth term of the arithmetic sequence with $a_1 = 2$ and $d = 7$. (Assume that n begins with 1.)

    1—O—Answer: 114

18. Find the sum of the first 50 terms of the arithmetic sequence: 25, 35, 45, 55, 65, ...

    (a) $27{,}000$ (b) $13{,}750$ (c) $12{,}875$

    (d) $13{,}500$ (e) None of these

    1—M—Answer: d

19. Find the sum of the first 50 positive integers that are multiples of 3.

    (a) 7500   (b) 3900   (c) 3825

    (d) 7650   (e) None of these

    1—M—Answer: c

20. Find the sum of the first 40 positive integers that are multiples of 4.

   1—O—Answer: 3280

21. Find the sum of the first 30 terms of the sequence: $\sqrt{2}$, $2\sqrt{2}$, $3\sqrt{2}$, $4\sqrt{2}$, $5\sqrt{2}$, ...

   2—O—Answer: $465\sqrt{2}$

22. Find the sum of the first n terms of the arithmetic sequence: -4, 5, 14, 23, 32, ...

   (a) $9n - 4$ (b) $\dfrac{n(9n - 17)}{2}$ (c) $\dfrac{1 - 9^n}{2}$

   (d) $\dfrac{n^2 - 9n}{2}$ (e) None of these

   1—M—Answer: b

23. Find the sum of the first 18 terms of the arithmetic sequence whose nth term is $a_n = 3n - 1$. (Assume that n begins with 1.)

   (a) 495   (b) 53   (c) 459   (d) 445   (e) None of these

   1—M—Answer: a

24. Find the sum of the first 19 terms of the arithmetic sequence whose nth term is $a_n = n + 1$. (Assume that n begins with 1.)

   1—O—Answer: 209

25. Find a formula for a_n for the arithmetic sequence with $a_1 = 5$ and $d = -4$. (Assume that n begins with 1.)

   (a) $a_n = -4n + 9$ (b) $a_n = -4n + 5$ (c) $a_n = 5n - 4$

   (d) $a_n = 9n - 4$ (e) None of these

   1—M—Answer: a

26. Find a formula for a_n for the arithmetic sequence with $a_3 = 15$ and $d = -2$. (Assume that n begins with 1.)

   (a) $a_n = -2n + 9$ (b) $a_n = -2n + 19$ (c) $a_n = -2n + 21$

   (d) $a_n = -2n + 15$ (e) None of these

   1—M—Answer: c

27. Find a formula for a_n for the arithmetic sequence with $a_2 = 12$ and $d = -3$. (Assume that n begins with 1.)

   (a) $a_n = 12n - 3$ (b) $a_n = -3n + 15$ (c) $a_n = -3n + 12$

   (d) $a_n = -3n + 18$ (e) None of these

   1—M—Answer: d

28. Find a formula for a_n for the arithmetic sequence with $a_2 = 15$ and $d = \frac{3}{2}$. (Assume that n begins with 1.)

1—O—Answer: $a_n = -\frac{3}{2}n + 12$

29. Find the sum: $\displaystyle\sum_{n=1}^{35} 3n$

1—O—Answer: 1890

30. Find the sum: $\displaystyle\sum_{n=1}^{50} (2n + 3)$

1—O—Answer: 2700

31. Find the sum: $\displaystyle\sum_{n=1}^{100} (3n - 2)$

(a) 14,850   (b) 29,900   (c) 1495
(d) 14,950   (e) None of these

1—M—Answer: d

32. Find the sum: $\displaystyle\sum_{n=1}^{500} (3n + 5)$

(a) 756,500   (b) 376,250   (c) 752,500
(d) 378,250   (e) None of these

1—M—Answer: d

33. Find the sum: $\displaystyle\sum_{i=1}^{7} 2(i + 1)$

1—O—Answer: 70

34. Insert 3 arithmetic means between 15 and 83.

(a) 30, 45, 60   (b) 23, 41, 75   (c) 32, 49, 66
(d) 17, 40, 71   (e) None of these

2—M—Answer: c

35. Insert 4 arithmetic means between 75 and 50.

(a) 53, 59, 65, 71   (b) 70, 65, 60, 55   (c) 72, 66, 60, 54
(d) 57, 63, 69, 72   (e) None of these

2—M—Answer: b

36. Insert 3 arithmetic means between 2 and 42.

2—O—Answer: 12, 22, 32

37. Insert 4 arithmetic means between 7 and 17.

2—O—Answer: 9, 11, 13, 15

38. Determine the seating capacity of an auditorium with 25 rows of seats if there are 20 seats in the first row, 24 seats in the second row, 28 seats in the third row, and so on.

(a) 1200   (b) 1500   (c) 1700   (d) 1900   (e) None of these

2—M—Answer: c

39. Determine the seating capacity of an auditorium with 30 rows of seats if there are 25 seats in the first row, 28 seats in the second row, 31 seats in the third row, and so on.

(a) 1635   (b) 1792   (c) 2055   (d) 3125   (e) None of these

2—M—Answer: c

10.3 Geometric Sequences

1. Which of the following is a geometric sequence?

(a) $1, -3, 5, -7, 9, \ldots$ (b) $6, 3, 0, -3, -6, \ldots$ (c) $2, 4, 8, 16, 32, \ldots$
(d) $-1, 0, -1, 0, -1, \ldots$ (e) None of these

1—M—Answer: c

2. Determine whether the sequence $3, -2, \frac{4}{3}, -\frac{8}{9}, \frac{16}{27}, \ldots$ is geometric. If it is, find its common ratio.

1—O—Answer: Yes, $r = -\frac{2}{3}$

3. Which of the following is a geometric sequence?

(a) $-2, 0, 2, 4, 6, \ldots$ (b) $2, 4, 8, 16, 32, \ldots$ (c) $2, 7, 3, 8, 4, \ldots$
(d) $2, \frac{1}{2}, \frac{1}{4}, \frac{1}{6}, \frac{1}{8}, \ldots$ (e) None of these

1—M—Answer: b

4. Which of the following is a geometric sequence?

(a) $-1, -3, -5, -7, -9, \ldots$ (b) $2, 3, 5, 7, 11, \ldots$ (c) $1, 2, 4, 7, 11, 16, \ldots$
(d) $-2, 4, -8, 16, -32, \ldots$ (e) None of these

1—M—Answer: d

5. Find the first five terms of the geometric sequence with $a_1 = 2$ and $r = \frac{2}{3}$.

(a) $2, \frac{4}{3}, \frac{8}{9}, \frac{16}{27}, \frac{32}{81}$

(b) $2, 3, \frac{9}{2}, \frac{27}{4}, \frac{81}{8}$

(c) $2, \frac{8}{3}, \frac{10}{3}, 4, \frac{14}{3}$

(d) $2, \frac{4}{3}, \frac{2}{3}, -\frac{2}{3}$

(e) None of these

1—M—Answer: a

6. Find the first five terms of the geometric sequence with $a_1 = 3$ and $r = \frac{3}{2}$.

(a) $3, \frac{9}{2}, \frac{27}{4}, \frac{81}{8}, \frac{243}{16}$

(b) $3, 2, \frac{4}{3}, \frac{8}{9}, \frac{16}{27}$

(c) $3, \frac{9}{2}, 6, \frac{15}{2}, 9$

(d) $3, \frac{3}{2}, 0, -\frac{3}{2}, -3$

(e) None of these

1—M—Answer: a

7. Write the first five terms of the geometric sequence with $a_1 = 3$ and $r = \frac{1}{2}$.

(a) $3, 3\frac{1}{2}, 4, 4\frac{1}{2}, 5$

(b) $3, 2\frac{1}{2}, 2, 1\frac{1}{2}, 1$

(c) $3, \frac{3}{2}, \frac{3}{4}, \frac{3}{8}, \frac{3}{16}$

(d) $3, \frac{3}{2}, \frac{3}{4}, \frac{3}{6}, \frac{3}{8}$

(e) None of these

1—M—Answer: c

8. Write the first five terms of the geometric sequence with $a_1 = -3$ and $r = \frac{2}{3}$.

(a) $-3, -2\frac{1}{3}, -1\frac{2}{3}, -1, -\frac{1}{3}$

(b) $-3, -3\frac{2}{3}, -4\frac{1}{3}, -5, -5\frac{2}{3}$

(c) $-3, -\frac{9}{2}, -\frac{27}{4}, -\frac{81}{8}, -\frac{243}{16}$

(d) $-3, -2, -\frac{4}{3}, -\frac{8}{9}, -\frac{16}{27}$

(e) None of these

1—M—Answer: d

9. Find the 20th term of the geometric sequence with $a_1 = 5$ and $r = 1.1$.

(a) 1.1665

(b) 37.0012

(c) 33.6375

(d) 30.5795

(e) None of these

1—M—Answer: d

10. Find the 23rd term of the geometric sequence with $a_1 = -23$ and $r = \sqrt{2}$.

(a) $-47104\sqrt{2}$

(b) $-2048\sqrt{2}$

(c) -2048

(d) -47104

(e) None of these

1—M—Answer: d

11. Find the 28th term of the geometric sequence: $2, 2.4, 2.88, 3.456, 4.1472, \ldots$

1—O—Answer: 274.7411

12. Find the 14th term of the geometric sequence with $a_1 = -11$ and $r = \sqrt{3}$.

1—O—Answer: $-8019\sqrt{3}$

13. Find the sum: $\displaystyle\sum_{n=0}^{10} 2\left(\frac{3}{5}\right)^n$ Round your answer to four decimal places.

(a) 4.9698   (b) 5.0000   (c) 4.9819

(d) 55.0000   (e) None of these

1—M—Answer: c

14. Find the sum: $\displaystyle\sum_{j=0}^{40} 3(1.05)^j$ Round your answer to two decimal places.

(a) 383.52   (b) 362.40   (c) 984.00

(d) 22.18   (e) None of these

1—M—Answer: a

15. Find the sum: $\displaystyle\sum_{k=1}^{10} 4\left(\frac{3}{2}\right)^{k-1}$ Round your answer to three decimal places.

1—O—Answer: 453.320

16. Find the sum: $\displaystyle\sum_{n=1}^{15} 3\left(\frac{5}{4}\right)^n$ Round your answer to two decimal places.

(a) 329.06   (b) 260.85   (c) 322.61

(d) 271.15   (e) None of these

1—M—Answer: a

17. Find the sum of the first 30 terms in the sequence. $2, \frac{5}{2}, \frac{25}{8}, \frac{125}{32}, \frac{625}{128}, \ldots$
Round your answer to two decimal places.

(a) 791.25   (b) 5161.88   (c) 6454.35

(d) 7116.42   (e) None of these

1—M—Answer: c

18. Find the sum of the first 30 terms in the sequence. $\sqrt{2}, 2\sqrt{2}, 3\sqrt{2}, 4\sqrt{2}, 5\sqrt{2}, \ldots$
1—O—Answer: $465\sqrt{2}$

19. Find the sum of the first six terms of the geometric sequence with $a_1 = 2$ and $a_2 = -4$.

(a) -42 (b) $\frac{130}{3}$ (c) 42   (d) $-\frac{62}{3}$ (e) None of these

1—M—Answer: a

20. Find the sum of the first 10 terms of the geometric sequence with $a_1 = 3$ and $a_2 = \frac{3}{2}$. Round to three decimal places.

(a) 5.994   (b) 7.286   (c) 6.984

(d) 9.117   (e) None of these

2—M—Answer: a

21. Find a formula for the nth term of the geometric sequence with $a_1 = 2$ and $r = -\frac{1}{3}$. (Assume that n begins with 1.)

(a) $a_n = \left(-\frac{2}{3}\right)^n$ (b) $a_n = 2 - \frac{1}{3}n$ (c) $a_n = 2\left(-\frac{1}{3}\right)^{n-1}$

(d) $a_n = 2\left(-\frac{1}{3}\right)^n$ (e) None of these

1—M—Answer: c

22. Find a formula for the nth term of the geometric sequence with $a_1 = 4$ and $r = \frac{1}{3}$. (Assume that n begins with 1.)

(a) $a_n = \left(\frac{1}{3}\right)^n$ (b) $a_n = 4\left(\frac{1}{3}\right)^{n-1}$ (c) $a_n = 4\left(\frac{1}{3}\right)^n$

(d) $a_n = 4 + \left(\frac{1}{3}\right)^n$ (e) None of these

1—M—Answer: b

23. Find a formula for the nth term of the geometric series with $a_1 = \frac{1}{2}$ and $r = -\frac{1}{3}$. (Assume that n begins at 1.)

(a) $a_n = \frac{1}{2}\left(-\frac{1}{3}\right)^{n-1}$ (b) $a_n = \frac{1}{2}\left(-\frac{1}{3}\right)^n$ (c) $a_n = \left(-\frac{1}{6}\right)^n$

(d) $a_n = \frac{1}{2} - \frac{1}{3^n}$ (e) None of these

1—M—Answer: a

24. Find a formula for the nth term of the geometric series with $a_1 = \frac{2}{3}$ and $r = -\frac{1}{5}$. (Assume that n begins at 1.)

(a) $a_n = \frac{2}{3}\left(-\frac{1}{5}\right)^n$ (b) $a_n = \left(-\frac{2}{15}\right)^n$ (c) $a_n = -\frac{1}{5}\left(\frac{2}{3}\right)^n$

(d) $a_n = \frac{2}{3}\left(-\frac{1}{5}\right)^{n-1}$ (e) None of these

1—M—Answer: d

25. Find the common ratio of the geometric series: -4, 3, $-\frac{9}{4}$, $\frac{27}{16}$, $-\frac{81}{16}$, $\cdots$

(a) $\frac{3}{4}$ (b) $-\frac{3}{4}$ (c) $\frac{4}{3}$

(d) $-\frac{4}{3}$ (e) None of these

1—M—Answer: b

26. Find the sum of the infinite geometric sequence: -7, $-\frac{7}{3}$, $-\frac{7}{9}$, $-\frac{7}{27}$, $\cdots$

(a) -5 (b) $-\frac{21}{4}$ (c) $-\frac{5}{2}$

(d) $-\frac{21}{2}$ (e) None of these

1—M—Answer: d

27. Find the sum of the infinite geometric sequence: 1, 0.9, 0.81, 0.729, $\cdots$

(a) 23 (b) 90 (c) 10

(d) 57 (e) None of these

1—M—Answer: c

28. Find the sum of the infinite geometric sequence: 1, $\frac{1}{3}$, $\frac{1}{9}$, $\frac{1}{27}$, $\cdots$

(a) $\frac{3}{2}$ (b) 3 (c) $\frac{5}{3}$

(d) $\frac{5}{2}$ (e) None of these

1—M—Answer: a

29. Find the sum of the infinite geometric sequence with $a_1 = 9$ and $r = 0.7$.

1—O—Answer: 30

30. Evaluate: $\displaystyle\sum_{n=0}^{\infty} 2\left(\frac{1}{2}\right)^n = 2 + 1 + \frac{1}{2} + \frac{1}{4} + \frac{1}{8} + \cdots$

(a) 4   (b) 6   (c) 8   (d) 10   (e) None of these

1—M—Answer: a

31. Evaluate: $\displaystyle\sum_{n=0}^{\infty} 4\left(\frac{2}{3}\right)^n = 4 + \frac{8}{3} + \frac{16}{9} + \frac{32}{27} + \cdots$

(a) 8   (b) 10   (c) 12   (d) 14   (e) None of these

1—M—Answer: c

32. Evaluate: $\displaystyle\sum_{n=0}^{\infty} 3\left(-\frac{1}{2}\right)^n$

(a) 6   (b) 4   (c) 2   (d) 0   (e) None of these

1—M—Answer: c

33. Evaluate: $\displaystyle\sum_{n=0}^{\infty} 5\left(-\frac{2}{3}\right)^{n}$

(a) 6　　　　(b) 3　　　　(c) 1　　　　(d) 0　　　　(e) None of these

1—M—Answer: b

34. An individual buys a \$100,000 term life insurance policy. During the next five years the value of the policy will depreciate at the rate of 4% per year. (That is, at the end of each year the depreciated value is 96% of the value at the beginning of the year.) Find the depreciated value of the policy at the end of five years.

(a) \$80,000　　　　　　　　(b) \$84,934.66　　　　　　　　(c) \$81,537.27

(d) \$78,275.78　　　　　　　(e) None of these

2—M—Answer: c

35. Suppose in 1985 you accepted a job at \$17,000. If you receive a 5% raise in salary each year, what will be your salary in 1995?

(a) \$25,116.74　　　　　　　(b) \$26,372.58　　　　　　　(c) \$27,691.21

(d) \$29,075.77　　　　　　　(e) None of these

2—M—Answer: c

36. In coming to rest, a CD player makes one half as many revolutions per second as in the previous second. How many revolutions does a CD make in coming to rest if it makes 20 revolutions in the first second after the stop function is activated?

1—O—Answer: 40

37. A square has sides of 10 inches each. A second square is inscribed in the original square by joining the midpoints of the sides, as shown. A third square is then inscribed inside the second square by joining the midpoints of the sides of the second square. This process is continued endlessly. What is the sum of the areas of the infinite sequence of squares?

(a)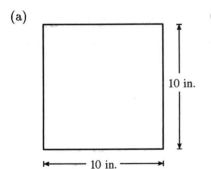

(b)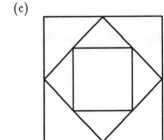

(c)

2—O—Answer: 200 square inches

$\boxed{10.4}$ Mathematical Induction

1. Find P_{k+1} for $P_k = k(k+2)$.
   (a) $(k+1)(k+2)$ (b) $(k+2)(k+3)$ (c) $(k+1)(k+3)$
   (d) $k(k+3)$ (e) None of these

   1—M—Answer: c

2. Find P_{k+1} for $P_k = (k+2)(k-1)^2$.
   (a) $k^2(k+2)$ (b) $k(k+3)$ (c) $(k+3)(k+2)^2$
   (d) $k^2(k+3)$ (e) None of these

   1—M—Answer: d

3. Find P_{k+1} for $P_k = \dfrac{1}{k(2k+1)}$.

   (a) $\dfrac{1}{(k+1)(2k+3)}$ (b) $\dfrac{1}{(k+1)(2k+2)}$ (c) $\dfrac{1}{k(2k+3)}$

   (d) $\dfrac{1}{(k+1)(2k+1)}$ (e) None of these

   1—M—Answer: a

4. Identify S_{k+1} given $S_k = \dfrac{2k-1}{3k(k+1)}$.

   (a) $\dfrac{2k+1}{(3k+1)(k+1)}$ (b) $\dfrac{2k+1}{3(k+1)(k+2)}$ (c) $\dfrac{2k}{3(k+1)(k+2)}$

   (d) $\dfrac{2k}{(3k+1)(k+2)}$ (e) None of these

   1—M—Answer: b

5. Identify S_{k+1} given $S_k = \dfrac{3}{k(k+2)}$.

   (a) $\dfrac{3}{(k+1)(k+3)}$ (b) $\dfrac{k^2+2k+3}{k+2}$ (c) $\dfrac{3}{(k+1)(k+2)}$

   (d) $\dfrac{k^2+5}{k(k+2)}$ (e) None of these

   1—M—Answer: a

6. Identify S_{k+1} given $S_k = \dfrac{(k+1)^2}{k(k-1)}$.

   (a) $\dfrac{2k^2 + 2k}{k(k-1)}$ (b) $\dfrac{(k+2)^2}{k(k-1)}$ (c) $\dfrac{(k+1)^2 + k(k-1)}{k(k-1)}$

   (d) $\dfrac{(k+2)^2}{k(k+1)}$ (e) None of these

   1—M—Answer: d

7. Identify S_{k+1} given $S_k = \dfrac{k(2k-1)}{3}$.

   (a) $\dfrac{2k(k+1)}{3}$ (b) $\dfrac{2k^2 - k + 3}{3}$ (c) $\dfrac{(k+1)(2k+1)}{3}$

   (d) $\dfrac{2k^2 - k + 1}{3}$ (e) None of these

   1—M—Answer: c

8. Identify S_{k+1} given $S_k = k(3k-1)$.

   (a) $(k+1)(3k+2)$ (b) $3k(k+1)$ (c) $k(3k-1)+1$

   (d) $3k^2 + 1$ (e) None of these

   1—M—Answer: a

9. Identify S_{k+1} given $S_k = k^2(k+1)^2$.

   (a) $(k^2 + 1)(k+2)^2$ (b) $k^2(k+1)^2 + 1$ (c) $(k+1)^2(k-1)^2$

   (d) $(k+1)^2(k+2)^2$ (e) None of these

   1—M—Answer: d

10. Identify S_{k+1} given $S_k = \dfrac{k}{2}(3k+2)$.

    (a) $\dfrac{3(k+1)^2}{2}$ (b) $\dfrac{k+1}{2}(3k+2)$ (c) $\dfrac{3k^2 + 2k + 2}{2}$

    (d) $\dfrac{k+1}{2}(3k+5)$ (e) None of these

    1—M—Answer: d

11. Identify S_{k+1} given $S_k = (k+1)(k-1)$.

    (a) $k(k+2)$ (b) k^2 (c) $k^2 - 2$

    (d) $(k+2)(k+1)$ (e) None of these

    1—M—Answer: a

12. Identify S_{k+1} given $S_k = \dfrac{k(k+1)}{2}$.

(a) $\dfrac{k^2 + k + 2}{2}$

(b) $\dfrac{k^2 + 2}{2}$

(c) $\dfrac{(k+1)(k+2)}{2}$

(d) $\dfrac{(k+1)(k+2)}{2k+1}$

(e) None of these

1—M—Answer: c

13. Prove by mathematical induction: $1 + 2 + 2^2 + 2^3 + \cdots + 2^{n-1} = 2^n - 1$

2—O—Answer: $S_1 : \quad 2^1 - 1 = 2 - 1 = 1$

$S_k : \quad 1 + 2 + 2^2 + 2^3 + \cdots + 2^{k-1} = 2^k - 1$

$S_{k+1} : 1 + 2 + 2^2 + 2^3 + \cdots + 2^k = 2^{k+1} - 1$

Assuming S_k, we have:

$$(1 + 2 + 2^2 + 2^3 + \cdots + 2^{k-1}) + 2^{(k+1)-1} = (1 + 2 + \cdots + 2^{k-1}) + 2^k$$
$$= (2^k - 1) + 2^k$$
$$= 2^{k+1} - 1$$

Hence, the formula is valid for all $n \geq 1$.

14. Prove by mathematical induction: $1^2 + 2^2 + 3^2 + \cdots + n^2 = \dfrac{n(n+1)(2n+1)}{6}$

2—O—Answer: Let $n = 1$, then $\dfrac{n(n+1)(2n+1)}{6} = \dfrac{(1)(2)(3)}{6} = 1 = 1^2$

For $n = k$, $S_k = 1^2 + 2^2 + 3^2 + \cdots + k^2 = \dfrac{k(k+1)(2k+1)}{6}$

For $n = k + 1$, $S_{k+1} = \dfrac{k(k+1)(2k+1)}{6} + (k+1)^2$

$$= (k+1)\left[\dfrac{k(2k+1) + 6(k+1)}{6}\right]$$
$$= \dfrac{(k+1)(2k^2 + 7k + 6)}{6}$$
$$= \dfrac{(k+1)(k+2)(2k+3)}{6}$$
$$= \dfrac{(k+1)[(k+1)+1][2(k+1)+1]}{6}$$

Thus, the formula is valid.

15. Use mathematical induction to prove:

$$\frac{1}{1 \cdot 3} + \frac{1}{3 \cdot 5} + \frac{1}{5 \cdot 7} + \cdots + \frac{1}{(2n-1)(2n+1)} = \frac{n}{2n+1}$$

2—O—Answer:

When $n = 1$, the formula is valid since $S_1 = \dfrac{1}{1 \cdot 3} = \dfrac{1}{3}$.

For $n = k$, assume S_k is true. $S_k = \dfrac{k}{2k+1}$

For $n = k+1$, show $S_{k+1} = \dfrac{k+1}{2k+3}$

$$S_{k+1} = \left[\frac{1}{1 \cdot 3} + \frac{1}{3 \cdot 5} + \frac{1}{5 \cdot 7} + \cdots + \frac{1}{(2k-1)(2k+1)} \right] + \frac{1}{(2k+1)(2k+3)}$$

$$= S_k + \frac{1}{(2k+1)(2k+3)}$$

$$= \frac{k}{2k+1} + \frac{1}{(2k+1)(2k+3)}$$

$$= \frac{k(2k+3)+1}{(2k+1)(2k+3)}$$

$$= \frac{2k^2 + 3k + 1}{(2k+1)(2k+3)}$$

$$= \frac{(2k+1)(k+1)}{(2k+1)(2k+3)}$$

$$= \frac{k+1}{2k+3}$$

Thus, the formula is valid.

16. Use mathematical induction to prove:

$$\frac{1}{1 \cdot 2} + \frac{1}{2 \cdot 3} + \frac{1}{3 \cdot 4} + \cdots + \frac{1}{n(n+1)} = \frac{n}{n+1}$$

2—O—Answer:

Let $n = 1$, $S_1 = \dfrac{1}{1 \cdot 2} = \dfrac{1}{2}$.

For $n = k$, assume $S_k = \dfrac{k}{k+1}$ is true.

For $n = k + 1$, show $S_{k+1} = \dfrac{k+1}{k+2}$

$$S_{k+1} = \left[\frac{1}{1 \cdot 2} + \frac{1}{2 \cdot 3} + \frac{1}{3 \cdot 4} + \cdots + \frac{1}{k(k+1)}\right] + \frac{1}{(k+1)(k+2)}$$

$$= S_k + \frac{1}{(k+1)(k+2)}$$

$$= \frac{k}{k+1} + \frac{1}{(k+1)(k+2)}$$

$$= \frac{k^2 + 2k + 1}{(k+1)(k+2)}$$

$$= \frac{(k+1)^2}{(k+1)(k+2)}$$

$$= \frac{k+1}{k+2}$$

Thus, the formula is valid.

17. Use mathematical induction to prove:

$$6 + 11 + 16 + 21 + \bullet + (5n + 1) = \frac{n(7 + 5n)}{2}$$

2—O—Answer: For $n = 1$, $S_1 = \dfrac{1(7 + 5)}{2} = 6$

For $n = k$, assume $S_k = \dfrac{k(7 + 5k)}{2}$ is true.

For $n = k + 1$, show $S_{k+1} = \dfrac{(k+1)(5k+12)}{2}$

$$S_{k+1} = [6 + 11 + 16 + \cdots + (5k + 1) + [5(k+1) + 1]$$

$$= S_k + (5k + 6)$$

$$= \frac{k(7 + 5k)}{2} + (5k + 6)$$

$$= \frac{7k + 5k^2}{2} + \frac{10k + 12}{2}$$

$$= \frac{5k^2 + 17k + 12}{2}$$

$$= \frac{(k+1)(5k+12)}{2}$$

Thus, the formula is valid.

18. Find the sum using the formulas for the sums of powers of integers: $\displaystyle\sum_{n=1}^{7} n^5$

   (a) 4219   (b) 4676   (c) 29008
   (d) 61776   (e) None of these

   1—M—Answer: c

19. Find the sum using the formulas for the sums of powers of integers: $\displaystyle\sum_{n=1}^{8} (n^2 - n^3)$

   (a) −994   (b) −1092   (c) −1296
   (d) −1538   (e) None of these

   1—M—Answer: b

20. Find the sum using the formulas for the sums of powers of integers: $\displaystyle\sum_{n=1}^{19} i^3$

   (a) 36,100   (b) 3581   (c) 44,100
   (d) 1,687,998   (e) None of these

   1—M—Answer: a

21. Find the sum using the formulas for the sums of powers of integers: $\displaystyle\sum_{n=1}^{15} i^4$

   (a) 2,299,200   (b) 1,337,340   (c) 445,780
   (d) 178,312   (e) None of these

   1—M—Answer: d

22. Find the sum using the formulas for the sums of powers of integers: $\displaystyle\sum_{n=1}^{50} (n^2 - n)$

   (a) 42,925   (b) 41,650   (c) 44,100
   (d) 43,150   (e) None of these

   1—M—Answer: b

23. Find the sum using the formulas for the sums of powers of integers: $\displaystyle\sum_{n=1}^{15} 4n^2$

   (a) 4960   (b) 1240   (c) 73,810
   (d) 74,400   (e) None of these

   1—M—Answer: a

24. Find the sum using the formulas for the sums of powers of integers: $\displaystyle\sum_{n=1}^{20} 3n^2$

   (a) 73,810   (b) 25,830   (c) 8610

   (d) 172,200   (e) None of these

   1—M—Answer: c

25. Find the sum using the formulas for the sums of powers of integers: $\displaystyle\sum_{n=1}^{19} 2n^2$

   (a) 19,019   (b) 4940   (c) 4921

   (d) 22,140   (e) None of these

   1—M—Answer: b

26. Find the sum using the formulas for the sums of powers of integers: $\displaystyle\sum_{i=1}^{20} i^4$

   (a) 718,312   (b) 4,933,320   (c) 44,100

   (d) 722,666   (e) None of these

   1—M—Answer: d

27. Use mathematical induction to prove: $1 + 3 + 3^2 + \cdots + 3^{n-1} = \dfrac{3^n - 1}{2}$

   2—O—Answer: For $n = 1$, $S_1 = \dfrac{3^1 - 1}{2} = 1$

   For $n = k$, assume $S_k = \dfrac{3^k - 1}{2}$

   For $n = k + 1$, show $S_{k+1} = \dfrac{3^{k+1} - 1}{2}$

   $$S_{k+1} = 1 + 3 + 3^2 + \cdots + 3^{k-1} + 3^k$$
   $$= S_k + 3^k$$
   $$= \frac{3^k - 1}{2} + 3^k$$
   $$= \frac{3^k - 1 + 2(3^k)}{2}$$
   $$= \frac{3(3^k) - 1}{2}$$
   $$= \frac{3^{k+1} - 1}{2}$$

   Thus, the formula is valid.

28. Use mathematical induction to prove:

$$\frac{1}{1\cdot2\cdot3}+\frac{1}{2\cdot3\cdot4}+\frac{1}{3\cdot4\cdot5}+\cdots+\frac{1}{n(n+1)(n+2)}=\frac{n(n+3)}{4(n+1)(n+2)}$$

2—O—Answer:

For $n=1$, $S_1=\dfrac{1}{1\cdot2\cdot3}$

For $n=k$, assume $S_k=\dfrac{k(k+3)}{4(k+1)(k+2)}$

For $n=k+1$,

show $S_{k+1}=\dfrac{(k+1)(k+4)}{4(k+2)(k+3)}$

$$S_{k+1}=\frac{1}{1\cdot2\cdot3}+\frac{1}{2\cdot3\cdot4}+\frac{1}{3\cdot4\cdot5}+\cdots+\frac{1}{k(k+1)(k+2)}+\frac{1}{(k+1)(k+2)(k+3)}$$

$$S_{k+1}=S_k+\frac{1}{(k+1)(k+2)(k+3)}$$

$$S_{k+1}=\frac{k(k+3)}{4(k+1)(k+2)}+\frac{1}{(k+1)(k+2)(k+3)}$$

$$S_{k+1}=\frac{k(k+3)^2+4}{4(k+1)(k+2)(k+3)}$$

$$=\frac{k^3+6k^2+9k+4}{4(k+1)(k+2)(k+3)}\quad\text{(factorable)}$$

$$=\frac{(k+1)(k+1)(k+4)}{4(k+1)(k+2)(k+3)}$$

$$=\frac{(k+1)(k+4)}{4(k+2)(k+3)}$$

Thus, the formula is valid.

29. Use mathematical induction to prove: $1^3 + 2^3 + 3^3 + \cdots + n^3 = \dfrac{n^2(n+1)^2}{4}$

2—O—Answer: For $n = 1$, $S_1 = 1 = \dfrac{1^2(1+1)^2}{4} = 1$

For $n = k$, assume $S_k = \dfrac{k^2(k+1)^2}{4}$

For $n = k+1$, show $S_{k+1} = \dfrac{(k+1)^2(k+2)^2}{4}$

$S_{k+1} = 1^3 + 2^3 + 3^3 + \cdots + k^3 + (k+1)^3$

$= \dfrac{k^2(k+1)^2}{4} + (k+1)^3$

$= \dfrac{k^2(k+1)^2 + 4(k+1)^3}{4}$

$= \dfrac{(k+1)^2[k^2 + 4(k+1)]}{4}$

$= \dfrac{(k+1)^2(k^2 + 4k + 4)}{4}$

$= \dfrac{(k+1)^2(k+2)^2}{4}$

Thus, the formula is valid.

30. Use mathematical induction to prove:

$-3 + 1 + 5 + 9 + 13 + \cdots + (4n - 7) = n(2n - 5)$

2—O—Answer: For $n = 1$, $S_1 = -3 = 1(2 - 5) = -3$

For $n = k$, assume $S_k = k(2k - 5)$

For $n = k + 1$, show $S_{k+1} = (k+1)(2k - 3)$

$S_{k+1} = -3 + 1 + 5 + 9 + 13 + \cdots + (4k - 7) + (4k - 3)$

$= S_k + (4k - 3)$

$= k(2k - 5) + (4k - 3)$

$= 2k^2 - k - 3$

$= (k+1)(2k - 3)$

Thus, the formula is valid.

31. Find a formula for the sum of the first n terms of the sequence:

$$\dfrac{1}{1 \cdot 3}, \ \dfrac{1}{3 \cdot 5}, \ \dfrac{1}{5 \cdot 7}, \ \dfrac{1}{7 \cdot 9}, \ \cdots, \ \dfrac{1}{(2n - 1)(2n + 1)}, \ \cdots$$

2—O—Answer: $\dfrac{n}{2n + 1}$

32. Find a formula for the sum of the first n terms of the sequence:

$$\frac{1}{2 \cdot 5}, \ \frac{1}{5 \cdot 8}, \ \frac{1}{8 \cdot 11}, \ \frac{1}{11 \cdot 14}, \ \cdots, \ \frac{1}{(3n-1)(3n+2)}, \cdots$$

2—O—Answer: $\dfrac{n}{6n+4}$

33. Find a formula for the sum of the first n terms of the sequence:

$$2, \ 6, \ 18, \ 54, \ \ldots, 2(3^{n-1}), \ldots$$

2—O—Answer: $3^n - 1$

34. Use mathematical induction to prove $n < 3^n$ for all positive integers n.

2—O—Answer: For $n = 1$, $1 < 3$

For $n = k$, assume $k < 3^k$

For $n = k + 1$, show $k + 1 < 3^{k+1}$

$$k < 3^k$$

$$k + 1 < 3^k + 1 < 3^k + 3^k$$

$$k + 1 < 2(3^k) < 3(3^k)$$

$$k + 1 < 3^{k+1}$$

Hence, $n < 3^n$ for $n \geq 1$.

35. Use mathematical induction to prove: $\dfrac{1}{2} + \dfrac{1}{4} + \dfrac{1}{8} + \cdots + \dfrac{1}{2^n} < 1$ for $n \geq 1$

2—O—Answer: For $n = 1, \dfrac{1}{2} < 1$

For $n = k$, assume $\dfrac{1}{2} + \dfrac{1}{4} + \dfrac{1}{8} + \cdots + \dfrac{1}{2^k} < 1$

For $n = k + 1$, show $\dfrac{1}{2} + \dfrac{1}{4} + \dfrac{1}{8} + \cdots + \dfrac{1}{2^k} + \dfrac{1}{2^{k+1}} < 1$ is true.

$$\frac{1}{2} + \frac{1}{4} + \frac{1}{8} + \cdots + \frac{1}{2^k} < 1$$

$$\frac{1}{2}\left(\frac{1}{2} + \frac{1}{4} + \frac{1}{8} + \cdots + \frac{1}{2^k}\right) < \frac{1}{2} \cdot 1$$

$$\frac{1}{4} + \frac{1}{8} + \frac{1}{16} + \cdots + \frac{1}{2^{k+1}} < \frac{1}{2}$$

$$\frac{1}{2} + \frac{1}{4} + \frac{1}{8} + \cdots + \frac{1}{2^{k+1}} < \frac{1}{2} + \frac{1}{2}$$

$$\frac{1}{2} + \frac{1}{2} + \frac{1}{8} + \cdots + \frac{1}{2^{k+1}} < 1$$

Hence, $\dfrac{1}{2} + \dfrac{1}{4} + \cdots + \dfrac{1}{2^n} < 1$ for $n \geq 1$.

36. Use mathematical induction to prove:

$$\frac{1}{3} + \frac{1}{9} + \frac{1}{27} + \cdots + \frac{1}{3^n} < 1 \text{ for } n \geq 1$$

2—O—Answer: For $n = 1$, $\frac{1}{3} < 1$

For $n = k$, assume $\frac{1}{3} + \frac{1}{9} + \frac{1}{27} + \cdots + \frac{1}{3^k} < 1$ is true.

For $n = k + 1$, show $\frac{1}{3} + \frac{1}{9} + \frac{1}{27} + \cdots + \frac{1}{3^k} + \frac{1}{3^{k+1}} < 1$

$$\frac{1}{3} + \frac{1}{9} + \frac{1}{27} + \cdots + \frac{1}{3^k} < 1$$

$$\frac{1}{3}\left[\frac{1}{3} + \frac{1}{9} + \frac{1}{27} + \cdots + \frac{1}{3^k}\right] < \frac{1}{3} \cdot 1$$

$$\frac{1}{9} + \frac{1}{27} + \frac{1}{81} + \cdots + \frac{1}{3^{k+1}} < \frac{1}{3}$$

$$\frac{1}{3} + \frac{1}{9} + \frac{1}{27} + \frac{1}{81} + \cdots + \frac{1}{3^{k+1}} < \frac{2}{3} < 1$$

Hence, $\frac{1}{3} + \frac{1}{9} + \frac{1}{27} + \cdots + \frac{1}{3^n} < 1$ for $n \geq 1$.

10.5 The Binomial Theorem

1. Evaluate: $_{12}C_{10}$

(a) $\frac{1}{66}$ (b) 66   (c) 132

(d) $\frac{1}{120}$ (e) None of these

1—M—Answer: b

2. Evaluate: $_{10}C_3$

(a) 1000   (b) 604,800   (c) 720

(d) 120   (e) None of these

1—M—Answer: d

3. Evaluate: $_{17}C_{14}$

(a) 5.9×10^{13} (b) 842,771   (c) 4080

(d) 680   (e) None of these

1—M—Answer: d

4. Evaluate: $_{12}C_9$ **5.** Evaluate: $_{45}C_2$

1—O—Answer: 220   **1—O—Answer:** 990

6. Evaluate: $_6C_2$

(a) 15

(b) 30

(c) 360

(d) 12

(e) None of these

1—M—Answer: a

7. Evaluate: $_9C_7$

(a) 181,440

(b) 63

(c) 72

(d) 36

(e) None of these

1—M—Answer: d

8. Evaluate: $_8C_5$

(a) 40

(b) 336

(c) 56

(d) 6720

(e) None of these

1—M—Answer: c

9. Evaluate: $_9C_5$

(a) 15,120

(b) 126

(c) 3024

(d) 45

(e) None of these

1—M—Answer: b

10. Evaluate: $_6C_4$

(a) 24

(b) 15

(c) 30

(d) 360

(e) None of these

1—M—Answer: b

11. Evaluate: $_7C_4$

(a) 35

(b) 28

(c) 210

(d) 840

(e) None of these

1—M—Answer: a

12. Evaluate using a graphing utility: $_{55}C_5$

1—O—Answer: 3,478,761

13. Evaluate using a graphing utility: $_{75}C_{73}$

1—O—Answer: 2775

14. Evaluate using a graphing utility: $_{42}C_{32}$

1—O—Answer: 1,471,442,973

15. Use the Binomial Theorem to expand then simplify: $(x-3)^5$

    (a) $x^5 - 15x^4 + 30x^3 - 30x^2 + 15x - 243$ (b) $x^5 - 15x^4 + 900x^3 - 27{,}000x^2 + 50{,}625x - 243$

    (c) $x^5 - 15x^4 + 90x^3 - 270x^2 + 405x - 243$ (d) $x^5 - 3x^4 + 9x^3 - 27x^2 + 81x - 243$

    (e) None of these

    1—M—Answer: c

16. Use the Binomial Theorem to expand, then simplify: $(2x-3)^3$

    (a) $8x^3 - 324x^2 + 324x - 27$ (b) $8x^3 - 36x^2 + 54x - 27$

    (c) $2x^3 - 18x^2 + 54x - 27$ (d) $8x^3 - 12x^2 + 27x - 27$

    (e) None of these

    1—M—Answer: b

17. Expand: $(3-2x)^3$

    (a) $27 - 3x + 3x^2 - 8x^3$ (b) $27 - 9x + 9x^2 - 8x^3$ (c) $27 - 27x + 6x^2 - 8x^3$

    (d) $27 - 54x + 36x^2 - 8x^3$ (e) None of these

    1—M—Answer: d

18. Use Pascal's Triangle to evaluate the complex number $(2-i)^4$.

    (a) 17 (b) $-7 - 24i$ (c) $13 + 6i$

    (d) 15 (e) None of these

    1—M—Answer: b

19. Use the Binomial Theorem to expand, then simplify: $(i-1)^4$

    (a) $4 - 8i$ (b) $-4 - 8i$ (c) -4

    (d) 6 (e) None of these

    1—M—Answer: c

20. Use the Binomial Theorem to expand, then simplify: $(i-2)^4$

    (a) $-24 + 9i$ (b) $7 + 16i$ (c) $31 - 40i$

    (d) $-7 - 24i$ (e) None of these

    1—M—Answer: d

21. Use Pascal's Triangle to expand $(x-2y)^4$.

    1—O—Answer: $x^4 - 8x^3y + 24x^2y^2 - 32xy^3 + 16y^4$

22. Use Pascal's Triangle to expand $(2x - y)^3$.

    (a) $2x^3 - 6x^2y + 6xy^2 - y^3$ (b) $8x^3 - 4x^2y + 2xy^2 - y^3$

    (c) $2x^3 + 3x^2y + 3xy^2 + y^3$ (d) $8x^3 - 12x^2y + 6xy^2 - y^3$

    (e) None of these

    1—M—Answer: d

23. Use Pascal's Triangle to expand $(x + 3y)^3$.

    (a) $x^3 + 6x^2y + 6xy^2 + 9y^3$ (b) $x^3 - 3x^2y + 6xy^2 - 27y^3$

    (c) $x^3 + 9x^2y + 27xy^2 + 27y^3$ (d) $x^3 + 9x^2y + 9xy^2 + 3y^3$

    (e) None of these

    1—M—Answer: c

24. Use Pascal's Triangle to expand $(3x + y)^4$.

    (a) $81x^4 + 108x^3y + 54x^2y^2 + 12xy^3 + y^4$ (b) $3x^4 + 12x^3y + 18x^2y^2 + 12xy^3 + y^4$

    (c) $81x^4 + 1728x^3y + 324x^2y^2 + 12xy^3 + y^4$ (d) $3x^4 - 12x^3y + 324x^2y^3 + 12xy^3 - y^4$

    (e) None of these

    1—M—Answer: a

25. Use Pascal's Triangle to expand $(5x + 2y)^3$.

    (a) $125x^3 + 450x^2y + 60xy^2 + 8y^3$ (b) $125x^3 + 150x^2y + 60xy^2 + 8y^3$

    (c) $125x^3 + 50x^2y + 20xy^2 + 8y^3$ (d) $5x^3 + 60x^2y + 30xy^2 + 2y^2$

    (e) None of these

    1—M—Answer: b

26. Use Pascal's Triangle to expand $(2x + y)^5$.

    (a) $32x^5 + 16x^4y + 8x^3y^2 + 4x^2y^3 + 2xy^4 + y^5$

    (b) $32x^5 + 80x^4y + 80x^3y^2 + 40x^2y^3 + 10xy^4 + y^5$

    (c) $2x^5 + 10x^4y + 20x^3y^2 + 20x^2y^3 + 10xy^4 + y^5$

    (d) $32x^5 + 10,000x^4y + 8,000x^3y^2 + 400x^2y^3 + 10xy^4 + y^5$

    (e) None of these

    1—M—Answer: b

27. Use Pascal's Triangle to expand: $(2a - b)^3$

    (a) $8a^3 - 4a^2b + 2ab^2 - b^3$ (b) $8a^3 + 12a^2b + 6ab^2 + b^3$ (c) $8a^3 - 12a^2b + 6ab^2 - b^3$

    (d) $8a^3 - b^3$ (e) None of these

    1—M—Answer: c

28. Use Pascal's Triangle to expand: $(3x + y)^3$

    (a) $27x^3 + 27x^2y + 9xy^2 + y^3$ (b) $27x^3 - 27x^2y + 9xy^2 - y^3$ (c) $27x^3 + 9x^2y + 3xy^2 + y^3$

    (d) $27x^3 + y^3$ (e) None of these

    1—M—Answer: a

29. Find the coefficient of x^4y^3 in the expansion of $(x + 2y)^7$.

    (a) 35   (b) 8   (c) 1,680   (d) 280   (e) None of these

    1—M—Answer: d

30. Find the coefficient of x^4y^3 in the expansion of $(2x + y)^7$.

    (a) 35   (b) 560   (c) 16   (d) 280   (e) None of these

    1—M—Answer: b

31. Determine the coefficient of x^5y^7 in the expansion of $(5x + 2y)^{12}$.

    (a) 316,800,000   (b) 400,000   (c) 792

    (d) 7920   (e) None of these

    1—M—Answer: a

32. Determine the coefficient of x^3y^5 in the expansion of $(3x + 2y)^8$.

    (a) 336   (b) 48,384   (c) 864

    (d) 52,488   (e) None of these

    1—M—Answer: b

33. Determine the coefficient of x^2y^7 in the expansion of $(3x - 2y)^9$.

    (a) -1152 (b) 1152   (c) 41,472

    (d) $-41,472$ (e) None of these

    1—M—Answer: d

34. Determine the coefficient of the x^2y^7 in the expansion of $(7x - 2y)^9$.

    1—O—Answer: $-225,792$

35. Find the 4th term in the expansion: $\left(\dfrac{1}{4} + \dfrac{3}{4}\right)^5$

1—O—Answer: $\dfrac{270}{4^5}$

36. Find the 5th term in the expansion: $\left(\dfrac{1}{3} + \dfrac{2}{3}\right)^5$

(a) $\dfrac{120}{243}$ (b) $\dfrac{16}{243}$ (c) $\dfrac{80}{243}$

(d) $\dfrac{32}{243}$ (e) None of these

1—M—Answer: a

37. Find the 4th term in the expansion: $(0.2 + 0.8)^5$

(a) 0.0064   (b) 0.4096   (c) 0.0512

(d) 0.2048   (e) None of these

1—M—Answer: d

38. Find the sum of the first 3 terms in the expansion of $(1 + 0.03)^7$.

(a) 1.2289   (b) 1.2299   (c) 1.1935

(d) 1.2415   (e) None of these

1—M—Answer: a

39. Find the sum of the first 3 terms in the expansion of $(1 + 0.02)^7$.

(a) 1.1260   (b) 1.1487   (c) 1.1484

(d) 1.1540   (e) None of these

1—M—Answer: c

40. Find the sum of the first 3 terms in the expansion of $(3 + 0.02)^7$.

(a) 2291.1240   (b) 2291.1012   (c) 2275.9380

(d) 2291.1141   (e) None of these

1—M—Answer: b

10.6   Counting Principles, Permutations, Combinations

1. Evaluate: $_{10}P_6$

   (a) 5040   (b) 151,200   (c) 210

   (d) 60   (e) None of these

   1—M—Answer: b

2. Evaluate: $_{14}P_4$

   (a) 24,024   (b) 8008   (c) 5040

   (d) 720   (e) None of these

   1—M—Answer: a

3. Evaluate: $_7P_4$

   (a) 840   (b) 35   (c) 10,920

   (d) 210   (e) None of these

   1—M—Answer: a

4. Evaluate: $_{20}P_3$

   (a) 1140   (b) 116,280   (c) 6840

   (d) 4.05×10^{17} (e) None of these

   1—M—Answer: c

5. Evaluate: $_7P_2$

   (a) 2520   (b) 210   (c) 21

   (d) 42   (e) None of these

   1—M—Answer: d

6. Evaluate: $_{14}P_3$

   (a) 1.45×10^{10} (b) 24,024   (c) 2184

   (d) 364   (e) None of these

   1—M—Answer: c

7. Find the number of distinguishable permutations using the letters in LETTERFILE.

   (a) 3,628,800   (b) 1024   (c) 151,200

   (d) 5040   (e) None of these

   1—M—Answer: c

8. In how many distinguishable ways can the letters in MISSISSIPPI be arranged?

   1—O—Answer: 34,650

9. Find the number of distinguishable ways the letters in OKEECHOBEE can be arranged.

   (a) 75,600   (b) 3,628,800   (c) 151,200

   (d) 1,814,400   (e) None of these

   1—M—Answer: a

10. Find the number of distinguishable permutations using the letters in the word ARKANSAS.

    (a) 40,320   (b) 13,440   (c) 6720

    (d) 3360   (e) None of these

    1—M—Answer: d

11. Find the number of distinguishable permutations using the letters in the word CALCULATOR.

    (a) 3,628,800   (b) 43,360   (c) 435,600

    (d) 907,200   (e) None of these

    1—M—Answer: c

12. Find the number of distinguishable permutations using the letters in the word MATHEMATICS.

    1—O—Answer: 4,989,600

13. Find the number of distinguishable permutations with the following letters:

    $\{A, A, A, B, B, C, C, C, C\}$

    (a) 2520   (b) 1260   (c) 362,880

    (d) 288   (e) None of these

    1—M—Answer: b

14. How many different ways (subject orders) can three algebra books, two trigonometry books and two arithmetic books be arranged on a shelf?

    (a) 5040   (b) 210   (c) 128

    (d) 823,543   (e) None of these

    1—M—Answer: b

15. How many different ways can three chocolate, four strawberry, and two butterscotch sundaes be served to nine people?

    1—O—Answer: 1260 ways

16. An organization consisting of 54 members is going to elect four officers. No person may hold more than one office. How many different outcomes are possible?

    (a) 354,294   (b) 8,503,056   (c) 316,251

    (d) 7,590,024   (e) None of these

    2—M—Answer: d

17. A class of nine students line up single file for lunch. How many different ways can this occur if the six boys in the class must line up first?

   (a) 18   (b) 60,480   (c) 4320
   (d) 504   (e) None of these

   1—M—Answer: c

18. How many ways can a ten-question multiple choice test be answered if each question has five possible answers?

   (a) 50   (b) 120   (c) 3,628,800
   (d) 9,765,625   (e) None of these

   1—M—Answer: d

19. An organization consisting of 36 members is going to elect three officers. No person may hold more than one office. How many different outcomes are possible?

   (a) 7140   (b) 42,840   (c) 6.2×10^{40}
   (d) 3.7×10^{41} (e) None of these

   1—M—Answer: b

20. How many ways can an eight-question multiple choice test be answered if each question has five possible answers?

   (a) 390,625   (b) 4,838,400   (c) 40,320
   (d) 120   (e) None of these

   1—M—Answer: a

21. There are 20 girls in a beauty pageant. A queen, a first runner-up and a second runner-up are to be chosen. How many different outcomes are possible?

   (a) 1140   (b) 6840   (c) 2.4×10^{18}
   (d) 4.1×10^{17} (e) None of these

   1—M—Answer: b

22. A group of six students are seated in a single row at a football game. In how many different orders can they be seated?

   1—O—Answer: 720

23. The flags of seven different countries are to be displayed in a row. In how many different orders can they be flown?

   (a) 5040   (b) 1258   (c) 128   (d) 49   (e) None of these

   1—M—Answer: a

24. Seven members of a family line up to have their picture taken. In how many different ways can they be arranged?

    (a) 49   (b) 128   (c) 5040   (d) 1258   (e) None of these

    1—M—Answer: c

25. If there are ten questions on a test, how many different versions of the same test can be made by rearranging the questions?

    (a) 1024   (b) 100   (c) 30,240

    (d) 3,628,800   (e) None of these

    1—M—Answer: d

26. Eight sailboats are entered in a race. In how many ways can they finish?

    (a) 6720   (b) 256   (c) 40,320

    (d) 1680   (e) None of these

    1—M—Answer: c

27. Six girls are chosen as cheerleaders. In how many different orders could they have been chosen?

    (a) 720   (b) 64   (c) 46,656

    (d) 17,280   (e) None of these

    1—M—Answer: a

28. There are seven possible digits in a phone number. How many different phone numbers are possible if the first digit cannot be 0 and no digit can be used more than once?

    (a) 128   (b) 181,440   (c) 544,320

    (d) 5040   (e) None of these

    1—M—Answer: c

29. How many different ways (subject order) can seven algebra books, five trigonometry books, and four calculus books be arranged on a shelf?

    (a) 140   (b) 1,441,440   (c) 65,536

    (d) 2.1×10^{13} (e) None of these

    1—M—Answer: b

30. A license plate number consists of three letters followed by three digits. How many distinct license plate numbers can be formed?

    (a) 17,576,000   (b) 30,844,800   (c) 11,232,000

    (d) 12,812,904   (e) None of these

    1—M—Answer: a

31. A group of nine students line up single file for lunch. How many different ways can this occur if the five boys must line up first?

(a) 362,880   (b) 2880   (c) 15,120

(d) 126   (e) None of these

1—M—Answer: b

32. A random number generator selects an integer from 1 to 50. Find the number of ways a square number can occur.

(a) 99,884,400   (b) 5040   (c) 128

(d) 7   (e) None of these

1—M—Answer: d

33. Determine the number of ways the last four digits of a telephone number can be arranged if the first of the four digits cannot be 0.

(a) 10,000   (b) 5040   (c) 9000

(d) 4536   (e) None of these

1—M—Answer: c

34. If a license plate number consists of two letters followed by two digits, how many different license plate numbers are possible?

(a) 58,500   (b) 67,600   (c) 256

(d) 24   (e) None of these

1—M—Answer: b

35. A scrabble tray contains the tiles F E R S X A I. How many different four-letter arrangements ("words") can be made?

1—O—Answer: 840

36. A ship has six flags available for signaling. If a signal consists of hoisting three of the flags, how many different signals are possible?

1—O—Answer: 120

37. A random number generator selects an integer from 1 to 20. Find the number of ways in which a number that is a multiple of three can be selected.

(a) 6   (b) 720   (c) 5   (d) 120   (e) None of these

1—M—Answer: a

38. A random number generator selects two integers from 1 to 20. Find the number of ways that the sum of these two integers is 8.

(a) 4   (b) 7   (c) 9   (d) 6   (e) None of these

1—M—Answer: b

39. An auto license plate is made using two letters followed by three digits. How many license plates are possible?

(a) 676,000   (b) 468,000   (c) 82

(d) 1,757,600   (e) None of these

1—M—Answer: a

40. Determine the number of possible 5 digit ZIP codes.

(a) 120   (b) 90,000   (c) 3,628,800

(d) 100,000   (e) None of these

1—M—Answer: d

41. Determine the number of seven digit telephone numbers that can be formed under the condition that each of the first three digits cannot be 0.

1—O—Answer: 7,290,000

42. How many different three-letter arrangements ("words") can be made from the letters A B C D E F G?

(a) 24   (b) 35   (c) 840   (d) 210   (e) None of these

1—M—Answer: d

43. A ship has eight flags available for signaling. If a signal consists of hoisting three of the flags, how many different signals are possible?

(a) 1680   (b) 336   (c) 56   (d) 40,320   (e) None of these

1—M—Answer: b

44. If a special at a diner offers a choice of one each of two appetizers, four entrees and five desserts, how many distinct meals are possible under the special?

(a) 20   (b) 40   (c) 60   (d) 80   (e) None of these

1—M—Answer: b

45. The chief designer for a large auto company is considering four different radiator grilles, two different headlight styles and five different front fender designs. How many front-end designs can be made using these three characteristics?

(a) 80   (b) 60   (c) 40   (d) 20   (e) None of these

1—M—Answer: c

46. If a menu at a diner offers a choice of three appetizers, six entrees and four desserts, how many distinct meals are possible?

(a) 72   (b) 216   (c) 24   (d) 103,680   (e) None of these

1—M—Answer: a

47. If a woman's wardrobe consists of two jackets, three skirts, and five blouses, how many different outfits consisting of a jacket, skirt, and blouse can be made?

    (a) 1440   (b) 10   (c) 90   (d) 30   (e) None of these

    1—M—Answer: d

48. In how many ways can a subcommittee of five people be selected from a committee of ten people?

    (a) 252   (b) 30,240   (c) 6048

    (d) 1260   (e) None of these

    1—M—Answer: a

49. A record club offers new customers six free selections from a list of 130 different recordings. How many different introductory offers are possible?

    1—O—Answer: $\dfrac{130!}{6!124!} = 5,963,412,000$

50. In how many ways can a subcommittee of six people be selected from a committee of 12 people?

    (a) 665,280   (b) 924   (c) 720

    (d) 520   (e) None of these

    1—M—Answer: b

51. In how many ways can a committee of nine people be selected from a group of 12 people?

    (a) 1320   (b) 79,833,600   (c) 362,880

    (d) 220   (e) None of these

    1—M—Answer: d

52. How many ways can four girls be picked from a group of 30 girls?

    1—O—Answer: 27,405

53. A committee composed of three math majors and four science majors is to be selected from a group of 20 math majors and 16 science majors. How many different committees can be formed?

    (a) 2,074,800   (b) 6840   (c) 4.05×10^{17}

    (d) 320   (e) None of these

    2—M—Answer: a

54. At a Boy Scout jamboree there are 12 senior patrol leaders, 10 assistant senior patrol leaders, 21 patrol leaders, and 84 other scouts. How many committees of two senior patrol leaders, one assistant patrol leader, three patrol leaders, and four regular scouts can be formed?

    (a) 3.2×10^{11} (b) 1.7×10^{12} (c) 2.4×10^9

    (d) 1.4×10^9 (e) None of these

    2—M—Answer: b

55. A band director is taking auditions for a special pep band which requires three trumpets, one trombone, one saxophone, and two clarinets. There were five trumpet players, four trombone players, three saxophone players and 10 clarinet players who came to audition. How many possible combinations does the band director have?

(a) 100 (b) 600 (c) 5400 (d) 32,400 (e) None of these

2—M—Answer: c

56. In how many ways can a committee consisting of two deacons and four regular church members be formed in a church that has five deacons and 120 regular members?

1—O—Answer: 82,145,700

57. A small college needs four additional faculty members: a mathematician, two chemists, and an engineer. In how many ways can these positions be filled if there are two applicants for mathematics, six applicants for chemistry and three applicants for engineering?

(a) 180 (b) 330 (c) 90 (d) 36 (e) None of these

2—M—Answer: c

58. In how many ways can a committee of two boys and three girls be formed from a group of 10 boys and 12 girls?

(a) 9900 (b) 1320 (c) 118,800

(d) 265 (e) None of these

1—M—Answer: a

59. In how many ways can a committee of three boys and three girls be formed from a group of 10 boys and 12 girls?

(a) 340 (b) 2040 (c) 26,400

(d) 960,400 (e) None of these

1—M—Answer: c

60. In how many ways can a committee of two boys and four girls be formed from a group of six boys and nine girls?

(a) 141 (b) 90,720 (c) 3054

(d) 1890 (e) None of these

1—M—Answer: d

61. Find the number of diagonals in a heptagon (7-sided polygon). A line segment connecting any two nonadjacent vertices is called a diagonal of the polygon.

(a) 21 (b) 14 (c) 35 (d) 28 (e) None of these

2—M—Answer: b

62. Find the number of diagonals in a nonagon (9-sided polygon). A line segment connecting any two nonadjacent vertices is called a diagonal of the polygon.

(a) 56   (b) 36   (c) 27

(d) 18   (e) None of these

2—M—Answer: c

10.7 Probability

1. Describe the sample space: "A number is chosen at random from the numbers one to five inclusive."

(a) {1, 2, 3, 4}   (b) 1   (c) $\frac{1}{5}$

(d) {1, 2, 3, 4, 5}   (e) None of these

1—M—Answer: d

2. Describe the sample space: "A student must select the correct answer to a multiple choice test question given five possible answers."

(a) The correct answer   (b) The five possible answers   (c) $\frac{1}{5}$

(d) The four wrong answers (e) None of these

1—M—Answer: b

3. Describe the sample space: "A letter is selected from the word MATHEMATICS."

(a) One of the letters   (b) $\frac{1}{11}$

(c) (M, A, T, H, E, M, A, T, I, C, S)   (d) {M, A, T, H, E, I, C, S}

(e) None of these

1—M—Answer: d

4. Describe the sample space: "A letter is selected from the word FINITE."

(a) {F, I, N, T, E}   (b) One of the letters   (c) (F, I, N, I, T, E)

(d) $\frac{1}{6}$ (e) None of these

1—M—Answer: a

5. Describe the sample space: "A ball is selected from a bag containing seven balls, numbered from 1 to 7."

(a) The ball numbered 3   (b) $\frac{1}{7}$ (c) The set of 7 balls

(d) The balls numbered 3, 4, and 7   (e) None of these

1—M—Answer: c

6. A card is drawn at random from a standard deck of 52 playing cards. Find the probability that the card is a spade.

(a) $\frac{1}{13}$ (b) $\frac{1}{4}$ (c) $\frac{12}{13}$

(d) $\frac{3}{4}$ (e) None of these

1—M—Answer: b

7. A card is drawn at random from a standard deck of 52 playing cards. Find the probability that the card is a 10 or an ace.

(a) $\frac{2}{13}$ (b) $\frac{1}{169}$ (c) $\frac{4}{13}$

(d) $\frac{1}{4}$ (e) None of these

1—M—Answer: a

8. A card is drawn at random from a standard deck of 52 playing cards. Find the probability that the card is an ace or spade.

(a) $\frac{17}{52}$ (b) $\frac{4}{13}$ (c) $\frac{1}{52}$

(d) $\frac{2}{13}$ (e) None of these

1—M—Answer: b

9. Two cards are randomly selected from a standard deck of 52 playing cards. Find the probability that one card will be an ace and the other will be a 10.

(a) $\frac{1}{52}$ (b) $\frac{8}{663}$ (c) $\frac{1}{169}$

(d) $\frac{2}{13}$ (e) None of these

1—M—Answer: c

10. Find the probability of choosing an E when selecting a letter at random from those in the word COLLEGE.

(a) $\frac{2}{7}$ (b) $\frac{1}{5}$ (c) $\frac{2}{5}$

(d) $\frac{1}{7}$ (e) None of these

1—M—Answer: a

11. Find the probability of choosing an A, B, or N when selecting a letter at random from those in the word BANANA.

(a) $\frac{1}{26}$ (b) 0   (c) 1

(d) $\frac{1}{2}$ (e) None of these

1—M—Answer: c

12. In a group of 10 children, 3 have blond hair and 7 have brown hair. If a child is chosen at random, what is the probability that the child will have brown hair?

1—O—Answer: $\frac{7}{10}$

13. A bag contains four red balls and seven white balls. If a ball is drawn at random, what is the probability that it is a red ball?

(a) $\frac{1}{4}$ (b) $\frac{4}{7}$ (c) $\frac{1}{11}$

(d) $\frac{4}{11}$ (e) None of these

1—M—Answer: d

14. A bag contains nine red balls and six white balls. If one ball is drawn at random from the bag, what is the probability that it is a red ball?

(a) $\frac{1}{9}$ (b) $\frac{3}{5}$ (c) $\frac{2}{5}$

(d) $\frac{3}{2}$ (e) None of these

1—M—Answer: b

15. A bag contains nine red balls numbered 1 – 9 and six white balls numbered 10 – 15. If one ball is drawn at random, what is the probability that the number on it is even?

(a) $\frac{3}{5}$ (b) $\frac{7}{15}$ (c) $\frac{4}{15}$

(d) $\frac{1}{5}$ (e) None of these

1—M—Answer: b

16. A bag contains nine red balls numbered 1 – 9 and six white balls numbered 10 – 15. If one ball is drawn at random, what is the probability that the number on it is divisible by three?

(a) $\frac{1}{3}$ (b) $\frac{1}{2}$ (c) $\frac{2}{3}$

(d) $\frac{2}{5}$ (e) None of these

1—M—Answer: a

17. A bag contains nine red balls numbered 1 – 9 and six white balls numbered 10 – 15. If one ball is drawn at random, what is the probability that the number on it is divisible by five?

(a) 3   (b) $\frac{2}{3}$ (c) $\frac{3}{5}$

(d) $\frac{1}{5}$ (e) None of these

1—M—Answer: d

18. A die is tossed three times. What is the probability that a two will come up all three times?

(a) $\frac{1}{172}$ (b) $\frac{1}{18}$ (c) $\frac{1}{120}$

(d) $\frac{1}{216}$ (e) None of these

1—M—Answer: d

19. What is the probability of drawing a white marble from a box containing six white, three red and five black marbles?

(a) $\frac{1}{6}$ (b) $\frac{1}{14}$ (c) $\frac{3}{7}$

(d) $\frac{1}{15}$ (e) None of these

1—M—Answer: c

20. A fair coin is tossed four times. What is the probability of getting heads on all four tosses?

1—O—Answer: $\frac{1}{16}$

21. A fair coin is tossed four times. What is the probability of getting a head on the first toss and tails on the other three tosses?

(a) $\frac{1}{8}$ (b) $\frac{1}{16}$ (c) $\frac{1}{12}$

(d) $\frac{3}{16}$ (e) None of these

1—M—Answer: b

22. A fair coin is tossed four times. What is the probability of getting exactly one head?

(a) $\frac{1}{2}$ (b) $\frac{1}{4}$ (c) $\frac{1}{8}$

(d) $\frac{1}{16}$ (e) None of these

1—M—Answer: b

23. Two six-sided dice are tossed. What is the probability that the total is 11?

(a) $\frac{1}{18}$ (b) $\frac{1}{6}$ (c) $\frac{1}{8}$

(d) $\frac{2}{15}$ (e) None of these

1—M—Answer: a

24. Two integers from 0 to 9 inclusive are chosen by a random number generator. What is the probability of choosing the number 2 both times?

(a) $\frac{1}{10}$ (b) $\frac{1}{100}$ (c) $\frac{1}{50}$

(d) $\frac{4}{5}$ (e) None of these

1—M—Answer: b

25. Two integers (between 1 and 40 inclusive) are chosen by a random number generator. What is the probability that both numbers chosen are divisible by 4?

1—O—Answer: $\frac{1}{16}$

26. What is the probability that in a group of 6 people at least 2 will have their birthdays within the same week?

(a) 0.74   (b) 0.50   (c) 0.26

(d) 0.47   (e) None of these

2—M—Answer: c

27. What is the probability that 2 people chosen at random from a group of 8 married couples are married to each other?

1—O—Answer: $\frac{1}{15}$

28. There are 5 red and 4 black balls in a box. If 3 balls are picked without replacement, what is the probability that at least one of them is red?

    1—O—Answer: $\frac{20}{21}$

29. A box holds 12 white, 5 red, and 6 black marbles. If 2 marbles are picked at random, without replacement, what is the probability that they will both be black?

    (a) $\frac{36}{529}$ (b) $\frac{247}{506}$ (c) $\frac{15}{253}$

    (d) $\frac{6}{23}$ (e) None of these

    1—M—Answer: c

30. Five cards are drawn from an ordinary deck of 52 playing cards. What is the probability of getting exactly one ace? Round your answer to three decimal places.

    (a) 0.060   (b) 0.299   (c) 0.064

    (d) 0.341   (e) None of these

    1—M—Answer: b

31. Two six-sided dice are tossed. What is the probability that the total is seven?

    (a) $\frac{1}{2}$ (b) $\frac{7}{12}$ (c) $\frac{1}{6}$

    (d) $\frac{1}{3}$ (e) None of these

    1—M—Answer: c

32. Two six-sided dice are tossed. What is the probability that the total is nine?

    (a) $\frac{1}{6}$ (b) $\frac{1}{9}$ (c) $\frac{1}{8}$

    (d) $\frac{1}{3}$ (e) None of these

    1—M—Answer: b

33. Two six-sided dice are tossed. What is the probability that the total is 12?

    (a) $\frac{1}{12}$ (b) $\frac{1}{18}$ (c) $\frac{1}{36}$

    (d) $\frac{1}{30}$ (e) None of these

    1—M—Answer: c

34. Two six-sided dice are tossed. What is the probability that the total is ten?

    (a) $\frac{1}{12}$ (b) $\frac{1}{4}$ (c) $\frac{1}{18}$

    (d) $\frac{1}{8}$ (e) None of these

    1—M—Answer: a

35. Two cards are drawn with replacement from a box containing six blue cards numbered 1 – 6 and eleven white cards numbered 7 – 17. What is the probability that both cards are even-numbered?

    (a) $\frac{64}{289}$ (b) $\frac{4}{17}$ (c) $\frac{1}{34}$

    (d) $\frac{7}{34}$ (e) None of these

    1—M—Answer: a

36. Two cards are drawn with replacement from a box containing six blue cards numbered 1 – 6 and eleven white cards numbered 7 – 17. What is the probability that the first card is odd-numbered and the second card is white?

    (a) $\frac{99}{136}$ (b) $\frac{99}{272}$ (c) $\frac{99}{289}$

    (d) $\frac{20}{289}$ (e) None of these

    1—M—Answer: c

37. Drawing from a standard deck of 52 cards, what is the probability that the card is an eight or a face card?

    (a) $\frac{3}{169}$ (b) $\frac{4}{13}$ (c) $\frac{2}{13}$

    (d) $\frac{1}{48}$ (e) None of these

    1—M—Answer: b

38. Drawing from a standard deck of 52 cards, what is the probability that the card is an ace, king or queen?

    (a) $\frac{3}{13}$ (b) $\frac{1}{13}$ (c) $\frac{1}{2197}$

    (d) $\frac{1}{64}$ (e) None of these

    1—M—Answer: a

39. Drawing from a standard deck of 52 cards, what is the probability that the card is a five or a red jack?

    (a) $\frac{1}{13}$ (b) $\frac{3}{26}$ (c) $\frac{3}{13}$

    (d) $\frac{1}{238}$ (e) None of these

    1—M—Answer: b

40. A small business college has 800 seniors, 700 juniors, 900 sophomores and 1,200 freshmen. If a student is randomly selected, what is the probability that the student is a junior or senior?

    (a) $\frac{13}{36}$ (b) $\frac{1}{4}$ (c) $\frac{5}{12}$

    (d) $\frac{5}{162}$ (e) None of these

    1—M—Answer: c

41. A small business college has 800 seniors, 700 juniors, 900 sophomores and 1,200 freshmen. If a student is randomly selected, what is the probability that the student is a freshman or a senior?

    (a) $\frac{1}{4}$ (b) $\frac{1}{54}$ (c) $\frac{5}{12}$

    (d) $\frac{5}{9}$ (e) None of these

    1—M—Answer: d

42. A small business college has 400 seniors, 300 juniors, 500 sophomores and 600 freshmen. If a student is randomly selected, what is the probability that the student is a junior or a senior?

(a) $\frac{1}{4}$ (b) $\frac{2}{9}$ (c) $\frac{7}{18}$

(d) $\frac{1}{27}$ (e) None of these

1—M—Answer: c

43. A small business college has 400 seniors, 300 juniors, 500 sophomores and 600 freshmen. If a student is randomly selected, what is the probability that the student is a freshman or a senior?

(a) $\frac{2}{27}$ (b) $\frac{5}{9}$ (c) $\frac{1}{4}$

(d) $\frac{5}{18}$ (e) None of these

1—M—Answer: b

44. In drawing one card from a standard deck of 52 playing cards, what is the probability of obtaining a king or a club?

(a) $\frac{1}{52}$ (b) $\frac{17}{52}$ (c) $\frac{4}{13}$

(d) $\frac{2}{13}$ (e) None of these

1—M—Answer: c

45. In drawing one card from a standard deck of 52 playing cards, what is the probability of obtaining an ace or a heart?

(a) $\frac{4}{13}$ (b) $\frac{1}{52}$ (c) $\frac{17}{52}$

(d) $\frac{2}{13}$ (e) None of these

1—M—Answer: a

46. In drawing one card from a standard deck of 52 playing cards, what is the probability of obtaining a queen or a diamond?

(a) $\frac{1}{52}$ (b) $\frac{2}{13}$ (c) $\frac{4}{13}$

(d) $\frac{17}{52}$ (e) None of these

1—M—Answer: c

47. In drawing one card from a standard deck of 52 playing cards, what is the probability that it is a jack or a spade?

(a) $\frac{1}{52}$ (b) $\frac{17}{52}$ (c) $\frac{2}{13}$

(d) $\frac{4}{13}$ (e) None of these

1—M—Answer: d

48. In drawing one card from a standard deck of 52 playing cards, what is the probability that the card is a diamond or a face card?

(a) $\frac{11}{26}$ (b) $\frac{17}{52}$ (c) $\frac{3}{13}$

(d) $\frac{1}{13}$ (e) None of these

1—M—Answer: a

49. Before an election, a sample of 120,000 people throughout the county showed that 79,386 people would vote for Candidate A. If a person from the sample is chosen at random, what is the probability the person is one of the people who said they would not vote for Candidate A?

(a) 0.66 (b) 0.34 (c) 0.47

(d) 0.53 (e) None of these

1—M—Answer: b

50. If the probability of getting a rotten apple in a basket of apples is 12%, what is the probability of getting 3 good apples choosing one from each of three different baskets?

(a) 0.9983 (b) 0.0017 (c) 0.8800

(d) 0.6815 (e) None of these

1—M—Answer: d

51. In an experiment in which 2 six-sided dice are tossed, what is the probability of *not* getting a sum of 10?

1—O—Answer: $\frac{11}{12}$

52. If $P(A) = \frac{6}{11}$, find $P(A')$.

(a) 0 (b) 1 (c) $\frac{5}{11}$

(d) $\frac{5}{6}$ (e) None of these

1—M—Answer: c

53. A "doctored" die is tossed 100,000 times and comes up six on 35,861 rolls. Find the probability of rolling a number other than 6 with this die.

(a) 0.36 (b) 0.64 (c) 0.17

(d) 0.83 (e) None of these

1—M—Answer: b

54. A sample of nursing homes in a state reveals that 112,000 of 218,000 residents are female. If a nursing home resident is chosen at random from this state, what is the probability that the resident is male?

1—O—Answer: $\frac{53}{109}$

55. There are 120 40-watt bulbs, 200 60-watt bulbs and 80 100-watt bulbs in an art gallery. All of the 60-watt bulbs and half of the 100-watt bulbs are transparent and the rest are not. While installing the bulbs, a worker dropped one of them. What is the probability that the broken bulb was not a transparent 100-watt bulb?

(a) $\frac{1}{10}$ (b) $\frac{1}{5}$ (c) $\frac{9}{10}$

(d) $\frac{2}{5}$ (e) None of these

1—M—Answer: c

CHAPTER ELEVEN
Parametric Equations and Polar Coordinates

11.1 Plane Curves and Parametric Equations

1. Use a graphing utility to identify the curve for the parametric equations: $x = 3t - 6$, $y = t - 4$

(a)

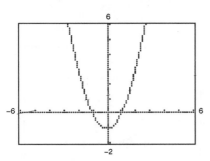

(b)

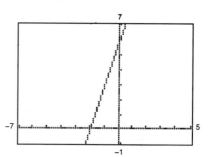

(c)

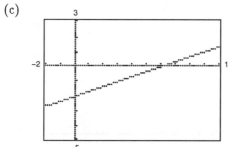

(d)

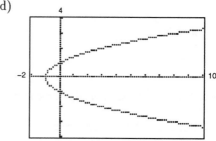

(e) None of these

1—M—Answer: c

2. Use a graphing utility to identify the curve for the parametric equations: $x = 3t^2$ $y = 1 - 2t^2$

(a)
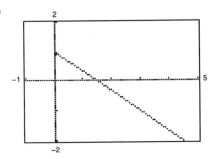

(b)
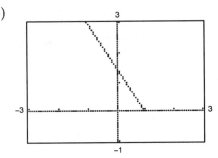

(c)
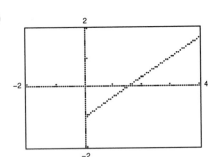

(d)
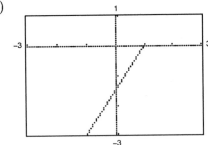

(e) None of these

1—M—Answer: a

3. Use a graphing utility to identify the curve for the parametric equation: $x = 3t + 2$, $y = t$

(a)
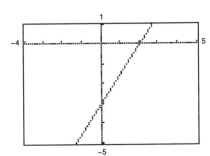

(b)
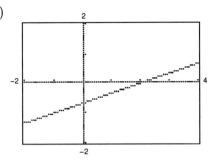

(c)
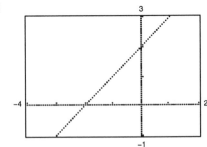

(d)
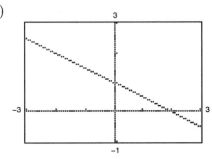

(e) None of these

1—M—Answer: b

4. Use a graphing utility to identify the curve for the parametric equations: $x = t^2$, $y = t - 1$

(a)

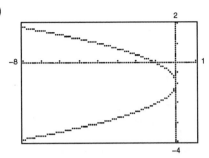

(b)

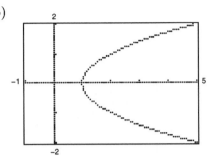

(c)

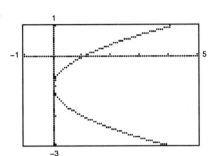

(d)

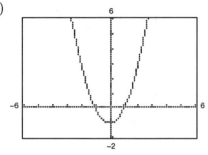

(e) None of these

1—M—Answer: c

5. Use a graphing utility to identify the curve for the parametric equations: $x = 2t^2$, $y = t + 1$

(a)

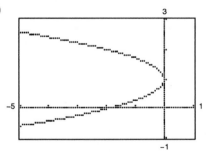

(b)

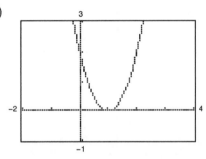

(c)

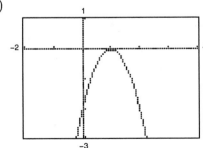

(d)

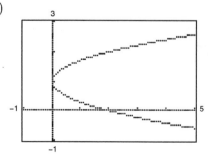

(e) None of these

1—M—Answer: d

6. Identify the curve for the parametric equations: $x = \cos\theta$, $y = 3\sin\theta$

(a)

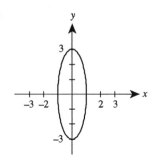

(b)

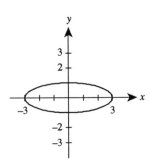

(c)

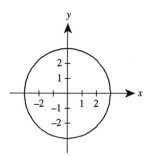

(d)

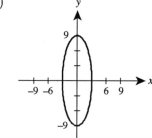

(e) None of these

1—M—Answer: a

7. Identify the curve for the parametric equations: $x = 4 + \cos\theta$, $y = -1 + \sin\theta$

(a)

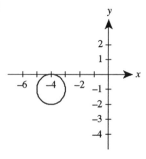

(b)

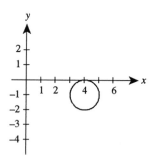

(c)

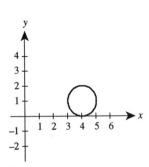

(d)

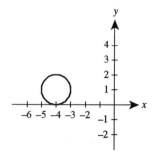

(e) None of these

1—M—Answer: b

8. Identify the curve for the parametric equations: $x = 4\cos t, \ y = -\sin t$

(a)

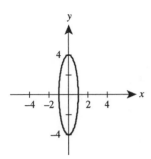

(b)

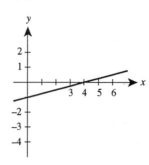

(c)

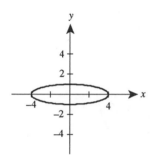

(d)

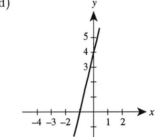

(e) None of these

1—M—Answer: c

9. Identify the curve for the parametric equations: $x = -2 + \cos t, \ y = \sin t$

(a)

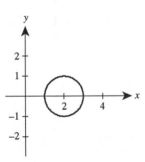

(b)

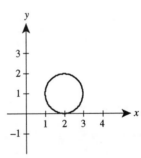

(c)

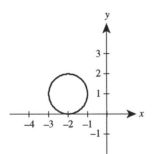

(d)

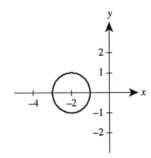

(e) None of these

1—M—Answer: d

10. Identify the wave for the parametric equations: $x = 2t, \ y = \sin t$

(a)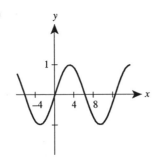

(b)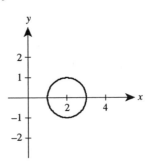

(c)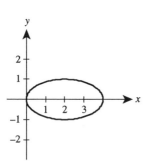

(d)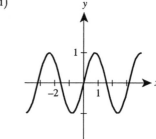

(e) None of these

1—M—Answer: a

11. Eliminate the parameter and find a corresponding rectangular equation: $x = 3t^2, \ y = 2t + 1$

(a) $2x^2 + 3y^2 - 1 = 0$ (b) $2x - 3y + 3 = 0$ (c) $3y^2 - 4x + 1 = 0$

(d) $3y^2 - 4x - 6y + 3 = 0$ (e) None of these

1—M—Answer: d

12. Eliminate the parameter and find a corresponding rectangular equation: $x = 2\cos\theta, \ y = \cos^2\theta$

(a) $x + y = \cos\theta(2 + \cos\theta)$ (b) $x - 2y = 0$ (c) $y = \left(1 - \dfrac{x}{2}\right)^2$

(d) $x^2 = 4y$ (e) None of these

1—M—Answer: d

13. Eliminate the parameter and find a corresponding rectangular equation: $x = 1 + \cos\theta, \ y = 2 - \sin\theta$

2—O—Answer: $x^2 + y^2 - 2x - 4y + 4 = 0$

14. Eliminate the parameter and find a corresponding rectangular equation: $x = 3 + \cos\theta, \ y = \sin\theta - 1$

2—O—Answer: $x^2 + y^2 - 6x + 2y + 9 = 0$

15. Eliminate the parameter and find a corresponding rectangular equation: $x = t^3, \ y = 1/t$

1—O—Answer: $xy^3 = 1$

16. Eliminate the parameter and find a corresponding rectangular equation: $x = 3t + 1$, $y = 2t$

(a) $2x - 3y - 2 = 0$ (b) $2x - 3y - 3 = 0$ (c) $x - 6y + 1 = 0$

(d) $2x - 3y - 6 = 0$ (e) None of these

1—M—Answer: a

17. Eliminate the parameter and find a corresponding rectangular equation: $x = t^2$, $y = t + 1$

(a) $x - y^2 - 1 = 0$ (b) $x - y^2 + 2y - 1 = 0$ (c) $x - y + 1 = 0$

(d) $x - y^2 - 2y - 1 = 0$ (e) None of these

1—M—Answer: b

18. Eliminate the parameter and find a corresponding rectangular equation: $x = 2\cos\theta$, $y = 4\sin\theta$

(a) $4x + 2y = 1$ (b) $16x^2 + 4y^2 = 1$ (c) $4x + 2y = 8$

(d) $16x^2 + 4y^2 = 64$ (e) None of these

1—M—Answer: d

19. Eliminate the parameter and find a corresponding rectangular equation: $x = -3 + 2\cos\theta$, $y = 1 + \sin\theta$

1—O—Answer: $\dfrac{(x + 3)^2}{4} + (y - 1)^2 = 1$ or $x^2 + 4y^2 + 6x - 8y + 9 = 0$

20. Eliminate the parameter and find a corresponding rectangular equation: $x = t^3$, $y = 1 - t$

(a) $y^3 - 3y^2 + 3y + x - 1 = 0$ (b) $y^3 - 3y^2 + 3y - x - 1 = 0$ (c) $y^3 + x - 1 = 0$

(d) $y^3 - x - 1 = 0$ (e) None of these

1—M—Answer: a

21. Given the line through (x_1, y_1) and (x_2, y_2) has parametric equations $x = x_1 + t(x_2 - x_1)$ and $y = y_1 + t(y_2 - y_1)$, find the parametric equations for the line passing through the points $(4, 3)$ and $(6, -10)$.

1—O—Answer: $x = 4 + 2t$

$y = 3 - 13t$

22. Given the line through (x_1, y_1) and (x_2, y_2) has parametric equations $x = x_1 + t(x_2 - x_1)$ and $y = y_1 + t(y_2 - y_1)$, find the parametric equations for the line passing through the points $(5, -4)$ and $(0, 5)$.

1—O—Answer: $x = 5 - 5t$

$y = -4 + 9t$

23. Given a circle with center (h, k) and radius r has parametric equations $x = h + r\cos\theta$ and $y = k + r\sin\theta$, find a set of parametric equations of a circle with centers $(-4, 5)$ and radius 4.

1—O—Answer: $x = -4 + 4\cos\theta$

$y = 5 + 4\sin\theta$

24. Given a circle with center $(h,\ k)$ and radius r has parametric equations $x = h + r\cos\theta$ and $y = k + r\sin\theta$, find a set of parametric equations of a circle with centers $\left(-10,\ \frac{1}{2}\right)$ and radius $\sqrt{7}$.

1—O—Answer: $x = -10 + \sqrt{7}\cos\theta$
$$y = \tfrac{1}{2} + \sqrt{7}\sin\theta$$

25. Given an ellipse in standard form with horizontal major axis has parametric equations $x = h + a\cos\theta$ and $y = k + b\sin\theta$, find a set of parametric equations with vertices $(4,\ 3)$, $(-4,\ 3)$ and foci $(2,\ 3)$, $(-2,\ 3)$.

1—O—Answer: $x = 4\cos\theta$
$$y = 3 + 2\sqrt{3}\sin\theta$$

26. Given an ellipse in standard form with horizontal major axis has parametric equations $x = h + a\cos\theta$ and $y = k + b\sin\theta$, find a set of parametric equations with vertices $(10,\ 2)$, $(-20,\ 2)$ and foci $(8,\ 2)$, $(-18,\ 2)$.

1—O—Answer: $x = -5 + 15\cos\theta$
$$y = 2 + 2\sqrt{14}\sin\theta$$

27. Given a hyperbola in standard form with horizontal traverse axis has parametric equations $x = h + a\sec\theta$ and $y = k + b\tan\theta$, find a set of parametric equations for the hyperbola with vertices $(\pm 10,\ 0)$ and foci $(\pm 12,\ 0)$.

1—O—Answer: $x = 10\sec\theta$
$$y = 2\sqrt{11}\tan\theta$$

28. Given a hyperbola in standard form with horizontal traverse axis has parametric equations $x = h + a\sec\theta$ and $y = k + b\tan\theta$, find a set of parametric equations for the hyperbola with vertices $(12,\ 1)$, $(22,\ 1)$ and foci $(24,\ 1)$, $(10,\ 1)$.

1—O—Answer: $x = 17 + 5\sec\theta$
$$y = 1 + 4\sqrt{6}\tan\theta$$

29. Find a set of parametric equations for the curve at the right.

(a) $x = -1 + \sin t$
   $y = -1 + 3\sin t$

(b) $x = 3\cos t + 8$
   $y = 2 + \cos t$

(c) $x = \cos 2t$
   $y = 2\cos^2 t - 1$

(d) $x = 1 + \cos t$
   $y = 3 + \cos t$

(e) None of these

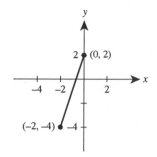

2—M—Answer: a

30. Find a set of parametric equations for the curve at the right.

(a) $x = \frac{3}{2}t$ (b) $x = t$

     $y = t + 3$ $y = -\frac{2}{3}t + 3$

(c) $x = -\frac{3}{2}t$ (d) $x = t$

     $y = t - 3$ $y = \frac{2}{3}t + 3$

(e) None of these

1—M—Answer: b

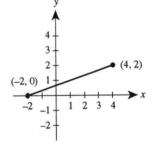

31. Find a set of parametric equations for the curve at the right.

(a) $x = t$ (b) $x = t$

     $y = t$ $y = 3t + \frac{2}{3}$

(c) $x = 3t$ (d) $x = 3t$

     $y = t + \frac{2}{3}$ $y = 3t + \frac{2}{3}$

(e) None of these

1—M—Answer: c

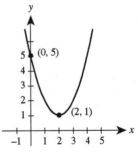

32. Find a set of parametric equations for the curve at the right.

2—O—Answer: $y = (x - 2)^2 + 1$

$$t = x - 2 \ \Rightarrow \ x = t + 2$$
$$y = (t)^2 + 1 \ \Rightarrow \ y = t^2 + 1$$

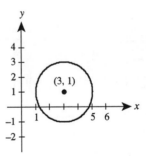

33. Find a set of parametric equations for the curve at the right.

2—O—Answer:

Circle with center $(3, 1)$, $r = 2$

$$(x - 3)^2 + (y - 1)^2 = 4$$
$$\frac{(x - 3)^2}{4} + \frac{(y - 1)^2}{4} = 1$$
$$\cos^2 t + \sin^2 t = 1$$
$$\cos t = \frac{x - 3}{2} \ \Rightarrow \ x = 3 + 2\cos t$$
$$\sin t = \frac{y - 1}{2} \ \Rightarrow \ y = 1 + 2\sin t$$

34. Use a graphing utility to graph the curve represented by the parametric equations $x = 1 + 3t$ and $y = t - 1$.

1—O—Answer:

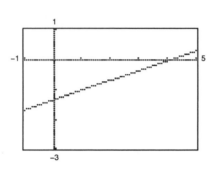

35. Use a graphing utility to graph the curve represented by the parametric equations $x = 4 + 2t$ and $y = t^2$.

1—O—Answer:

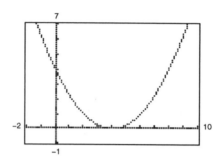

36. Use a graphing utility to graph the curve represented by the parametric equations $x = 6 + t$ and $y = t^3$.

1—O—Answer:

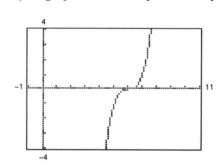

37. Use a graphing utility to graph the curve represented by the parametric equations $x = 2t$ and $y = t + 1$.

1—O—Answer:

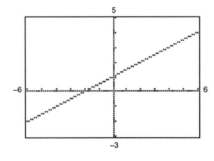

38. Use a graphing utility to graph the curve represented by the parametric equations $x = \frac{1}{4}t$ and $y = -t^2$.

1—O—Answer:

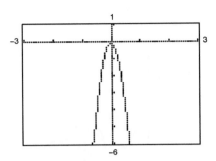

39. If an object moves according to the parametric equations $x = 2t$, $y = 3t^2$, sketch a graph of its motion for $0 \leq t \leq 3$.

1—O—Answer:

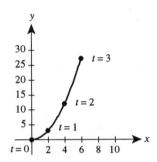

40. A ball is thrown at an angle of θ and initial velocity V_0. The path of the ball has parametric equations $x = V_0 \cos\theta t$ and $y = V_0 \sin\theta t - 16t^2$. Sketch the curve of a ball if it is thrown at an angle of $45°$ and with initial velocity of 60 feet per second.

2—O—Answer: $\theta = 45°$, $V_0 = 60$

$$x = 60\cos 45°t \;\Rightarrow\; x = \frac{60}{\sqrt{2}}t$$

$$y = 60\sin 45°t - 16t^2 \;\Rightarrow\; y = \frac{60}{\sqrt{2}}t - 16t^2$$

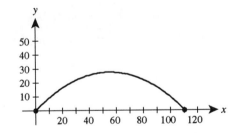

11.2 Polar Coordinates

1. Plot the point whose polar coordinates are $\left(3, \dfrac{\pi}{6}\right)$.

(a)

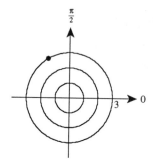

(b)

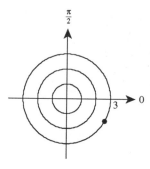

(c)

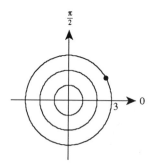

(d)

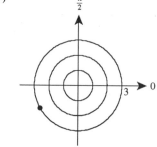

(e) None of these

1—M—Answer: c

2. Plot the point whose polar coordinates are $\left(4, -\dfrac{\pi}{3}\right)$.

(a)

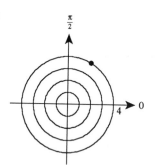

(b)

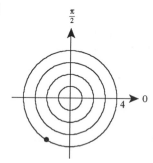

2. —CONTINUED—

(c)

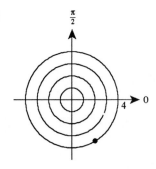

(d)

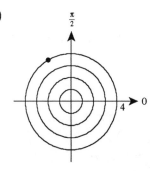

(e) None of these

1—M—Answer: c

3. Plot the point whose polar coordinates are $\left(-2, \ -\dfrac{2\pi}{3}\right)$.

(a)

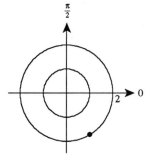

(b)

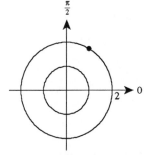

(c)

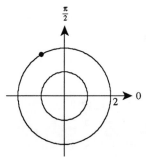

(d)

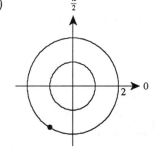

(e) None of these

1—M—Answer: b

4. Plot the point whose polar coordinates are $\left(-2, \dfrac{15\pi}{4}\right)$.

(a)

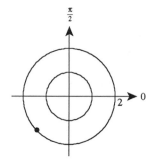

(b)

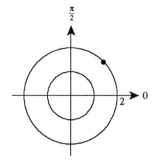

(c)

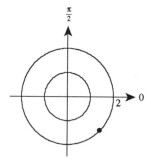

(d)

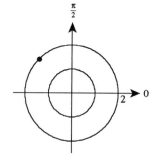

(e) None of these

1—M—Answer: d

5. Plot the point whose polar coordinates are $\left(-3, \dfrac{\pi}{3}\right)$.

(a)

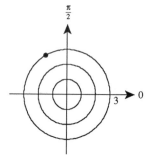

(b)

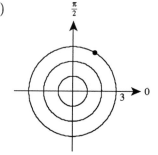

5. —CONTINUED—

(c)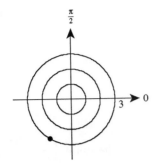

(d)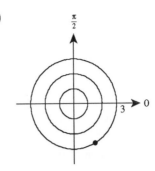

(e) None of these

1—M—Answer: c

6. Plot the points whose polar coordinates are:

(a) $\left(3, \dfrac{\pi}{2}\right)$ (b) $\left(-2, \dfrac{\pi}{4}\right)$ (c) $\left(3, -\dfrac{\pi}{6}\right)$

1—O—Answer:

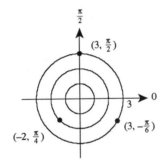

7. In polar coordinates, which of the following is *not* a correct representation for the point $(3, \pi/4)$?

(a) $\left(-3, -\dfrac{3\pi}{4}\right)$ (b) $\left(-3, -\dfrac{\pi}{4}\right)$ (c) $\left(3, \dfrac{9\pi}{4}\right)$

(d) $\left(-3, \dfrac{5\pi}{4}\right)$ (e) None of these

1—M—Answer: b

8. In polar coordinates, which of the following is *not* a correct representation for the point $\left(2, \dfrac{5\pi}{6}\right)$?

(a) $\left(-2, -\dfrac{\pi}{6}\right)$ (b) $\left(-2, \dfrac{11\pi}{6}\right)$ (c) $\left(2, -\dfrac{11\pi}{6}\right)$

(d) $\left(2, -\dfrac{7\pi}{6}\right)$ (e) None of these

1—M—Answer: c

9. In polar coordinates, which of the following are correct representations for the point $\left(-3, -\frac{\pi}{3}\right)$?

(a) $\left(3, -\frac{4\pi}{3}\right)$

(b) $\left(3, \frac{2\pi}{3}\right)$

(c) $\left(3, \frac{8\pi}{3}\right)$

(d) $\left(-3, -\frac{8\pi}{3}\right)$

(e) None of these

1—M—Answer: a, b, c

10. In polar coordinates, which of the following are correct representations for the point $\left(-1, \frac{5\pi}{4}\right)$?

(a) $\left(1, \frac{\pi}{4}\right)$

(b) $\left(-1, -\frac{3\pi}{4}\right)$

(c) $\left(-1, -\frac{7\pi}{4}\right)$

(d) $\left(1, -\frac{15\pi}{4}\right)$

(e) None of these

1—M—Answer: a, b, d

11. In polar coordinates, which of the following are correct representations for the point $\left(3, \frac{6\pi}{5}\right)$?

(a) $\left(-3, -\frac{4\pi}{5}\right)$

(b) $\left(-3, -\frac{\pi}{5}\right)$

(c) $\left(-3, \frac{4\pi}{5}\right)$

(d) $\left(-3, -\frac{14\pi}{5}\right)$

(e) None of these

1—M—Answer: e

12. Convert from polar to rectangular coordinates: $\left(3, \frac{5\pi}{3}\right)$

(a) $\left(\frac{3\sqrt{3}}{2}, -\frac{3}{2}\right)$

(b) $\left(-\frac{3}{2}, \frac{3\sqrt{3}}{2}\right)$

(c) $\left(\frac{3\sqrt{2}}{2}, -\frac{3\sqrt{2}}{2}\right)$

(d) $\left(\frac{3}{2}, -\frac{3\sqrt{3}}{2}\right)$

(e) None of these

1—M—Answer: d

13. Convert from polar to rectangular coordinates: $\left(8, \frac{7\pi}{6}\right)$

(a) $(-4\sqrt{3}, -4)$

(b) $(4, 4\sqrt{3})$

(c) $(-4, 4\sqrt{3})$

(d) $(-4, -4\sqrt{3})$

(e) None of these

1—M—Answer: a

14. Convert from polar to rectangular coordinates: $\left(-6, \dfrac{3\pi}{2}\right)$

(a) $(-6, 0)$ (b) $(0, 6)$ (c) $(0, -6)$

(d) $(6, 0)$ (e) None of these

1—M—Answer: b

15. Convert from polar to rectangular coordinates: $\left(-1, -\dfrac{5\pi}{3}\right)$

(a) $\left(\dfrac{1}{2}, \dfrac{\sqrt{3}}{2}\right)$ (b) $\left(-\dfrac{\sqrt{3}}{2}, -\dfrac{1}{2}\right)$ (c) $\left(-\dfrac{1}{2}, -\dfrac{\sqrt{3}}{2}\right)$

(d) $\left(\dfrac{\sqrt{3}}{2}, \dfrac{1}{2}\right)$ (e) None of these

1—M—Answer: c

16. Convert from polar to rectangular coordinates: $(3, -\pi)$

(a) $(3, 0)$ (b) $(-3, 0)$ (c) $(0, 3)$

(d) $(0, -3)$ (e) None of these

1—M—Answer: b

17. Convert from rectangular to polar coordinates: $(-4, 4)$

(a) $\left(4\sqrt{2}, \dfrac{\pi}{4}\right)$ (b) $\left(4\sqrt{2}, \dfrac{3\pi}{4}\right)$ (c) $\left(4\sqrt{2}, -\dfrac{\pi}{4}\right)$

(d) $\left(-4\sqrt{2}, -\dfrac{7\pi}{4}\right)$ (e) None of these

1—M—Answer: b

18. Convert from rectangular to polar coordinates: $(-1, -\sqrt{3})$

(a) $\left(2, -\dfrac{4\pi}{4}\right)$ (b) $\left(-2, \dfrac{\pi}{3}\right)$ (c) $\left(-2, \dfrac{4\pi}{3}\right)$

(d) $\left(-2, -\dfrac{\pi}{3}\right)$ (e) None of these

1—M—Answer: b

19. Convert from rectangular to polar coordinates: $(5\sqrt{2}, -5\sqrt{2})$

(a) $\left(-10, \dfrac{\pi}{4}\right)$ (b) $\left(2\sqrt{5}, \dfrac{7\pi}{4}\right)$ (c) $\left(10, \dfrac{7\pi}{4}\right)$

(d) $\left(10\sqrt{2}, \dfrac{7\pi}{4}\right)$ (e) None of these

1—M—Answer: c

20. Convert from rectangular to polar coordinates: $(0, -4)$

(a) $\left(-4, \dfrac{\pi}{2}\right)$ (b) $\left(-4, \dfrac{3\pi}{2}\right)$ (c) $\left(-4, -\dfrac{\pi}{2}\right)$

(d) $\left(4, -\dfrac{3\pi}{2}\right)$ (e) None of these

1—M—Answer: a

21. Convert from rectangular to polar coordinates: $(-\sqrt{6}, \sqrt{2})$

(a) $\left(8, \dfrac{5\pi}{6}\right)$ (b) $\left(-2\sqrt{2}, \dfrac{\pi}{6}\right)$ (c) $\left(2, -\dfrac{\pi}{6}\right)$

(d) $\left(2\sqrt{2}, \dfrac{17\pi}{6}\right)$ (e) None of these

1—M—Answer: d

22. Change from polar to rectangular coordinates and graph the equation: $r = 2\cos\theta$

1—O—Answer: $x^2 + y^2 - 2x = 0$

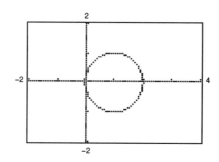

23. Change from polar to rectangular coordinates and graph the equation: $r\sin\theta = -3$

(a) $x + 3 = 0$ (b) $y + 3 = 0$ (c) $y^2 + 3 = 0$

(d) $y - 3 = 0$ (e) None of these

1—M—Answer: b

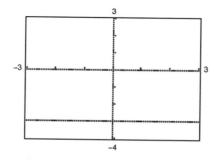

24. Change from polar to rectangular coordinates and graph the equation: $r = 5$

(a) $x + y = 5$ (b) $x^2 + y^2 = 5$ (c) $x^2 + y^2 = 25$

(d) $x + y = 25$ (e) None of these

1—M—Answer: c

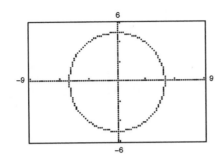

25. Change from polar to rectangular coordinates and graph the equation: $\theta = \dfrac{5\pi}{4}$

(a) $\sqrt{2}y - x = 0$ (b) $y + x = 0$ (c) $y - x = 0$

(d) $\sqrt{2}y + x = 0$ (e) None of these

1—M—Answer: c

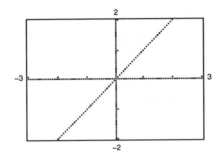

26. Change from polar to rectangular coordinates and graph the equation: $r = 5\cos\theta$

(a) $x^2 + y^2 - 25x = 0$ (b) $x^2 + y^2 - 5x = 0$ (c) $x - 5 = 0$

(d) $x + 5 = 0$ (e) None of these

1—M—Answer: b

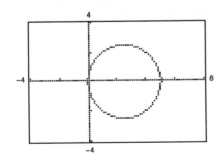

27. Change from polar to rectangular coordinates and graph the equation: $r \sin^2 \theta = 3 \cos \theta$

(a) $y^2 - 3x = 0$ (b) $xy - 3y = 0$ (c) $x^2 + y^2 - 3x = 0$

(d) $x^2 + y^2 - 9x = 0$ (e) None of these

1—M—Answer: a

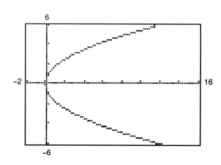

28. Convert from rectangular to polar coordinates: $3x + 2y - 1 = 0$

(a) $r = \dfrac{1}{3 \sin \theta + 2 \cos \theta}$ (b) $r = 3 \cos \theta + 2 \sin \theta - 1$ (c) $r = \dfrac{1}{3 \cos \theta + 2 \sin \theta}$

(d) $r = 3 \sin \theta - 2 \cos \theta - 1$ (e) None of these

1—M—Answer: c

29. Convert from rectangular to polar coordinates: $x^2 + y^2 - 4x + 2y = 0$

(a) $r = 4 \cos \theta - 2 \sin \theta$ (b) $r = 4 \sin \theta - 2 \cos \theta$ (c) $r = \cos^2 2\theta$

(d) $r = \dfrac{4}{1 - 2 \sin \theta}$ (e) None of these

1—M—Answer: a

30. Convert from rectangular to polar coordinates: $(-\sqrt{3},\ -1)$ Give two representations.

1—O—Answer: $\left(2,\ \dfrac{7\pi}{6}\right),\ \left(-2,\ \dfrac{\pi}{6}\right)$

31. Convert from rectangular to polar coordinates: $x^2 + y^2 - 4x + 6y = 0$

1—O—Answer: $r = 4 \cos \theta - 6 \sin \theta$

32. Change from rectangular to polar coordinates: $x^2 + y^2 + 2x + 5y = 0$

(a) $r^2 + 2 \cos \theta + 5 \sin \theta = 0$ (b) $r + 2 \cos \theta + 5 \sin \theta = 0$ (c) $r^2 + 7 = 0$

(d) $2 \cos \theta + 5 \sin \theta + 1 = 0$ (e) None of these

1—M—Answer: b

33. Change from rectangular to polar equation: $x^3 = 4y^2$

(a) $r = 4 \cot^2 \theta \cos \theta$ (b) $r = 4 \cos \theta$ (c) $r = 4 \tan^2 \theta \cos \theta$

(d) $r = 4 \tan^2 \theta \sec \theta$ (e) None of these

1—M—Answer: d

34. The town of Clinton is located 60 miles east and 90 miles south of the town of Clearfield. A small weather station in Clearfield detects on their radar screen a severe thunderstorm centered over Clinton. What polar coordinates would the weather station report the storm to be centered?

1—O—Answer: Rectangular coordinates: $(60, -90)$

Polar coordinates: $r = \sqrt{(60)^2 + (-90)^2} \approx 108.2$ miles

$$\theta = \tan\left(-\tfrac{90}{60}\right) \approx 303.7°$$

$(108.2$ miles, $303.7°)$

35. A polar bear discovers a source of food located 2.0 miles west and 5.0 miles south of the den. Find the polar coordinates of the food source from the den.

1—O—Answer: Rectangular coordinates: $(-2.0, -5.0)$

Polar coordinates: $r = \sqrt{(-2.0)^2 + (-5.0)^2} \approx 5.4$ miles

$$\theta = \tan\left(\frac{-5.0}{-2.0}\right) \approx 248.2°$$

$(5.4$ miles, $248.2°)$

11.3 | Graphs of Polar Equations

1. Determine the type of symmetry: $r = 2\sin\theta$

(a) Symmetric to the line $\theta = \dfrac{\pi}{2}$

(b) Symmetric to the polar axis

(c) Symmetric to the pole

(d) Symmetric to the line $\theta = \dfrac{\pi}{2}$, the polar axis and the pole.

(e) None of these

1—M—Answer: a

2. Determine the type of symmetry: $r = 2$

(a) Symmetric to $\theta = \dfrac{\pi}{2}$

(b) Symmetric to the polar axis

(c) Symmetric to the pole

(d) Symmetric to the line $\theta = \dfrac{\pi}{2}$, the polar axis and the pole

(e) None of these

1—M—Answer: d

3. Determine the type of symmetry: $r = 2 + \sin\theta$

(a) Symmetric to $\theta = \dfrac{\pi}{2}$

(b) Symmetric to the polar axis

(c) Symmetric to the pole

(d) No symmetry

(e) None of these

1—M—Answer: a

4. Determine the type of symmetry: $r = 2\cos 3\theta$

    (a) Symmetric to the line $\theta = \dfrac{\pi}{2}$

    (b) Symmetric to the polar axis

    (c) Symmetric to the pole

    (d) Symmetric to the line $\theta = \dfrac{\pi}{2}$ and the polar axis

    (e) None of these

    1—M—Answer: b

5. Determine the type of symmetry: $r = \sin\left(\theta + \dfrac{\pi}{3}\right)$

    (a) Symmetric to line $\theta = \dfrac{\pi}{2}$

    (b) Symmetric to the polar axis

    (c) Symmetric to the pole

    (d) No symmetry

    (e) None of these

    1—M—Answer: d

6. Determine the type of symmetry: $r = 7\cos 2\theta$

    (a) Symmetric to the line $\theta = \dfrac{\pi}{2}$

    (b) Symmetric to the polar axis

    (c) Symmetric to the pole

    (d) Symmetric to the line $\theta = \dfrac{\pi}{2}$, the polar axis, and the pole.

    (e) None of these

    1—M—Answer: d

7. Determine the type(s) of symmetry of the graph of each of the following:

    (a) $r = 3 + 4\cos\theta$

    (b) $r = \sin 2\theta$

    1—O—Answer: (a) Symmetric to the polar axis.

    (b) Symmetric to the line $\theta = \dfrac{\pi}{2}$, the polar axis, and the pole.

8. Find the values of θ for which $|r|$ is a maximum: $r = \sin 4\theta$

    (a) $0,\ \pi$

    (b) $0,\ \dfrac{\pi}{4},\ \dfrac{\pi}{2},\ \dfrac{3\pi}{4},\ \pi,\ \dfrac{5\pi}{4},\ \dfrac{3\pi}{2},\ \dfrac{7\pi}{4}$

    (c) $\dfrac{\pi}{2},\ \dfrac{3\pi}{2}$

    (d) $\dfrac{\pi}{8},\ \dfrac{3\pi}{8},\ \dfrac{5\pi}{8},\ \dfrac{7\pi}{8},\ \dfrac{9\pi}{8},\ \dfrac{11\pi}{8},\ \dfrac{13\pi}{8},\ \dfrac{15\pi}{8}$

    (e) None of these

    1—M—Answer: d

9. Find the value of θ for which $|r|$ is a maximum: $r = \cos\left(\theta - \frac{\pi}{2}\right)$

   (a) $0, \pi$ (b) $\frac{\pi}{2}, \frac{3\pi}{2}$ (c) 0

   (d) $0, \frac{\pi}{2}, \pi, \frac{3\pi}{2}$ (e) None of these

   1—M—Answer: b

10. Find the values of θ for which $|r|$ is a maximum: $r = 5 - 4\sin\theta$

    (a) $0, \pi$ (b) $\frac{\pi}{2}, \frac{3\pi}{2}$ (c) $\frac{\pi}{2}$

    (d) $\frac{3\pi}{2}$ (e) None of these

    1—M—Answer: d

11. Find the values of θ for which $|r|$ is a maximum: $r = 2 - 4\cos\theta$

    (a) $0, \pi$ (b) $\frac{\pi}{2}, \frac{3\pi}{2}$ (c) π

    (d) $\frac{3\pi}{2}$ (e) None of these

    1—M—Answer: c

12. Find the maximum value of $|r|$: $r = 1 + \sin 2\theta$

    (a) 1   (b) 3   (c) 5   (d) 2   (e) None of these

    1—M—Answer: d

13. Find the maximum value of $|r|$: $r = 15(1 - 2\cos\theta)$

    (a) -15 (b) 15   (c) 30

    (d) 45   (e) None of these

    1—M—Answer: d

14. Find the maximum value of $|r|$: $r = 3(1 + 2\sin\theta)$

    (a) 3   (b) $\frac{3}{2}$ (c) 1   (d) 9   (e) None of these

    1—M—Answer: d

15. Find the maximum value of $|r|$: $r = \frac{3}{5} - \frac{1}{2}\cos\theta$

    (a) $\frac{1}{10}$ (b) $\frac{3}{5}$ (c) $\frac{11}{10}$ (d) $\frac{7}{20}$ (e) None of these

    1—M—Answer: c

16. Find any zeros of r: $r = 8 + 16 \sin \theta$

    (a) $\dfrac{\pi}{6}$ (b) $0, \pi$ (c) $\dfrac{7\pi}{6}, \dfrac{11\pi}{6}$

    (d) $\dfrac{\pi}{2}, \dfrac{3\pi}{2}$ (e) None of these

    1—M—Answer: c

17. Find any zeros of r: $r = 6 \left(\dfrac{1}{2} - \cos \theta \right)$

    (a) $0, \pi$ (b) $\dfrac{\pi}{3}, \dfrac{5\pi}{3}$ (c) $\dfrac{2\pi}{3}, \dfrac{5\pi}{3}$

    (d) $\dfrac{\pi}{3}$ (e) None of these

    1—M—Answer: b

18. Find any zeros of r: $r = 1 + \cos 3\theta$

    (a) π (b) $\dfrac{\pi}{3}, \pi, \dfrac{5\pi}{3}$ (c) $\dfrac{\pi}{6}, \dfrac{\pi}{2}, \dfrac{5\pi}{6}$

    (d) $\dfrac{\pi}{3}$ (e) None of these

    1—M—Answer: b

19. Find any zeros for r: $r = 2 - 4 \sin 2\theta$

    (a) $\dfrac{\pi}{6}, \dfrac{5\pi}{6}$ (b) $0, \dfrac{\pi}{2}, \pi, \dfrac{3\pi}{2}$ (c) $\dfrac{\pi}{4}, \dfrac{3\pi}{4}, \dfrac{5\pi}{4}, \dfrac{7\pi}{4}$

    (d) $\dfrac{\pi}{12}, \dfrac{5\pi}{12}, \dfrac{13\pi}{12}, \dfrac{17\pi}{12}$ (e) None of these

    1—M—Answer: d

20. Find an equation for the graph at the right.

    (a) $r = 4 - 3 \cos \theta$ (b) $r^2 = 9 \cos \theta$

    (c) $r = 2 \cos 3\theta$ (d) $r = 4 + 3 \cos \theta$

    (e) None of these

    1—M—Answer: d

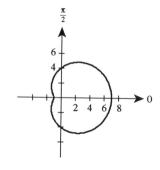

21. Find an equation for the graph at the right.

    (a) $r = 3 \sin 4\theta$ (b) $r^2 = 1 + 4 \sin \theta$

    (c) $r = 3 - 4 \cos \theta$ (d) $r^2 = 4 \cos 3\theta$

    (e) None of these

    1—M—Answer: a

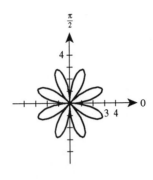

22. Find an equation for the graph at the right.

    (a) $r^2 = 9 \cos 2\theta$ (b) $r = 3 - 3 \sin \theta$

    (c) $r^2 = 3 \cos 2\theta$ (d) $r^2 = 9 \sin 2\theta$

    (e) None of these

    1—M—Answer: d

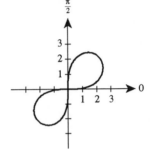

23. Sketch the graph of $r = 5 \sin 2\theta$.

    1—O—Answer:

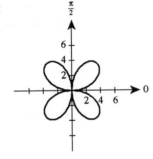

24. Sketch the graph of $r = 1 - 2 \sin \theta$.

    1—O—Answer:

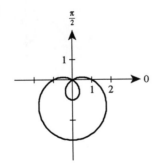

25. Find an equation for the graph at the right.

(a) $r = 5 + 4\sin\theta$ (b) $r = 4 - 5\sin\theta$

(c) $r = 4 + 5\sin\theta$ (d) $r = 5 - 4\sin\theta$

(e) None of these

1—M—Answer: d

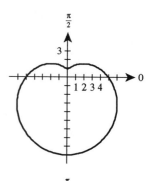

26. Find an equation for the graph at the right.

(a) $r = -5\sin 5\theta$ (b) $r = 5\sin\theta$

(c) $r = -5\sin\theta$ (d) $r = \sin 5\theta$

(e) None of these

1—M—Answer: a

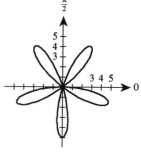

27. Find an equation for the graph at the right.

(a) $r = \frac{1}{3}\csc\theta$ (b) $r = 3\sin\theta$

(c) $r = 3\csc\theta$ (d) $r = \frac{1}{3}\sin\theta$

(e) None of these

1—M—Answer: c

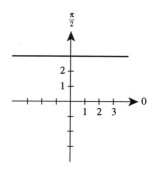

28. Find an equation for the graph at the right.

(a) $r = 2 - 2\sin\theta$ (b) $r = 2(1 - 2\sin\theta)$

(c) $r = 2(1 + 2\sin\theta)$ (d) $r = 2 + 2\sin\theta$

(e) None of these

1—M—Answer: b

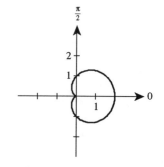

29. Find an equation for the graph at the right.

(a) $r = 1 - \cos\theta$ (b) $r = 1 - \sin\theta$

(c) $r = 1 + \cos\theta$ (d) $r = 1 + \sin\theta$

(e) None of these

1—M—Answer: c

30. Sketch the graph of $r = \sin 8\theta$.

1—O—Answer:

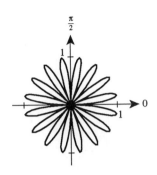

31. Sketch the graph of $r^2 = 4\sin 2\theta$.

1—O—Answer:

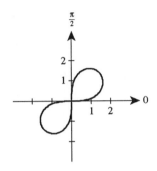

32. Identify the graph: $r = 2 + 3\sin\theta$

(a) Cardioid   (b) Limaçon with inner loop   (c) Dimpled limaçon

(d) Rose curve   (e) None of these

1—M—Answer: b

33. Classify each of the following as a cardioid, limaçon with inner loop, dimpled limaçon or rose curve. (State the number of petals.)

(a) $r = 8\sin 3\theta$ (b) $r = 1 - 2\cos\theta$

(c) $r = 5 + 3\cos\theta$ (d) $r = 2(1 + \sin\theta)$

1—O—Answer: (a) 3 petal rose curve
                      (b) Limaçon with inner loop
                      (c) Dimpled limaçon
                      (d) Cardioid

34. Classify each of the following as a cardioid, limaçon with inner loop, dimpled limaçon, or rose curve. (State the number of petals.)

(a) $r = 3 + 2\cos\theta$ (b) $r = 2\sin 3\theta$

(c) $r = 1 + \sin\theta$ (d) $r = 3\cos 2\theta$

1—O—Answer: (a) Limaçon with one flattened loop
                      (b) 3 petal rose curve
                      (c) Cardioid
                      (d) 4 petal rose curve

35. A speedway built in the shape of a lemniscate with an overpass at the point of intersection has an equation of $r^2 = 9.0 \times 10^6 \cos 2\theta$. Sketch the graph of this equation.

1—O—Answer:

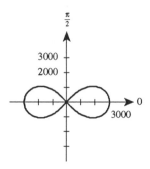

11.4 | Polar Equations of Conics

1. Identify the graph: $r = \dfrac{3}{1 + 2\cos\theta}$

(a) Ellipse   (b) Hyperbola   (c) Parabola

(d) Circle   (e) None of these

1—M—Answer: b

2. Identify the graph: $r = \dfrac{10}{3 - 3\cos\theta}$

(a) Parabola   (b) Ellipse   (c) Hyperbola

(d) Cardioid   (e) None of these

1—M—Answer: a

3. Identify the graph: $r = \dfrac{4}{2 + \cos\theta}$

(a) Ellipse   (b) Parabola   (c) Hyperbola

(d) Circle   (e) None of these

1—M—Answer: a

4. Identify the graph: $r = \dfrac{5}{5 + \frac{1}{5}\cos\theta}$

(a) Ellipse   (b) Parabola   (c) Hyperbola

(d) Circle   (e) None of these

1—M—Answer: a

5. Identify the graph: $r = \dfrac{1}{2 + 2\cos\theta}$

(a) Ellipse (b) Parabola (c) Hyperbola

(d) Circle (e) None of these

1—M—Answer: b

6. Identify and use a graphing utility to sketch the graph of the polar equation: $r = \dfrac{5}{1 - 3\sin\theta}$

(a) Ellipse (b) Parabola (c) Hyperbola

(d) Circle (e) None of these

1—M—Answer: c

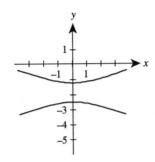

7. Identify and use a graphing utility to sketch the graph of the polar equation: $r = \dfrac{10}{3 + \cos\theta}$

(a) Ellipse (b) Parabola (c) Hyperbola

(d) Circle (e) None of these

1—M—Answer: a

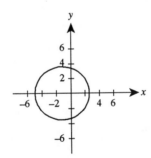

8. Identify and use a graphing utility to sketch the graph of the polar equation: $r = \dfrac{\frac{1}{2}}{\frac{1}{2} + \sin\theta}$

(a) Ellipse (b) Parabola (c) Hyperbola

(d) Circle (e) None of these

1—M—Answer: c

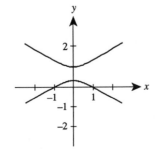

9. Identify and use a graphing utility to sketch the graph of the polar equation: $r = \dfrac{6}{16 - 3\sin\theta}$

   (a) Ellipse   (b) Parabola   (c) Hyperbola

   (d) Circle   (e) None of these

   1—M—Answer: a

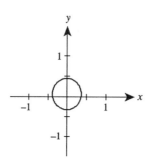

10. Identify and use a graphing utility to sketch the graph of the polar equation: $r = \dfrac{1}{4 - 4\cos\theta}$

    (a) Ellipse   (b) Parabola   (c) Hyperbola

    (d) Circle   (e) None of these

    1—M—Answer: b

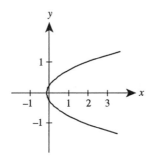

11. Find a polar equation of the parabola with its focus at the pole and directrix $x = 3$.

    (a) $r = \dfrac{3}{1 - \cos\theta}$ (b) $r = \dfrac{3}{1 + 3\cos\theta}$ (c) $r = \dfrac{3}{1 + \cos\theta}$

    (d) $r = \dfrac{3}{1 + \sin\theta}$ (e) None of these

    1—M—Answer: c

12. Find a polar equation of the parabola with its focus at the pole and directrix $y = -\frac{1}{2}$.

    (a) $r = \dfrac{2}{2 - \sin\theta}$ (b) $r = \dfrac{\frac{1}{2}}{1 - \sin\theta}$ (c) $r = \dfrac{2}{2 + \sin\theta}$

    (d) $r = \dfrac{\frac{1}{2}}{1 - \cos\theta}$ (e) None of these

    1—M—Answer: b

13. Find a polar equation of the parabola with its focus at the pole and directrix $x = -7$.

(a) $r = \dfrac{7}{1 + 7\sin\theta}$

(b) $r = \dfrac{7}{1 + \cos\theta}$

(c) $r = \dfrac{7}{1 - \cos\theta}$

(d) $r = \dfrac{7}{1 - 7\cos\theta}$

(e) None of these

1—M—Answer: c

14. Find a polar equation of the parabola whose focus is the pole and whose directrix is the line $y = \frac{3}{8}$.

(a) $r = \dfrac{\frac{3}{8}}{1 + \cos\theta}$

(b) $r = \dfrac{\frac{3}{8}}{1 - \sin\theta}$

(c) $r = \dfrac{\frac{3}{8}}{1 - \cos\theta}$

(d) $r = \dfrac{\frac{3}{8}}{1 + \sin\theta}$

(e) None of these

1—M—Answer: d

15. Find a polar equation of the conic with eccentricity $e = \frac{1}{4}$ with its focus at the pole and directrix $x = 2$.

(a) $r = \dfrac{\frac{1}{2}}{1 + \frac{1}{4}\cos\theta}$

(b) $r = \dfrac{\frac{1}{4}}{1 + \frac{1}{4}\cos\theta}$

(c) $r = \dfrac{\frac{1}{2}}{1 - \frac{1}{4}\cos\theta}$

(d) $r = \dfrac{\frac{1}{2}}{1 + \frac{1}{4}\sin\theta}$

(e) None of these

1—M—Answer: a

16. Find a polar equation of the conic with eccentricity $e = 3$, with its focus at the pole and directrix $y = -9$.

(a) $r = \dfrac{27}{1 - 9\sin\theta}$

(b) $r = \dfrac{27}{1 - 3\sin\theta}$

(c) $r = \dfrac{27}{1 - 27\sin\theta}$

(d) $r = \dfrac{27}{1 + 3\sin\theta}$

(e) None of these

1—M—Answer: b

17. Find a polar equation of the conic with eccentricity $e = \frac{1}{8}$ with its focus at the pole and directrix $x = -16$.

(a) $r = \dfrac{2}{1 - \cos\theta}$

(b) $r = \dfrac{16}{8 - \cos\theta}$

(c) $r = \dfrac{16}{8 + \cos\theta}$

(d) $r = \dfrac{2}{1 - \frac{1}{8}\sin\theta}$

(e) None of these

1—M—Answer: b

18. Find a polar equation of the conic with eccentricity $e = 4$ with focus at the pole and directrix $y = \frac{1}{16}$.

(a) $r = \dfrac{\frac{1}{4}}{1 + \frac{1}{4}\sin\theta}$

(b) $r = \dfrac{\frac{1}{4}}{1 + 4\cos\theta}$

(c) $r = \dfrac{4}{4 + \sin\theta}$

(d) $r = \dfrac{1}{4 + 16\sin\theta}$

(e) None of these

1—M—Answer: d

19. Find a polar equation of a parabola with vertex $\left(2, \dfrac{\pi}{2}\right)$ and focus at the pole.

(a) $r = \dfrac{4}{1 + \sin\theta}$

(b) $r = \dfrac{4}{1 - \sin\theta}$

(c) $r = \dfrac{2}{1 + \sin\theta}$

(d) $r = \dfrac{4}{1 + \cos\theta}$

(e) None of these

1—M—Answer: a

20. Find a polar equation of the parabola with vertex $(3, \pi)$ and focus at the pole.

(a) $r = \dfrac{3}{1 + \cos\theta}$

(b) $r = \dfrac{6}{1 - \cos\theta}$

(c) $r = \dfrac{3}{1 - \cos\theta}$

(d) $r = \dfrac{6}{1 - \sin\theta}$

(e) None of these

1—M—Answer: b

21. Find a polar equation of the parabola with vertex $(-5, 0)$ and focus at the pole.

(a) $r = \dfrac{10}{1 - \cos\theta}$

(b) $r = \dfrac{5}{1 + \cos\theta}$

(c) $r = \dfrac{10}{1 + \cos\theta}$

(d) $r = \dfrac{10}{1 - \sin\theta}$

(e) None of these

1—M—Answer: a

22. Find a polar equation of the ellipse having a focus at the pole and vertices at $\left(3, \dfrac{\pi}{2}\right)$ and $\left(5, -\dfrac{\pi}{2}\right)$.

(a) $r = \dfrac{15}{4 - \cos\theta}$

(b) $r = \dfrac{15}{4 + \cos\theta}$

(c) $r = \dfrac{15}{4 + \sin\theta}$

(d) $r = \dfrac{15}{4 - \sin\theta}$

(e) None of these

2—M—Answer: c

23. Find a polar equation of the ellipse with vertices $(6, 0)$, $(2, \pi)$ and focus at the pole.

(a) $r = \dfrac{3}{1 - \cos\theta}$

(b) $r = \dfrac{3}{1 - \frac{1}{2}\cos\theta}$

(c) $r = \dfrac{6}{1 - \cos\theta}$

(d) $r = \dfrac{6}{1 + \cos\theta}$

(e) None of these

2—M—Answer: b

24. Find a polar equation of the ellipse with vertices $\left(5, \frac{\pi}{2}\right)$, $\left(15, \frac{3\pi}{2}\right)$ and focus at the pole.

(a) $r = \dfrac{\frac{5}{6}}{1 + \frac{1}{2}\sin\theta}$
(b) $r = \dfrac{5}{1 + \frac{1}{2}\sin\theta}$
(c) $r = \dfrac{\frac{15}{2}}{1 + \frac{1}{2}\sin\theta}$

(d) $r = \dfrac{\frac{15}{2}}{1 - \frac{1}{2}\sin\theta}$
(e) None of these

2—M—Answer: c

25. Find a polar equation of the ellipse with vertices $(1, 0)$, $(5, \pi)$ and focus at the pole.

(a) $r = \dfrac{\frac{10}{6}}{1 + \cos\theta}$
(b) $r = \dfrac{10}{6 + 4\cos\theta}$
(c) $r = \dfrac{10}{6 - 4\cos\theta}$

(d) $r = \dfrac{10}{6 + 4\sin\theta}$
(e) None of these

2—M—Answer: b

26. Find a polar equation of the ellipse with vertices $\left(10, \frac{\pi}{2}\right)$, $\left(2, \frac{3\pi}{2}\right)$ and focus at the pole.

(a) $r = \dfrac{\frac{10}{3}}{1 + \frac{2}{3}\sin\theta}$
(b) $r = \dfrac{5}{1 - \sin\theta}$
(c) $r = \dfrac{5}{1 + \sin\theta}$

(d) $r = \dfrac{\frac{10}{3}}{1 - \frac{2}{3}\sin\theta}$
(e) None of these

2—M—Answer: d

27. Find a polar equation of the hyperbola with vertices $(3, 0)$, $(13, 0)$ and focus at the pole.

(a) $r = \dfrac{\frac{39}{5}}{1 + \frac{8}{5}\cos\theta}$
(b) $r = \dfrac{\frac{9}{8}}{1 - \frac{8}{5}\cos\theta}$
(c) $r = \dfrac{\frac{9}{5}}{1 + \frac{8}{5}\cos\theta}$

(d) $r = \dfrac{\frac{9}{8}}{1 - \frac{8}{5}\sin\theta}$
(e) None of these

2—M—Answer: a

28. Find a polar equation of the hyperbola with vertices $\left(2, \frac{3\pi}{2}\right)$, $\left(20, \frac{3\pi}{2}\right)$ and focus at the pole.

(a) $r = \dfrac{4}{9 - 11\sin\theta}$
(b) $r = \dfrac{4}{9 + 11\sin\theta}$
(c) $r = \dfrac{40}{9 + 11\sin\theta}$

(d) $r = \dfrac{40}{9 - 11\sin\theta}$
(e) None of these

2—M—Answer: d

29. Find a polar equation of the hyperbola with vertices $(4, \pi)$, $(6, \pi)$ and focus at the pole.

(a) $r = \dfrac{16}{1 - 5\cos\theta}$

(b) $r = \dfrac{24}{1 - 5\cos\theta}$

(c) $r = \dfrac{24}{1 + 5\cos\theta}$

(d) $r = \dfrac{16}{1 + 5\cos\theta}$

(e) None of these

2—M—Answer: b

30. Find a polar equation of the hyperbola with vertices $\left(6, \dfrac{\pi}{2}\right)$, $\left(-20, \dfrac{3\pi}{2}\right)$ and focus at the pole.

(a) $r = \dfrac{\frac{36}{7}}{1 + \frac{13}{7}\sin\theta}$

(b) $r = \dfrac{\frac{120}{7}}{1 - \frac{13}{7}\sin\theta}$

(c) $r = \dfrac{\frac{36}{7}}{1 - \frac{13}{7}\sin\theta}$

(d) $r = \dfrac{\frac{120}{7}}{1 + \frac{13}{7}\sin\theta}$

(e) None of these

2—M—Answer: d

31. Find a polar equation of the ellipse with vertices at $(1, 0)$, $(7, \pi)$ and focus at $(0, 0)$.

2—O—Answer: $r = \dfrac{7}{4 + 3\cos\theta}$

32. Find a polar equation of the parabola with vertex at $(3, \pi)$ and focus at $(0, 0)$.

2—O—Answer: $r = \dfrac{6}{1 - \cos\theta}$

33. Find a polar equation for the graph at the right.

(a) $r = \dfrac{33}{4 - 7\sin\theta}$

(b) $r = \dfrac{33}{4 + 7\sin\theta}$

(c) $r = \dfrac{33}{7 - 4\sin\theta}$

(d) $r = \dfrac{33}{7 + 4\cos\theta}$

(e) None of these

1—M—Answer: b

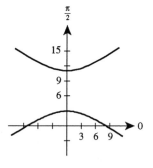

34. Identify the conic, then sketch the graph of the polar equation : $r = \dfrac{4}{1 + \sin\theta}$

1—O—Answer: Parabola

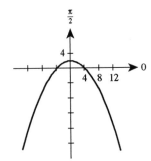

35. Given that $r^2 = \dfrac{-b^2}{1 - e^2 \cos^2 \theta}$ is a polar equation of the hyperbola

$\dfrac{x^2}{a^2} - \dfrac{y^2}{b^2} = 1$, find a polar equation of the hyperbola $\dfrac{x^2}{20} - \dfrac{y^2}{16} = 1$.

(a) $r^2 = \dfrac{-1280}{5 - \cos^2 \theta}$ 　　(b) $r^2 = \dfrac{-2000}{5 - 9 \cos^2 \theta}$ 　　(c) $r^2 = \dfrac{-144}{9 - 5 \cos^2 \theta}$

(d) $r^2 = \dfrac{-80}{5 - 9 \cos^2 \theta}$ 　　(e) None of these

1—M—Answer: d

36. A racetrack is made in the shape of an ellipse. It is 1000 yards long at its longest point. A camera tower is 100 yards from the near end of the track. Find a polar equation of the track using the camera tower as a focus and the pole.

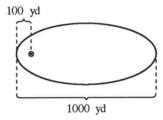

100 yd

1000 yd

2—O—Answer:

Vertices: $(100, \pi)$, $(900, 0)$

$a = 500$

$c = 400$

$e = \dfrac{c}{a} = \dfrac{400}{500} = \dfrac{4}{5}$

$r = \dfrac{ep}{1 - e \cos \theta} \Rightarrow 900 = \dfrac{\frac{4}{5}p}{1 - \frac{4}{5}\cos \theta} \Rightarrow 900 = \dfrac{\frac{4}{5}p}{\frac{1}{5}} \Rightarrow$

$900 = 4p \Rightarrow$

$\dfrac{900}{4} = p \Rightarrow$

$p = 225$

so $r = \dfrac{(225)\left(\frac{4}{5}\right)}{1 - \frac{4}{5}\cos \theta} \Rightarrow r = \dfrac{180}{1 - \frac{4}{5}\cos \theta} \Rightarrow r = \dfrac{900}{5 - 4\cos \theta}$

37. The swimming course for a triathlon includes a turnaround point marked by a stationary buoy. The swimmers must pass between the buoy and the straight shoreline. The swimmers follow a parabolic path past the buoy, which is 80 feet from the shoreline. Find a polar equation to represent the parabolic path so that the swimmers remain equidistant from the buoy and the straight shoreline, using the buoy as the focus.

1—O—Answer: $p = 80$, $e = 1$

$$r = \dfrac{80}{1 - \sin \theta}$$

Test Form A   Name _____   Date _____

Chapter 1   Class _____   Section _____

1. Identify the graph of the equation: $y = \sqrt{4 - x^2}$

(a)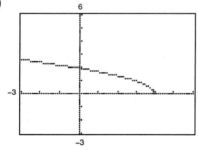

(b)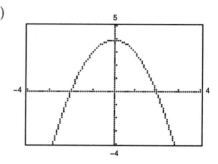

(c)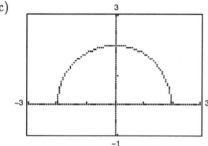

(d)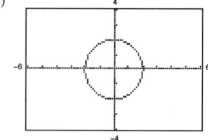

(e) None of these

2. Determine the slope of the line that passes through $(-2,\ 5)$ and $(1,\ -4)$.

   (a) -3 (b) 3 (c) 1 (d) $\frac{1}{3}$ (e) None of these

3. Find an equation of the line that passes through $(4,\ 4)$ with a slope of $\frac{1}{2}$.

   (a) $y = \frac{1}{2}x + 1$ (b) $y = \frac{1}{2}x + 4$ (c) $y = 4x + \frac{1}{2}$
   (d) $y = \frac{1}{2}x + 2$ (e) None of these

4. Find an equation of the line that passes through $(1,\ -1)$ parallel to the line $y = 2x + 10$.

   (a) $y = 2x - 1$ (b) $y = 2x - 3$ (c) $y = -\frac{1}{2}x - \frac{1}{2}$
   (d) $y = -2x + 1$ (e) None of these

5. Given $f(x) = \begin{cases} x - 4, & x \le 0 \\ x^2 + 3, & x > 0 \end{cases}$, find $f(3)$.

   (a) -12 (b) -1 (c) 1 (d) 9 (e) None of these

6. Find the domain of $f(x) = \dfrac{3}{\sqrt{x+5}}$.

(a) $(-\infty, \infty)$ (b) $(-5, \infty)$ (c) $[-5, \infty)$

(d) $(-5, 5)$ (e) None of these

7. Determine which of the following represents y as a function of x.

(a)

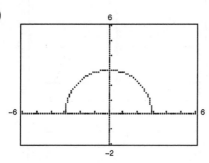

(b)

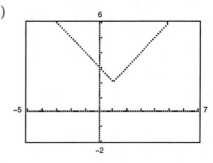

(c)

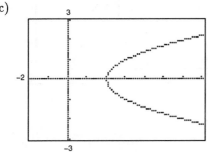

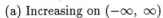

(d) Both **a** and **b**

(e) Both **a** and **c**

8. Determine the open intervals in which the function is increasing, decreasing, or constant.

(a) Increasing on $(-\infty, \infty)$

(b) Decreasing on $(-\infty, \infty)$

(c) Increasing on $(-\infty, 1)$
    Decreasing on $(1, \infty)$

(d) Increasing on $(0, \infty)$
    Decreasing on $(-\infty, 0)$

(e) None of these

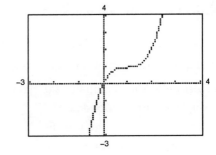

9. Use a graphing utility to graph the function:

$$f(x) = \begin{cases} -2x - 1, & x \le 1 \\ |x + 2| - 6, & x > 1 \end{cases}$$

(a)
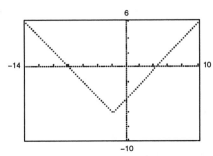

(b)
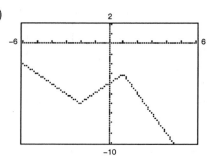

(c)
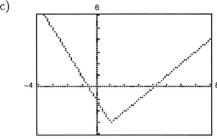

(d)
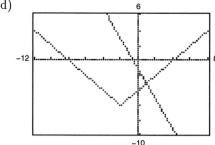

(e) None of these

10. Determine which of the following are odd functions.

(a) $y = x^3 + x^2$ (b) $y = x^5 + 2x^3$ (c) $y = 3x^2 - x$

(d) All of these are odd functions.   (e) None of these are odd functions.

11. Describe the transformation of the graph of $f(x) = |x|$ for the graph of $g(x) = |x - 7| + 8$.

(a) Horizontal shift 7 units to the right   (b) Horizontal shift 8 units to the right
     Vertical shift 8 units down   Vertical shift 7 units down

(c) Horizontal shift 7 units to the left   (d) Horizontal shift 8 units to the left
     Vertical shift 8 units up   Vertical shift 7 units down

(e) None of these

12. Graph $g(x) = -x^2 + 3$ using a transformation of the graph of $f(x) = x^2$.

(a)

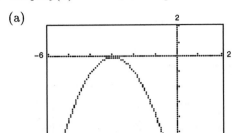

(b)

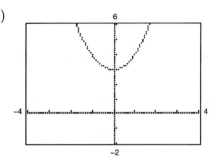

(c)

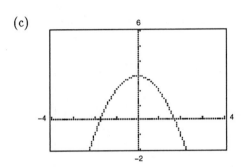

(d)

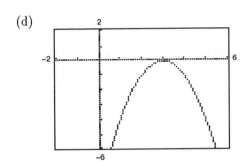

(e) None of these

13. Given $f(x) = 3x - 4$ and $g(x) = 5$, find $(f + g)(x)$.

(a) $15x - 20$ (b) $8x - 4$ (c) $3x + 9$

(d) $3x + 1$ (e) None of these

14. Given $f(x) = 9x$ and $g(x) = 1 - 2x$, find $(fg)(1)$.

(a) -9 (b) 9 (c) 8 (d) 27 (e) None of these

15. Given $f(x) = \sqrt{x}$ and $g(x) = x - 1$, find $(f \circ g)(5)$.

(a) -2 (b) 2 (c) 4 (d) $\sqrt{5} - 1$ (e) None of these

16. Find the inverse of $f(x) = 4x + 6$.

(a) $f^{-1}(x) = 6x + 4$ (b) $f^{-1}(x) = \dfrac{x + 3}{4}$ (c) $f^{-1}(x) = \dfrac{1}{4}x - 6$

(d) $f^{-1}(x) = \dfrac{x - 6}{4}$ (e) None of these

17. Determine which function is one-to-one.

(a) $y = |x| + 1$ (b) $y = (x - 1)^2$ (c) $y = \dfrac{9}{x + 1}$

(d) $y = \sqrt{1 + x^2}$ (e) None of these

18. Given $f(x) = x^2$ and $g(x) = x - 3$, find $(f^{-1} \circ g^{-1})(13)$.

   (a) 4   (b) 46   (c) 2   (d) -4 (e) None of these

19. The population, y, in a certain city between 1980 and 1990 can be modeled by

   $$y = 3x^4 + 5x^3 - 35x^2 + 815x + 7000,$$

   where x is the year with $x = 0$ corresponding to 1980. Use a graphing utility to estimate the population in 1987.

   (a) 5000   (b) 10,000   (c) 15,000
   (d) 20,000   (e) 25,000

20. The perimeter of a rectangle is 20 feet. Find the maximum area of the rectangle.

   (a) 20 ft^2 (b) 25 ft^2 (c) 100 ft^2
   (d) 400 ft^2 (e) None of these

Test Form B   Name _____   Date _____

Chapter 1   Class _____   Section _____

1. Match the equation with the graph.

   (a) $y = |1 + x|$ (b) $y = 1 + x$
   (c) $y = \sqrt{1 + x}$ (d) $y = (1 + x)^2$
   (e) None of these

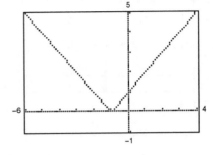

2. What is the slope of the line that passes through the points $(2, -5)$ and $(-4, 1)$?

   (a) 0   (b) 1   (c) -1 (d) $\frac{5}{6}$ (e) None of these

3. Find an equation of the line that passes through the points $(4, -5)$ and $(-6, 0)$.

   (a) $y = \frac{1}{2}x - 7$ (b) $y = \frac{1}{2}x + 3$ (c) $y = -\frac{1}{2}x - 6$
   (d) $y = -\frac{1}{2}x - 3$ (e) None of these

4. Find an equation of the line that passes through $(-2, 1)$ perpendicular to the line $y = -\frac{1}{4}x + 4$.

   (a) $y = 4x + 9$ (b) $y = -4x - 7$ (c) $y = \frac{1}{4}x + \frac{3}{2}$
   (d) $y = -\frac{1}{4}x + \frac{1}{2}$ (e) None of these

5. Given $f(x) = x^3 + 4x^2 - 1$, find $f(-2)$.

   (a) 23   (b) 7   (c) 15   (d) -1 (e) None of these

6. Find the domain of $y = |x^2 - 4|$.

   (a) $(-2, 2)$ (b) $[-2, 2]$ (c) $(-\infty, -2], [2, \infty)$
   (d) $(-\infty, \infty)$ (e) None of these

7. Determine which of the following does not represent y as a function of x.

(a)

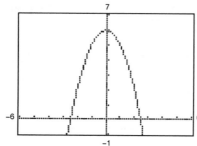

(b)

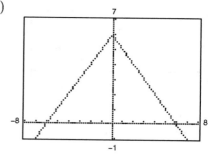

(c)

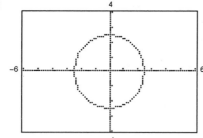

(d) All of these represent y as a function of x.

(e) None of these represent y as a function of x.

8. Determine the open intervals in which the function is increasing, decreasing, or constant.

(a) Increasing on $(-\infty, \infty)$

(b) Increasing on $(-\infty, -2)$
Decreasing on $(-2, \infty)$

(c) Increasing on $(-2, \infty)$
Decreasing on $(-\infty, -2)$

(d) Increasing on $(-\infty, 2)$
Decreasing on $(2, \infty)$

(e) None of these

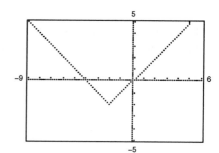

9. Graph the function: $f(x) = [[x]] - 1$

(a)

(b)

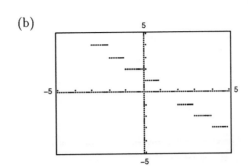

(c)

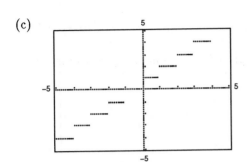

(d)

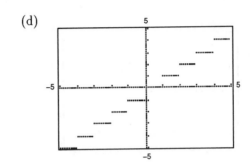

(e) None of these

10. Determine which functions are even.

(a) $f(x) = 10$

(b) $f(x) = x^2 + 9$

(c) $f(x) = x^8 + x^2$

(d) All of these are even.

(e) None of these are even.

11. Describe the transformations of the graph of $f(x) = \sqrt[3]{x}$ for the graph of $g(x) = -\sqrt[3]{x+4}$.

(a) Horizontal shift 4 units to the left
Vertical shift 2 unit down

(b) Horizontal shift 4 units to the left
Reflection in the x -axis

(c) Vertical shift 4 units up
Reflection in the y -axis

(d) Horizontal shift 4 units to the right
Vertical shift 1 unit down

12. Graph: $f(x) = |x + 3| - 3$

(a)

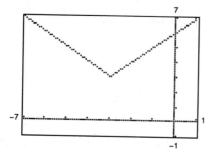

(b)

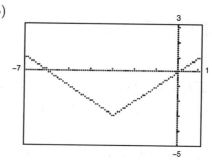

(c)

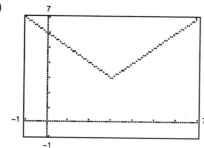

(d)

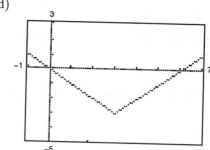

(e) None of these

13. Given $f(x) = x^2$ and $g(x) = x - 9$, find $(f + g)(3)$.

(a) 54   (b) 15   (c) 3   (d) −18   (e) None of these

14. Given $f(x) = x^3 - x$ and $g(x) = \frac{1}{2}x$, find $(f/g)(x)$.

(a) $2(x^2 - 1)$ (b) $\frac{1}{2}(x^2 - 1)$ (c) $\frac{1}{2}x^2(x^2 - 1)$

(d) $\frac{1}{2}x^2$ (e) None of these

15. Given $f(x) = 2x - 7$ and $g(x) = x + 5$, find $(f \circ g)(x)$.

(a) $2x - 3$ (b) $2x^2 - 2$ (c) $2x^2 + 3x - 35$

(d) $2x - 2$ (e) None of these

16. Given $f(x) = (x + 1)^2 - 9$, find $f^{-1}(x)$.

(a) $\sqrt{x - 9} - 1$ (b) $\sqrt{x - 9} + 1$ (c) $\sqrt{x + 9} + 1$

(d) $\sqrt{x + 9} - 1$ (e) None of these

17. Determine which function is not one-to-one.

(a) $y = x^2$ (b) $y = |x|$ (c) $y = \sqrt{x^2 + 4}$

(d) All of these are one-to-one.   (e) None of these are one-to-one.

18. Given $f(x) = x + 8$ and $g(x) = x^2 - 9$, find $(f^{-1} \circ g^{-1})(0)$.

(a) -5 (b) -1 (c) -72 (d) 5 (e) None of these

19. You invest $8000 to start a business. Each unit costs $2.20 and is sold for $6.50. Write the profit, P, as a function of the number of units produced, x.

(a) $P = 4.30x + 8000$ (b) $P = 4.30x - 8000$ (c) $P = 8.70x - 8000$

(d) $P = 8.70x + 8000$ (e) None of these

20. The perimeter of a rectangle is 8 feet. What are the dimensions of the rectangle that yields a maximum area?

(a) 1 ft by 1 ft   (b) 4 ft by 4 ft   (c) 2 ft by 2 ft

(d) 6 ft by 6 ft   (e) None of these

Test Form C   Name _____   Date _____

Chapter 1   Class _____   Section _____

1. Match the equation with the graph.

    (a) $y = (x + 5)^2$ (b) $y = |x - 5|$

    (c) $y = (x - 5)^2$ (d) $y = \sqrt{x - 5}$

    (e) None of these

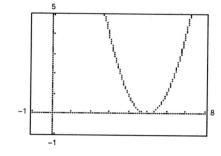

2. Determine the slope of the line that passes through $(1, 2)$ and $(-2, -7)$.

    (a) 3   (b) -3 (c) $-\frac{1}{3}$ (d) $\frac{5}{2}$ (e) None of these

3. Find an equation of the line that passes through $(-3, 3)$ with a slope of $-\frac{1}{3}$.

    (a) $y = -\frac{1}{3}x + 3$ (b) $y = -\frac{1}{3}x - 3$ (c) $y = -\frac{1}{3}x - 2$

    (d) $y = -\frac{1}{3}x + 2$ (e) None of these

4. Find an equation of the line that passes through $(-5, 5)$ perpendicular to the line $y = \frac{1}{2}x + 9$.

    (a) $y = \frac{1}{2}x + \frac{15}{2}$ (b) $y = -2x - 5$ (c) $y = 2x + 15$

    (d) $y = -\frac{1}{2}x + \frac{5}{2}$ (e) None of these

5. Given $f(x) = \begin{cases} 2x^2 + 3, & x < -3 \\ x - 9, & x \geq -3 \end{cases}$, find $f(-2)$.

    (a) 11   (b) -11 (c) -7 (d) -5 (e) None of these

6. Find the domain of $f(x) = \dfrac{1}{x + 4}$.

    (a) All real numbers   (b) All real numbers $x \neq 4$

    (c) All real numbers $x \neq -4$ (d) All real numbers $x > -4$

    (e) None of these

7. Determine which of the following represents y as a function of x.

(a)

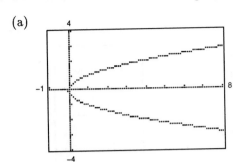

(b)

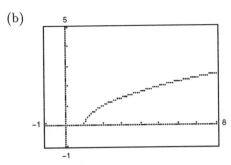

(d) Both **a** and **b**

(c)

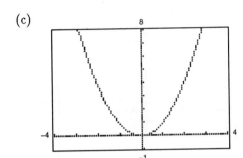

(e) Both **b** and **c**

8. Approximate any relative minimum or relative maximum of $f(x) = 3x^2 - x + 4$.

(a) Relative minimum at $(0.17, 3.92)$

(b) Relative maximum at $(0.17, 3.92)$

(c) Relative minimum at $(0, 4)$

(d) Relative maximum at $(0, 4)$

(e) None of these

9. Graph the function: $f(x) = \begin{cases} \frac{1}{2}x^2 - 1, & x \le 0 \\ 2x - 1, & x > 0 \end{cases}$

(a)

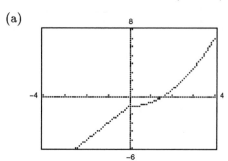

(b)

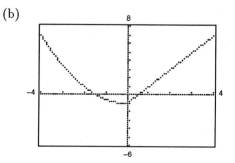

(c)

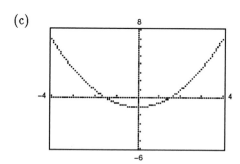

(d)

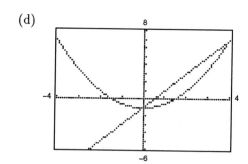

(e) None of these

10. Determine which functions are odd.

(a) $y = 10$ (b) $y = x + 4$ (c) $y = x^3 + x$

(d) Both **b** and **c**   (e) **a**, **b**, and **c**

11. Write an equation of the function.

(a) $y = \sqrt{x+1} - 2$ (b) $y = \sqrt{x-1} + 2$

(c) $y = \sqrt{x-1} - 2$ (d) $y = \sqrt{x+1} + 2$

(e) None of these

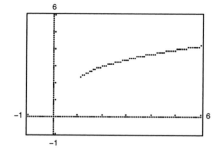

12. Graph: $y = (x + 1)^3 + 1$

(a)

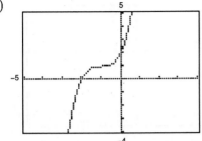

(b)

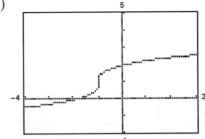

(c)

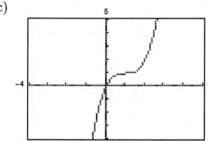

(d)

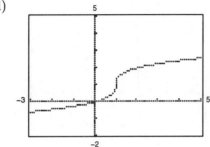

(e) None of these

13. Given $f(x) = x^3 - 1$ and $g(x) = x - 4$, find $(f - g)(x)$.

(a) $x^3 + x - 5$ (b) $x^3 - x - 5$ (c) $x^2 + 3$

(d) $x^3 - x + 3$ (e) None of these

14. Given $f(x) = x - 3$ and $g(x) = 2$, graph $(f/g)(x)$.

(a)

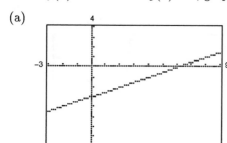

(b)

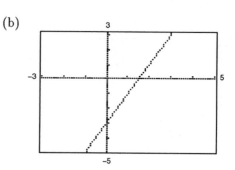

(c)

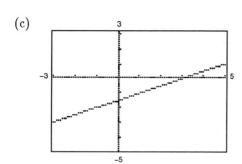

(d)

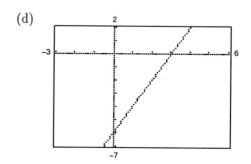

(e) None of these

15. Given $f(x) = \sqrt{x + 10}$ and $g(x) = 4 - x$, find $(f \circ g)(-2)$.

(a) 4   (b) −4   (c) $6\sqrt{2}$

(d) $12\sqrt{2}$ (e) None of these

16. Find the inverse of $f(x) = \dfrac{x - 3}{5}$.

(a) $f^{-1}(x) = \dfrac{5}{x - 3}$ (b) $f^{-1}(x) = 5x + 3$ (c) $f^{-1}(x) = 5(x + 3)$

(d) $f^{-1}(x) = \dfrac{5}{x} + 3$ (e) None of these

17. Determine which function is one-to-one.

(a) $y = 4 + x^2$ (b) $y = |4 + x|$ (c) $y = \sqrt{4 + x^2}$

(d) $y = \sqrt{4 + x}$ (e) None of these

18. Given $f(x) = 3x + 6$ and $g(x) = \dfrac{1}{2}x$, find $(f^{-1} \circ g^{-1})(x)$.

(a) $\dfrac{2x + 6}{6}$

(b) $\dfrac{3x - 6}{2}$

(c) $\dfrac{2x - 6}{3}$

(d) $\dfrac{2x - 3}{6}$

(e) None of these

19. In 1980, enrollment at a certain college was 940 students. In 1990, the enrollment was 2200 students. Write a linear equation giving the enrollment, y, in terms of the year, x. Let $x = 0$ represent 1980.

(a) $y = 126x + 940$

(b) $y = 1260x - 320$

(c) $y = 940x + 2200$

(d) $y = 126x + 2200$

(e) None of these

20. Determine the interval(s) on the real axis for which $f(x) \geq 0$ for $f(x) = (x - 9)^3 + 8$.

(a) $[9, \infty)$

(b) $[7, \infty)$

(c) $[1, \infty)$

(d) $[16, \infty)$

(e) None of these

Test Form D

Chapter 1

Name _____ Date _____

Class _____ Section _____

1. Graph: $2x^2 + y^2 = 8$

2. Find the slope of the line that passes through the points $(2, 1)$ and $(-3, 16)$.

3. Find an equation of the line that passes through the points $(-4, 1)$ and $(0, 3)$.

4. Describe the behavior of the line that passes through the points $(1, 3)$ and $(-9, 3)$.

5. Find an equation of the line that passes through the point $(6, 7)$ parallel to the line $2x - y = 14$.

6. Does $9x^2 - y = 5$ represent y as a function of x?

7. Given $f(x) = x^2 + x$, find $\dfrac{f(x + \Delta x) - f(x)}{\Delta x}$.

8. Given $f(x) = \begin{cases} x - 14, & x \le -9 \\ 2x^2, & x > -9 \end{cases}$, find $f(-11)$.

9. Find the range of the function shown at the right.

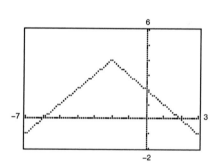

10. The perimeter of a rectangle is 60 feet. Find the maximum area of the rectangle.

11. Graph $y = [[x - 3]]$.

12. Is $f(x) = x^5 + x - 2$ even, odd, or neither?

13. Describe the transformation of the graph of $f(x) = \sqrt[3]{x}$ for the graph of $g(x) = \sqrt[3]{x + 1} - 7$.

14. Graph $y = -(x - 2)^2$.

15. Given $f(x) = x^2 - 4$ and $g(x) = 3x + 1$, find $(f + g)(x)$.

16. Given $f(x) = -x^2$ and $g(x) = \sqrt{-x+1}$, find $(f \circ g)(x)$.

17. Given $f(x) = x - 4$ and $g(x) = 2x + 2$, graph $(f \circ g)(x)$.

18. Find the inverse of $f(x) = \sqrt{x} - 5$.

19. Does the graph represent y as a one-to-one function of x?

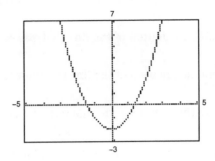

20. Given $f(x) = x - 9$ and $g(x) = 3x$, find $(f^{-1} \circ g^{-1})(-3)$.

Test Form E

Name _____ Date _____

Chapter 1

Class _____ Section _____

1. Graph $3x^2 + 2y^2 = 6$.

2. Find the slope of the line that passes through $(-4, -4)$ and $(8, 5)$.

3. Find an equation of the line that passes through the point $(5, 1)$ with a slope of 2.

4. Find an equation of the line that passes through the point $(-6, 1)$ perpendicular to the line $y = 2x + 1$.

5. Does the graph shown at the right represent y as a function of x?

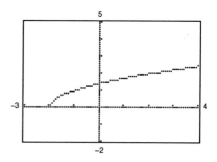

6. Given $f(x) = x^3 - 5x - 1$, find $f(2)$.

7. Given $f(x) = \begin{cases} -(x-1)^2, & x \le 1 \\ \sqrt{x-1}, & x > 1 \end{cases}$, find $f(10)$.

8. Find the domain of $f(x) = \dfrac{2x}{\sqrt{9+x^2}}$.

9. Approximate any relative minimum or relative maximum of $f(x) = \frac{2}{3}x^3 - 8x$.

10. Graph: $f(x) = \begin{cases} -(x+2)^2 + 1, & x \le 0 \\ (x-4)^2 - 19, & x > 0 \end{cases}$

11. Find the domain of $y = [[x - 3]]$.

12. Is the function shown at the right even, odd, or neither?

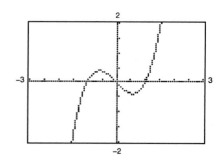

13. Determine the intervals on the real axis for which $f(x) \geq 0$ for $f(x) = \sqrt{16 - x}$.

14. Find an equation for the function shown at the right.

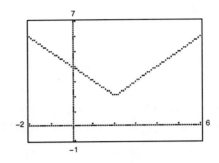

15. Given $f(x) = x^2 - 1$ and $g(x) = x$, find $(fg)(2)$.

16. Given $f(x) = x$ and $g(x) = -x + 3$, graph $(f + g)(x)$.

17. Given $f(x) = \sqrt{x} - 7$ and $g(x) = (x + 1)^2$, find $(f \circ g)(6)$.

18. Find the inverse of $f(x) = \dfrac{4}{x + 1}$.

19. Is the function $f(x) = \dfrac{2}{x}$ one-to-one?

20. Given $f(x) = x - 4$ and $g(x) = x + 4$, find $(f^{-1} \circ g^{-1})(x)$.

Test Form A   Name _____ Date _____

Chapter 2   Class _____ Section _____

1. Is $3x + 4(x - 2) = 10x$ a conditional equation or an identity?

   (a) Conditional   (b) Identity   (c) Neither   (d) Both

2. Eleanor invests $18,000 in two funds paying $9\frac{1}{4}\%$ and $10\frac{1}{2}\%$ simple interest. How much is invested at $9\frac{1}{4}\%$ if the total yearly interest is $1827.50?

   (a) $1300   (b) $5000   (c) $8000   (d) $10,000   (e) None of these

3. 29 is what percent of 37?

   (a) 7.8%   (b) 78.4%   (c) 12.76%   (d) 127.6%   (e) None of these

4. Complete the square in the denominator: $\dfrac{3}{4x^2 + 10x - 7}$

   (a) $\dfrac{3}{4[x + \frac{5}{4}]^2 - \frac{53}{4}}$

   (b) $\dfrac{3}{4[x + \frac{5}{2}]^2 - 32}$

   (c) $\dfrac{3}{4[x + \frac{5}{4}]^2 - \frac{3}{4}}$

   (d) $\dfrac{3}{4[x + \frac{5}{2}]^2 + 18}$

   (e) None of these

5. Use the discriminant to determine the number of real solutions: $4x^2 - 2x - 7 = 0$

   (a) 0   (b) 1   (c) 2   (d) 3   (e) None of these

6. Two airplanes leave simultaneously from the same airport, one flying due east, and the other flying due north. The eastbound plane is flying 20 miles per hour slower than the northbound one. If after 3 hours they are 1128 miles apart, how fast is the northbound plane traveling?

   (a) 178 mph   (b) 198 mph   (c) 256 mph
   (d) 276 mph   (e) None of these

7. Find the domain of $\sqrt{x^2 - 7x - 8}$.

   (a) $(-\infty, -1] \cup [8, \infty)$ (b) $(-\infty, -1) \cup (8, \infty)$ (c) $[-1, 8]$
   (d) $(-1, 8)$ (e) None of these

In Problems 8–15, solve for x.

8. $8x - 2 = 13 - 2x$

   (a) $\frac{2}{3}$ (b) $\frac{3}{2}$ (c) $\frac{11}{6}$ (d) $-\frac{2}{3}$ (e) None of these

9. $3x^2 = 4x + 2$

   (a) $\frac{-2 \pm \sqrt{10}}{6}$ (b) $2 \pm \sqrt{10}$ (c) $4 \pm 2\sqrt{10}$

   (d) $\frac{2 \pm \sqrt{10}}{3}$ (e) None of these

10. $2x^2 = 162$

    (a) 9 (b) -9 (c) $-9, 9$ (d) 81 (e) None of these

11. $5x^2 - 2 = 3x$

    (a) $\frac{2}{5}, -1$ (b) $-\frac{1}{5}, 2$ (c) $-\frac{2}{5}, 1$ (d) $\frac{1}{5}, -2$ (e) None of these

12. $|3x + 10| = 13$

    (a) 1 (b) $1, -1$ (c) $1, -\frac{23}{3}$ (d) $1, \frac{23}{3}$ (e) None of these

13. $x^3 + 2x^2 + 2x + 4 = 0$

    (a) -2 (b) ± 2 (c) $\pm 2, \pm \sqrt{2}$ (d) $-2, -\sqrt{2}$ (e) None of these

14. $\sqrt{15x + 4} = 4 - \sqrt{2x + 3}$

    (a) 3 (b) $\frac{11}{169}$ (c) $3, \frac{11}{169}$ (d) $-3, -\frac{11}{169}$ (e) None of these

15. $\dfrac{3x + 25}{x + 7} - 5 = \dfrac{3}{x}$

    (a) $\frac{3}{2}, 7$ (b) $\frac{7}{2}, 3$ (c) $-\frac{3}{2}, -7$ (d) $-\frac{7}{2}, -3$ (e) None of these

16. Use a graphing utility to approximate the solution(s) of $x^3 + 3x^2 - 4x + 9 = 0$.

   (a) -4.38 (b) 0.05 (c) -2.52 (d) No solution   (e) None of these

17. Solve for P: $A = P + PRT$

   (a) $A - PRT$ (b) $A - RT$ (c) $\dfrac{A}{RT}$ (d) $\dfrac{A}{1 + RT}$ (e) None of these

18. Graph the solution: $3 - 2x < 15$

   (a)

   (b)

   (c)

   (d)

   (e) None of these

19. Graph the solution: $|3x - 1| \geq 5$

   (a)

   (b)

   (c)

   (d)

   (e) None of these

20. Solve for x: $\dfrac{x + 16}{3x + 2} \leq 5$

   (a) $\left(-\infty, -\dfrac{2}{3}\right] \cup \left[\dfrac{3}{7}, \infty\right)$ (b) $\left[-\dfrac{2}{3}, \dfrac{3}{7}\right]$ (c) $\left(-\infty, -\dfrac{2}{3}\right) \cup \left[\dfrac{3}{7}, \infty\right)$

   (d) $\left(-\dfrac{2}{3}, \dfrac{3}{7}\right]$ (e) None of these

Test Form B   Name _____   Date _____

Chapter 2   Class _____   Section _____

1. The formula to find the volume of a cone is $V = \dfrac{\pi}{3}r^2h$. Solve this formula for h.

   (a) $\dfrac{V}{3\pi r^2}$ (b) $\dfrac{\pi r^2 V}{3}$ (c) $\dfrac{\pi r^2}{3V}$ (d) $\dfrac{3V}{\pi r^2}$ (e) None of these

2. 460 is what percent of 340?

   (a) 74%   (b) 0.74%   (c) 1.35%   (d) 135.3%   (e) None of these

3. Maria inherited $15,000. She decided to invest it in two funds, one paying $9\frac{1}{4}\%$ simple interest, the other paying $11\frac{1}{2}\%$ simple interest. Her annual income from these investments will total $1623.75. How much did she invest in the fund that pays $9\frac{1}{4}\%$ simple interest?

   (a) $4500   (b) $10,500   (c) $488   (d) $14,512   (e) None of these

In Problems 4–12, solve for x.

4. $|2 - 4x| = 12$

   (a) $-\frac{5}{2}, \frac{7}{2}$ (b) $-\frac{5}{2}, -\frac{7}{2}$ (c) $\frac{5}{2}, -\frac{5}{2}$ (d) $-\frac{5}{2}$ (e) None of these

5. $4x - 7(3x + 6) = 4x - 9$

   (a) $\frac{7}{11}$ (b) $-\frac{11}{7}$ (c) $-\frac{33}{13}$ (d) $-\frac{17}{7}$ (e) None of these

6. $\dfrac{7x}{x-2} + \dfrac{2x}{x+2} = 9$

   (a) $-\dfrac{18}{5}$ (b) $\dfrac{2}{3}$ (c) $-\dfrac{2}{5}$ (d) $\dfrac{5}{18}$ (e) None of these

7. $2x^2 + 4x = 9x + 18$

   (a) $-2, \frac{9}{2}$ (b) $2, -\frac{9}{2}$ (c) $\frac{9}{2}$ (d) $-\frac{9}{2}$ (e) None of these

8. $x^2 - 2x - 10 = 0$

   (a) $-5, 2$ (b) $-2, 5$ (c) $1 \pm \sqrt{11}$

   (d) $2 \pm 4\sqrt{11}$ (e) None of these

9. $(x + 2)^2 = -16x$

   (a) $-8 \pm 2\sqrt{15}$ (b) $-10 \pm 4\sqrt{6}$ (c) $-10 \pm 2\sqrt{26}$

   (d) $-8 \pm 4\sqrt{15}$ (e) None of these

10. $3x^3 - 27x = 0$

(a) 3   (b) $-3, 3$ (c) $-3, 0, 3$ (d) $0, 3$ (e) None of these

11. $\sqrt{2 - 5x} = 5x$

(a) $\frac{1}{5}$ (b) $-\frac{2}{5}$ (c) $\frac{1}{5}, -\frac{2}{5}$ (d) $\frac{1}{10}$ (e) None of these

12. $(x^2 + 4)^{2/3} = 25$

(a) $-5.8, 5.8$ (b) $-4.6, 4.6$ (c) 21   (d) $-11, 11$ (e) None of these

13. Use a graphing utility to approximate the solution(s) of $2x^3 - 3x^2 + 9x - 3$.

(a) -1.91 (b) 0.37 (c) 3.43 (d) No solution   (e) None of these

14. Complete the square: $2x^2 + 9x - 4$

(a) $2\left(x + \frac{9}{4}\right)^2 - \frac{113}{8}$ (b) $2\left(x + \frac{9}{4}\right)^2 - \frac{145}{16}$ (c) $2\left(x + \frac{9}{4}\right)^2 + \frac{49}{8}$

(d) $2\left(x + \frac{9}{4}\right)^2 + \frac{17}{16}$ (e) None of these

15. Use the discriminant to determine the number of real solutions: $7x^2 - 3x + 15 = 0$

(a) 0   (b) 1   (c) 2   (d) 3   (e) None of these

16. Two trains traveling the same speed leave the city. The southbound train reaches its destination in 45 minutes. The eastbound train reaches its destination in 1 hour. How fast were the trains traveling if their destinations are 88 miles apart?

(a) 70.4 mph   (b) 1.2 mph   (c) 2 mph

(d) 49.6 mph   (e) None of these

17. Graph the solution: $-6 < 7x + 2 \le 5$

(a)

(b)

(c)

(d)

(e) None of these

18. Graph the solution: $|x + 2| < 9$

(a)

(b)

(c)

(d)

(e) None of these

19. Find the domain of $\sqrt{169 - 9x^2}$.

(a) $\left(-\frac{13}{3}, \frac{13}{3}\right)$ (b) $\left[-\frac{13}{3}, \frac{13}{3}\right]$ (c) $\left(-\infty, -\frac{13}{3}\right] \cup \left[\frac{13}{3}, \infty\right)$

(d) $\left(-\infty, -\frac{13}{3}\right) \cup \left(\frac{13}{3}, \infty\right)$ (e) None of these

20. Solve for x: $\dfrac{4}{x + 1} \le \dfrac{3}{x + 2}$

(a) $(-\infty, -5] \cup (-2, -1)$ (b) $(-5, -2) \cup [-1, \infty)$ (c) $(-\infty, -5) \cup (-2, -1)$

(d) $(-5, -2] \cup [-1, \infty)$ (e) None of these

Test Form C Name _____ Date _____

Chapter 2 Class _____ Section _____

1. Identify the Quadratic Formula.

   (a) $x = -b \pm \dfrac{\sqrt{b^2 - 4ac}}{2a}$

   (b) $x = \dfrac{-b \pm \sqrt{b^2 - 4a}}{2c}$

   (c) $x = \dfrac{-b \pm \sqrt{b^2 - 4ac}}{2a}$

   (d) $x = \dfrac{-b \pm \sqrt{b^2 - 4ac}}{2}$

   (e) None of these

2. Is the statement $3(x^2 + 2) = 5x - 9$ a conditional equation or an identity?

   (a) Conditional   (b) Identity   (c) Neither   (d) Both

3. Two brothers, Bob and Bill, live 450 miles apart. Starting at the same time they plan to drive until they meet. Bill averages 10 miles per hour faster than Bob who averages 50 mph. How long will it take them to meet?

   (a) $3\frac{2}{15}$ hours

   (b) $3\frac{9}{11}$ hours

   (c) $4\frac{1}{11}$ hours

   (d) $4\frac{1}{2}$ hours

   (e) None of these

4. Use the discriminant to determine the number of real solutions: $\frac{1}{3}x^2 - 2x + 5 = 0$

   (a) 0   (b) 1   (c) 2   (d) 3   (e) None of these

5. Complete the square: $3x^2 - 2x + 1$

   (a) $(3x - 1)^2$

   (b) $3(x - 1)^2 + 1$

   (c) $3\left(x - \dfrac{1}{3}\right)^2 + \dfrac{1}{9}$

   (d) $3\left(x - \dfrac{1}{3}\right)^2 + \dfrac{2}{3}$

   (e) None of these

6. An open box is to be constructed from a square piece of material by cutting a 3-inch square from each corner. Find the dimensions of the square piece of material if the box is to have a volume of 363 cubic inches.

   (a) 14″ by 14″

   (b) 17″ by 17″

   (c) 20″ by 20″

   (d) 23″ by 23″

   (e) None of these

7. Solve for h: $A = \dfrac{1}{2}(a + b)h$

   (a) $\dfrac{A}{2(a + b)}$

   (b) $\dfrac{2A}{a + b}$

   (c) $2A(a + b)$

   (d) $A - \dfrac{1}{2}(a + b)$

   (e) None of these

8. Use a graphing utility to solve the equation $x^4 + 3x^2 - 6x + 3 = 0$.

(a) 0.79   (b) 0.52   (c) 1.93

(d) No solution   (e) None of these

In Problems 9–19, solve for x.

9. $13x - 9 = 3x + 10$

(a) $\frac{19}{10}$ (b) $\frac{10}{19}$ (c) $\frac{1}{10}$ (d) $\frac{19}{16}$ (e) None of these

10. $3 - \dfrac{4x + 5}{x - 2} = \dfrac{7x - 9}{x - 2}$

(a) $-\frac{1}{4}$ (b) -1 (c) 1 (d) No solution   (e) None of these

11. $3x^2 = x + 14$

(a) $-7, \dfrac{2}{3}$ (b) $\dfrac{7}{3}, -2$ (c) $\dfrac{x + 14}{3x}$

(d) $-\dfrac{1}{6} \pm \dfrac{\sqrt{167}}{6}$ (e) None of these

12. $8x^2 = 2x + 3$

(a) $-\frac{1}{2}$ (b) $-\frac{3}{4}, \frac{1}{2}$ (c) $\frac{3}{4}$ (d) $\frac{1}{2}, \frac{3}{4}$ (e) None of these

13. $3x^3 - 24x^2 + 21x = 0$

(a) $7, 1$ (b) $-7, -1$ (c) $0, 1, 7$

(d) $0, -1, -7$ (e) None of these

14. $\sqrt{x + 16} = 3 + \sqrt{x - 2}$

(a) 3 (b) $\frac{17}{4}$ (c) $\frac{1}{2}$ (d) No solution   (e) None of these

15. $(x^2 - 9x + 2)^{3/2} = 216$

(a) $-\dfrac{1}{2}, 9$ (b) $\dfrac{3}{2}, \dfrac{15}{2}$ (c) $\dfrac{9}{2} \pm \dfrac{\sqrt{217}}{2}$

(d) $9 \pm \dfrac{\sqrt{217}}{2}$ (e) None of these

16. $3x - 2\sqrt{x} - 5 = 0$

(a) $\frac{5}{3}$ (b) $-1, \frac{5}{3}$ (c) $1, \frac{25}{9}$ (d) $\frac{25}{9}$ (e) None of these

17. $14 - 2x \leq 5$

    (a) $(-\infty, \frac{9}{2})$ (b) $(-\infty, \frac{9}{2}]$ (c) $(\frac{9}{2}, \infty)$

    (d) $[\frac{9}{2}, \infty)$ (e) None of these

18. $|3x - 1| > 2$

    (a) $(-\frac{1}{3}, 1)$ (b) $[-\frac{1}{3}, 1]$ (c) $(-\infty, -\frac{1}{3}) \cup (1, \infty)$

    (d) $(-\infty, -\frac{1}{3}] \cup [1, \infty)$ (e) None of these

19. $\dfrac{x + 7}{3x - 1} < 1$

    (a) $\left(\frac{1}{3}, 4\right)$ (b) $\left[\frac{1}{3}, 4\right]$ (c) $\left(-\infty, \frac{1}{3}\right) \cup (4, \infty)$

    (d) $\left(-\infty, \frac{1}{3}\right] \cup [4, \infty)$ (e) None of these

20. Jan has \$2.80 in quarters and nickels. If there are 20 coins in all, how many quarters does Jan have?

    (a) 12   (b) 11   (c) 10   (d) 9   (e) None of these

Test Form D   Name _____   Date _____

Chapter 2   Class _____   Section _____

1. Solve for x: $5(3x - 2) + 5x - 7 = 16 + 2x$

2. Solve by completing the square: $2x^2 - 7x - 12 = 0$

3. Solve for x: $3x^2 + 19x - 14 = 0$

4. Use the Quadratic Formula to solve for x: $5x^2 - 2x - 6 = 0$

5. Solve for p: $g = \dfrac{4\pi^2 p}{r^2}$

6. What is 0.17% of 432?

7. Complete the square: $2x^2 - 6x + 9$

8. Use the discriminant to determine the number of real solutions: $10x = x^2 - 14x + 50$

9. Solve for x: $x^{2/3} - 6x^{1/3} = 7$

10. Graph the solution of the inequality: $\frac{1}{2} < 3 - x < 5$

11. Graph the solution of the inequality: $|x + 5| \leq 2$

12. Solve the inequality: $\dfrac{3x - 7}{x + 2} < 1$

13. Find two consecutive positive integers m and n such that $n^2 - m^2 = 27$.

14. Ann invested $8000 in a fund that pays $2\frac{1}{2}$% more simple interest per year than a similar fund in which her husband had invested $10,000. At the end of a year their interest totaled $1690. What rate of interest did Ann receive?

15. Solve for x: $\dfrac{14}{3x-1} + \dfrac{6x}{3x+7} = 2$

16. Solve for x: $7(x+2)^2 = 12$

17. Solve for x: $20x^3 - 500x = 0$

18. Approximate the solutions of $-2x^4 + 3x^3 - x + 4 = 0$.

19. Use absolute values to define the interval: $-7 \le x \le 7$

20. Find the domain of $\sqrt{36 - x^2}$.

Test Form E   Name _____   Date _____

Chapter 2   Class _____   Section _____

1. Solve for x: $3x + 5 = \sqrt{2 - 2x}$

2. Is the equation $3x + 2 = 9x^2 - 1$ conditional or an identity?

3. Solve for x: $\dfrac{3x}{5} + x = \dfrac{2}{3}$

4. The formula to find the volume of a cone is $V = \dfrac{\pi}{3}r^2h$. Solve for h.

5. 35 is what percent of 748?

6. A 15-quart radiator contains a 40% concentration of antifreeze. How much of the solution must be drained and replaced by 100% antifreeze to bring the solution up to 70%?

7. Solve for x: $2x^2 + x = 3$

8. Solve by completing the square: $x^2 - 8x + 2 = 0$

9. Solve for x: $(x + 7)^2 = 5$

10. Approximate the solutions of $x^4 + 2x^3 - x^2 - 9 = 0$.

11. The Curriers have decided to fence in part of their back yard to form a rectangular region with an area of 1248 square feet. The fence will extend 2 feet on each side of their 48-foot-wide house. How many feet of fencing will they need to enclose the play area? (There is no fence along the house wall.)

12. Use the Quadratic Formula to solve for x: $2x^2 - 4x - 3 = 0$

13. Use the discriminant to determine the number of real solutions: $5x^2 - 7x + 16 = 0$

14. Solve for x: $7x^3 = 252x$

15. Solve for x: $\sqrt[3]{4x-1}=3$

16. Solve for x: $2x^4-7x^2+5=0$

17. Solve for x: $\sqrt{x+1}=9-\sqrt{x}$

18. Solve the inequality $-16 \leq 7-2x < 5$, then sketch the solution on the real number line.

19. Solve the inequality $|3x-1| > 9$, then sketch the solution on the real number line.

20. Find the domain: $\sqrt{16-4x^2}$

Test Form A   Name _____   Date _____

Chapter 3   Class _____   Section _____

1. Identify the correct quadratic function for the graph at the right.

   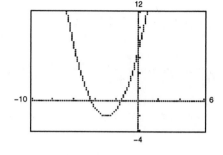

   (a) $y = (x - 3)^2 + 2$ (b) $y = (x - 3)^2 - 2$

   (c) $y = (x + 3)^2 + 2$ (d) $y = (x + 3)^2 - 2$

   (e) None of these

2. Find the vertex of the parabola: $y = x^2 - 8x + 2$

   (a) $(4, -18)$ (b) $(4, -14)$ (c) $(8, 66)$

   (d) $(4, 18)$ (e) None of these

3. Find the x-intercept(s) of the quadratic function: $f(x) = x^2 - 3x - 4$

   (a) -4 (b) $4, -1$ (c) $-4, -1, 4$

   (d) $2, -2$ (e) None of these

4. The perimeter of a rectangle is 108 feet. Find the width of the rectangle that would yield a maximum area.

   (a) 27 feet   (b) 36 feet   (c) 54 feet

   (d) 18 feet   (e) None of these

5. Determine the right and left behavior of the function: $f(x) = -x^5 + 2x^2 - 1$

   (a) Up to the left, down to the right.
   (b) Down to the left, up to the right.
   (c) Up to the left, up to the right.
   (d) Down to the left, down to the right.
   (e) None of these

6. Find all of the real zeros of the function: $f(x) = 3x^4 - 27x^3 + 54x^2$

   (a) 0, 3, 9, 2   (b) 0, 6, 3   (c) 0, 9, 2

   (d) 0, 6   (e) None of these

7. Find a polynomial that has the zeros 0, 3, and -4.

   (a) $x^3 + 3x^2 - 4x$ (b) $x^3 - x^2 - 6x$ (c) $x^3 + x^2 - 12x$

   (d) $x^3 - x^2 - 12x$ (e) None of these

8. Determine the function shown at the right.

   (a) $f(x) = x^4 + 1$ (b) $f(x) = x^3 + 1$

   (c) $f(x) = -x^4 + 1$ (d) $f(x) = -x^3 + 1$

   (e) None of these

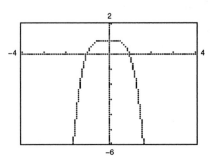

9. Divide: $(6x^3 + 7x^2 - 15x + 6) \div (2x - 1)$

   (a) $3x^2 + 2x - \dfrac{17}{2} - \dfrac{5}{2(2x-1)}$ (b) $3x^2 + 5x - 5 + \dfrac{1}{2x-1}$

   (c) $3x^2 + 5x + 5 + \dfrac{11}{2x-1}$ (d) $3x^2 + 4x - 17 + \dfrac{29/2}{2x-1}$

   (e) None of these

10. Use synthetic division to perform the following division: $(5x^4 - 2x^2 + 1) \div (x + 1)$

   (a) $5x^3 - 5x^2 + 3x - 3 + \dfrac{4}{x+1}$ (b) $5x^2 - 7x + 8$

   (c) $5x^2 + 3x + 4$ (d) $5x^3 + 5x^2 + 3x + 3 + \dfrac{4}{x+1}$

   (e) None of these

11. Given $f(x) = 4x^3 + 3x + 10$, find $f(-2)$.

   (a) 20   (b) -20 (c) 36   (d) -28 (e) None of these

12. Use Descartes's Rule of Signs to determine the possible number of positive and negative zeros:

   $f(x) = 5x^4 - 3x^3 - 4x + 2$

   (a) 2 positive, 2 negative   (b) 2 or 0 positive, 0 negative   (c) 4 positive, 0 negative

   (d) 0 positive, 4 negative   (e) None of these

13. Find all of the real zeros of the function: $f(x) = x^3 - \frac{11}{3}x^2 + \frac{5}{3}x + 1$

    (a) $-\frac{1}{3}$, 1, 3   (b) 3, ± 1 (c) 1, ± 3

    (d) 3, $1 \pm \sqrt{2}$ (e) None of these

14. Write in standard form: $2i - \sqrt{-25} + 2$

    (a) $2 + 7i$ (b) $7 + 2i$ (c) $2 - 3i$

    (d) $2 + 3i$ (e) None of these

15. Simplify: $(5 - 3i) - (6 - i)$

    (a) $-1 - 2i$ (b) $11 - 4i$ (c) $-1 - 4i$

    (d) $-1 + 2i$ (e) None of these

16. Solve: $3x^2 + 48 = 0$

    (a) ± 4 (b) $\pm 4i$ (c) ± 4, $\pm 4i$

    (d) $\pm 16i$ (e) None of these

17. Which point is plotted at the right?

    (a) $-3 + 4i$ (b) $3 - 4i$

    (c) $-4 + 3i$ (d) $4 - 3i$

    (e) None of these

18. Write $f(x) = x^4 - 5x^3 + 8x^2 - 20x + 16$ as a product of linear factors.

    (a) $(x + 2)(x - 2)(x - 4)(x - 1)$ (b) $(x + 4)(x + 1)(x - 2i)(x + 2i)$

    (c) $(x - 4)(x - 1)(x + 2i)(x - 2i)$ (d) $(x + 4)(x + 1)(x + 2i)(x + 2i)$

    (e) None of these

19. Use synthetic division to determine which of the following are zeros of the function

    $f(x) = x^4 + x^3 - x^2 + 5x - 30$.

    (a) $\sqrt{5}\,i$ (b) 2   (c) -3 (d) All of these   (e) None of these

20. Find a polynomial with real coefficients that has the following zeros: 0, 3, -3, i, and $-i$.

    (a) $f(x) = x^5 - 8x^3 - 9x$ (b) $f(x) = x^5 - 10x^3 + 9x$

    (c) $f(x) = x^3 - 4x^2 + 3$ (d) $f(x) = x^5 - 9x$

    (e) None of these

Test Form B   Name 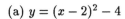 _____ Date _____

Chapter 3   Class _____ Section _____

1. Identify the correct quadratic function for the graph at the
   right.

   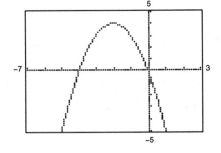

   (a) $y = (x - 2)^2 - 4$ (b) $y = -(x + 2)^2 + 4$

   (c) $y = -(x + 2)^2$ (d) $y = -(x - 2)^2 + 4$

   (e) None of these

2. Find the vertex of the parabola: $y = x^2 - 6x + 10$

   (a) $(-3,\ 1)$ (b) $(3,\ -1)$ (c) $(-3,\ 10)$

   (d) $(3,\ 1)$ (e) None of these

3. Find the quadratic function that has a maximum point at $(-1,\ 17)$ and passes through the point $(7,\ 1)$.

   (a) $y = \frac{1}{4}(-x^2 - 2x + 16)$ (b) $y = -\frac{1}{4}(x + 1)^2 + 17$

   (c) $y = (x - 7)^2 + 1$ (d) $y = (x - 1)^2 + 17$

   (e) None of these

4. The perimeter of a rectangle is 46 inches. Find the width of the rectangle that would yield a maximum
   area.

   (a) 4 inches   (b) 23 inches   (c) $11\frac{1}{2}$ inches

   (d) 9 inches   (e) None of these

5. Determine the right and left behavior of the graph of the function: $f(x) = 3x^5 - 7x^2 + 2$

   (a) Down to the left, up to the right   (b) Up to the left, down to the right

   (c) Up to the left, up to the right   (d) Down to the left, down to the right

   (e) None of these

6. Find all of the real zeros of the function: $f(x) = 6x^4 + 32x^3 - 70x^2$

   (a) $0,\ -1,\ 5$ (b) $0,\ -7,\ \frac{5}{3}$ (c) $\frac{7}{3},\ 5$

   (d) $0,\ -1,\ -7,\ \frac{5}{3}$ (e) None of these

7. Find a polynomial that has the zeros 0, −6, and 2.

    (a) $f(x) = x^3 - 6x - 2$ (b) $f(x) = x^3 - 4x^2 - 12x$ (c) $f(x) = x^3 - 2x - 6$

    (d) $f(x) = x^3 + 4x^2 - 12x$ (e) None of these

8. Determine the function shown at the right.

    (a) $f(x) = x^5 + 3$ (b) $f(x) = -x^5 + 3$

    (c) $f(x) = x^4 + 3$ (d) $f(x) = -x^4 - 3$

    (e) None of these

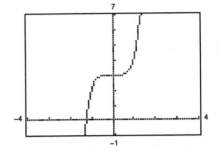

9. Divide: $(2x^4 + 3x^3 + x + 4) \div (x^2 - 2)$

    (a) $2x^2 - 3x - 2 + \dfrac{4x - 1}{x^2 - 2}$ (b) $2x^2 + 3x - 2 + \dfrac{2x + 2}{x^2 - 2}$

    (c) $2x^2 + 3x + 4 + \dfrac{7x + 12}{x^2 - 2}$ (d) $2x^2 - 3x + 4 + \dfrac{2x - 1}{x^2 - 2}$

    (e) None of these

10. Use synthetic division to divide: $(5x^4 + 2x^3 - x + 4) \div (x + 1)$

    (a) $5x^3 - 3x^2 + 3x - 4$ (b) $5x^3 - 3x^2 + 3x - 4 + \dfrac{8}{x + 1}$

    (c) $5x^3 - 3x^2 + 2x + 2$ (d) $5x^3 - 3x + 2 + \dfrac{2}{x + 1}$

    (e) None of these

11. Use synthetic division to find $f(-3)$ for $f(x) = 3x^3 + 2x^2 - 5x + 2$.

    (a) −46   (b) 86   (c) −4   (d) 20   (e) None of these

12. List the possible rational zeros of the function: $f(x) = 2x^4 + 3x^2 - 2x - 6$.

    (a) $\pm\frac{1}{6}$, $\pm\frac{1}{3}$, $\pm\frac{1}{2}$, ±1, ±2, ±3, ±6 (b) ±1, ±2, ±3, ±6

    (c) $\pm\frac{1}{6}$, $\pm\frac{1}{2}$, ±1, $\pm\frac{3}{2}$, ±2, ±3, ±6 (d) $\pm\frac{1}{2}$, ±1, $\pm\frac{3}{2}$, ±2, ±3, ±6

    (e) None of these

13. Find all the real solutions of $x^3 - x^2 - 10x - 8 = 0$.

    (a) −1, 2, 4   (b) −2, −1, 4   (c) −4, −2, 1

    (d) −4, 1, 2   (e) None of these

14. Write in standard form: $\sqrt{-4} - 2i + 6$

    (a) $6 - 4i$ (b) $8 - 2i$ (c) 6

    (d) $4 - 2i$ (e) None of these

15. Divide, then write the result in standard form: $\dfrac{6 + 10i}{2i}$

    (a) $\dfrac{3}{i} + 5$ (b) $5 - 3i$ (c) $5 + 3i$

    (d) $3 + 5i$ (e) None of these

16. Solve: $x^4 + 16x^2 - 225 = 0$

    (a) $\pm 3,\ \pm 5i$ (b) $\pm 5i$ (c) $\pm 4,\ \pm 5$

    (d) $\pm 4,\ \pm 5i$ (e) None of these

17. Which point is plotted at the right?

    (a) $1 - 3i$ (b) $1 + 3i$

    (c) $-3 + i$ (d) $3 - i$

    (e) None of these

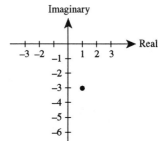

18. Write as a product of linear factors: $x^4 + 25x^2 + 144$

    (a) $(x^2 + 9)(x^2 + 16)$ (b) $(x + 3i)(x + 3i)(x + 4i)(x + 4i)$

    (c) $(x + 3i)(x - 3i)(x + 4i)(x - 4i)$ (d) $(x - 3i)(x - 3i)(x - 4i)(x - 4i)$

    (e) None of these

19. Find a polynomial with real coefficients that has the following zeros: $0,\ 2,\ -2,\ 2i,\ -2i$

    (a) $f(x) = x^5 + 16x$ (b) $f(x) = x^4 + 16$ (c) $f(x) = x^4 - 16$

    (d) $f(x) = x^5 - 16x$ (e) None of these

20. Which of the following are zeros of the function $f(x) = x^3 + 4x^2 - 9x - 36$?

    (a) $\sqrt{3}i$ (b) $-\sqrt{3}i$ (c) 4 (d) All of these   (e) None of these

Test Form C   Name _____   Date _____

Chapter 3   Class _____   Section _____

1. Identify the correct quadratic function for the graph at the right.

   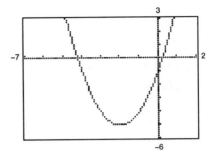

   (a) $y = (x - 2)^2 - 5$ (b) $y = -(x - 2)^2 - 1$

   (c) $y = (x + 2)^2 - 5$ (d) $y = (x + 2)^2 - 1$

   (e) None of these

2. Find the vertex of the parabola: $y = 4x^2 + 4x + 10$

   (a) $\left(-\frac{1}{2},\ 9\right)$ (b) $\left(\frac{1}{2},\ 9\right)$ (c) $(1,\ 10)$

   (d) $(-1,\ 10)$ (e) None of these

3. Find the intercepts of the function: $f(x) = x^2 + 3x - 10$

   (a) $(0,\ -10)$ (b) $(-10,\ 0),\ (0,\ -5),\ (0,\ 2)$

   (c) $(-5,\ 0),\ (2,\ 0),\ (0,\ -10)$ (d) $(-2,\ 0),\ (5,\ 0),\ (0,\ -10)$

   (e) None of these

4. The perimeter of the rectangle is 256 inches. Find the width of the rectangle that would yield a maximum area.

   (a) 16 inches   (b) 64 inches   (c) 128 inches

   (d) 32 inches   (e) None of these

5. Identify the right and left behavior of the graph of $y = 4x^2 - 2x + 1$.

   (a) Up to the left, down to the right.
   (b) Down to the left, up to the right.
   (c) Up to the left, up to the right.
   (d) Down to the left, down to the right.
   (e) None of these

6. Find all the real zeros of the function: $f(x) = x^4 + 10x^3 + 24x^2$

   (a) 0, 4, 6   (b) 0, 3, 8   (c) −8, −3, 0

   (d) −6, −4, 0   (e) None of these

7. Find a polynomial that has the zeros 0, −1, and −5.

(a) $f(x) = x^3 + 6x^2 + 5x$ (b) $f(x) = x^3 - 6x^2 + 5x$ (c) $f(x) = x^3 - x - 5$

(d) $f(x) = x^3 - 4x + 5x$ (e) None of these

8. Determine the function shown at the right.

(a) $f(x) = -(x - 3)^2$ (b) $f(x) = x^3 + 3$

(c) $f(x) = -x^4 + 3$ (d) $f(x) = -x^3 + 3$

(e) None of these

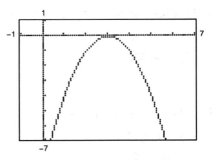

9. Divide: $(3x^4 + 2x^3 - 3x + 1) \div (x^2 + 1)$

(a) $3x^2 + 2x + 3 - \dfrac{5x + 2}{x^2 + 1}$ (b) $3x^2 + 2x - 3 + \dfrac{-5x + 4}{x^2 + 1}$

(c) $3x^2 - x^2 + x - 4 + \dfrac{5}{x^2 + 1}$ (d) $3x^2 - x + 1 + \dfrac{-4x + 5}{x^2 + 1}$

(e) None of these

10. Use synthetic division to divide: $(3x^4 + 4x^3 - 2x^2 + 1) \div (x + 2)$

(a) $3x^3 + 10x^2 + 18x + 37$ (b) $3x^3 - 2x^2 + 2x - 3$

(c) $3x^3 - 2x^2 + 2x - 4 + \dfrac{9}{x + 2}$ (d) $3x^3 + 10x^2 + 18x + 36 + \dfrac{73}{x + 2}$

(e) None of these

11. Use synthetic division to find $f(8)$ for $f(x) = x^4 - 7x^3 - 4x^2 - 6x - 1$.

(a) 7471   (b) 1079   (c) −418

(d) 207   (e) None of these

12. List the possible rational zeros of the function: $f(x) = 3x^5 + 2x^2 - 3x + 2$

(a) $\pm 3, \pm 2, \pm \frac{3}{2}, \pm 1, \pm \frac{2}{3}$ (b) $\pm 3, \pm \frac{1}{3}, \pm 2, \pm \frac{1}{2}, \pm 1$

(c) $\pm 2, \pm 1, \pm \frac{2}{3}, \pm \frac{1}{3}$ (d) $\pm 3, \pm 1, \pm \frac{3}{2}, \pm \frac{1}{2}$

(e) None of these

13. Find all the real solutions of $x^3 - 6x^2 + 5x + 12 = 0$.

(a) −1, 3, 4   (b) −3, 1, 4   (c) −3, −1, 4

(d) −4, −3, 1   (e) None of these

14. Write in standard form: $\sqrt{-8} + \sqrt{2}i - 4$

    (a) $-4 - \sqrt{10}i$ (b) $-4 + 3\sqrt{2}i$ (c) $(-4 + \sqrt{2}) + \sqrt{2}i$

    (d) $-4 - \sqrt{2}i$ (e) None of these

15. Multiply, then express your answer in standard form: $(3 + 7i)(6 - 2i)$

    (a) $18 + 22i$ (b) $4 + 48i$ (c) $4 + 36i$

    (d) $32 + 36i$ (e) None of these

16. Solve: $x^4 + 6x^2 + 8 = 0$

    (a) $\pm\sqrt{2}i, \pm 2$ (b) ± 2 (c) $\pm\sqrt{2}, \pm 2$

    (d) $-4, -2$ (e) None of these

17. Which point is plotted at the right?

    (a) $3 - i$ (b) $1 - i$

    (c) $-1 + i$ (d) $-3 - i$

    (e) None of these

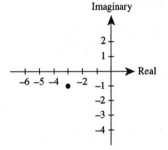

18. Write $f(x) = x^4 - 3x^2 - 28$ as a product of linear factors.

    (a) $(x^2 + 4)(x^2 - 7)$ (b) $(x - 2i)(x + 2i)(x - \sqrt{7})(x + \sqrt{7})$

    (c) $(x + 2i)(x + 2i)(x + \sqrt{7})(x - \sqrt{7})$ (d) $(x - 2i)(x - 2i)(x - \sqrt{7})(x + \sqrt{7})$

    (e) None of these

19. Find a polynomial with real coefficients that has the following zeros: $3, \pm 3i$

    (a) $f(x) = x^3 + 3x^2 + 9x + 27$ (b) $f(x) = x^3 + 6x^2 - 27$

    (c) $f(x) = x^3 + 12x^2 + 27$ (d) $f(x) = x^3 - 3x^2 + 9x - 27$

    (e) None of these

20. Which of the following are zeros of the function $f(x) = x^3 + 3x^2 + x + 3$?

    (a) 3   (b) $-i$ (c) $2i$ (d) All of these   (e) None of these

Test Form D   Name _____   Date _____

Chapter 3   Class _____   Section _____

1. Write the standard form of the equation of the parabola shown in the graph at the right.

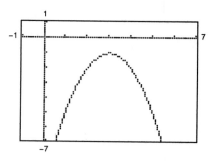

2. Find the vertex of the parabola: $f(x) = (x + 5)^2 - 4$

3. Find the quadratic function whose maximum point is $(-1,\ 2)$ and passes through the point $(0,\ 1)$.

4. Determine the left and right behavior of the function: $f(x) = -4x^3 + 3x^2 - 1$

5. Find all the real zeros of the function: $f(x) = 2x^3 + 14x^2 + 24x$

6. Use the following data table to estimate the zero (to the nearest tenth) of the function in the interval $[0,\ 1]$:

    $f(x) = x^5 + x - 1$

x	0.0	0.1	0.2	0.3	0.4
y	-1.0	-0.90	-0.80	-0.70	-0.59

x	0.5	0.6	0.7	0.8	0.9	1.0
y	-0.47	-0.32	-0.13	0.13	0.49	1.0

7. Perform the following division: $(6x^4 - 4x^3 + x^2 + 10x - 1) \div (3x + 1)$

8. Find a function that has the given zeros: $0,\ \pm1,\ 6$

9. Determine the function for the given graph.

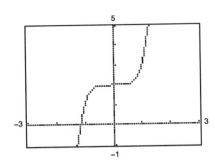

10. List the possible rational zeros: $f(x) = 3x^5 - 2x^3 + 3x - 5$

11. Find the rational zeros: $f(x) = x^3 - \frac{4}{3}x^2 - \frac{5}{3}x + \frac{2}{3}$

12. Use Descartes's Rule of Signs to determine the possible number of positive and negative zeros:

$f(x) = x^3 + 2x - 1$

13. Write $x^4 - 16$ as a product of linear factors.

14. Simplify, then write your result in standard form: $3(2 - \sqrt{-9}) + 2i(4i - 7)$

15. Use the Quadratic Formula to solve for x: $5x^2 - 2x + 6 = 0$

16. Use the fact that $3i$ is a zero of f to find all the zeros of the function:

$f(x) = x^4 - 6x^3 + 14x^2 - 54x + 45$

17. Use the Bisection Method to approximate the zero of $f(x) = x^3 + 4x + 2$ in the interval $[-1, \ 0]$. (Use an accuracy of ± 0.001.)

Test Form E   Name _____   Date _____

Chapter 3   Class _____   Section _____

1. Sketch the graph of the function: $f(x) = (x - 2)^2 + 6$

2. Write in standard (parabolic) form: $f(x) = -x^2 + 3x - 2$

3. Find the quadratic function whose graph opens upward and has x-intercepts at $(0, 0)$ and $(6, 0)$.

4. Use the leading coefficient test to determine the left and right behavior of the graph of:
$$f(x) = 3x^4 + 2x^3 + 7x^2 + x - 1$$

5. Find a fourth degree polynomial function that has 1, -1, 0, and 2 as zeros.

6. Sketch the graph of the function $f(x) = -(x - 3)^3$.

7. Use synthetic division to find $f(-3)$: $f(x) = 3x^3 + 2x^2 - 1$

8. Divide: $(2x^4 + 7x - 2) \div (x^2 + 3)$

9. Given $r = i$ is a zero, find the remaining zeros: $f(x) = x^4 - 5x^3 + 7x^2 - 5x + 6$

10. List the possible rational zeros: $f(x) = 3x^5 + 7x^3 - 3x^2 + 2$

11. Find the rational zeros: $f(x) = x^3 - \dfrac{9}{2}x^2 + \dfrac{11}{2}x - \dfrac{3}{2}$

12. Given $f(x) = 3x^3 + 4x - 1$, determine if $x = -2$ is an upper bound for the zeros of f, a lower bound for the zeros of f, or neither.

13. Find all real zeros: $f(x) = x^4 - 7x^2 + 12$

14. Write $f(x) = x^4 - 100$ as a product of linear factors.

15. Find all solutions: $x^4 - 5x^3 + 7x^2 - 5x + 6 = 0$

16. Approximate the zero of the function $f(x) = x^3 + x + 3$ in the interval $[-2, \ -1]$. (Use an accuracy of ± 0.001.)

17. Divide, then write the result in standard form: $\dfrac{2 + 3i}{1 - i}$

Test Form A   Name _____   Date _____

Chapter 4   Class _____   Section _____

1. Identify the vertical asymptote of the graph of $f(x) = \dfrac{7}{x+2}$.

   (a) $x = -2$ (b) $x = 2$ (c) $(0, -2)$

   (d) $y = 0$ (e) None of these

2. Identify the horizontal or slant asymptote(s) of $f(x) = \dfrac{3x^2 + 2x - 1}{x - 1}$.

   (a) $x = 1$ (b) $x = -1, \; x = \dfrac{1}{3}$ (c) $y = 3x + 5$

   (d) $y = 3$ (e) None of these

3. Match the rational function with the correct graph: $f(x) = \dfrac{3 + x}{x - 1}$

   (a)   (b)

   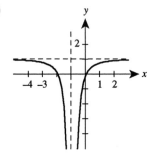   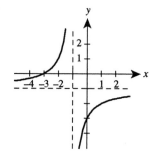

   (c)   (d)

   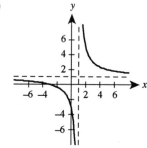   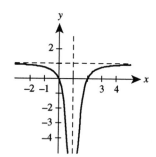

   (e) None of these

4. Find the partial fraction decomposition: $\dfrac{9x^2 + x - 1}{x^2(x + 1)}$

(a) $\dfrac{2}{x} - \dfrac{1}{x^2} + \dfrac{7}{x + 1}$

(b) $\dfrac{20}{x} - \dfrac{1}{x^2} - \dfrac{11}{x + 1}$

(c) $\dfrac{9}{x} + \dfrac{1}{x^2} - \dfrac{1}{x + 1}$

(d) $\dfrac{-1}{x^2} + \dfrac{9}{x + 1}$

(e) None of these

5. Find the partial fraction decomposition: $\dfrac{x^2 - 4x + 1}{(x - 3)(x^2 + 1)}$

(a) $\dfrac{-1/5}{x - 3} + \dfrac{2}{x + 1} + \dfrac{4/5}{x + 1}$

(b) $\dfrac{1}{x - 3} + \dfrac{-4x + 1}{x^2 + 1}$

(c) $\dfrac{1}{x - 3} - \dfrac{4}{x + 1} + \dfrac{1}{x + 1}$

(d) $\dfrac{-1/5}{x - 3} + \dfrac{(6/5)x - (2/5)}{x^2 + 1}$

(e) None of these

6. Match the graph at the right with the correct equation.

(a) $\dfrac{x^2}{16} - \dfrac{y^2}{4} = 1$

(b) $\dfrac{x^2}{4} - \dfrac{y^2}{16} = 1$

(c) $\dfrac{y^2}{16} - \dfrac{x^2}{4} = 1$

(d) $\dfrac{y^2}{4} - \dfrac{x^2}{16} = 1$

(e) None of these

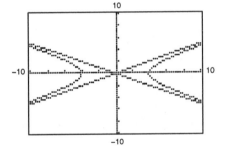

7. What is the equation of the parabola with vertex $(0, 0)$ and focus $(-3, 0)$?

(a) $x^2 = -12y$

(b) $y^2 = -12x$

(c) $x^2 = 12y$

(d) $y^2 = 12x$

(e) None of these

8. Find the foci of the ellipse: $\dfrac{x^2}{9} + \dfrac{y^2}{5} = 1$

(a) $(-2, 0)$, $(2, 0)$

(b) $(0, -2)$, $(0, 2)$

(c) $(-4, 0)$, $(4, 0)$

(d) $(0, -4)$, $(0, 4)$

(e) None of these

9. Find the center of the ellipse: $9x^2 + 4y^2 - 36x - 24y - 36 = 0$

(a) $(2, 3)$

(b) $(3, -2)$

(c) $(2\sqrt{3}, 3\sqrt{3})$

(d) $(6, 48)$

(e) None of these

10. Find the standard form of the equation of a parabola with a vertical axis, the vertex at $(7, -3)$ and passes through the point $(11, 1)$.

    (a) $(y + 3)^2 = \frac{1}{8}(x - 7)$ (b) $(y + 3)^2 = 4(x - 7)$ (c) $(x - 7)^2 = 16(y + 3)$

    (d) $(x - 7)^2 = 4(y + 3)$ (e) None of these

11. Identify the graph of $3x^2 + 6x - 4y + 12 = 0$.

    (a) Circle   (b) Hyperbola   (c) Ellipse

    (d) Parabola   (e) None of these

12. Find the vertices of the hyperbola given by $\dfrac{(x - 2)^2}{9} - \dfrac{(y + 7)^2}{12} = 1$.

    (a) $(5, -7)$, $(-1, -7)$ (b) $(2, -4)$, $(2, -10)$ (c) $(-2, 10)$, $(-2, 4)$

    (d) $(1, 7)$, $(-5, 7)$ (e) None of these

Test Form B　　　　　　　Name _____　Date _____

Chapter 4　　　　　　　　Class _____　Section _____

1. Match the graph at the right with the correct equation.

    (a) $f(x) = \dfrac{1}{2x+1}$　　　　　(b) $f(x) = \dfrac{x-1}{2x+1}$

    (c) $f(x) = \dfrac{x^2+2x+2}{2x-1}$　　(d) $f(x) = \dfrac{x^3+2x^2+x-2}{2x+1}$

    (e) None of these

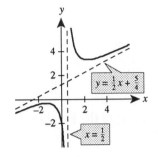

2. Find the x-intercept: $f(x) = \dfrac{2x-1}{x^2+2}$

    (a) $-\sqrt{2}$　　　　　　　　(b) $\dfrac{1}{2}$　　　　　　　　(c) $-\sqrt{2}, \dfrac{1}{2}$

    (d) $\sqrt{2}$　　　　　　　　(e) None of these

3. Find the horizontal asymptote of the graph of $f(x) = \dfrac{7}{x-4}$.

    (a) $x = 4$　　　　　　　(b) $y = 7$　　　　　　　(c) $y = 0$

    (d) $x = 0$　　　　　　　(e) None of these

4. Find the partial fraction decomposition: $\dfrac{-9}{(x+1)^2(x-2)}$

    (a) $\dfrac{1}{x+1} + \dfrac{3}{(x+1)^2} - \dfrac{1}{x-2}$　　　　(b) $\dfrac{10}{x+1} - \dfrac{4}{(x+1)^2} - \dfrac{15}{x-2}$

    (c) $\dfrac{2}{x+1} - \dfrac{1}{(x+1)^2} - \dfrac{1}{x-2}$　　　　(d) $\dfrac{1}{x+1} - \dfrac{3}{(x+1)^2} + \dfrac{5}{x-2}$

    (e) None of these

5. Find the partial fraction decomposition: $\dfrac{-x^2-7x+27}{x(x^2+9)}$

    (a) $\dfrac{3}{x} + \dfrac{4}{x+3} - \dfrac{7}{x^2+9}$　　　　(b) $\dfrac{3}{x} - \dfrac{4x+7}{x^2+9}$

    (c) $\dfrac{2}{x} + \dfrac{3x+5}{x^2+9}$　　　　　　　(d) $\dfrac{2}{x} + \dfrac{3}{x+3} - \dfrac{5}{x^2+9}$

    (e) None of these

6. Match the graph at the right with the correct equation.

(a) $\dfrac{x^2}{9} + \dfrac{y^2}{25} = 1$ (b) $\dfrac{x^2}{25} + \dfrac{y^2}{9} = 1$

(c) $\dfrac{x^2}{9} - \dfrac{y^2}{25} = 1$ (d) $\dfrac{y^2}{25} - \dfrac{x^2}{9} = 1$

(e) None of these

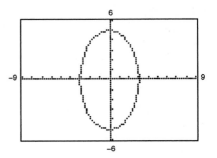

7. Find the focus of the parabola: $y^2 = -32x$

(a) $(8,\ 0)$ (b) $(-8,\ 0)$ (c) $(0,\ 8)$

(d) $(0,\ -8)$ (e) None of these

8. Write in standard form: $4x^2 + 9y^2 - 8x + 72y + 4 = 0$

(a) $\dfrac{(x-1)^2}{36} + \dfrac{(y+4)^2}{16} = 1$ (b) $\dfrac{(x-1)^2}{144} + \dfrac{(y+8)^2}{64} = 1$

(c) $\dfrac{(x-1)^2}{13/4} + \dfrac{(y+4)^2}{13/9} = 1$ (d) $\dfrac{(x-4)^2}{327} + \dfrac{(y+36)^2}{436/3} = 1$

(e) None of these

9. Find the foci of the hyperbola given by $2y^2 - 9x^2 - 18 = 0$.

(a) $(\pm\sqrt{11},\ 3)$ (b) $(0,\ \pm\sqrt{7})$ (c) $(0,\ \pm\sqrt{11})$

(d) $(\pm\sqrt{7},\ 0)$ (e) None of these

10. Find the vertex of the parabola: $(x+3)^2 - 8(y+6) = 0$

(a) $(3,\ 6)$ (b) $(-3,\ -6)$ (c) $(-3,\ -4)$

(d) $(-1,\ -6)$ (e) None of these

11. Identify the graph of $4x^2 + y^2 - 8x + 6y + 9 = 0$.

(a) Circle   (b) Hyperbola   (c) Parabola

(d) Ellipse   (e) None of these

12. Find the equation of the ellipse whose center is $(-1, 3)$, has a vertex at $(3, 3)$ and a minor axis of length 2.

(a) $\dfrac{x^2}{16} + \dfrac{y^2}{4} = 1$ (b) $\dfrac{x^2}{4} + \dfrac{y^2}{16} = 1$

(c) $\dfrac{(x+1)^2}{1} + \dfrac{(y-3)^2}{16} = 1$ (d) $\dfrac{(x+1)^2}{16} + \dfrac{(y-3)^3}{1} = 1$

(e) None of these

Test Form C   Name _____   Date _____

Chapter 4   Class _____   Section _____

1. Match the graph at the right with the correct equation.

   (a) $f(x) = \dfrac{x+3}{x-1}$ (b) $f(x) = x + 3$

   (c) $f(x) = \dfrac{x-1}{x^2+2x-3}$ (d) $f(x) = \dfrac{x^2+2x-3}{x-1}$

   (e) None of these

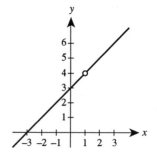

2. Find the horizontal (or slant) asymptote: $f(x) = \dfrac{3x^2+2x-16}{x^2-7}$

   (a) $x = \pm\sqrt{7}$ (b) $y = 3$ (c) $y = 3x + 7$

   (d) $y = 0$ (e) None of these

3. Find the vertical asymptote(s): $f(x) = \dfrac{1}{(x+2)(x-5)}$

   (a) $x = -2,\ x = 5$ (b) $y = 1$ (c) $y = 0$

   (d) $y = 1,\ y = 0$ (e) None of these

4. Find the partial fraction decomposition: $\dfrac{-5x^2-19x-28}{x^3+4x^2+4x}$

   (a) $-\dfrac{5x^2}{x^3} - \dfrac{19x}{4x^2} - \dfrac{28}{4x}$

   (b) $-\dfrac{5x^2}{x} - \dfrac{19x}{x+2} - \dfrac{28}{(x+2)^2}$

   (c) $\dfrac{2}{x} - \dfrac{5}{x+2} + \dfrac{16}{(x+2)^2}$

   (d) $-\dfrac{7}{x} + \dfrac{2}{x+2} + \dfrac{5}{(x+2)^2}$

   (e) None of these

5. Find the partial fraction decomposition: $\dfrac{5x^2-9x+12}{(x-2)(x^2+x+1)}$

   (a) $\dfrac{5x^2}{x-2} - \dfrac{9x+12}{x^2+x+1}$

   (b) $-\dfrac{4/9}{x-2} + \dfrac{22/9}{x+1} - \dfrac{26/3}{(x+1)^2}$

   (c) $\dfrac{2}{x-2} + \dfrac{3x-5}{x^2+x+1}$

   (d) $\dfrac{5}{x-2} + \dfrac{2x-7}{x^2+x+1}$

   (e) None of these

6. Match the graph with the correct equation.

    (a) $\dfrac{x^2}{1} - \dfrac{y^2}{9} = 1$

    (b) $\dfrac{x^2}{1} - \dfrac{y}{9} = 1$

    (c) $\dfrac{y^2}{9} - x = 1$

    (d) $\dfrac{x^2}{1} + \dfrac{y^2}{9} = 1$

    (e) None of these

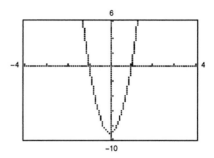

7. Find the directrix of the parabola: $y^2 = x$

    (a) $y = \frac{1}{4}$

    (b) $x = \frac{1}{4}$

    (c) $y = -\frac{1}{4}$

    (d) $x = -\frac{1}{4}$

    (e) None of these

8. Find the foci of the ellipse: $\dfrac{x^2}{81} + \dfrac{y^2}{225} = 1$

    (a) $(0,\ 12),\ (0,\ -12)$

    (b) $(12,\ 0),\ (-12,\ 0)$

    (c) $(0,\ 3\sqrt{34}),\ (0,\ -3\sqrt{34})$

    (d) $(3\sqrt{34},\ 0),\ (-3\sqrt{34},\ 0)$

    (e) None of these

9. Find the equation of the hyperbola with center $(0,\ 0)$, vertices $(\pm 3,\ 0)$ and foci $(\pm 3\sqrt{5},\ 0)$.

    (a) $\dfrac{x^2}{9} - \dfrac{y^2}{45} = 1$

    (b) $\dfrac{y^2}{9} - \dfrac{x^2}{45} = 1$

    (c) $\dfrac{x^2}{9} - \dfrac{y^2}{36} = 1$

    (d) $\dfrac{x^2}{9} - \dfrac{y^2}{54} = 1$

    (e) None of these

10. Classify the graph of $3x^2 - 2y^2 + 6x - 8y + 1 = 0$.

    (a) Parabola

    (b) Circle

    (c) Ellipse

    (d) Hyperbola

    (e) None of these

11. Find the center of the ellipse: $3x^2 + 4y^2 - 6x + 16y + 7 = 0$

    (a) $(1,\ -2)$

    (b) $(4,\ 3)$

    (c) $(1,\ -8)$

    (d) $(3,\ -8)$

    (e) None of these

12. Find the equation of the parabola with vertex $(2,\ -3)$ and focus $(2,\ 0)$.

    (a) $y^2 + 6y - 12x + 33 = 0$

    (b) $x^2 - 4x + 12y + 40 = 0$

    (c) $x^2 - 4x - 12y - 32 = 0$

    (d) $y^2 + 6y + 12x - 15 = 0$

    (e) None of these

Test Form D   Name _____ Date _____

Chapter 4   Class _____ Section _____

1. Find the intercepts and asymptotes: $f(x) = \dfrac{3}{x - 5}$

2. Find the asymptotes: $f(x) = \dfrac{x^3 - 2x^2 + 5}{x^2}$

3. Sketch the graph: $f(x) = \dfrac{x + 2}{x + 1}$

4. Write the partial fraction decomposition: $\dfrac{12x^2 - 13x - 3}{(x - 1)^2(x + 3)}$

5. Write the partial fraction decomposition: $\dfrac{x^2 - x - 4}{x(x^2 + 2)}$

6. Classify the graph of $f(x) = 3x^2 + 3y^2 - 6x + 18y + 10$.

7. Find an equation of the parabola with vertex $(0, 0)$ and directrix $x = 7$.

8. Find the center, vertices, and foci and sketch the graph of the conic given by
   $$\frac{x^2}{9} - \frac{y^2}{4} = 1.$$

9. Find an equation of the ellipse with foci at $(0, 2)$ and $(0, 8)$ and vertices at $(0, 0)$ and $(0, 10)$.

10. Write the equation of the parabola in standard form: $x^2 + 4x - 8y + 4 = 0$

Test Form E   Name _____   Date _____

Chapter 4   Class _____   Section _____

In Problems 1 and 2, find the vertical and horizontal (or slant) asymptotes.

1. $f(x) = \dfrac{x-2}{x^2 - 2x - 3}$

2. $f(x) = \dfrac{3x^2 - 2x + 4}{x - 3}$

3. Sketch the graph of the function $f(x) = \dfrac{3x+2}{x-5}$. Label all asymptotes and intercepts.

In Problems 4 and 5, write the partial fraction decomposition for the rational expression.

4. $\dfrac{3x^2 - 7x + 1}{(x-1)^3}$

5. $\dfrac{3x^2 - 31x - 25}{(x+1)(x^2 - 7x - 8)}$

In Problems 6–8, write the standard equation for the given conic section.

6. Parabola – Vertex: $(0,\, 0)$, Directrix: $x = 5$

7. Ellipse – Center: $(0,\, 0)$, Focus: $(3,\, 0)$, Length of major axis: 12

8. Hyperbola – Center: $(2,\, 5)$, Focus: $(2,\, 15)$, Length of transverse axis: 12

9. Find the center of the ellipse: $5x^2 + 2y^2 - 20x + 24y + 82 = 0$

10. Sketch the graph of $y^2 = -3x$.

Test Form A   Name _____   Date _____

Chapter 5   Class _____   Section _____

1. Match the graph at the right with the correct function.

   (a) $f(x) = 4^x - 5$ (b) $f(x) = 4^x + 5$

   (c) $f(x) = 4^{-x} + 5$ (d) $f(x) = 4^{-x} - 5$

   (e) None of these

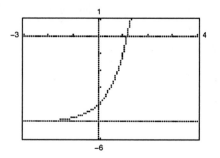

2. Solve for x: $3^{2x} = 81$

   (a) $x = 13.5$ (b) $x = \frac{1}{4}$ (c) $x = 4$

   (d) $x = 2$ (e) None of these

3. Evaluate: $300e^{-0.076t}$ for $t = 15$

   (a) 95.95   (b) 39.31   (c) 0.000479718

   (d) -1906.12 (e) None of these

4. Write in logarithmic form: $4^3 = 64$

   (a) $4 \log 3 = 64$ (b) $\log_4 64 = 3$ (c) $\log_3 4 = 64$

   (d) $\log_3 64 = 4$ (e) None of these

5. Evaluate $\log_a 24$ using the fact that $\log_a 2 = 0.4307$ and $\log_a 3 = 0.6826$.

   (a) 0.8820   (b) 1.9747   (c) 0.2940

   (d) 1.1133   (e) None of these

6. Solve for x: $\log_x 8 = -3$

   (a) 2   (b) 512   (c) $\frac{1}{2}$ (d) -2 (e) None of these

7. Write as a sum, difference, or multiple of logarithms: $\log \sqrt[3]{\dfrac{a^2 b}{c}}$

   (a) $\sqrt[3]{\dfrac{2 \log a + \log b}{\log c}}$

   (b) $\dfrac{1}{3}\left(\dfrac{2 \log a + \log b}{\log c}\right)$

   (c) $\dfrac{1}{3}(2 \log a + \log b - \log c)$

   (d) $\sqrt[3]{2 \log a^2 + \log b - \log c}$

   (e) None of these

8. Evaluate $\log_4 7$ using the change of base formula.

   (a) 0.2430   (b) 0.5596   (c) 0.7124

   (d) 1.4037   (e) None of these

9. Evaluate: $\dfrac{15\ln 23}{\ln 7 - \ln 2}$

   (a) 37.5429   (b) 23.4767   (c) 34.8698

   (d) $22,218,828.26$ (e) None of these

10. Simplify using the properties of logarithms: $\ln 5e^3$

    (a) $3 + \ln 5$ (b) $3\ln 5$ (c) $3 + 3\ln 5$

    (d) $5e^3$ (e) None of these

11. Determine the domain of the function: $f(x) = \ln(3x + 1)$

    (a) $(-\infty,\ \infty)$ (b) $\left(-\frac{1}{3},\ \infty\right)$ (c) $(0,\ \infty)$

    (d) $\left(\frac{1}{3},\ \infty\right)$ (e) None of these

12. Identify the correct function for the graph at the right.

    (a) $f(x) = -3 + \ln x$ (b) $f(x) = 3 + \ln x$

    (c) $f(x) = \ln(x - 3)$ (d) $f(x) = \ln(x + 3)$

    (e) None of these

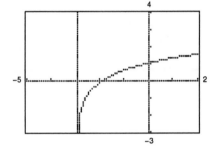

13. Solve for x: $\log(3x + 7) + \log(x - 2) = 1$

    (a) $\frac{8}{3}$ (b) $3,\ -\frac{8}{3}$ (c) 2   (d) $2,\ -\frac{5}{3}$ (e) None of these

14. Solve for x: $3^{5x+1} = 5$

    (a) 0.1022   (b) 0.0930   (c) 0.1333

    (d) 0.2218   (e) None of these

15. Determine the principal, P, that must be invested at a rate of 8% compounded quarterly so that the balance, B, in 40 years will be \$200,000. $\left[B = P\left(1 + \frac{r}{n}\right)^{nt} \right]$

    (a) \$90,578.10   (b) \$47,539.00   (c) \$12,416.00

    (d) \$8,414.00   (e) None of these

Test Form B

Chapter 5

Name _____ Date _____

Class _____ Section _____

1. Match the graph at the right with the correct function.

   (a) $f(x) = 3^{x-1}$ (b) $f(x) = 3^x - 1$

   (c) $f(x) = 3^{1-x}$ (d) $f(x) = 3^{-x} - 1$

   (e) None of these

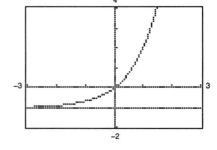

2. If \$3700 is invested at $11\frac{1}{2}\%$ interest compounded continuously, find the balance B in the account after 5 years. $(B = Pe^{rt})$

   (a) \$3,918.99   (b) \$20,754.65   (c) \$6,575.38

   (d) \$7,376.75   (e) None of these

3. Evaluate: $\log_7 7$

   (a) 1   (b) 0   (c) 2   (d) 49   (e) None of these

4. Write as a single log: $\frac{1}{4} \log_b 16 - 2 \log_b 5 + \log_b 7$

   (a) $\frac{14}{25}$ (b) $\log_b \frac{2}{175}$ (c) 1

   (d) $\log_b \frac{14}{25}$ (e) None of these

5. Write in exponential form: $\log_b 37 = 2$

   (a) $37^2 = b$ (b) $2^b = 37$ (c) $b = 10$

   (d) $b^2 = 37$ (e) None of these

6. Solve for x: $16 = 2^{7x-5}$

   (a) 0.1143   (b) -0.3010 (c) $\frac{13}{7}$

   (d) $\frac{9}{7}$ (e) None of these

7. Evaluate $\log_7 15$ using the change of base formula.

   (a) 1.3917   (b) 12.6765   (c) 2.1429

   (d) 0.7186   (e) None of these

8. Evaluate: $\dfrac{3\ln 5}{7\ln 6 - 2\ln 7}$

   (a) -3.8222 (b) -2.6559 (c) 0.5582

   (d) -11.6058 (e) None of these

9. Determine the domain of the function: $f(x) = 3\log(5x - 2)$

   (a) $(-\infty,\ \infty)$ (b) $(0,\ \infty)$ (c) $\left(\frac{2}{5},\ \infty\right)$

   (d) $(0.064,\ \infty)$ (e) None of these

10. Match the graph at the right with the correct function.

   (a) $f(x) = 3 + \log x$ (b) $f(x) = \log(x + 3)$

   (c) $f(x) = \frac{1}{3}\log x$ (d) $f(x) = 3\log x$

   (e) None of these

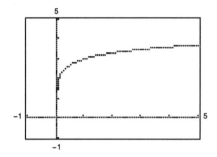

11. Solve for x: $3^{2x} = 5^{x-1}$

   (a) -0.5563 (b) -1 (c) -2.7381

   (d) 15.2755 (e) None of these

12. Solve for x: $\ln(7 - x) + \ln(3x + 5) = \ln(24x)$

   (a) $\frac{6}{11}$ (b) $\frac{7}{3}$ (c) $\frac{7}{3},\ -5$

   (d) $\frac{6}{11},\ 5$ (e) None of these

13. Solve for x: $\ln e^{4x} = 60$

   (a) 2.7832 (b) 15 (c) 1.0236

   (d) 2.7081 (e) None of these

14. Evaluate: $\dfrac{3e^{(0.0721)(52)}}{(1 - 0.0721)}$

(a) 4.2727   (b) 180.6908   (c) 137.3653

(d) −410.3055   (e) None of these

15. Which of the following is not true?

(a) $b^{\log_b c} = c$ (b) $\log_1 b = b$ (c) $\log_b b = 1$

(d) All of these statements are false.   (e) All of these statements are true.

Test Form C   Name _____ Date _____

Chapter 5   Class _____ Section _____

1. Match the graph at the right with the correct function.

   (a) $f(x) = \left(\frac{1}{2}\right)^x - 1$ (b) $f(x) = 3^{-x^2} - 1$

   (c) $f(x) = 3^{x+1}$ (d) $f(x) = 4^{-x}$

   (e) None of these

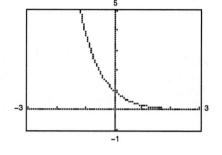

2. Evaluate for $t = 3$: $y = \dfrac{300}{1 + e^{-2t}}$

   (a) 299.2582   (b) 213.3704   (c) 300.0025

   (d) 107.4591   (e) None of these

3. Solve for x: $27^x = 81$

   (a) $\frac{3}{4}$ (b) $-\frac{1}{3}$ (c) $\frac{4}{3}$ (d) $\frac{2}{3}$ (e) None of these

4. Evaluate $\log_{1/2} 13$ using the change of base formula.

   (a) 2.5649   (b) 1.1139   (c) -0.2702

   (d) -3.7004 (e) None of these

5. Write in exponential form: $\log_b 7 = 13$

   (a) $7^{13} = b$ (b) $b^{13} = 7$ (c) $b^7 = 13$

   (d) $7^b = 13$ (e) None of these

6. Write as a sum, difference, or multiple of logarithms: $\log_b \left(\dfrac{x^3 y^2}{\sqrt{w}} \right)$

   (a) $x^3 + y^3 - \sqrt{w}$ (b) $\frac{1}{3} \log_b x + \frac{1}{2} \log_b y - 2 \log_b w$

   (c) $3 \log_b x + 2 \log_b y - \frac{1}{2} \log_b w$ (d) $\dfrac{3 \log x + 2 \log y}{(1/2) \log w}$

   (e) None of these

7. Given $\log_b 2 = 0.2789$, $\log_b 3 = 0.4421$, and $\log_b 7 = 0.7831$, find $\log_b \left(\dfrac{14}{3b} \right)$.

   (a) -0.3801 (b) 0.6199 (c) 0.5119

   (d) 0.7364 (e) None of these

8. Evaluate: $\dfrac{16 \ln 5}{1 + 2 \ln 3}$

   (a) 918.3228 (b) 27.9482 (c) 8.0542

   (d) 22.5538 (e) None of these

9. Solve for x: $\ln e^{2x+1} = 9$

   (a) $\dfrac{-1 + \ln 9}{2}$ (b) $\dfrac{9}{2 \ln e} - \dfrac{1}{2}$ (c) 23

   (d) 4 (e) None of these

10. Match the graph at the right with the correct function.

    (a) $f(x) = e^x$ (b) $f(x) = e^{x-1}$

    (c) $f(x) = \ln x$ (d) $f(x) = \ln(x - 1)$

    (e) None of these

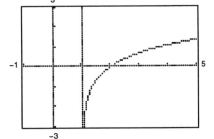

11. Determine the domain of the function: $f(x) = 3 + \ln(x - 1)$

    (a) $(-\infty, \infty)$ (b) $(0, \infty)$ (c) $(1, \infty)$

    (d) $(3, \infty)$ (e) None of these

12. The pH of a solution is determined by $\text{pH} = -\log_{10}[H^+]$ where pH is a measure of the hydrogen ion concentration $[H^+]$, measured in moles per liter. Find the pH of a solution for which $[H^+] = 7.61 \times 10^{-6}$.

    (a) -5.12 (b) 5.12 (c) -11.79

    (d) 11.79 (e) None of these

13. Solve for x: $\log(4 + x) - \log(2x - 1) = 1$

    (a) $\frac{14}{19}$ (b) $-\frac{9}{3}$ (c) $\frac{7}{2}$

    (d) $\frac{2}{7}$ (e) None of these

14. An initial deposit of \$2000 is compounded continuously at an annual percentage rate of 9%. Find the effective yield.

    (a) 9.4%   (b) 9.2%   (c) \$188.00

    (d) 180.00   (e) None of these

15. Solve for t: $e^{-0.0097t} = 12$

    (a) -256.1759 (b) -1237.1134 (c) $16,778,844.47$

    (d) -2.5886 (e) None of these

Test Form D

Name _____   Date _____

Chapter 5

Class _____   Section _____

1. Graph the function: $f(x) = 2^x - 3$

2. Find the balance B after 10 years if \$800 is invested in an account that pays $11\frac{1}{2}\%$ interest compounded monthly. $[B = P(1 + \frac{r}{n})^{nt}]$

In Problems 3–5, evaluate the given expression.

3. $200 - 5e^{0.002x}$ for $x = 65$

4. $\dfrac{16\ln(1/2)}{3\ln 10}$

5. $\log_5 22$

6. Write the expression as a single logarithm: $\frac{1}{5}[3\log(x + 1) + 2\log(x - 1) - \log 7]$

7. Write in logarithmic form: $3^5 = 243$

8. Solve for x: $\ln x = 5.3670$

9. Simplify: $b^{\log_b x}$

10. Graph the function: $f(x) = \log(x^2 - 1)$

11. Find the domain of the function: $f(x) = 3 - \log(x^2 - 1)$

12. The demand equation for a certain product is given by $p = 450 - 0.4e^{0.007x}$. Find the demand x if the price charged is \$300.

In Problems 13–15, solve for x.

13. $\log x + \log(x + 3) = 1$

14. $2^{x-1} = 5^{2x+6}$

15. $\log_x 16 = 5$

Test Form E   Name _____   Date _____

Chapter 5   Class _____   Section _____

1. Graph the function: $f(x) = 4^x + 1$

2. Solve for x: $16^x = 8^{2x-1}$

3. Evaluate $16e^{-0.015x}$ for $x = -20$.

4. Evaluate: $\log_5 17$

5. Solve for x: $x^2 - 4x = \log_2 32$

6. Evaluate $\log_b \sqrt{10b}$ given $\log_b 2 = 0.3562$, $\log_b 5 = 0.8271$.

7. Graph the function: $f(x) = 1 - \log_5 x$

8. Determine the domain of the function: $f(x) = \log_3(x^2 - 4)$

9. Solve for x: $\log_3(x^2 + 5) = \log_3(4x^2 - 2x)$

10. Find the constant, k, so that the exponential function $y = 5e^{kt}$ passes through the points $(0, 5)$ and $(5, 12)$.

Test Form A   Name _____   Date _____

Chapter 6   Class _____   Section _____

1. Which of the following angles is coterminal to $\theta = -\dfrac{7\pi}{12}$?

   (a) $\dfrac{5\pi}{12}$ (b) $\dfrac{17\pi}{12}$ (c) $-\dfrac{19\pi}{12}$

   (d) Both **a** and **c**   (e) None of these

2. Convert to radians: $42°15'$

   (a) 0.7374   (b) 0.7346   (c) 2420.7467

   (d) 0.7357   (e) None of these

3. Convert to degrees: $\theta = \dfrac{3\pi}{5}$ rad.

   (a) 0.0329°   (b) 108°   (c) 216°

   (d) 54°   (e) None of these

4. Convert to (degree) decimal form: $-13°42'15''$

   (a) −13.95°   (b) −12.05°   (c) −13.7042°

   (d) −12.2958°   (e) None of these

5. A circle of radius r has a central angle of $\theta = 45°$ which subtends an arc of 16 inches. Find r.

   (a) 0.3556 inch   (b) 12.5664 inches   (c) 2.8125 inches

   (d) 20.3718 inches   (e) None of these

6. A right triangle has an acute angle θ such that $\cot\theta = 15$. Find $\cos\theta$.

   (a) $\sqrt{226}$ (b) $\dfrac{\sqrt{226}}{226}$ (c) $\dfrac{15\sqrt{226}}{226}$

   (d) $\dfrac{\sqrt{226}}{15}$ (e) None of these

7. Using the two similar triangles shown at the right, find a.

(a) $\dfrac{15\sqrt{6}}{6}$

(b) $\dfrac{\sqrt{74}}{30}$

(c) $\dfrac{15\sqrt{74}}{37}$

(d) $\dfrac{21\sqrt{74}}{37}$

(e) None of these

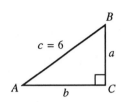 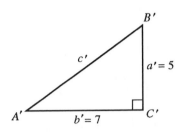

8. Given $\sec\theta = 3$, find $\csc(90 - \theta)$.

(a) $\dfrac{1}{3}$

(b) $\dfrac{3\sqrt{2}}{4}$

(c) 3

(d) $\dfrac{2\sqrt{2}}{3}$

(e) None of these

9. Evaluate: $\csc 14°$

(a) 4.0960

(b) 4.1336

(c) 1.0306

(d) 0.9999

(e) None of these

10. Find θ in radians if $\tan\theta = 1.2617$.

(a) 0.0220

(b) 0.9006

(c) 1.0145

(d) 0.3193

(e) None of these

11. For the triangle shown at the right, solve for x.

(a) $7\sqrt{3}$

(b) $\dfrac{7}{\sqrt{3}}$

(c) 14

(d) $\dfrac{7}{2}$

(e) None of these

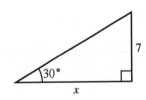

12. Find the reference angle for $\theta = 305°$.

(a) 35°

(b) −55°

(c) 55°

(d) 125°

(e) None of these

13. Find $\cos \theta$, given $\sin \theta = -\dfrac{1}{5}$ and $\tan \theta < 0$.

(a) $-\dfrac{\sqrt{26}}{5}$

(b) $\dfrac{\sqrt{26}}{5}$

(c) $-\dfrac{2\sqrt{6}}{5}$

(d) $\dfrac{2\sqrt{6}}{5}$

(e) None of these

14. Match the graph at the right with the correct function.

(a) $y = \dfrac{1}{2}\cos\left(\dfrac{2x}{3}\right)$

(b) $y = \dfrac{1}{2}\sin\left(\dfrac{2x}{3}\right)$

(c) $y = \dfrac{1}{2}\cos\left(\dfrac{3x}{2}\right)$

(d) $y = \dfrac{1}{2}\sin\left(\dfrac{3x}{2}\right)$

(e) None of these

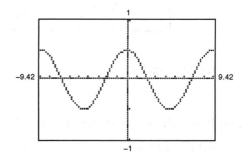

15. Match the graph at the right with the correct function.

(a) $y = 3 - \sec x$

(b) $y = x + \csc x$

(c) $y = x + \sec x$

(d) $y = 3 + \csc x$

(e) None of these

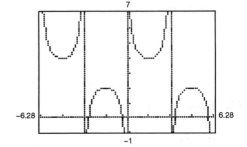

16. Match the function $y = 2\sin(4x + \pi)$ with the correct graph.

(a)

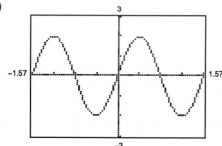

(b)

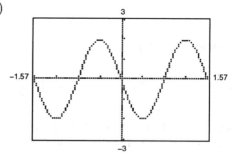

16. —CONTINUED—

(c)

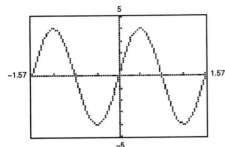

(d)

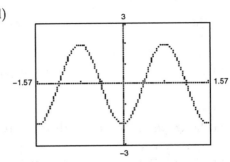

(e) None of these

17. Match the graph at the right with the correct function.

    (a) $y = 2x \cos x$ (b) $y = 2x \sin x$

    (c) $y = 2x + \cos x$ (d) $y = 2x + \sin x$

    (e) None of these

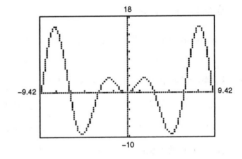

18. Evaluate: $\sec[\arctan 3]$

    (a) $\sqrt{10}$ (b) $\dfrac{\sqrt{2}}{4}$ (c) $2\sqrt{2}$

    (d) $\dfrac{\sqrt{10}}{3}$ (e) None of these

19. Evaluate: $\arccos\left(-\dfrac{1}{2}\right)$

    (a) $\dfrac{\pi}{6}$ (b) $\dfrac{\pi}{3}$ (c) $-\dfrac{\pi}{3}$ (d) $\dfrac{2\pi}{3}$ (e) None of these

20. A guy wire attached to the top of a 90 foot antenna is fastened to the ground 40 feet from the base of the antenna. Find the angle of elevation of the wire with the ground.

    (a) 50°   (b) 66°   (c) 75°   (d) 79°   (e) None of these

21. The pilot of an airplane flying at an altitude of 3000 feet sights two ships traveling in the same direction as the plane. The angle of depression of the farther ship is 20° and the angle of depression of the other ship is 35°. Find the distance between the two ships.

    (a) 470 feet   (b) 3541 feet   (c) 3958 feet

    (d) 1009 feet   (e) None of these

Test Form B   Name _____ Date _____

Chapter 6   Class _____ Section _____

1. Convert to radians: 240°

   (a) $\dfrac{3\pi}{4}$ (b) $\dfrac{43200}{\pi}$ (c) $\dfrac{3\pi}{2}$

   (d) $\dfrac{4\pi}{3}$ (e) None of these

2. Convert to (degree) decimal form: 72°15″

   (a) 72.25°   (b) 72.0042°   (c) 72.09°

   (d) 72.00054°   (e) None of these

3. A central angle θ of a circle with radius 16 inches subtends an arc 19.36 inches. Find θ.

   (a) 47.3519°   (b) 1.21°   (c) 69.3279°

   (d) 0.8264°   (e) None of these

4. Given θ as an acute angle of a right triangle and $\csc\theta = \dfrac{7}{3}$, find $\tan\theta$.

   (a) $\dfrac{2\sqrt{10}}{7}$ (b) $\dfrac{3\sqrt{10}}{20}$ (c) $\dfrac{2\sqrt{10}}{3}$

   (d) $\dfrac{3}{7}$ (e) None of these

5. Evaluate: $\cot 15°$

   (a) 3.7321   (b) 0.0012   (c) 86.1859

   (d) 1.0353   (e) None of these

6. Given $\cos\theta = 0.9872$, find θ.

   (a) 80.8229°   (b) 0.9998°   (c) 9.1771°

   (d) 1.0001°   (e) None of these

7. Evaluate: $\sec\left(\dfrac{\pi}{3}\right)$

   (a) $\dfrac{\sqrt{2}}{2}$ (b) $\dfrac{\sqrt{3}}{2}$ (c) $\dfrac{\sqrt{3}}{3}$

   (d) 2   (e) None of these

8. A man that is 6 feet tall casts a shadow 14 feet long. Find the angle of elevation of the sun.

   (a) 23.2°   (b) 66.8°   (c) 25.4°

   (d) 64.6°   (e) None of these

9. For the angle θ shown at the right, find the $\tan\theta$.

   (a) $-\dfrac{9\sqrt{130}}{7}$ (b) $\dfrac{\sqrt{130}}{7}$ (c) $-\dfrac{7}{9}$

   (d) $-\dfrac{9}{7}$ (e) None of these

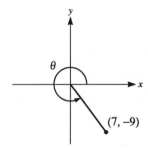

10. Given $\sin\theta = \dfrac{7}{13}$, and $\tan\theta < 0$, find $\tan\theta$.

   (a) $-\dfrac{7\sqrt{3}}{2}$ (b) $-\dfrac{2\sqrt{3}}{7}$ (c) $-\dfrac{2\sqrt{3}}{13}$

   (d) $-\dfrac{7\sqrt{30}}{60}$ (e) None of these

11. Describe the horizontal shift of the graph of g with respect to the graph of f:

   $$g(x) = 4\sin\left(2x - \frac{\pi}{3}\right) \quad \text{and} \quad f(x) = 4\sin(2x)$$

   (a) $\dfrac{\pi}{6}$ units to the left   (b) $\dfrac{\pi}{6}$ units to the right

   (c) $\dfrac{2\pi}{3}$ units to the left   (d) $\dfrac{2\pi}{3}$ units to the right

   (e) None of these

12. Match the graph at the right with the correct function.

   (a) $y = 3\sin 4x$ (b) $y = 3\sin\left(\dfrac{x}{4}\right)$

   (c) $y = 3\cos 4x$ (d) $y = 3\cos\left(\dfrac{x}{4}\right)$

   (e) None of these

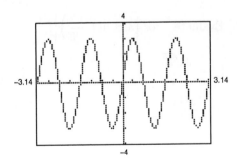

13. Find the period of the function: $y = 3\tan 7x$

    (a) $\dfrac{\pi}{3}$ (b) $\dfrac{\pi}{7}$ (c) $\dfrac{2\pi}{7}$

    (d) 6π (e) None of these

14. Match the graph at the right with the correct function.

    (a) $y = \cos 2x + \sin x$ (b) $y = \cos x + \sin 2x$

    (c) $y = 2\cos x + \sin x$ (d) $y = \cos x + 2\sin x$

    (e) None of these

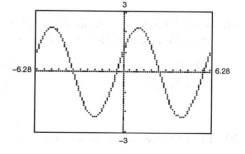

15. Match the graph at the right with the correct function.

    (a) $y = |x|\cos x$ (b) $y = 2^x \sin x$

    (c) $y = |x|\sin 2x$ (d) $y = x\sin x$

    (e) None of these

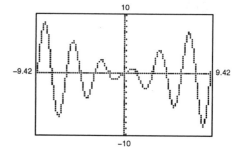

16. Evaluate: $\arccos 0$

    (a) 0 (b) π (c) $\dfrac{\pi}{2}$

    (d) $-\dfrac{\pi}{2}$ (e) None of these

17. Evaluate: $\cos\left[\arctan\left(-\dfrac{2}{3}\right)\right]$

    (a) $-\dfrac{3\sqrt{13}}{13}$ (b) $\dfrac{3\sqrt{13}}{13}$ (c) $-\dfrac{2\sqrt{13}}{13}$

    (d) $\dfrac{2\sqrt{13}}{13}$ (e) None of these

18. Write an algebraic expression for tan[arcsin x].

(a) $\dfrac{x\sqrt{1+x^2}}{1+x^2}$

(b) $\dfrac{1}{x}$

(c) $\dfrac{\sqrt{1-x^2}}{x}$

(d) $\dfrac{x\sqrt{1-x^2}}{1-x^2}$

(e) None of these

19. A ladder is leaning against the side of a house. The base of the ladder is 5 feet from the wall and makes an angle of 39° with the ground. Find the length of the ladder.

(a) 3.89 feet

(b) 6.43 feet

(c) 4.05 feet

(d) 7.95 feet

(e) None of these

20. Find the frequency of the simple harmonic motion described by $d = 7\cos 16\pi t$.

(a) $3\frac{1}{2}$

(b) 7

(c) 16

(d) 8

(e) None of these

Test Form C

Name _____   Date _____

Chapter 6

Class _____   Section _____

1. Which of the following angles is coterminal to $\theta = -73°$?

    (a) 107°   (b) 287°   (c) −253°

    (d) 17°   (e) None of these

2. Convert to radians: 25°

    (a) $\dfrac{5\pi}{36}$ (b) $\dfrac{36}{5\pi}$ (c) $\dfrac{4500}{\pi}$

    (d) $\dfrac{5\pi}{18}$ (e) None of these

3. Convert to degrees, minutes, and seconds: 178.463°

    (a) 178°77′50″   (b) 178°46′30″   (c) 178°7′12″

    (d) 178°27′47″   (e) None of these

4. The central angle of a circle with radius 9 inches subtends an arc of 20 inches. Find the central angle.

    (a) 2.22°   (b) 127.32°   (c) 0.45°

    (d) 25.78°   (e) None of these

5. A right triangle has an acute angle θ such that $\sin\theta = \dfrac{7}{9}$. Find $\tan\theta$.

    (a) $\dfrac{7\sqrt{2}}{8}$ (b) $\dfrac{4\sqrt{2}}{7}$ (c) $\dfrac{\sqrt{130}}{7}$

    (d) $\dfrac{9\sqrt{130}}{130}$ (e) None of these

6. Evaluate: $\sec(4°15′42″)$

    (a) 13.4569   (b) 0.9999   (c) 1.0028

    (d) 13.8043   (e) None of these

7. Find x for the triangle shown at the right.

(a) 0.1047   (b) 11.9638   (c) 5.4256

(d) 9.5547   (e) None of these

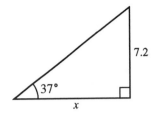

8. Find the reference angle for $\theta = \dfrac{19\pi}{15}$.

(a) $\dfrac{4\pi}{15}$ (b) $\dfrac{7\pi}{30}$ (c) $\dfrac{11\pi}{30}$

(d) $\dfrac{49\pi}{15}$ (e) None of these

9. Determine the period of the function: $y = \dfrac{1}{2}\sin\left(\dfrac{x}{3} - \pi\right)$

(a) $\dfrac{1}{2}$ (b) $\dfrac{2\pi}{3}$ (c) 6π

(d) 3π (e) None of these

10. Match the graph at the right with the correct function.

(a) $y = 4\cos\left(3x - \dfrac{\pi}{2}\right)$ (b) $y = 4\cos\left(x + \dfrac{\pi}{6}\right)$

(c) $y = 4\sin\left(2x - \dfrac{\pi}{3}\right)$ (d) $y = 4\cos\left(2x + \dfrac{\pi}{3}\right)$

(e) None of these

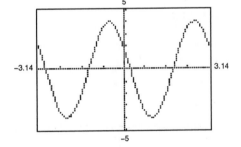

11. Match the graph at the right with the correct function.

(a) $y = 2\sec 2\pi x$ (b) $y = -2\csc\left(\dfrac{\pi x}{2}\right)$

(c) $y = -2\cot\left(\dfrac{\pi x}{4}\right)$ (d) $y = -\sin\left(\dfrac{x}{2}\right)$

(e) None of these

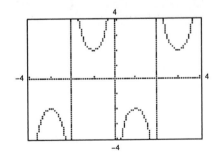

12. Match the graph at the right with the correct function.

   (a) $y = 3 + \sin\left(x + \dfrac{\pi}{2}\right)$ (b) $y = 3 + \sin\left(x - \dfrac{\pi}{2}\right)$

   (c) $y = 3 + \cos\left(x + \dfrac{\pi}{2}\right)$ (d) $y = 3 + \cos\left(x - \dfrac{\pi}{2}\right)$

   (e) None of these

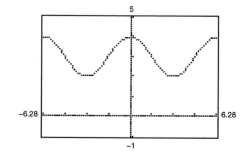

13. Match the graph at the right with the correct function.

   (a) $y = x \sin x$ (b) $y = -x \sin x$

   (c) $y = -x + \sin x$ (d) $y = -x - \sin x$

   (e) None of these

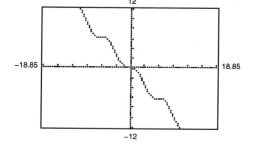

14. Evaluate: $\sin\left[\arccos\left(-\dfrac{2}{7}\right)\right]$

   (a) $\dfrac{\sqrt{53}}{7}$ (b) $-\dfrac{\sqrt{53}}{7}$ (c) $\dfrac{3\sqrt{5}}{7}$

   (d) $-\dfrac{3\sqrt{5}}{7}$ (e) None of these

15. A boy and his father are walking on a street with their backs to the sun. The father is 5'8" tall and casts a shadow 9 feet long. The boy is 4'9" tall. How long is his shadow?

   (a) 6.7 feet   (b) 7.5 feet   (c) 5.9 feet

   (d) 8.2 feet   (e) None of these

Test Form D Name _____ Date _____

Chapter 6 Class _____ Section _____

1. Find an angle θ that is coterminal to $-423°$ such that $0 \le \theta < 360°$.

2. Convert $330°$ to radian measure. (Write your answer as a multiple of π.)

3. Convert the angle $\theta = 128°35'18''$ to (degree) decimal form.

4. A bicycle wheel with an 18 inch diameter rotates $120°$. What distance has the bicycle traveled?

5. In the triangle shown at the right, use the fact that $\sin \theta = 2/5$ to find $\tan \theta$.

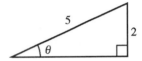

6. Evaluate $\cot \left(\dfrac{\pi}{3} \right)$ without the use of a calculator.

7. Find θ such that $0 \le \theta < \dfrac{\pi}{2}$ and $\csc \theta = 1.4736$.

8. Find x for the triangle shown at the right.

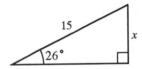

9. Given $\tan \theta = -\dfrac{7}{8}$ and $\cos \theta > 0$, find $\csc \theta$.

10. Determine the period and amplitude of the function:
$f(x) = -7 \cos 3x$

11. Graph the function $f(x) = \dfrac{1}{2} \sec \left(x - \dfrac{\pi}{2} \right)$.

12. Graph the function $f(x) = \dfrac{1}{3} x - \cos x$.

13. Graph the function $f(x) = x \sin 2x$.

14. Evaluate: $\cos \left[\arctan \left(-\dfrac{3}{10} \right) \right]$

15. The angle of depression from the top of one building to the foot of a building across the street is $63°$. The angle of depression to the top of the same building is $33°$. The two buildings are 40 feet apart. What is the height of the shorter building?

Test Form E   Name _____   Date _____

Chapter 6   Class _____   Section _____

1. Find an angle θ that is coterminal to $-495°$ such that $0 \leq \theta < 360°$.

2. Convert 1.4267 radians to degree measure.

3. Convert $12.4762°$ to degrees, minutes, and seconds.

4. Find the arclength, s, shown in the figure at the right.

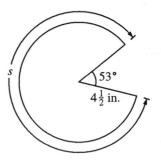

5. Two similar triangles are shown at the right. Find b.

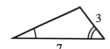   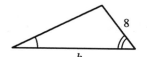

6. Solve for x in the triangle at the right.

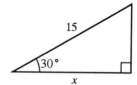

7. Evaluate: $\cot 49°$

8. Given $\sin \theta = -\dfrac{2}{9}$, and $\tan \theta > 0$, find $\cos \theta$.

9. Find the magnitude of the reference angle for $\theta = -155°$.

10. Find the $\csc\theta$ as indicated in the graph at the right.

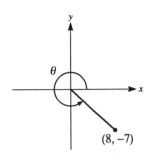

$(8, -7)$

11. Graph the function $f(x) = 4\sin(2x - \pi)$.

12. Determine the period and amplitude of the function: $f(x) = 5\cos\dfrac{x}{2}$

13. Determine the period of the function: $f(x) = \dfrac{1}{5}\tan\left(3x + \dfrac{\pi}{2}\right)$

14. Graph the function $f(x) = -\csc\left(x + \dfrac{\pi}{3}\right)$.

15. Graph the function $f(x) = 7 + \tan x$.

16. Graph the function $f(x) = e^{-x}\sin x$.

17. Evaluate: $\arccos(-0.8923)$

18. Evaluate: $\sin(\arctan 3)$

19. Find the maximum displacement for the simple harmonic motion described by $d = 2\cos 40\pi t$.

20. From a point on a cliff 75 feet above water level an observer can see a ship. The angle of depression to the ship is 4°. How far is the ship from the base of the cliff?

Test Form A   Name _____ Date _____

Chapter 7   Class _____ Section _____

1. Find $\sin x$, given $\cos\left(\dfrac{\pi}{2} - x\right) = \dfrac{2}{7}$.

   (a) $\dfrac{3\sqrt{5}}{7}$ (b) $\dfrac{7}{2}$ (c) $\dfrac{3\sqrt{5}}{2}$

   (d) $\dfrac{2}{7}$ (e) None of these

2. Rewrite in terms of $\sin\theta$ and $\cos\theta$: $\dfrac{\cot^2\theta}{\csc\theta + 1} + 1$

   (a) $\sin^2\theta - \cos\theta$ (b) $\dfrac{1}{\sin\theta}$ (c) $\dfrac{1 + \sin\theta}{\sin\theta}$

   (d) $\dfrac{\cos^2\theta - (1 + \sin\theta)}{\sin^3\theta}$ (e) None of these

3. For what values of θ, $0 \le \theta < 2\pi$ is it true that $\sin\theta = -\sqrt{1 - \cos^2\theta}$?

   (a) $\dfrac{\pi}{2} \le \theta \le \pi, \ \dfrac{3\pi}{2} \le \theta < 2\pi$ (b) $0 \le \theta \le \pi$

   (c) $\dfrac{\pi}{2} \le \theta \le \dfrac{3\pi}{2}$ (d) $\pi \le \theta < 2\pi$

   (e) None of these

4. Simplify: $\dfrac{\tan x}{\csc x + \cot x}$

   (a) $\sec x - 1$ (b) $\sec x + 1$ (c) $\tan x \csc x + \tan x \cot x$

   (d) $1 - \dfrac{1}{\cos x}$ (e) None of these

5. Rewrite in factored form: $2\sin^2 x - 5\sin x - 3$

   (a) $(2\sin x - 3)(\sin x + 1)$ (b) $(2\sin x - 1)(\sin x + 3)$
   (c) $(2\sin x + 1)(\sin x - 3)$ (d) $(2\sin x - 3)(\sin x - 1)$
   (e) None of these

6. Simplify: $\dfrac{1}{\sec x + 1} + \dfrac{1}{\sec x - 1}$

   (a) $\dfrac{2\sin^2 x}{\cos^4 x}$ (b) $2\cot x \csc x$ (c) $2\csc x$

   (d) $\dfrac{\cos x}{2\sin^2 x}$ (e) None of these

7. Evaluate: $\sin 105°$ (Use the fact that $105° = 60° + 45°$.)

(a) $\dfrac{\sqrt{6} + \sqrt{2}}{4}$

(b) $\dfrac{\sqrt{6} - \sqrt{2}}{4}$

(c) $\dfrac{\sqrt{2} - \sqrt{6}}{4}$

(d) $\dfrac{1 + \sqrt{3}}{2}$

(e) None of these

8. Use a sum or difference formula to simplify: $\dfrac{\tan 37° - \tan 13°}{1 + (\tan 37°)(\tan 13°)}$

(a) $\tan 50°$

(b) $\tan 24°$

(c) $\cot 50°$

(d) $\cot 24°$

(e) None of these

9. Find $\cos 2u$, given $\cos u = -\dfrac{4}{7}$.   (Assume $\pi < u < 3\pi/2$.)

(a) $\dfrac{\sqrt{33}}{7}$

(b) $-\dfrac{17}{49}$

(c) $-\dfrac{4\sqrt{33}}{14}$

(d) $-\dfrac{33}{49}$

(e) None of these

10. Use trigonometric identities to rewrite $\cos^4\left(\dfrac{x}{2}\right)$.

(a) $\dfrac{1}{8}(3 + 4\cos x + \cos 2x)$

(b) $\dfrac{1}{8}(3 - 4\cos x - \cos 2x)$

(c) $\dfrac{1}{4}(2 + 2\cos x + \cos 2x)$

(d) $\dfrac{1}{8}(3 + \cos 2x)$

(e) None of these

11. Find $\cos\left(\dfrac{u}{2}\right)$, given $\sin u = -\dfrac{8}{13}$.   (Assume $\dfrac{3\pi}{2} < u < 2\pi$.)

(a) $-\sqrt{\dfrac{13 - \sqrt{105}}{26}}$

(b) $-\sqrt{\dfrac{13 + \sqrt{105}}{26}}$

(c) $-\sqrt{\dfrac{13 - \sqrt{233}}{26}}$

(d) $\sqrt{\dfrac{13 + \sqrt{105}}{26}}$

(e) None of these

12. Rewrite as a sum: $9 \sin 3x \cos 7x$

(a) $\dfrac{9}{2}(\cos 4x + \cos 10x)$

(b) $\dfrac{9}{2}(\sin 10x + \sin 4x)$

(c) $\dfrac{9}{2}(\cos 4x - \cos 10x)$

(d) $\dfrac{9}{2}(\sin 10x - \sin 4x)$

(e) None of these

13. Rewrite as a product: $\sin x + \sin 3x$

(a) $2 \sin 2x \cos x$ (b) $-2 \sin x \cos 2x$ (c) $-2 \cos 2x \cos x$

(d) $2 \sin 2x \sin x$ (e) None of these

14. Find all solutions in the interval $[0, \, 2\pi)$: $\quad 4 \sin^2 x + 2(1 - \sqrt{3}) \sin x - \sqrt{3} = 0$

(a) $\dfrac{\pi}{3}, \dfrac{2\pi}{3}, \dfrac{7\pi}{6}, \dfrac{11\pi}{6}$ (b) $\dfrac{\pi}{6}, \dfrac{5\pi}{6}, \dfrac{4\pi}{3}, \dfrac{5\pi}{3}$ (c) $\dfrac{\pi}{6}, \dfrac{\pi}{3}, \dfrac{2\pi}{3}, \dfrac{5\pi}{6}$

(d) $\dfrac{7\pi}{6}, \dfrac{4\pi}{3}, \dfrac{5\pi}{3}, \dfrac{11\pi}{6}$ (e) None of these

15. Find all solutions in the interval $[0, \, 2\pi)$: $\quad \sec 3x = \sqrt{2}$

(a) $\dfrac{\pi}{4}, \dfrac{7\pi}{4}$

(b) $\dfrac{\pi}{12}, \dfrac{7\pi}{12}, \dfrac{9\pi}{12}, \dfrac{15\pi}{12}, \dfrac{17\pi}{12}, \dfrac{23\pi}{12}$

(c) $\dfrac{\pi}{12}, \dfrac{5\pi}{12}, \dfrac{7\pi}{12}, \dfrac{9\pi}{12}, \dfrac{11\pi}{12}, \dfrac{13\pi}{12}, \dfrac{15\pi}{12}, \dfrac{17\pi}{12}, \dfrac{19\pi}{12}, \dfrac{23\pi}{12}$

(d) $\dfrac{\pi}{12}, \dfrac{7\pi}{12}$

(e) None of these

Test Form B   Name _____ Date _____

Chapter 7   Class _____ Section _____

1. Simplify: $\sec x \cos\left(\dfrac{\pi}{2} - x\right)$

   (a) 1   (b) $\dfrac{1}{\cos^2 x}$ (c) $\tan x$

   (d) $\cot x$ (e) None of these

2. Given $\csc x = -3$ and $\tan x > 0$, find $\cos x$.

   (a) $\dfrac{2\sqrt{2}}{3}$ (b) $-\dfrac{3\sqrt{2}}{2}$ (c) $-\dfrac{2\sqrt{2}}{3}$

   (d) $\dfrac{3\sqrt{2}}{2}$ (e) None of these

3. Rewrite: $\dfrac{\cot^2 \theta + 1}{\cos^2 \theta - 1}$

   (a) $-\dfrac{1}{\sin^4 \theta}$ (b) -1 (c) $\csc^4 \theta$

   (d) $\cot^2 \theta$ (e) None of these

4. Simplify: $\dfrac{1 + \cos \theta}{\sin \theta} + \dfrac{\sin \theta}{1 + \cos \theta}$

   (a) $\dfrac{1 + \cos \theta + \sin \theta}{\sin \theta + \sin \theta \cos \theta}$ (b) $1 + 2\cos \theta + \cos^2 \theta$ (c) $\dfrac{2}{\sin \theta}$

   (d) $\cos^2 \theta$ (e) None of these

5. Simplify: $\dfrac{\cos x}{1 + \sin x}$

   (a) $\cos x + \cot x$ (b) $\sec x - \tan x$ (c) $\sec x - \cot x$

   (d) $\cos x + \tan x$ (e) None of these

6. Factor and simplify: $\sec^4 x - 2\sec^2 x \tan^2 x + \tan^4 x$

   (a) -1 (b) $\sec x - \tan x$ (c) $\sec x + \tan x$

   (d) 1   (e) None of these

7. Evaluate: $\sin 255°$ (Use the fact that $255° = 210° + 45°$.)

(a) $\dfrac{\sqrt{6} - \sqrt{2}}{4}$

(b) $\dfrac{\sqrt{2} - \sqrt{6}}{4}$

(c) $-\dfrac{\sqrt{2} + \sqrt{6}}{4}$

(d) $\dfrac{\sqrt{2} + \sqrt{6}}{4}$

(e) None of these

8. Simplify: $\sin 8x \cos 2x + \cos 8x \sin 2x$

(a) $\sin 10x$

(b) $\sin 6x$

(c) $\cos 10x$

(d) $\cos 6x$

(e) None of these

9. Evaluate: $\tan \dfrac{13\pi}{12}$ $\left(\text{Use the fact that } \dfrac{13\pi}{12} = \dfrac{4\pi}{3} - \dfrac{\pi}{4}.\right)$

(a) 1

(b) $1 + \sqrt{3}$

(c) $\sqrt{3} - 1$

(d) $2 - \sqrt{3}$

(e) None of these

10. Given $\cos \theta = -\dfrac{7}{9}$ and $\tan \theta < 0$, find $\sin 2\theta$.

(a) $-\dfrac{14}{9}$

(b) $-\dfrac{56\sqrt{2}}{81}$

(c) $-\dfrac{32}{81}$

(d) $\dfrac{49}{81}$

(e) None of these

11. Simplify: $y = \pm\sqrt{\dfrac{1 - \cos 16x}{2}}$

(a) $y = \sin 32x$

(b) $y = \cos 32x$

(c) $y = \sin 8x$

(d) $y = \cos 8x$

(e) None of these

12. Rewrite as a product: $\sin 7\theta - \sin 3\theta$

(a) $2 \sin 5\theta \cos 2\theta$

(b) $2 \cos 5\theta \sin 2\theta$

(c) $2 \cos 5\theta \cos 2\theta$

(d) $-2 \sin 5\theta \cos 2\theta$

(e) None of these

13. Rewrite as a sum: $\sin 3x \cos 4y$

(a) $\frac{1}{2}[\sin(3x + 4y) + \sin(3x - 4y)]$

(b) $\frac{1}{2}[\sin(3x + 4y) - \sin(3x - 4y)]$

(c) $2[\cos(3x + 4y) + \cos(3x - 4y)]$

(d) $2[\sin(3x - 4y) + \cos(3x - 4y)]$

(e) None of these

14. Find all solutions in the interval $[0, 2\pi)$: $\tan \dfrac{x}{4} = \dfrac{\sqrt{3}}{3}$

(a) $\dfrac{2\pi}{3}$

(b) $\dfrac{10\pi}{3}$

(c) $\dfrac{\pi}{4}$

(d) $\dfrac{\pi}{4}, \dfrac{5\pi}{4}$

(e) None of these

15. Find all solutions in the interval $[0, 2\pi)$: $2 \sin x \cos x + \cos x = 0$

(a) $\dfrac{\pi}{6}, \dfrac{\pi}{2}, \dfrac{5\pi}{6}, \dfrac{3\pi}{2}$

(b) $\dfrac{\pi}{2}, \dfrac{7\pi}{6}, \dfrac{3\pi}{2}, \dfrac{11\pi}{6}$

(c) $\dfrac{5\pi}{6}, \dfrac{11\pi}{6}$

(d) $0, \pi$

(e) None of these

Test Form C   Name _____ Date _____

Chapter 7   Class _____ Section _____

1. Simplify: $\dfrac{\csc x}{\tan x + \cot x}$

   (a) $\cos x + \tan x$ (b) $\sin^2 x + \cos x$ (c) $\csc^2 x \sec x$

   (d) $\cos x$ (e) None of these

2. For what values of x, $0 \leq x < 2\pi$ is it true that $\csc x = \sqrt{\cot^2 x + 1}$?

   (a) $0 < x < \pi$ (b) $\pi < x < 2\pi$ (c) $\dfrac{\pi}{2} \leq x \leq \dfrac{3\pi}{2}$

   (d) $0 \leq x < \dfrac{\pi}{2},\ \pi < x < \dfrac{3\pi}{2}$ (e) None of these

3. Simplify: $\dfrac{\tan^2 x}{\csc^2 x - 1}$

   (a) -1 (b) 1 (c) $\tan^4 x$

   (d) $-\cot^4 x$ (e) None of these

4. Simplify: $\dfrac{\tan x}{1 - \sec x}$

   (a) $-\cot x(1 + \sec x)$ (b) $\dfrac{1 + \sec x}{\tan x}$ (c) $\cot x$

   (d) $1 - \sin x \sec^2 x$ (e) None of these

5. Factor and simplify: $\cos^4 x + 2\cos^2 x \sin^2 x + \sin^4 x$

   (a) -1 (b) 1 (c) $2\sin^2 x \cos^2 x$

   (d) $\sin^4 x + 1$ (e) None of these

6. Evaluate: $\tan 165°$ (Use the fact that $165° = 210° - 45°$.)

   (a) $3 + 2\sqrt{3}$ (b) $-2 + \sqrt{3}$ (c) $2 - \sqrt{3}$

   (d) $-3 - 2\sqrt{3}$ (e) None of these

7. Simplify: $\cos(5\pi + x)$

   (a) $\cos x$

   (b) $\sin x$

   (c) $-\sin x$

   (d) $-\cos x$

   (e) None of these

8. Simplify: $\sin 345° \cos 45° + \cos 345° \sin 45°$

   (a) $-\dfrac{\sqrt{3}}{2}$

   (b) $\dfrac{1}{2}$

   (c) $\dfrac{\sqrt{3}}{2}$

   (d) $-\dfrac{1}{2}$

   (e) None of these

9. Given $\tan\theta = \dfrac{3}{4}$ and $\sin\theta < 0$, find $\tan 2\theta$.

   (a) $\dfrac{1}{3}$

   (b) $\dfrac{\sqrt{5}}{3}$

   (c) $\dfrac{5}{9}$

   (d) $\dfrac{24}{7}$

   (e) None of these

10. Given $\tan u = -\dfrac{1}{3}$, and $\sin u < 0$, find $\sin\left(\dfrac{u}{2}\right)$.   (Assume $0 \le u < 2\pi$.)

    (a) $-\sqrt{\dfrac{10 + 3\sqrt{10}}{20}}$

    (b) $\sqrt{\dfrac{10 - 3\sqrt{10}}{20}}$

    (c) $\sqrt{\dfrac{10 + 3\sqrt{10}}{20}}$

    (d) $-\sqrt{\dfrac{10 - 3\sqrt{10}}{20}}$

    (e) None of these

11. Use trigonometric identities to rewrite: $\cos^4 x \tan^4 x$

    (a) $\frac{1}{8}(3 + 4\cos 2x + \cos 4x)$

    (b) $-\frac{1}{4}\cos 4x$

    (c) $\frac{1}{4}(2 + \cos 4x)$

    (d) $\frac{1}{8}(3 - 4\cos 2x + \cos 4x)$

    (e) None of these

12. Use a sum-to-product formula to simplify: $\dfrac{\sin 3\theta + \sin 5\alpha}{\cos 3\theta + \cos 5\alpha}$

    (a) $\tan(3\theta + 5\alpha)$

    (b) $\tan\left(\dfrac{3\theta + 5\alpha}{2}\right)$

    (c) 1

    (d) $\cot\left(\dfrac{3\theta - 5\alpha}{2}\right)$

    (e) None of these

13. Use a product-to-sum formula to rewrite: $\sin 7x \cos 3x$

(a) $\frac{1}{2}(\sin 4x + \cos 10x)$ (b) $\frac{1}{2}(\sin 10x + \sin 4x)$ (c) $\frac{1}{2}(\cos 4x + \cos 10x)$

(d) $\sin 2x + \cos 5x$ (e) None of these

14. Find all solutions in the interval $[0,\ 2\pi)$: $2\sin^3 x + \sin^2 x = 0$

(a) $\dfrac{5\pi}{6},\ \dfrac{11\pi}{6}$ (b) $\dfrac{4\pi}{3},\ \dfrac{5\pi}{3}$ (c) $0,\ \dfrac{7\pi}{6},\ \pi,\ \dfrac{11\pi}{6}$

(d) $0,\ \dfrac{\pi}{2},\ \pi,\ \dfrac{4\pi}{3},\ \dfrac{3\pi}{2},\ \dfrac{5\pi}{3}$ (e) None of these

15. Find all solutions in the interval $[0,\ 2\pi)$: $2\cos^2(2\theta) - 1 = 0$

(a) $\dfrac{\pi}{4},\ \dfrac{3\pi}{4},\ \dfrac{5\pi}{4},\ \dfrac{7\pi}{4}$ (b) $\dfrac{\pi}{8},\ \dfrac{3\pi}{8},\ \dfrac{5\pi}{8},\ \dfrac{7\pi}{8},\ \dfrac{9\pi}{8},\ \dfrac{11\pi}{8},\ \dfrac{13\pi}{8},\ \dfrac{15\pi}{8}$

(c) $\dfrac{\pi}{8},\ \dfrac{\pi}{4},\ \dfrac{3\pi}{8},\ \dfrac{3\pi}{4}$ (d) $\dfrac{\pi}{2},\ \dfrac{\pi}{4},\ \dfrac{3\pi}{2},\ \dfrac{3\pi}{4},\ \dfrac{5\pi}{2},\ \dfrac{5\pi}{4},\ \dfrac{7\pi}{2},\ \dfrac{7\pi}{4}$

(e) None of these

Test Form D   Name _____   Date _____

Chapter 7   Class _____   Section _____

1. Use trigonometric identities to simplify: $\dfrac{\csc x \cos^2 x}{1 + \csc x}$

2. For what values of θ, $0 \le \theta < 2\pi$ is it true that $\sec\theta = -\sqrt{1 + \tan^2\theta}$?

3. Simplify: $\sin\left(\dfrac{\pi}{2} + x\right)\cos(-x)$

4. Factor and simplify: $1 + 2\tan^2\theta + \tan^4\theta$

5. Subtract and simplify: $\dfrac{1 + \sin\theta}{\cos\theta} - \dfrac{\cos\theta}{\sin\theta - 1}$

6. Verify the identity: $\dfrac{\tan^2 x + 1}{\tan^2 x} = \csc^2 x$

7. Evaluate: $\sin 255°$ (Use the fact that $255° = 300° - 45°$.)

8. Simplify: $\dfrac{\tan 7x + \tan 5x}{1 - \tan 7x \tan 5x}$

9. Given $\sin x = -\frac{1}{8}$ and $\tan x < 0$, find $\sin 2x$.

10. Given $\cos x = -\dfrac{3}{7}$ and $\dfrac{\pi}{2} < x < \pi$, find $\cos\left(\dfrac{x}{2}\right)$.

11. Rewrite in terms of the first power of the cosine: $\cos^2 2x \sin^2 2x$

12. Rewrite as a sum: $\frac{1}{4}\cos 12x \cos 4x$

13. Rewrite as a product: $\sin(x + 2y) - \sin(x - 2y)$

14. Find all solutions in the interval $[0,\ 2\pi)$: $3\tan^2 2x - 1 = 0$

15. Find all solutions in the interval $[0,\ 2\pi)$: $2\sin^2 x = \sin x$

16. Use a graphing utility to find all solutions in the interval $[0,\ \pi)$: $2\sin x + \cos x = 0$

Test Form E

Chapter 7

Name _____   Date _____

Class _____   Section _____

1. Use trigonometric identities to simplify: $\dfrac{\cos^4 x - \sin^4 x}{\cos^2 x - \sin^2 x}$

2. For what values of θ, $0 \le \theta < 2\pi$ is it true that $\sin \theta = -\sqrt{1 - \cos^2 \theta}$?

3. Verify the identity: $\sec x \csc^2 x - \csc^2 x = \dfrac{\sec x}{1 + \cos x}$

4. Add and simplify: $\dfrac{1}{\csc x - 1} + \dfrac{1}{\csc x + 1}$

5. Given $\sin x = \dfrac{4}{7}$ and $\cos x = -\dfrac{\sqrt{33}}{7}$, find $\cot x$.

6. Evaluate: $\sin(-15°)$ (Use the fact that $-15° = 45° - 60°$.)

7. Simplify: $\dfrac{\tan 325° - \tan 25°}{1 + \tan 325° \tan 25°}$

8. Given $\tan x = -5$ and $\sin x > 0$, find $\sin 2x$.

9. Given $\cos x = \dfrac{2}{3}$ and $\dfrac{3\pi}{2} < x < 2\pi$, find $\cos\left(\dfrac{x}{2}\right)$.

10. Rewrite in terms of the first power of the cosine: $\tan^4 2x$

11. Rewrite as a sum: $3\cos 5x \sin(-2x)$

12. Verify the identity: $\sin(\pi + 2x)\sin(\pi - 2x) = -\sin^2 2x$

13. Find all solutions in the interval $[0, 2\pi)$: $\tan^2 \theta \csc \theta = \tan^2 \theta$

14. Find all solutions in the interval $[0, 2\pi)$: $2\sin^2 2x + 5\sin 2x - 3 = 0$

15. Find all solutions in the interval $[0, 2\pi)$: $2\cos\left(\dfrac{x}{2}\right) - \sqrt{3} = 0$

16. Use a graphing utility to find all solutions in the interval $[0, \pi)$: $3\sin(2x) + \cos x = 0$

Test Form A   Name _____   Date _____

Chapter 8   Class _____   Section _____

In Problems 1–8, consider a triangle with angles A, B, and C whose opposing sides are a, b, and c, respectively.

1. Given an oblique triangle with $C = 72°$, $A = 15°$, and $b = 342.6$, find a.

   (a) 1258.92   (b) 88.79   (c) 6323.1
   (d) 326.28   (e) None of these

2. Given a triangle with $a = 80$, $b = 51$, and $c = 113$, find C.

   (a) 117.5°   (b) 27.5°   (c) 157.4°
   (d) 62.5°   (e) None of these

3. Given an oblique triangle with $C = 80.3°$, $c = 52.7$, and $b = 41.6$, find B.

   (a) 77.7°   (b) 82.4°   (c) 51.1°
   (d) 0.8°   (e) None of these

4. Given a triangle with $a = 2178$, $B = 23°$, $c = 1719$, and find b.

   (a) 2184.9   (b) 805,937.8   (c) 2062.1
   (d) 897.7   (e) None of these

5. Given a triangle with $c = 24.19$, $a = 91.6$, and $B = 37°$, find the area.

   (a) 1769.6 square units   (b) 666.8 square units   (c) 1107.9 square units
   (d) 1333.5 square units   (e) None of these

6. Given a triangle with $B = 61°$, $c = 18$, and $b = 17$, find A. If there are two solutions, find both A_1 and A_2.

   (a) 6.8°, 173.2°   (b) 51.2°   (c) 112.2°
   (d) 6.8°, 51.2°   (e) None of these

7. Given a triangle with $c = 634$, $b = 600$, and $B = 78°$, find the number of solutions for a.

   (a) 0   (b) 1   (c) 2
   (d) 3   (e) 6

8. Given a triangle with $a = 80$, $b = 90$, and $c = 110$, use Heron's formula to find the area.

   (a) 12,600,000   (b) 69,135.8   (c) 262.9

   (d) 3549.6   (e) None of these

9. A vector **v** has initial point $(1, 8)$ and terminal point $(3, -7)$. Find its magnitude.

   (a) $\sqrt{229}$ (b) $\sqrt{5}$ (c) $4\sqrt{14}$

   (d) $\sqrt{15}$ (e) None of these

10. A vector **v** has a magnitude of 8 and makes an angle of 120° with the positive x-axis. Find the component form of **v**.

    (a) $\left\langle \dfrac{8\sqrt{3}}{3}, \ -8\sqrt{3} \right\rangle$ (b) $\left\langle 8\sqrt{3}, \ \dfrac{8\sqrt{3}}{3} \right\rangle$ (c) $\langle 4\sqrt{3}, \ -4 \rangle$

    (d) $\langle -4, \ 4\sqrt{3} \rangle$ (e) None of these

11. Given $\mathbf{u} = 3\mathbf{i} + 2\mathbf{j}$, $\mathbf{w} = \mathbf{i} - \mathbf{j}$, and $\mathbf{v} = 3\mathbf{u} - 2\mathbf{w}$, find the component form of **v**.

    (a) $\langle 11, \ 4 \rangle$ (b) $\langle 7, \ 8 \rangle$ (c) $\langle \sqrt{77}, \ 4\sqrt{2} \rangle$

    (d) $\langle \sqrt{85}, \ 2\sqrt{10} \rangle$ (e) None of these

12. Given $\mathbf{v} = 3\mathbf{i} + 2\mathbf{j}$ and $\mathbf{w} = 7\mathbf{i} - 5\mathbf{j}$, find the angle θ, $0° < \theta \le 180°$ between **v** and **w**. (Assume that the initial point of each vector is the origin.)

    (a) 16.7°   (b) 110.8°   (c) 50.4°

    (d) 69.2°   (e) None of these

13. Rewrite the complex number in trigonometric form: $16 - 4i$

    (a) $4\sqrt{15}(\cos 14° + i\sin 14°)$ (b) $4\sqrt{15}(\cos 346° + i\sin 346°)$

    (c) $4\sqrt{17}(\cos 346° + i\sin 346°)$ (d) $4\sqrt{17}(\cos 194° + i\sin 194°)$

    (e) None of these

14. Multiply: $[5(\cos 15° + i\sin 15°)][12(\cos 23° + i\sin 23°)]$

    (a) $60(\cos 345° + i\sin 345°)$ (b) $60(\cos 38° + i\sin 38°)$

    (c) $17(\cos 38° + i\sin 38°)$ (d) $17(\cos 345° + i\sin 345°)$

    (e) None of these

15. Give the standard form: $10\left(\cos\dfrac{2\pi}{3} + i\sin\dfrac{2\pi}{3}\right)$

(a) $5\sqrt{3} + 5i$ (b) $10\sqrt{3}\,i$ (c) $5 + 5\sqrt{3}\,i$

(d) $-5 + 5\sqrt{3}\,i$ (e) None of these

16. Rewrite the complex number in trigonometric form: $-4i$

(a) $4\left(\cos\dfrac{3\pi}{2} + i\sin\dfrac{3\pi}{2}\right)$ (b) $4(\cos\pi + i\sin\pi)$ (c) $4\left(\cos\dfrac{\pi}{2} + i\sin\dfrac{\pi}{2}\right)$

(d) $4(\cos 0 + i\sin 0)$ (e) None of these

17. Use DeMoivre's Theorem to find $(3 + 3i)^8$.

(a) $104{,}976$ (b) 6561 (c) 16

(d) $6561 + 6561i$ (e) None of these

18. Find the square roots: $64\left(\cos\dfrac{\pi}{3} + i\sin\dfrac{\pi}{3}\right)$

(a) $8\left(\cos\dfrac{\pi}{3} + i\sin\dfrac{\pi}{3}\right),\ 8\left(\cos\dfrac{2\pi}{3} + i\sin\dfrac{2\pi}{3}\right)$

(b) $8\left(\cos\dfrac{\pi}{6} + i\sin\dfrac{\pi}{6}\right),\ 8\left(\cos\dfrac{7\pi}{6} + i\sin\dfrac{7\pi}{6}\right)$

(c) $8\left(\cos\dfrac{\pi}{3} + i\sin\dfrac{\pi}{3}\right),\ 8\left(\cos\dfrac{\pi}{6} + i\sin\dfrac{\pi}{6}\right)$

(d) $4\sqrt{2} + 4\sqrt{3}\,i,\ 4\sqrt{2} - 4\sqrt{3}\,i$

(e) None of these

19. Find all solutions: $x^2 - 4i = 0$

(a) $\sqrt{2} - \sqrt{2}\,i,\ -\sqrt{2} + \sqrt{2}\,i$ (b) $2 + i,\ -2 - i$

(c) $2 - i,\ 2 + i$ (d) $\sqrt{2} + \sqrt{2}\,i,\ -\sqrt{2} - \sqrt{2}\,i$

(e) None of these

20. Find the quotient: $\dfrac{7(\cos 75° + i\sin 75°)}{2(\cos 25° + i\sin 25°)}$

(a) $\dfrac{7}{2}(\cos 50° - i\sin 50°)$ (b) $\dfrac{7}{2}(\cos 3° + i\sin 3°)$ (c) $\dfrac{7}{2}(\cos 50° + i\sin 50°)$

(d) $\dfrac{7}{2}(\cos 3° - i\sin 3°)$ (e) None of these

Test Form B   Name _____   Date _____

Chapter 8   Class _____   Section _____

In Problems 1–5, consider a triangle with angles A, B, and C whose opposing sides are a, b, and c, respectively.

1. Given an oblique triangle with $A = 39°$, $B = 106°$, and $c = 78$, find a.

   (a) 71.1   (b) 85.6   (c) 74.0

   (d) 82.2   (e) None of these

2. Given an oblique triangle with $a = 72$, $b = 51$, and $A = 27°$, find the area.

   (a) 833.5 square units   (b) 1315.3 square units   (c) 1635.9 square units

   (d) 2630.6 square units   (e) None of these

3. Given an oblique triangle with $B = 81°$, $a = 15$, and $c = 72$, find b.

   (a) 57.2   (b) 3275.6   (c) 5071

   (d) 71.2   (e) None of these

4. Given an oblique triangle with $A = 12°$, $a = 12$, and $c = 37$, find the two possible values of b.

   (a) 3.04, 14.95   (b) 44.30, 45.40   (c) 7.57, 10.85

   (d) 26.98, 45.40   (e) None of these

5. Given a triangle with $a = 17$, $b = 39$, and $c = 50$, find A.

   (a) 16.88°   (b) 73.12°   (c) 163.12°

   (d) 106.88°   (e) None of these

6. Ship A is 72 miles from a lighthouse on the shore. Its bearing from the lighthouse is N 15° E. Ship B is 81 miles from the same lighthouse. Its bearing from the lighthouse is N 52° E. Find the number of miles between the two ships.

   (a) 84.57   (b) 44.44   (c) 49.29

   (d) 90.75   (e) None of these

7. Find the component form of the vector at the right.

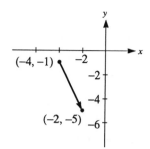

(a) $\langle -2,\ 4 \rangle$ (b) $\langle 2,\ -4 \rangle$ (c) $\langle -6,\ -6 \rangle$

(d) $\langle 6,\ 6 \rangle$ (e) None of these

8. Given $\mathbf{v} = \dfrac{2}{3}\mathbf{w} + \dfrac{1}{2}\mathbf{u}$ where $\mathbf{w} = \mathbf{i}$ and $\mathbf{u} = 4\mathbf{i} - 2\mathbf{j}$, find $\mathbf{v}$.

(a) $\dfrac{8}{3}\mathbf{i} - \mathbf{j}$ (b) $\dfrac{8}{3}\mathbf{i} - 2\mathbf{j}$ (c) $\dfrac{8}{3}\mathbf{i} + \mathbf{j}$

(d) $\dfrac{8}{3}\mathbf{i} + 2\mathbf{j}$ (e) None of these

9. Two forces, one of 120 pounds and the other of 200 pounds, act on the same object at angles of 30° and −30° respectively, with the positive x-axis. Find the direction of the resultant of these two forces.

(a) 14°   (b) −8.2°   (c) 0°

(d) −18°   (e) None of these

10. Which of the following graphs correctly expresses $7 - 2i$ in trigonometric form?

(a)

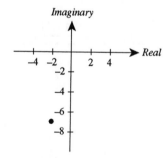

(b)

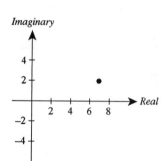

(c)

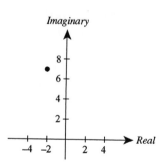

(d)

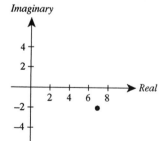

(e) None of these

11. Write in trigonometric form: $-2 + 3i$

   (a) $\sqrt{13}(\cos 56.3° + i \sin 56.3°)$ (b) $\sqrt{13}(\cos 123.7° + i \sin 123.7°)$

   (c) $\sqrt{13}(\cos 236.3° + i \sin 236.3°)$ (d) $\sqrt{13}(\cos 303.7° + i \sin 303.7°)$

   (e) None of these

12. Multiply: $[5(\cos 30° + i \sin 30°)][7(\cos 30° + i \sin 30°)]$

   (a) $35(\cos 60° + i \sin 60°)$ (b) $35(\cos 30° + i \sin 30°)$

   (c) $35(\cos 900° + i \sin 900°)$ (d) $12(\cos 30° + i \sin 30°)$

   (e) None of these

13. Find $(-2 + 2i)^8$.

   (a) $-2896.3 + 2896.3i$ (b) $-16i$ (c) $4096i$

   (d) 4096 (e) None of these

14. Which of the following is *not* a solution to $x^3 - 1 = 0$?

   (a) 1 (b) $\dfrac{1}{2} + \dfrac{\sqrt{3}}{2} i$ (c) $-\dfrac{1}{2} + \dfrac{\sqrt{3}}{2} i$

   (d) $-\dfrac{1}{2} - \dfrac{\sqrt{3}}{2} i$ (e) All are solutions.

15. Evaluate: $[3(\cos 120° + i \sin 120°)]^5$

   (a) $\dfrac{-243}{2} - \dfrac{243\sqrt{3}}{2} i$ (b) $\dfrac{-243}{2} + \dfrac{243\sqrt{3}}{2} i$ (c) $\dfrac{243}{2} + \dfrac{243\sqrt{3}}{2} i$

   (d) $\dfrac{243}{2} - \dfrac{243\sqrt{3}}{2} i$ (e) None of these

Test Form C   Name _____   Date _____

Chapter 8   Class _____   Section _____

In Problems 1–6, consider a triangle with angles A, B, and C whose opposing sides are a, b, and c, respectively.

1. Given a triangle with $A = 98°$, $a = 27$, and $b = 16$, find the area.

    (a) 155.56 square units (b) 149.86 square units (c) 311.11 square units

    (d) 213.90 square units (e) None of these

2. Find the two possible magnitudes of angle B, given a triangle with $A = 74°$, $a = 59.2$, and $c = 60.3$.

    (a) 78.3°, 101.7° (b) 4.3°, 27.7° (c) 73.7°, 106.3°

    (d) 32.3°, 0.3° (e) None of these

3. Given an oblique triangle with $A = 102°$, $B = 23°$, and $c = 576.1$, find a.

    (a) 687.9 (b) 208.8 (c) 1442.2

    (d) 274.8 (e) None of these

4. Given a triangle with $a = 121$, $b = 82$, and $c = 90$, find the area.

    (a) 9922 (b) 4961 (c) 523.2

    (d) 3689.7 (e) None of these

5. Given a triangle with $a = 117$, $b = 230$, and $c = 185$, find B.

    (a) 96.6° (b) 6.6° (c) 53.0°

    (d) 37.0° (e) None of these

6. Given a triangle with $A = 58°20'$, $b = 23$, and $c = 18$, find a.

    (a) 20.41 (b) 20.45 (c) 25.21

    (d) 35.88 (e) None of these

7. A television antenna sits on the roof. Two 78-foot guy wires are positioned on opposite sides of the antenna. The angle of elevation each makes with the ground is 23°. How far apart are the ends of the two guy wires?

    (a) 71.8 feet (b) 76.3 feet (c) 143.6 feet

    (d) 152.6 feet (e) None of these

8. A vector **v** has initial point $(3, 7)$ and terminal point $(3, -2)$. Find the component form of **v**.

   (a) $\langle 0, \ 9 \rangle$ (b) $\langle 9, \ 0 \rangle$ (c) $\langle 0, \ -9 \rangle$

   (d) $\langle -9, \ 0 \rangle$ (e) None of these

9. Find $\mathbf{v} + \mathbf{w}$ given that **v** has a magnitude of 200 and a direction of 215° and **w** has a magnitude of 150 and a direction of 162°.

   (a) $-21.2\mathbf{i} - 161.1\mathbf{j}$ (b) $350\mathbf{i} + 350\mathbf{j}$ (c) $50\mathbf{i} - 50\mathbf{j}$

   (d) $-306.5\mathbf{i} - 68.4\mathbf{j}$ (e) None of these

10. Find a unit vector in the direction of $\mathbf{v} = 3\mathbf{i} - 2\mathbf{j}$.

    (a) $\langle 3\sqrt{13}, \ -2\sqrt{13} \rangle$ (b) $\left\langle \dfrac{3\sqrt{13}}{13}, \ -\dfrac{2\sqrt{13}}{13} \right\rangle$ (c) $\langle \sqrt{13}, \ -\sqrt{13} \rangle$

    (d) $\langle 1, \ -1 \rangle$ (e) None of these

11. Rewrite in trigonometric form: $7 - 2i$

    (a) $\sqrt{53}(\cos 344.1° + i \sin 344.1°)$ (b) $3\sqrt{5}(\cos 344.1° + i \sin 344.1°)$

    (c) $3\sqrt{5}(\cos 15.9° + i \sin 15.9°)$ (d) $\sqrt{53}(\cos 15.9° + i \sin 15.9°)$

    (e) None of these

12. Find the product: $[3(\cos 85° + i \sin 85°)][12(\cos 10° + i \sin 10°)]$

    (a) $4(\cos 75° + i \sin 75°)$ (b) $36(\cos 850° + i \sin 850°)$

    (c) $36(\cos 95° + i \sin 95°)$ (d) $4(\sin 95° + i \cos 95°)$

    (e) None of these

13. Represent the complex number graphically: $-5(3 - \sqrt{2}\,i)$

(a)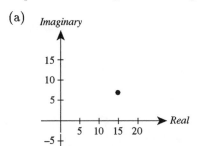

(b)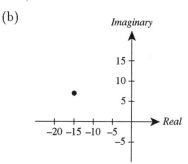

(c)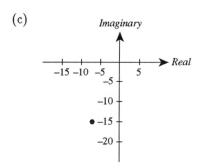

(d)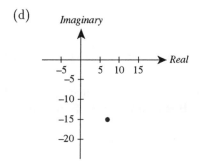

(e) None of these

14. Evaluate: $[2(\cos 15° + i \sin 15°)]^{12}$

(a) 4096

(b) 4096i

(c) -4096

(d) $-4096i$

(e) None of these

15. Find the fourth roots of $81i$.

(a) $\pm 3,\ \pm 3i$

(b) $3\left(\cos\dfrac{\pi}{8} + i\sin\dfrac{\pi}{8}\right),\ \ 3\left(\cos\dfrac{17\pi}{8} + i\sin\dfrac{17\pi}{8}\right),\ \ 3\left(\cos\dfrac{33\pi}{8} + i\sin\dfrac{33\pi}{8}\right),$

$\quad 3\left(\cos\dfrac{49\pi}{8} + i\sin\dfrac{49\pi}{8}\right)$

(c) $3\left(\cos\dfrac{\pi}{2} + i\sin\dfrac{\pi}{2}\right),\ \ -3\left(\cos\dfrac{\pi}{2} + i\sin\dfrac{\pi}{2}\right),\ \ 3\left(\cos\dfrac{3\pi}{2} + i\sin\dfrac{3\pi}{2}\right),\ \ -3\left(\cos\dfrac{3\pi}{2} + i\sin\dfrac{3\pi}{2}\right)$

(d) $3\left(\cos\dfrac{\pi}{8} + i\sin\dfrac{\pi}{8}\right),\ \ 3\left(\cos\dfrac{5\pi}{8} + i\sin\dfrac{5\pi}{8}\right),\ \ 3\left(\cos\dfrac{9\pi}{8} + i\sin\dfrac{9\pi}{8}\right),\ \ 3\left(\cos\dfrac{13\pi}{8} + i\sin\dfrac{13\pi}{8}\right)$

(e) None of these

Test Form D   Name _____   Date _____

Chapter 8   Class _____   Section _____

1. Given the triangle to the right, find B.

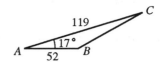

2. Given an oblique triangle with $B = 56°$, $a = 98$ and $b = 85$, find the two possible values for angle C.

3. From firetower A, a fire with a bearing N 78° E is sighted. The same fire is sighted from tower B at N 51° W. Tower B is 70 miles east of tower A. How far is it from tower A to the fire?

4. Given a triangle with $A = 37°$, $B = 78°$, and $c = 250$, find the area.

5. Given a triangle with $a = 78$, $b = 15$, and $c = 91$, find the area.

6. Given a triangle with $a = 78$, $b = 15$, and $c = 91$, find A, B, and C.

7. Find the component form of a unit vector that makes an angle of 120° with the positive x-axis.

8. Find the angle θ, $0° < \theta \le 180°$, between vector $\mathbf{v}$ and vector $\mathbf{w}$, given $\mathbf{v} = 3\mathbf{i} - 2\mathbf{j}$ and $\mathbf{w} = 6\mathbf{i} + \mathbf{j}$. (Assume that the initial point of each vector is the origin.)

9. Given $\mathbf{u} = 3\mathbf{i} - 2\mathbf{j}$ and $\mathbf{w} = 9\mathbf{i} + 5\mathbf{j}$, find $\mathbf{v} = \frac{1}{2}\mathbf{u} + 4\mathbf{w}$.

10. Write the complex number in trigonometric form: $-2 + \sqrt{3}\,i$

11. Find the quotient: $\dfrac{16[\cos(3\pi/4) + i\sin(3\pi/4)]}{2[\cos(\pi/2) + i\sin(\pi/2)]}$

12. Write in standard form and represent graphically: $3(\cos 150° + i\sin 150°)$

13. Evaluate: $\left[2\left(\cos\dfrac{\pi}{4} + i\sin\dfrac{\pi}{4}\right)\right]^{12}$

14. Find the cube roots of $8\left(\cos\dfrac{\pi}{3} + i\sin\dfrac{\pi}{3}\right)$.

15. Find all of the solutions to $x^2 + 4i = 0$.

Test Form E   Name _____   Date _____

Chapter 8   Class _____   Section _____

1. Given a triangle with $A = 61°$, $B = 49°$, and $c = 5396$, find a, b, and C.

2. Given a triangle with $A = 71°$, $b = 10$, and $c = 19$, find the area.

3. Given a triangle with $a = 135$, $b = 71.6$, and $c = 69$, find B.

4. A surveyor wishes to find the distance from a rock on the east side of a river to a tree on the opposite bank. On the east side of the river he locates a second rock 135 feet from the first one. From each rock he measures the angle between the line connecting the two rocks and the tree. The angle from the first rock is 87° and from the second rock is 82°. Find the desired distance.

5. Determine the number of solutions to each of the following triangles.

(a) $C = 58°$, $c = 50$, $a = 67$

(b) $A = 107°$, $b = 17$, $a = 25$

(c) $B = 27°$, $a = 78$, $b = 28$

6. Given an oblique triangle with $A = 38°$, $b = 22$, and $c = 98$, find a.

7. Given a vector **v** with initial point $(2, 5)$ and terminal point $(-1, 9)$, find the magnitude and direction of **v**.

8. Given a vector **v** with magnitude 27 and direction $\theta = 216°$, find the component form of **v**.

9. Two forces, one of 45 pounds and the other 52 pounds, act upon the same object. The angle between these forces is 25°. Find the magnitude of the resultant force.

10. Write the complex number in trigonometric form: $-17 + 32i$

11. Multiply: $[16(\cos 33° + i \sin 33°)][8(\cos 17° + i \sin 17°)]$

12. Represent the complex number graphically: $6 - 2i$

13. Use DeMoivre's Theorem to find $(\sqrt{3} - i)^7$.

14. Find the cube roots of -64.

15. Given a triangle with $a = 36$, $b = 91$, and $c = 72$, find the area.

Test Form A

Name _____ **Date** _____

Chapter 9

Class _____ **Section** _____

1. A wage of x dollars per hour is increased by 9%. Find a mathematical model for y, the new wage, in terms of x, the old wage.

   (a) $y = 0.09x$

   (b) $y = 9x$

   (c) $y = 1.09x$

   (d) $y = x + 0.09$

   (e) None of these

In Problems 2–4, find all solutions to each of the given systems of equations.

2. $x + y = 1$
   $x^2 + 3y^2 = 21$

   (a) $\left(\frac{3}{2}, -3\right)$

   (b) $\left(3, -\frac{3}{2}\right)$

   (c) $\left(-\frac{3}{2}, \frac{5}{2}\right), (3, -2)$

   (d) $\left(\frac{3}{2}, -\frac{1}{2}\right), (-3, 4)$

   (e) No solution

3. $2x^2 + 2y^2 = 7$
   $x + y^2 = 7$

   (a) $(2.8, 2.0), (-0.5, 7.3)$

   (b) $(4.6, 1.5), (-2.6, 3.1)$

   (c) $(2.8, -0.5)$

   (d) $(4.6), (-2.6)$

   (e) No solution

4. $x - y + z = 5$
   $3x + 2y - z = -2$
   $2x + y + 3z = 10$

   (a) $(1, -1, 3)$

   (b) $(2, -5, -2)$

   (c) $(-1, 7, 13)$

   (d) $(3, -9, -7)$

   (e) No solution

5. Use elimination to find all solutions.

   $7x - 3y = 26$
   $2x + 5y = 25$

   (a) $\left(-5, -\frac{61}{3}\right)$

   (b) $(5, 3)$

   (c) Infinitely many solutions

   (d) No solution

   (e) None of these

6. Write the matrix in reduced echelon form:
$\begin{bmatrix} 3 & 1 & 1 & 7 \\ 1 & -2 & 0 & 5 \\ 1 & 1 & 2 & 6 \end{bmatrix}$

(a) $\begin{bmatrix} 1 & 1 & 2 & 6 \\ 0 & 3 & 2 & 1 \\ 0 & 0 & 11 & 31 \end{bmatrix}$

(b) $\begin{bmatrix} 1 & 0 & 0 & \frac{21}{11} \\ 0 & 1 & 0 & -\frac{17}{11} \\ 0 & 0 & 1 & \frac{31}{11} \end{bmatrix}$

(c) $\begin{bmatrix} 1 & -2 & 0 & 5 \\ 0 & 1 & \frac{1}{7} & -\frac{8}{7} \\ 0 & 0 & 11 & 31 \end{bmatrix}$

(d) $\begin{bmatrix} 1 & 0 & 0 & \frac{3}{11} \\ 0 & 1 & 0 & \frac{7}{11} \\ 0 & 0 & 1 & -\frac{14}{11} \end{bmatrix}$

(e) None of these

7. Use matrices to solve the following system of linear equations:
$$x + 2y + z = 7$$
$$3x \qquad + z = 2$$
$$x - y - z = 1$$

(a) $\left(\frac{2}{3}, \frac{20}{3}, -7\right)$

(b) $\left(-\frac{7}{3}, \frac{1}{6}, 9\right)$

(c) $\left(\frac{11}{6}, \frac{13}{3}, -\frac{7}{2}\right)$

(d) $\left(-\frac{19}{3}, -\frac{2}{3}, \frac{44}{3}\right)$

(e) None of these

8. Given $A = \begin{bmatrix} 3 & 6 & -1 \\ 0 & 5 & 2 \end{bmatrix}$ and $B = \begin{bmatrix} 1 & 0 & 5 \\ -1 & 2 & 7 \end{bmatrix}$, find $3A - 2B$.

(a) $\begin{bmatrix} 7 & 18 & -13 \\ 2 & 11 & -8 \end{bmatrix}$

(b) $\begin{bmatrix} 7 & 18 & 2 \\ 0 & 11 & -8 \end{bmatrix}$

(c) $\begin{bmatrix} 11 & 18 & 7 \\ -2 & 19 & 20 \end{bmatrix}$

(d) $\begin{bmatrix} 7 & 18 & -13 \\ -2 & 9 & 20 \end{bmatrix}$

(e) None of these

9. Given $A = \begin{bmatrix} 2 & 1 \\ 3 & -2 \end{bmatrix}$ and $B = \begin{bmatrix} -1 & 5 \\ 6 & 2 \end{bmatrix}$, find AB.

(a) $\begin{bmatrix} 4 & 12 \\ -15 & 11 \end{bmatrix}$

(b) $\begin{bmatrix} 13 & -11 \\ 18 & 2 \end{bmatrix}$

(c) $\begin{bmatrix} 16 & 16 \\ -13 & 1 \end{bmatrix}$

(d) $\begin{bmatrix} -2 & 5 \\ 18 & -4 \end{bmatrix}$

(e) None of these

10. Given $A = \begin{bmatrix} 1 & 2 \\ -3 & 5 \end{bmatrix}$, find A^{-1}.

(a) $\begin{bmatrix} -1 & -2 \\ 3 & -5 \end{bmatrix}$

(b) $\begin{bmatrix} 1 & \frac{1}{2} \\ -\frac{1}{3} & \frac{1}{5} \end{bmatrix}$

(c) $\begin{bmatrix} -\frac{4}{15} & \frac{1}{3} \\ -\frac{2}{3} & \frac{11}{15} \end{bmatrix}$

(d) $\begin{bmatrix} \frac{5}{11} & -\frac{2}{11} \\ \frac{3}{11} & \frac{1}{11} \end{bmatrix}$

(e) None of these

11. Write the matrix equation for the following system of equations.

$$
\begin{aligned}
2x_1 + x_2 &= 0 \\
3x_1 + x_2 + x_3 &= -1 \\
2x_2 - x_3 + 3x_4 &= 1 \\
2x_3 - 3x_4 &= 4
\end{aligned}
$$

(a) $\begin{bmatrix} 2 & 1 & 0 & 0 \\ 3 & 1 & 1 & 0 \\ 0 & 2 & -1 & 3 \\ 0 & 0 & 2 & -3 \end{bmatrix} \begin{bmatrix} x_1 \\ x_2 \\ x_3 \\ x_4 \end{bmatrix} = \begin{bmatrix} 0 \\ -1 \\ 1 \\ 4 \end{bmatrix}$

(b) $\begin{bmatrix} 2 & 3 & 0 & 0 \\ 1 & 1 & 2 & 0 \\ 0 & 1 & -1 & 2 \\ 0 & 0 & 3 & -3 \end{bmatrix} \begin{bmatrix} x_1 \\ x_2 \\ x_3 \\ x_4 \end{bmatrix} = \begin{bmatrix} 0 \\ -1 \\ 1 \\ 4 \end{bmatrix}$

(c) $\begin{bmatrix} 2 & 1 & 0 & 0 \\ 3 & 1 & 1 & 0 \\ 0 & 2 & -1 & 3 \\ 0 & 0 & 2 & -3 \end{bmatrix} \begin{bmatrix} 0 \\ -1 \\ 1 \\ 4 \end{bmatrix} = \begin{bmatrix} x_1 \\ x_2 \\ x_3 \\ x_4 \end{bmatrix}$

(d) $\begin{bmatrix} 2 & 3 & 0 & 0 \\ 1 & 1 & 2 & 0 \\ 0 & 1 & -1 & 2 \\ 0 & 0 & 3 & -3 \end{bmatrix} \begin{bmatrix} 0 \\ -1 \\ 1 \\ 4 \end{bmatrix} = \begin{bmatrix} x_1 \\ x_2 \\ x_3 \\ x_4 \end{bmatrix}$

(e) None of these

12. Match the graph at the right with the correct inequality.

(a) $y < x^2 + 3x - 1$

(b) $y > x^2 + 3x - 1$

(c) $y \leq x^2 + 3x - 1$

(d) $y \geq x^2 + 3x - 1$

(e) None of these

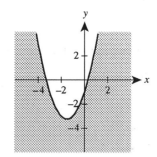

13. Match the graph at the right with the correct system of inequalities.

(a) $3x + y \leq 5$
$y \geq 1$
$x \geq 1$

(b) $3x + y \leq 5$
$y \leq 1$
$x \geq 1$

(c) $y \geq 5 + 3x$
$y \leq 1$
$x \leq 1$

(d) $3x + y \leq 5$
$y \geq 1$
$x \leq 1$

(e) None of these

14. Find all of the solutions to the following system of linear equations.

$$3x + 4y - 2z = 6$$
$$x + y + z = 2$$
$$x + 2y - 4z = 2$$

(a) $(20, -15, -3)$

(b) $\left(\dfrac{a}{2}, \dfrac{5a}{4}, \dfrac{a}{4} \right)$

(c) $(2 - 6a, 5a, a)$

(d) No solution

(e) None of these

15. Find the equation of the parabola, $y = ax^2 + bx + c$, passing through the points $(1, 4)$, $(-1, 0)$, and $(2, -3)$.

(a) $y = 4x^2 + 2x - 2$

(b) $y = 3x^2 + 2x - 7$

(c) $y = -3x^2 + 2x + 5$

(d) $y = 4x^2$

(e) None of these

16. Find the maximum value of the objective function, $P = 8x + 10y$, subject to the following constraints.

$$y \geq 0$$
$$x \geq 0$$
$$x + y \leq 160$$
$$x - 3y \geq 0$$

(a) 1280

(b) 1360

(c) 1500

(d) 0

(e) None of these

Test Form B   Name _____ Date _____

Chapter 9   Class _____ Section _____

1. Assume y is proportional to x, find a linear model that relates y and x, given y equals 50 when x equals 150.

   (a) $y = 3x$ (b) $y = \dfrac{x}{3}$ (c) $y = 100 + x$

   (d) $y = 100 - x$ (e) None of these

In Problems 2 and 3, use substitution to find all solutions to each of the given systems of equations.

2. $x^2 + y^2 = 25$

   $x - y = 1$

   (a) $(5, 0), (0, 5)$ (b) $(-4, -3), (3, 4)$ (c) $(4, 3), (-3, -4)$
   (d) $(-5, 0), (5, 0)$ (e) No solution

3. $x + y + 3z = 0$

   $2x - y - 3z = -9$

   $x + 2y + 3z = 1$

   (a) $\left(-3a,\ a,\ \dfrac{2a}{3}\right)$ (b) $\left(-1,\ 2,\ -\dfrac{1}{3}\right)$ (c) $\left(-3,\ 1,\ \dfrac{2}{3}\right)$

   (d) No solution   (e) None of these

In Problems 4–5, use elimination to find all solutions to each of the given systems of equations.

4. $2x + 4y = 7$

   $3x + 6y = 5$

   (a) $\left(1, \frac{5}{4}\right)$ (b) $(0, 0)$
   (c) Infinitely many solutions   (d) No solution
   (e) None of these

5. $\dfrac{2}{x} - \dfrac{3}{y} = 8$

   $\dfrac{3}{x} + \dfrac{3}{y} = 2$

   (a) $\left(2,\ -\dfrac{4}{3}\right)$ (b) $\left(\dfrac{1}{2},\ -\dfrac{3}{4}\right)$
   (c) Infinitely many solutions   (d) No solution
   (e) None of these

6. Find all solutions to the following system of linear equations.

$$2x + y - z = 3$$
$$x - 3y + z = 7$$
$$3x + 5y - 3z = -1$$

(a) $\left(a, \dfrac{3a - 10}{2}, \dfrac{7a - 16}{2} \right)$

(b) $\left(\dfrac{3a + 10}{3}, a, 6a - 21 \right)$

(c) $(2, -2, -1)$

(d) No solution

(e) None of these

7. Find an equation of the circle $x^2 + y^2 + Dx + Ey + F = 0$ that passes through the points $(9, -3)$, $(2, 4)$, and $(-5, -3)$.

(a) $x^2 + y^2 + 3x - 2y + 10 = 0$

(b) $x^2 + y^2 - 4x + 6y - 36 = 0$

(c) $x^2 + y^2 - 8x + 2y - 12 = 0$

(d) $x^2 + y^2 + 2x - 7y + 1 = 0$

(e) None of these

8. A twenty pound mixture of candy sells for \$30.52. One kind of candy in the mixture sells for \$1.35 per pound. The other kind sells for \$1.79 per pound. How much of the cheaper priced candy is in the mixture?

(a) 8 pounds

(b) 10 pounds

(c) 12 pounds

(d) 14 pounds

(e) None of these

9. Write the matrix in reduced echelon form: $\begin{bmatrix} 3 & 6 & -2 & 28 \\ -2 & -4 & 5 & -37 \\ 1 & 2 & 9 & -39 \end{bmatrix}$

(a) $\begin{bmatrix} 1 & 2 & 1 & 1 \\ 0 & 0 & 1 & -5 \\ 0 & 0 & 0 & 0 \end{bmatrix}$

(b) $\begin{bmatrix} 0 & 0 & 0 & 0 \\ 1 & 2 & 0 & 6 \\ 0 & 0 & 1 & -5 \end{bmatrix}$

(c) $\begin{bmatrix} 1 & 2 & 0 & 6 \\ 0 & 0 & 1 & -5 \\ 0 & 0 & 0 & 0 \end{bmatrix}$

(d) $\begin{bmatrix} 1 & 2 & 1 & 1 \\ 0 & 0 & 1 & -5 \\ 0 & 0 & 0 & 3 \end{bmatrix}$

(e) None of these

10. Perform the indicated operations: $2 \begin{bmatrix} 4 & 7 \\ 2 & 0 \end{bmatrix} - 3 \begin{bmatrix} 1 & 2 \\ -1 & 5 \end{bmatrix}$

(a) $\begin{bmatrix} 5 & 8 \\ 7 & -15 \end{bmatrix}$

(b) $\begin{bmatrix} 5 & 9 \\ 1 & -15 \end{bmatrix}$

(c) $-1 \begin{bmatrix} 3 & 5 \\ 3 & 5 \end{bmatrix}$

(d) $-1 \begin{bmatrix} 5 & 9 \\ 1 & 5 \end{bmatrix}$

(e) None of these

11. Given $A = \begin{bmatrix} 5 & 1 \\ -2 & 3 \end{bmatrix}$, find A^{-1}.

(a) $\begin{bmatrix} \frac{5}{17} & \frac{1}{17} \\ -\frac{2}{17} & \frac{3}{17} \end{bmatrix}$

(b) $\begin{bmatrix} \frac{3}{17} & -\frac{1}{17} \\ \frac{2}{17} & \frac{5}{17} \end{bmatrix}$

(c) $\begin{bmatrix} 85 & 17 \\ 34 & 51 \end{bmatrix}$

(d) $\begin{bmatrix} -\frac{2}{5} & \frac{1}{3} \\ \frac{3}{2} & -\frac{1}{2} \end{bmatrix}$

(e) None of these

12. Multiply: $\begin{bmatrix} 2 & 3 & 4 \\ -1 & 0 & 2 \end{bmatrix} \begin{bmatrix} -1 & 4 \\ 0 & 1 \\ 5 & 2 \end{bmatrix}$

(a) $\begin{bmatrix} 18 & 19 \\ 11 & 0 \end{bmatrix}$

(b) $\begin{bmatrix} -2 & 0 & 20 \\ -4 & 0 & 4 \end{bmatrix}$

(c) $\begin{bmatrix} -6 & -3 & 4 \\ -2 & 0 & 6 \\ -1 & 2 & 4 \end{bmatrix}$

(d) $\begin{bmatrix} -6 \\ 0 \\ 24 \end{bmatrix}$

(e) None of these

13. Write the matrix equation for the following system of equations.

$3x + 2y = 5$

$7x - 6y = 1$

(a) $\begin{bmatrix} x & y \end{bmatrix} = \begin{bmatrix} 3 & 7 \\ 2 & -6 \end{bmatrix} \begin{bmatrix} 5 \\ 1 \end{bmatrix}$

(b) $\begin{bmatrix} x \\ y \end{bmatrix} = \begin{bmatrix} 3 & 2 \\ 7 & -6 \end{bmatrix} \begin{bmatrix} 5 \\ 1 \end{bmatrix}$

(c) $\begin{bmatrix} 3 & 2 \\ 7 & -6 \end{bmatrix} \begin{bmatrix} x \\ y \end{bmatrix} = \begin{bmatrix} 5 \\ 1 \end{bmatrix}$

(d) $\begin{bmatrix} x & y \end{bmatrix} \begin{bmatrix} 5 \\ 1 \end{bmatrix} = \begin{bmatrix} 3 & 7 \\ 2 & -6 \end{bmatrix}$

(e) None of these

14. Given the system of linear equations with coefficient matrix A, use A^{-1} to find (x, y, z, w).

$$\begin{aligned} x + y + z + w &= 0 \\ 2x - y &= -2 \\ 3z - 2w &= 0 \\ y - 3z &= 6 \end{aligned} \qquad A^{-1} = \begin{bmatrix} \frac{3}{14} & \frac{11}{28} & \frac{3}{28} & \frac{5}{28} \\ \frac{3}{7} & -\frac{3}{14} & \frac{3}{14} & \frac{5}{14} \\ \frac{1}{7} & -\frac{1}{14} & \frac{1}{14} & -\frac{3}{14} \\ \frac{3}{14} & -\frac{3}{28} & -\frac{11}{28} & -\frac{9}{28} \end{bmatrix}$$

(a) $(10, -15, -5, 0)$

(b) $\left(\frac{2}{7}, \frac{18}{7}, -\frac{8}{7}, -\frac{12}{7} \right)$

(c) $\left(\frac{3}{11}, \frac{18}{11}, -\frac{7}{11}, \frac{16}{11} \right)$

(d) $(0, 1, -1, 0)$

(e) None of these

15. Match the graph at the right with the correct inequality.

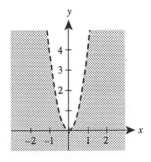

(a) $4x^2 - y \leq 0$ (b) $4x^2 - y > 0$

(c) $4x^2 - y < 0$ (d) $4x^2 - y^2 \geq 0$

(e) None of these

16. Match the graph at the right with the correct system of inequalities.

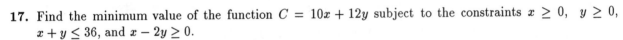

(a) $x + 2y \leq 6$ (b) $x + 2y \geq 6$

$\qquad x - y \leq 2$ $\qquad x - y \geq 2$

$\qquad\qquad y \geq 0$ $\qquad\qquad x \geq 0$

(c) $x + 2y \leq 6$ (d) $x + 2y \geq 6$

$\qquad x - y \geq 2$ $\qquad x - y \geq 2$

$\qquad\qquad x \geq 0$ $\qquad\qquad y \geq 0$

(e) None of these

17. Find the minimum value of the function $C = 10x + 12y$ subject to the constraints $x \geq 0$, $y \geq 0$, $x + y \leq 36$, and $x - 2y \geq 0$.

(a) 0 (b) 360 (c) 384

(d) 432 (e) None of these

Test Form C   Name _____ Date _____

Chapter 9   Class _____ Section _____

1. A new car worth \$12,500 depreciates \$1250 per year. Find a linear model that gives the value of the car, V, in terms of the years, x, since the car was purchased.

   (a) $V = \dfrac{12{,}000}{x}$ (b) $V = 12{,}500 - 1250x$ (c) $V = 10x$

   (d) $V = 12{,}500 - 10x$ (e) None of these

In Problems 2–6, find all solutions to the given system of equations.

2. $x^2 - 4y = 17$

   $x - 2y = 1$

   (a) $(5, \, -3)$ (b) $(5, \, 2), \, (-3, \, -2)$ (c) $\left(2, \, -\tfrac{1}{2}\right), \, \left(-2, \, -\tfrac{3}{2}\right)$

   (d) No solution   (e) None of these

3. $6x - 5y = 4$

   $3x + 2y = 1$

   (a) $\left(\tfrac{13}{27}, \, -\tfrac{2}{9}\right)$ (b) $\left(-\tfrac{2}{9}, \, -\tfrac{8}{5}\right)$ (c) $\left(-\tfrac{8}{5}, \, -\tfrac{68}{25}\right)$

   (d) $\left(2, \, \tfrac{8}{5}\right)$ (e) None of these

4. $x + y + z = 2$

   $3x - 2y + z = 7$

   $5y + 2z = -1$

   (a) $\left(\dfrac{2}{5}, \, -\dfrac{7}{5}, \, 3\right)$ (b) $\left(a, \, \dfrac{2a}{3}, \, \dfrac{a}{3}\right)$

   (c) $\left(\dfrac{11 - 3a}{5}, \, \dfrac{-1 - 2a}{5}, \, a\right)$ (d) No solution

   (e) None of these

5. $2x + 3y - z = 6$

   $x - y + 2z = 1$

   (a) $\left(a, \, \dfrac{13 - 5a}{5}, \, \dfrac{9 - 5a}{5}\right)$ (b) $\left(\dfrac{10 - 2a}{3}, \, a, \, \dfrac{5 - 2a}{3}\right)$ (c) $\left(3, \, -\dfrac{2}{5}, \, -\dfrac{6}{5}\right)$

   (d) No solution   (e) None of these

6. $x^2 + y^2 = 3$

$2x^2 - y = 0$

(a) $\left(\dfrac{3}{2}, -2\right)$

(b) $\left(\pm\dfrac{\sqrt{3}}{2}, \dfrac{3}{2}\right)$

(c) $\left(\pm\dfrac{\sqrt{3}}{2}, \dfrac{3}{2}\right)$, $(\pm 1, -2)$

(d) No solution

(e) None of these

7. Find the equation of the parabola $y = ax^2 + bx + c$ that passes through the points $(0,\ 5)$, $(2,\ -5)$, and $(-3,\ -40)$.

(a) $y = 3x^2 - 2x - 7$

(b) $y = -4x^2 + 3x + 5$

(c) $y = 4x^2 + 3x + 5$

(d) $y = 9x^2 - 121$

(e) None of these

8. Write the matrix in reduced echelon form: $\begin{bmatrix} 1 & 3 & -8 & 13 \\ 2 & -1 & 6 & -19 \\ -5 & 1 & 2 & 44 \end{bmatrix}$

(a) $\begin{bmatrix} 1 & 0 & 0 & -7 \\ 0 & 1 & 0 & 8 \\ 0 & 0 & 1 & \frac{1}{2} \end{bmatrix}$

(b) $\begin{bmatrix} 1 & 0 & 6 & -4 \\ 0 & 1 & 2 & 9 \\ 0 & 0 & 2 & 1 \end{bmatrix}$

(c) $\begin{bmatrix} 1 & 0 & 6 & -4 \\ 0 & 1 & -4 & 6 \\ 0 & 0 & 0 & 0 \end{bmatrix}$

(d) $\begin{bmatrix} 1 & 1 & 8 & 5 \\ 0 & 1 & 2 & 9 \\ 0 & 0 & 2 & 1 \end{bmatrix}$

(e) None of these

9. Given $A = \begin{bmatrix} 1 & 2 & 3 \\ 4 & 7 & 1 \\ 0 & 3 & 2 \end{bmatrix}$ and $B = \begin{bmatrix} 0 & 0 & 1 \\ 1 & 4 & 0 \\ 2 & 3 & 7 \end{bmatrix}$, find $6A - 2B$.

(a) $\begin{bmatrix} 30 & 72 & 52 \\ 32 & 10 & 6 \\ 1 & 6 & -8 \end{bmatrix}$

(b) $\begin{bmatrix} 30 & 12 & 4 \\ 3 & 10 & 6 \\ 1 & 6 & -8 \end{bmatrix}$

(c) $\begin{bmatrix} 6 & 12 & 16 \\ 22 & 34 & 6 \\ -4 & 12 & -2 \end{bmatrix}$

(d) $\begin{bmatrix} 30 & 22 & 20 \\ 66 & 28 & 26 \\ 24 & 16 & 14 \end{bmatrix}$

(e) None of these

10. Given $A = \begin{bmatrix} 1 & -1 & 2 \\ 0 & 5 & 1 \\ -2 & 0 & -1 \end{bmatrix}$ and $B = \begin{bmatrix} -1 & 2 & 0 \\ 5 & -7 & 1 \\ 2 & 3 & -2 \end{bmatrix}$, find AB.

(a) $\begin{bmatrix} -1 & -2 & 0 \\ 0 & -35 & 1 \\ -4 & 0 & 2 \end{bmatrix}$

(b) $\begin{bmatrix} -1 & 11 & 0 \\ 3 & -40 & 2 \\ 6 & 13 & 9 \end{bmatrix}$

(c) $\begin{bmatrix} 6 & 3 & -2 \\ 0 & -10 & -1 \\ -12 & 0 & 1 \end{bmatrix}$

(d) $\begin{bmatrix} -2 & 15 & -5 \\ 27 & -32 & 3 \\ 0 & -7 & 2 \end{bmatrix}$

(e) None of these

11. Find A^{-1}, given $A = \begin{bmatrix} 1 & 2 & 2 \\ 4 & 1 & 3 \\ -1 & 5 & 0 \end{bmatrix}$.

(a) $\dfrac{1}{21} \begin{bmatrix} -15 & 10 & 4 \\ -3 & 2 & 5 \\ 21 & -7 & -7 \end{bmatrix}$

(b) $\dfrac{1}{21} \begin{bmatrix} -15 & -22 & 28 \\ -3 & 27 & 25 \\ 21 & -7 & -7 \end{bmatrix}$

(c) $\begin{bmatrix} 1 & 0 & 0 \\ 0 & 1 & 0 \\ 0 & 0 & 1 \end{bmatrix}$

(d) $\begin{bmatrix} 1 & \frac{1}{2} & \frac{1}{2} \\ \frac{1}{4} & 1 & \frac{1}{3} \\ -1 & \frac{1}{5} & 0 \end{bmatrix}$

(e) None of these

12. Given the system of linear equations with coefficient matrix A, use A^{-1} to find (x, y, z, w).

$$
\begin{aligned}
x + 2y \qquad\qquad &= 1 \\
3x + 8y \qquad + 5w &= 0 \\
x + 4y + 3z + 10w &= -1 \\
x \qquad - 3z \qquad &= -1
\end{aligned}
\qquad
A^{-1} = \begin{bmatrix} 3 & -1 & \frac{1}{2} & \frac{1}{2} \\ -1 & \frac{1}{2} & -\frac{1}{4} & -\frac{1}{4} \\ 1 & -\frac{1}{3} & \frac{1}{6} & -\frac{1}{6} \\ -\frac{1}{5} & 0 & \frac{1}{10} & \frac{1}{10} \end{bmatrix}
$$

(a) $\left(2, -\frac{1}{2}, 1, -\frac{2}{5}\right)$

(b) $(3, -1, -1, 0)$

(c) $\left(\frac{2}{3}, \frac{1}{6}, -\frac{5}{9}, \frac{2}{3}\right)$

(d) $\left(1, 0, \frac{2}{3}, -\frac{5}{3}\right)$

(e) None of these

13. Find x: $\begin{bmatrix} 3x+2 & 5 & 2 \\ 7 & 2y & x \\ 4 & -1 & y+1 \end{bmatrix} = \begin{bmatrix} x-4 & 5 & \frac{y}{2} \\ 7 & 8 & -3 \\ 4 & -1 & 5 \end{bmatrix}$

(a) 4

(b) −3

(c) −1

(d) 6

(e) None of these

14. Match the graph at the right with the correct system of inequalities.

(a) $x + 2y \le 4$
$\quad x \le y$
$\quad x \ge 0$

(b) $x + 2y \ge 4$
$\quad x \le y$
$\quad y \ge 0$

(c) $x + 2y \le 4$
$\quad x \le y$
$\quad y \ge 0$

(d) $x + 2y \le 4$
$\quad y \le x$
$\quad y \ge 0$

(e) None of these

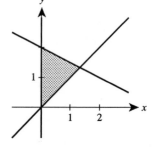

15. Solve the following system of equations:

$$\frac{6}{x} + \frac{2}{y} = 8$$

$$\frac{9}{x} + \frac{5}{y} = 16$$

(a) $\left(\frac{2}{3},\ 2\right)$

(b) $\left(\frac{3}{2},\ \frac{1}{2}\right)$

(c) $\left(2,\ \frac{3}{2}\right)$

(d) $\left(\frac{1}{2},\ \frac{2}{3}\right)$

(e) None of these

16. Find the consumer surplus if the demand equation is $p = 110 - 20x$ and the supply equation is $p = 50 + 10x$.

(a) $20

(b) $30

(c) $40

(d) $50

(e) None of these

17. Find the maximum value of the function, $P = 6x + 5y$, subject to the constraints $x \geq 0$, $y \geq 0$, $x + y \leq 76$, and $x - 3y \geq 0$.

(a) 380

(b) 437

(c) 456

(d) 519

(e) None of these

Test Form D   Name _____   Date _____

Chapter 9   Class _____   Section _____

1. The number of rugby clubs in the region between 1985 and 1990 can be approximated by the linear model $y = 47.2t - 135$, where y is the number of clubs and t is the calendar year with $t = 5$ corresponding to 1985. If this pattern continues, when will there be 200 rugby clubs in the region?

2. Solve the system of linear equations by the elimination method.

$$5x + 2y = -1$$
$$-15x + 8y = 10$$

3. Solve the system of equations by the substitution method.

$$x^2 + 2y - 5 = 0$$
$$3x^2 - y - 1 = 0$$

In Problems 4–7, find all the solutions to the given system of equations.

4.
$$x + y - z = -1$$
$$2x + 3y - z = -2$$
$$-3x - 2y + 2z = -3$$

5.
$$2x + y - z = 1$$
$$x + 4y + 2z = 7$$
$$-5x + y + 5z = 4$$

6.
$$x + y - 2z = 1$$
$$3x + y + z = 4$$
$$-x - 3y + 9z = 10$$

7.
$$\frac{6}{x} + \frac{1}{y} = -2$$
$$\frac{4}{x} - \frac{3}{y} = 17$$

8. Find an equation of the parabola, $y = ax^2 + bx + c$, that passes through the points $(0, -5)$, $(2, 1)$, and $(-1, -14)$.

9. Write the matrix in reduced echelon form: $\begin{bmatrix} 1 & 2 & -1 & 3 \\ 7 & -1 & 0 & 2 \\ 3 & 2 & 1 & -1 \end{bmatrix}$

10. Perform the indicated operations: $3\begin{bmatrix} 2 & 7 \\ 9 & -1 \end{bmatrix} + 3\begin{bmatrix} 4 & 1 \\ 6 & 2 \end{bmatrix}$

11. Find AB, given $A = \begin{bmatrix} 1 & 3 & 6 \\ 4 & 1 & 3 \end{bmatrix}$ and $B = \begin{bmatrix} 0 & 1 & 6 \\ 3 & -1 & 1 \\ 5 & 2 & 3 \end{bmatrix}$.

12. Use an augmented matrix to find A^{-1}: $\begin{bmatrix} 1 & 3 & -1 \\ 0 & 2 & 1 \\ -1 & 1 & -2 \end{bmatrix}$

13. Use an inverse matrix to solve the following system of linear equations.

$$3x + 2y + z = 1$$
$$x - y = 10$$
$$-x + 2z = 5$$

14. Use Gauss-Jordan elimination to solve the following system of equations.

$$x + 2y + z = 5$$
$$2x - y - 3z = 5$$
$$-2x + 3y + z = -11$$

15. Use a graphing utility to sketch the graph of the inequality $x^2 + (y - 1)^2 \le 25$.

16. Sketch the graph of the solution set of the system of inequalities:

$$y \ge -|x + 2|$$
$$x \le 0$$
$$y \le 0$$

17. Find the minimum value of the function, $C = 2x + y$, subject to the following constraints.

$$x \ge 0$$
$$y \ge 0$$
$$3x + 2y \ge 90$$
$$2x + 3y \le 105$$

Test Form E   Name _____   Date _____

Chapter 9   Class _____   Section _____

1. Scientists determine that a certain type of plant is growing at a linear rate. If the plant has a height of 4 inches on day 5 and a height of 8 inches on day 6, find a linear model that relates h, the height, in terms of the day, d.

2. Solve the system of equations using the substitution method.

$$y = \frac{1}{x}$$
$$x + 5y = 6$$

3. Solve the system of linear equations using the elimination method.

$$7x + y = 3$$
$$21x + 5y = 11$$

In Problems 4–6, find all of the solutions for the given system of linear equations.

4. $2x + 3y - 3z = 7$
     $-3x + y + z = 2$

5. $x - 3y + 2z = -11$
     $x + 4y - 5z = 17$
     $-2x + y - z = 6$

6. $2x - 4y + z = 7$
     $x + 3y - z = 2$
     $-5x + 15y - 4z = 10$

7. How many liters of a 40% solution of acid must be combined with a 15% solution to obtain 30 liters of a 20% solution?

8. Find the equation of the parabola $y = ax^2 + bx + c$ that passes through the points $(1, 1)$, $(-1, 11)$, and $(3, 23)$.

9. Write the following matrix in reduced echelon form: $\begin{bmatrix} 21 & 14 & -7 & 10 \\ 7 & 7 & 7 & -1 \\ 7 & -14 & 28 & 23 \end{bmatrix}$

10. Evaluate: $3 \begin{bmatrix} 7 & 5 & 2 \\ -1 & 1 & 0 \\ 0 & 3 & 6 \end{bmatrix} + 2 \begin{bmatrix} 1 & 0 & 0 \\ 0 & 1 & 0 \\ 0 & 0 & 1 \end{bmatrix} - 4 \begin{bmatrix} 1 & -1 & 2 \\ 7 & 1 & -1 \\ 2 & 5 & 1 \end{bmatrix}$

11. Find AB, given $A = \begin{bmatrix} 1 & 3 & 5 & 2 \\ -1 & 6 & 4 & 8 \end{bmatrix}$ and $B = \begin{bmatrix} 3 & 2 & 0 \\ 0 & 0 & 1 \\ 1 & 2 & -1 \\ 0 & 0 & 3 \end{bmatrix}$.

12. Use an augmented matrix to find A^{-1}: $\begin{bmatrix} 1 & 5 & -1 \\ 2 & 3 & -2 \\ -1 & -4 & 3 \end{bmatrix}$

In Problems 13 and 14, use the indicated method to solve the given system.

13. Gauss-Jordan elimination

$3x + 2y - 5z = -10$

$2x + 4y + z = 0$

$x - 6y - 4z = -3$

14. Inverse matrix method

$6x + 6y - 5z = 11$

$3x + 6y - z = 6$

$9x - 3y + z = 0$

15. Use a graphing utility to sketch the graph of the inequality $3x^2 + y \geq 6$.

16. Sketch the graph of the solution set of the system of inequalities:

$2y - 3x \leq 10$ and $2y \geq x^2$

17. Find the maximum value of the function, $C = 3x + 2y$, subject to the constraints $x \geq 0$, $y \geq 0$, $3x + 4y \leq 25$, and $3x - y \leq 5$.

Test Form A

Name _____   Date _____

Chapter 10

Class _____   Section _____

1. Find the sum: $\displaystyle\sum_{n=3}^{6}\frac{3}{n-2}$

   (a) $\dfrac{12}{9}$

   (b) $\dfrac{25}{4}$

   (c) $\dfrac{3}{16}$

   (d) $\dfrac{1}{2}$

   (e) None of these

2. Write an expression for the nth term of the sequence: $\left\{\dfrac{3}{2}, \dfrac{6}{4}, \dfrac{9}{12}, \dfrac{12}{48}, \dfrac{15}{240}, \ldots\right\}$

   (a) $\dfrac{3n}{2n!}$

   (b) $\dfrac{3n}{n(n+1)}$

   (c) $\dfrac{3n}{n!(n+1)!}$

   (d) $\dfrac{3n}{2(n-1)!}$

   (e) None of these

3. Find the first 5 terms of the sequence whose nth term is $a_n = (-1)^n(2n+9)$.

   (a) $\{-11, -13, -15, -17, -19, \ldots\}$

   (b) $\{-11, 13, -15, 17, -19, \ldots\}$

   (c) $\{-11, 2, -13, 4, -15, \ldots\}$

   (d) $\{-11, -24, -39, -56, -75, \ldots\}$

   (e) None of these

4. Find the sum: $\displaystyle\sum_{n=1}^{500}(3n+5)$

   (a) 756,500

   (b) 376,250

   (c) 752,500

   (d) 378,250

   (e) None of these

5. Find a_n for the arithmetic sequence with $a_1 = 5$, $d = -4$, and $n = 98$.

   (a) -392

   (b) -387

   (c) -383

   (d) 393

   (e) None of these

6. Which of the following is an arithmetic sequence?

   (a) $\{1, 3, 9, 27, 81, \ldots\}$

   (b) $\{1, 16, 36, 64, 100, \ldots\}$

   (c) $\{2, 11, 20, 29, 38, \ldots\}$

   (d) $\{3, -5, 7, -9, 11, \ldots\}$

   (e) None of these

7. Evaluate: $\displaystyle\sum_{n=0}^{10} 2\left(\frac{3}{5}\right)^n$

(a) 4.9698

(b) 5.0000

(c) 4.9819

(d) 55.0000

(e) None of these

8. Find the 10th term of the sequence: $\left\{\dfrac{3^1}{2^0}, \dfrac{3^2}{2^1}, \dfrac{3^3}{2^2}, \dfrac{3^4}{2^3}, \dfrac{3^5}{2^4}, \cdots\right\}$

(a) $\dfrac{3^{10}}{2^{10}}$

(b) $\dfrac{3^{11}}{2^{10}}$

(c) $\dfrac{3^{10}}{2^{9}}$

(d) $\dfrac{3^{11}}{2^{11}}$

(e) None of these

9. Find the sum of the infinite geometric series: $-7 - \frac{7}{3} - \frac{7}{9} - \frac{7}{27} - \cdots$

(a) -5

(b) $-\frac{21}{4}$

(c) $-\frac{5}{2}$

(d) $-\frac{21}{2}$

(e) None of these

10. Find a formula for the nth partial sum of the arithmetic sequence: $\{-4, 5, 14, 23, 32, \ldots\}$

(a) $9n - 4$

(b) $\dfrac{n(9n - 17)}{2}$

(c) $\dfrac{1 - 9^n}{2}$

(d) $\dfrac{n^2 - 9n}{2}$

(e) None of these

11. Evaluate: $_{12}C_{10}$

(a) $\frac{1}{66}$

(b) 66

(c) 132

(d) $\frac{1}{120}$

(e) None of these

12. Expand: $(3 - 2x)^3$

(a) $27 - 3x + 3x^2 - 8x^3$

(b) $27 - 9x + 9x^2 - 8x^3$

(c) $27 - 27x + 6x^2 - 8x^3$

(d) $27 - 54x + 36x^2 - 8x^3$

(e) None of these

13. Identify S_{k+1} given $S_k = \dfrac{k}{2}(3k + 2)$.

(a) $\dfrac{3(k + 1)^2}{2}$

(b) $\dfrac{k + 1}{2}(3k + 2)$

(c) $\dfrac{3k^2 + 2k + 2}{2}$

(d) $\dfrac{k + 1}{2}(3k + 5)$

(e) None of these

14. What is the coefficient of x^5y^7 in the expansion of $(5x + 2y)^{12}$?

(a) 7920

(b) 400,000

(c) 792

(d) 316,800,000

(e) None of these

15. Evaluate: $_{10}P_6$

(a) 5040

(b) 151,200

(c) 210

(d) 60

(e) None of these

16. Find the number of distinguishable permutations using the letters in LETTERFILE.

(a) 3,628,800

(b) 151,200

(c) 1024

(d) 5040

(e) None of these

17. How many different ways (subject orders) can 3 algebra books, 2 trigonometry books and 2 arithmetic books be arranged on a shelf?

(a) 5040

(b) 210

(c) 128

(d) 823,543

(e) None of these

18. A committee composed of 3 math majors and 4 science majors is to be selected from a group of 20 math majors and 16 science majors. How many different committees can be formed?

(a) 2,074,800

(b) 6840

(c) 4.05×10^{17}

(d) 320

(e) None of these

19. If the probability of getting a rotten apple in a basket of apples is 12%, what is the probability of getting 3 good apples choosing one from each of three different baskets?

(a) 0.9983

(b) 0.0017

(c) 0.8800

(d) 0.6815

(e) None of these

20. Two integers from 0 to 9 inclusive are chosen by a random number generator. What is the probability of choosing the number 2 both times?

(a) $\frac{1}{10}$

(b) $\frac{1}{100}$

(c) $\frac{1}{50}$

(d) $\frac{8}{10}$

(e) None of these

Test Form B　　　　　　　　Name _____   Date _____

Chapter 10　　　　　　　　Class _____   Section _____

1. Write out the first 5 terms of the sequence whose nth term is $a_n = n!$ (Assume that n begins with 0.)

(a) 0, 1, 2, 6, 24　　　　　　(b) 1, 1, 2, 6, 24　　　　　　(c) 1, 1, 2, 6, 12

(d) 0, 1, 2, 6, 12　　　　　　(e) None of these

2. Find the sum: $\displaystyle\sum_{n=1}^{4} \frac{n+1}{n+2}$

(a) $\dfrac{61}{20}$　　　　　　(b) $\dfrac{31}{20}$　　　　　　(c) $\dfrac{143}{60}$

(d) $\dfrac{131}{60}$　　　　　　(e) None of these

3. Write an expression for the nth term of the sequence. (Assume that n begins with 1.)

$$\left\{ \frac{1}{4}, \frac{2}{9}, \frac{3}{16}, \frac{4}{25}, \cdots \right\}$$

(a) $a_n = 1 - \dfrac{3n}{n^2}$　　　　(b) $a_n = \dfrac{n}{(n+1)!}$　　　　(c) $a_n = \dfrac{1}{2} + \dfrac{n}{(n+1)^3}$

(d) $a_n = \dfrac{n}{(n+1)^2}$　　　　(e) None of these

4. Find the 99th term of the arithmetic sequence with $a_1 = 7$ and $d = -3$.

(a) -287　　　　　　(b) -290　　　　　　(c) -293

(d) -297　　　　　　(e) None of these

5. Find the sum of the first 50 terms of the arithmetic sequence: $\{25, 35, 45, 55, 65, \ldots\}$

(a) 27,000　　　　　　(b) 13,750　　　　　　(c) 12,875

(d) 13,500　　　　　　(e) None of these

6. Insert 3 arithmetic means between 15 and 83.

(a) 30, 45, 60　　　　　　(b) 23, 41, 75　　　　　　(c) 32, 49, 66

(d) 17, 40, 71　　　　　　(e) None of these

7. Write the first five terms of the geometric sequence with $a_1 = 2$ and $r = \frac{2}{3}$.

(a) $2, \frac{4}{3}, \frac{8}{9}, \frac{16}{27}, \frac{32}{81}$

(b) $2, 3, \frac{9}{2}, \frac{27}{4}, \frac{81}{8}$

(c) $2, \frac{8}{3}, \frac{10}{3}, 4, \frac{14}{3}$

(d) $2, \frac{4}{3}, \frac{2}{3}, -\frac{2}{3}$

(e) None of these

8. Find the sum of the infinite series: $1 + 0.9 + 0.81 + 0.729 + \cdots$

(a) 23

(b) 90

(c) 10

(d) 57

(e) None of these

9. Find the 20th term of the geometric sequence with $a_1 = 5$ and $r = 1.1$.

(a) 1.1665

(b) 37.0012

(c) 33.6375

(d) 30.5795

(e) None of these

10. Find the sum using the formulas for the sums of powers of integers: $\displaystyle\sum_{n=1}^{19} i^3$

(a) 36,100

(b) 3581

(c) 44,100

(d) 1,687,998

(e) None of these

11. Find the first five terms of the geometric sequence with $a_1 = 3$ and $r = \frac{3}{2}$.

(a) $3, \frac{9}{2}, \frac{27}{4}, \frac{81}{8}, \frac{243}{16}$

(b) $3, 2, \frac{4}{3}, \frac{8}{9}, \frac{16}{27}$

(c) $3, \frac{9}{2}, 6, \frac{15}{2}, 9$

(d) $3, \frac{3}{2}, 0, -\frac{3}{2}, -3$

(e) None of these

12. Find a formula for the nth partial sum of the sequence.

$$\left\{ \frac{1}{1 \cdot 3}, \frac{1}{3 \cdot 5}, \frac{1}{5 \cdot 7}, \frac{1}{7 \cdot 9}, \frac{1}{9 \cdot 11}, \cdots, \frac{1}{(2n-1)(2n+1)}, \cdots \right\}$$

(a) $\dfrac{n(n^2 - 1)}{3}$

(b) $\dfrac{n}{n+1}$

(c) $\dfrac{n}{2n+1}$

(d) $\dfrac{n+1}{2n}$

(e) None of these

13. Evaluate: $_{10}C_3$

(a) 1000

(b) 604,800

(c) 720

(d) 120

(e) None of these

14. What is the coefficient of $x^3 y^5$ in the expansion of $(3x + 2y)^8$?

(a) 336

(b) 48,384

(c) 864

(d) 52,488

(e) None of these

15. An organization consisting of 54 members is going to elect four officers. No person may hold more than one office. How many different outcomes are possible?

(a) 354,294

(b) 8,503,056

(c) 316,251

(d) 7,590,024

(e) None of these

16. Evaluate: $_{14}P_4$

(a) 24,024

(b) 8008

(c) 5040

(d) 720

(e) None of these

17. At a Boy Scout jamboree there are 12 senior patrol leaders, 10 assistant senior patrol leaders, 21 patrol leaders, and 84 other scouts. How many committees of 2 senior patrol leaders, 1 assistant patrol leader, 3 patrol leaders, and 4 regular scouts can be formed?

(a) 3.2×10^{11}

(b) 1.7×10^{12}

(c) 2.4×10^9

(d) 1.4×10^9

(e) None of these

18. A box holds 12 white, 5 red, and 6 black marbles. If 2 marbles are picked at random, without replacement, what is the probability that they will both be black?

(a) $\frac{36}{529}$

(b) $\frac{247}{506}$

(c) $\frac{15}{253}$

(d) $\frac{6}{23}$

(e) None of these

19. Five cards are drawn from an ordinary deck of 52 playing cards. What is the probability of getting exactly one ace?

(a) 0.060

(b) 0.299

(c) 0.064

(d) 0.341

(e) None of these

20. A die is tossed 3 times. What is the probability that a 2 will come up all three times?

(a) $\frac{1}{172}$

(b) $\frac{1}{18}$

(c) $\frac{1}{120}$

(d) $\frac{1}{216}$

(e) None of these

Test Form C   Name _____ Date _____

Chapter 10   Class _____ Section _____

1. Use sigma notation to write the sum: $\dfrac{2}{3} + \dfrac{4}{4} + \dfrac{6}{5} + \dfrac{8}{6} + \cdots + \dfrac{14}{9}$

    (a) $\displaystyle\sum_{n=1}^{7} \dfrac{2n}{n+2}$ (b) $\displaystyle\sum_{n=2}^{8} \dfrac{n+2}{n+1}$ (c) $\displaystyle\sum_{n=0}^{6} \dfrac{n+2}{n+3}$

    (d) $\displaystyle\sum_{n=3}^{9} \dfrac{n-1}{n}$ (e) None of these

2. Write the first 5 terms of the sequence whose nth term is $1 - \dfrac{1}{n}$.
    (Assume that n begins with 1.)

    (a) $\dfrac{1}{2}, \dfrac{1}{4}, \dfrac{1}{8}, \dfrac{1}{16}, \dfrac{1}{32}$ (b) $0, \dfrac{1}{2}, \dfrac{2}{3}, \dfrac{3}{4}, \dfrac{4}{5}$ (c) $0, \dfrac{1}{2}, \dfrac{1}{3}, \dfrac{1}{4}, \dfrac{1}{5}$

    (d) $1, \dfrac{1}{2}, \dfrac{2}{3}, \dfrac{3}{4}, \dfrac{4}{5}$ (e) None of these

3. Find the 40th term of the sequence whose nth term is $500 \left(1 + \dfrac{0.095}{12}\right)^n$.

    (a) 363.83   (b) 752.19   (c) 690.84
    (d) 685.42   (e) None of these

4. Write the first 5 terms of the arithmetic sequence with $a_1 = 23$ and $d = -\tfrac{1}{2}$.

    (a) $23, 22\tfrac{1}{2}, 22, 21\tfrac{1}{2}, 21$ (b) $23, 23\tfrac{1}{2}, 24, 24\tfrac{1}{2}, 25$ (c) $23, -\tfrac{23}{2}, \tfrac{23}{4}, -\tfrac{23}{8}, \tfrac{23}{16}$
    (d) $23, -46, 92, -184, 368$ (e) None of these

5. Find the sum of the first 50 positive integers that are multiples of 3.

    (a) 7500   (b) 3900   (c) 3825
    (d) 7650   (e) None of these

6. Insert 4 arithmetic means between 75 and 50.

    (a) 53, 59, 65, 71   (b) 70, 65, 60, 55   (c) 72, 66, 60, 54
    (d) 57, 63, 69, 72   (e) None of these

7. Find the sum: $\displaystyle\sum_{j=0}^{40} 3(1.05)^j$

   (a) 383.52   (b) 362.40   (c) 984.00

   (d) 22.18   (e) None of these

8. Find the 23rd term of the geometric sequence with $a_1 = -23$ and $r = \sqrt{2}$.

   (a) $-47104\sqrt{2}$ (b) $-2048\sqrt{2}$ (c) -2048

   (d) -47104 (e) None of these

9. Find the sum of the first 30 terms in the sequence.

   $\left\{2, \frac{5}{2}, \frac{25}{8}, \frac{125}{32}, \frac{625}{128}, \cdots\right\}$

   (a) 791.25   (b) 5161.88   (c) 6454.35

   (d) 7116.42   (e) None of these

10. Find the sum of the infinite series: $1 + \frac{1}{3} + \frac{1}{9} + \frac{1}{27} + \cdots$

    (a) $\frac{3}{2}$ (b) 3   (c) $\frac{5}{3}$

    (d) $\frac{5}{2}$ (e) None of these

11. Find the nth partial sum of the sequence.

    $\left\{\dfrac{1}{1 \cdot 2}, \dfrac{1}{2 \cdot 3}, \dfrac{1}{3 \cdot 4}, \cdots, \dfrac{1}{n(n+1)}, \cdots\right\}$

    (a) $\dfrac{n(n+3)}{4(n+1)(n+2)}$ (b) $\dfrac{n}{n+1}$ (c) $n+1$

    (d) $\dfrac{n}{2n+1}$ (e) None of these

12. Find the nth term of the sequence: $\left\{\dfrac{2}{1}, \dfrac{3}{2}, \dfrac{4}{3}, \dfrac{5}{4}, \dfrac{6}{5}, \cdots\right\}$

    (a) $1 + \dfrac{1}{n}$ (b) $2 - \dfrac{1}{n}$ (c) $\dfrac{n+1}{n-1}$

    (d) $\dfrac{2n-1}{n}$ (e) None of these

13. Evaluate: $_{17}C_{14}$

    (a) 5.9×10^{13} (b) 842,771   (c) 4080

    (d) 680   (e) None of these

14. Determine the coefficient of the x^2y^7 term in the expansion of $(3x - 2y)^9$.

(a) -1152 (b) 1152   (c) 41,472

(d) $-41,472$ (e) None of these

15. A class of 9 students line up single file for lunch. How many different ways can this occur if the 6 boys in the class must line up first?

(a) 18   (b) 60,480   (c) 4320

(d) 504   (e) None of these

16. Evaluate: $_7P_4$

(a) 840   (b) 35   (c) 10,920

(d) 210   (e) None of these

17. A band director is taking auditions for a special pep band which requires 3 trumpets, 1 trombone, 1 saxophone, and 2 clarinets. There were 5 trumpet players, 4 trombone players, 3 saxophone players and 10 clarinet players who came to audition. How many possible combinations does the band director have?

(a) 100   (b) 600   (c) 5400

(d) 32,400   (e) None of these

18. Find the number of distinguishable permutations with the following letters:

  $\{A, A, A, B, B, C, C, C, C\}$

(a) 2520   (b) 1260   (c) 362,880

(d) 288   (e) None of these

19. What is the probability of drawing a white marble from a box containing 6 white, 3 red, and 5 black marbles?

(a) $\frac{1}{6}$ (b) $\frac{1}{14}$ (c) $\frac{3}{7}$

(d) $\frac{1}{15}$ (e) None of these

20. What is the probability that in a group of 6 people at least 2 will have their birthdays within the same week?

(a) 0.74   (b) 0.50   (c) 0.26

(d) 0.47   (e) None of these

Test Form D

Name _____ Date _____

Chapter 10

Class _____ Section _____

1. Write the first 5 terms of the sequence whose nth term is $\dfrac{n!}{(n+2)!}$.

   (Assume that n begins with 0.)

2. Find the sum: $\displaystyle\sum_{i=1}^{7} 2(i+1)$

3. Find a_n for the arithmetic sequence with $a_1 = 12$, $d = \frac{1}{3}$, and $n = 52$.

4. Find the sum of the first 30 terms in the sequence.

   $\sqrt{2},\ 2\sqrt{2},\ 3\sqrt{2},\ 4\sqrt{2},\ 5\sqrt{2},\ \ldots$

5. Insert 3 arithmetic means between 2 and 42.

6. Determine if the sequence $\left\{3, -2, \frac{4}{3}, -\frac{8}{9}, \frac{16}{27}, \ldots\right\}$ is geometric. If it is, find its common ratio.

7. Find the sum of the infinite geometric series with $a = 9$ and $r = 0.7$.

8. Prove by mathematical induction:

   $$1^2 + 2^2 + 3^3 + \cdots + n^2 = \frac{n(n+1)(2n+1)}{6}$$

9. Find the sum of the first n terms of the arithmetic sequence:

   $\{6, 11, 16, 21, 26, \ldots\}$

10. Evaluate: $_{12}C_9$

11. What is the coefficient of the $x^2 y^7$ term in the expansion of $(7x - 2y)^9$?

12. How many different ways can 3 chocolate, 4 strawberry, and 2 butterscotch sundaes be served to 9 people?

13. How many ways can 4 girls be picked from a group of 30 girls?

14. What is the probability that 2 people chosen at random from a group of 8 married couples are married to each other?

15. A coin is tossed four times. What is the probability of getting heads on all 4 tosses?

Test Form E   Name _____ Date _____

Chapter 10   Class _____ Section _____

1. Write the first five terms of the sequence whose nth term is $\dfrac{n-2}{n^2+1}$.
   (Assume that n begins with 1.)

2. Write the sum using sigma notation: $\frac{1}{2} + \frac{2}{6} + \frac{3}{24} + \frac{4}{120} + \frac{5}{720}$

3. Find the 30th term of the arithmetic sequence with $a_1 = -5$ and $d = \frac{1}{3}$.

4. Find the sum of the first 40 positive integers that are multiples of 4.

5. Insert 4 arithmetic means between 7 and 17.

6. Find the 28th term of the geometric sequence: $\{2, 2.4, 2.88, 3.456, 4.1472, \ldots\}$

7. Find the sum: $\displaystyle\sum_{k=1}^{10} 4\left(\frac{3}{2}\right)^{k-1}$

8. Find the sum of the first n terms of the arithmetic sequence: $\{-3, 1, 5, 9, 13, \ldots\}$

9. Prove by mathematical induction: $1 + 2 + 2^2 + 2^3 + \cdots + 2^{n-1} = 2^n - 1$

10. Evaluate: $_{45}C_2$

11. Find the 4th term in the expansion: $\left(\dfrac{1}{4} + \dfrac{3}{4}\right)^5$

12. In how many distinguishable ways can the letters in MISSISSIPPI be arranged?

13. A group of 6 students are seated in a single row at a football game. In how many different orders can they be seated?

14. Two integers (between 1 and 40 inclusive) are chosen by a random number generator. What is the probability that both numbers chosen are divisible by 4?

15. There are 5 red and 4 black balls in a box. If 3 balls are picked without replacement, what is the probability that at least one of them is red?

Test Form A   Name _____ Date _____

Chapter 11   Class _____ Section _____

1. Find the curve for the parametric equations $x = 3t - 6$ and $y = t - 4$.

(a)
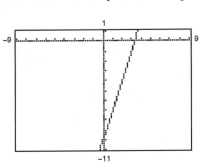

(b)
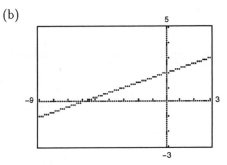

(c)
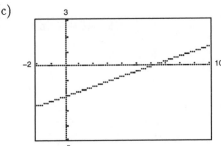

(d)
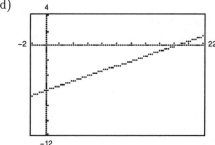

(e) None of these

2. Find the parametric equations for the curve at the right.

(a) $x = 2t$
  $y = t - 3$

(b) $x = t - 3$
  $y = 2t$

(c) $x = 2t$
  $y = t + 3$

(d) $x = t + 3$
  $y = 2t$

(e) None of these

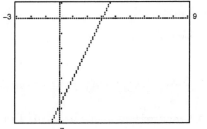

3. Find the rectangular equation for the curve represented by the parametric equations $x = 3t^2$ and $y = 2t + 1$.

(a) $2x^2 + 3y^2 - 1 = 0$

(b) $2x - 3y + 3 = 0$

(c) $3y^2 - 4x + 1 = 0$

(d) $3y^2 - 4x - 6y + 3 = 0$

(e) None of these

4. In polar coordinates, which of the following is *not* a correct representation for the point $(3, \pi/4)$?

(a) $\left(-3, -\dfrac{3\pi}{4}\right)$ (b) $\left(-3, -\dfrac{\pi}{4}\right)$ (c) $\left(3, \dfrac{9\pi}{4}\right)$

(d) $\left(-3, \dfrac{5\pi}{4}\right)$ (e) None of these

5. Convert from polar to rectangular coordinates: $\left(16, \dfrac{7\pi}{4}\right)$

(a) $(8\sqrt{3}, -4)$ (b) $(-8\sqrt{2}, 8\sqrt{2})$ (c) $(4, -8\sqrt{3})$
(d) $(8\sqrt{2}, -8\sqrt{2})$ (e) None of these

6. Convert from rectangular to polar form: $3x + 2y - 1 = 0$

(a) $r = \dfrac{1}{3\sin\theta + 2\cos\theta}$ (b) $r = 3\cos\theta + 2\sin\theta - 1$ (c) $r = \dfrac{1}{3\cos\theta + 2\sin\theta}$

(d) $r = 3\sin\theta - 2\cos\theta - 1$ (e) None of these

7. Convert from polar to rectangular form: $r = 2\sin\theta$

(a) $x^2 + y^2 = 4$ (b) $x^2 + y^2 - 2x = 0$ (c) $x^2 + y^2 - 4y = 0$
(d) $x^2 + y^2 - 2y = 0$ (e) None of these

8. Find the type of graph for $r = \dfrac{3}{1 + 2\cos\theta}$.

(a) Ellipse   (b) Hyperbola   (c) Parabola
(d) Circle   (e) None of these

9. Match the graph at the right to the correct equation.

(a) $r = \dfrac{1}{1 + \cos\theta}$ (b) $r = \dfrac{1}{1 - \sin\theta}$

(c) $r = \dfrac{1}{1 - \cos\theta}$ (d) $r = \dfrac{1}{1 + \sin\theta}$

(e) None of these

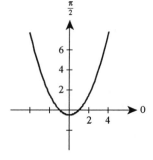

10. Find a polar equation for the ellipse having a focus at the pole and vertices at $(3, \pi/2)$ and $(5, -\pi/2)$.

(a) $r = \dfrac{15}{4 - \cos\theta}$ (b) $r = \dfrac{15}{4 + \cos\theta}$ (c) $r = \dfrac{15}{4 + \sin\theta}$

(d) $r = \dfrac{15}{4 - \sin\theta}$ (e) None of these

Test Form B   Name _____   Date _____

Chapter 11   Class _____   Section _____

1. Find the parametric equations for the curve at the right.

   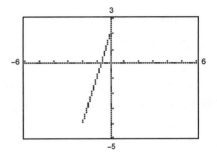

   (a) $x = -1 + \sin t, \ y = -1 + 3\sin t$

   (b) $x = 3\cos t + 8, \ y = 2 + \cos t$

   (c) $x = \cos 2t, \ y = 2\cos^2 t - 1$

   (d) $y = 1 + \cos t, y = 3 + \cos t$

   (e) None of these

2. Match the graph to the correct set of parametric equations.

   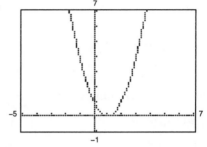

   (a) $x = t - 1$ (b) $x = t^2$

       $y = t^2$ $y = t + 1$

   (c) $x = t^2$ (d) $x = t + 1$

       $y = t - 1$ $y = t^2$

   (e) None of these

3. Find the rectangular equation for the curve represented by the parametric equations $x = 2\cos\theta$ and $y = \cos^2\theta$.

   (a) $x + y = \cos\theta(2 + \cos\theta)$ (b) $x - 2y = 0$ (c) $y = \left(1 - \dfrac{x}{2}\right)^2$

   (d) $x^2 = 4y$ (e) None of these

4. Convert from polar to rectangular coordinates: $\left(3, \dfrac{5\pi}{3}\right)$

   (a) $\left(\dfrac{3\sqrt{3}}{2}, -\dfrac{3}{2}\right)$ (b) $\left(-\dfrac{3}{2}, \dfrac{3\sqrt{3}}{2}\right)$ (c) $\left(\dfrac{3\sqrt{2}}{2}, -\dfrac{3\sqrt{2}}{2}\right)$

   (d) $\left(\dfrac{3}{2}, -\dfrac{3\sqrt{3}}{2}\right)$ (e) None of these

5. Convert from rectangular to polar form: $x + y = 5$

   (a) $r = \dfrac{5}{\cos\theta + \sin\theta}$ (b) $r = \dfrac{5}{\cos\theta - \sin\theta}$ (c) $r = \dfrac{\cos\theta + \sin\theta}{5}$

   (d) $r = 5(\cos\theta + \sin\theta)$ (e) None of these

6. Determine the type of symmetry: $r = 7\cos 2\theta$

   (a) Symmetric to the line $\theta = \dfrac{\pi}{2}$.

   (b) Symmetric to the polar axis.

   (c) Symmetric to the pole.

   (d) Symmetric to the line $\theta = \dfrac{\pi}{2}$, the polar axis, and the pole.

   (e) None of these

7. Find the equation for the graph at the right.

   (a) $r = 3\sin 4\theta$ (b) $r^2 = 1 + 4\sin\theta$

   (c) $r = 3 - 4\cos\theta$ (d) $r^2 = 4\cos 3\theta$

   (e) None of these

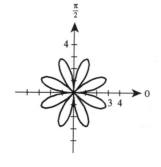

8. Find the type of graph for $r = \dfrac{10}{3 - 3\cos\theta}$.

   (a) Parabola   (b) Ellipse   (c) Hyperbola

   (d) Cardioid   (e) None of these

9. Find the equation for the graph at the right.

   (a) $r = \dfrac{33}{4 - 7\sin\theta}$ (b) $r = \dfrac{33}{4 + 7\sin\theta}$

   (c) $r = \dfrac{33}{7 - 4\sin\theta}$ (d) $r = \dfrac{33}{7 + 4\cos\theta}$

   (e) None of these

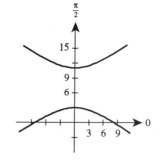

10. Convert from polar to rectangular form: $r = \dfrac{2}{\cos\theta - 1}$

   (a) $y^2 - 4 = 0$ (b) $x^2 + 4y - 4 = 0$ (c) $x^2 + y^2 - y + 2 = 0$

   (d) $y^2 + 4x - 4 = 0$ (e) None of these

Test Form C   Name _____ Date _____

Chapter 11   Class _____ Section _____

1. Find the curve represented by the parametric equations $x = 3t^2$ and $y = 1 - 2t^2$.

   (a)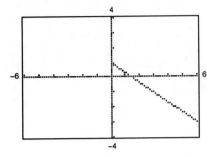

   (b)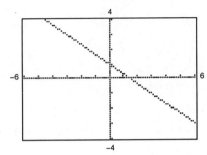

   (c)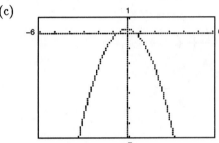

   (d)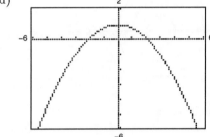

   (e) None of these

2. Find a set of parametric equations that correspond to the rectangular equation: $y = x^2 + 3$

   (a) $x = t^2 + 3$
       $y = t$

   (b) $x = t$
       $y = t^2 + 3$

   (c) $x = t^2$
       $y = t + 3$

   (d) $x = t + 3$
       $y = t^2$

   (e) None of these

3. Find the point corresponding to the polar coordinate $\left(-3, \dfrac{\pi}{3}\right)$.

(a)

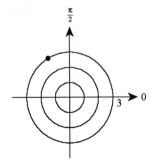

(b)

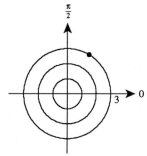

(c)

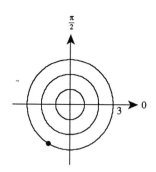

(d)

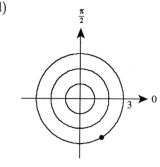

(e) None of these

4. Convert from rectangular to polar form: $x^2 + y^2 - 4x + 2y = 0$

(a) $r = 4\cos\theta - 2\sin\theta$ (b) $r = 4\sin\theta - 2\cos\theta$ (c) $r = \cos^2 2\theta$

(d) $r = \dfrac{4}{1 - 2\sin\theta}$ (e) None of these

5. Find the type of graph for $r = \dfrac{4}{2 + \cos\theta}$.

(a) Ellipse   (b) Parabola   (c) Hyperbola

(d) Circle   (e) None of these

6. Given that $r^2 = \dfrac{-b^2}{1 - e^2\cos^2\theta}$ is the corresponding polar equation of the hyperbola $\dfrac{x^2}{a^2} - \dfrac{y^2}{b^2} = 1$, find the polar equation for the hyperbola $\dfrac{x^2}{20} - \dfrac{y^2}{16} = 1$.

(a) $r^2 = \dfrac{-1280}{5 - \cos^2\theta}$ (b) $r^2 = \dfrac{-2000}{5 - 9\cos^2\theta}$ (c) $r^2 = \dfrac{-144}{9 - 5\cos^2\theta}$

(d) $r^2 = \dfrac{-80}{5 - 9\cos^2\theta}$ (e) None of these

7. Identify the type of curve for $r = 2 + 3\sin\theta$.

(a) Cardioid   (b) Limaçon with inner loop   (c) Dimpled limaçon

(d) Rose curve   (e) None of these

8. Find the equation for the graph at the right.

(a) $r^2 = 9\cos 2\theta$ (b) $r = 3 - 3\sin\theta$

(c) $r^2 = 3\cos 2\theta$ (d) $r^2 = 9\sin 2\theta$

(e) None of these

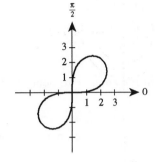

9. Find the equation for the graph at the right.

(a) $r = 5 - \sin\theta$ (b) $r = 5 + \sin\theta$

(c) $r = 5 + \cos\theta$ (d) $r = 5 - \cos\theta$

(e) None of these

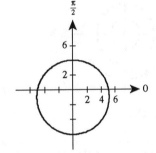

10. Write the equation $r = \dfrac{4}{2 - \cos\theta}$ in rectangular form.

(a) $4x^2 + 3y^2 + 8y + 16 = 0$ (b) $3x^2 + 4y^2 + 8x + 16 = 0$

(c) $3x^2 + 4y^2 - 8x - 16 = 0$ (d) $4x^2 + 3y^2 - 8y - 16 = 0$

(e) None of these

Test Form D

Chapter 11

Name _____ Date _____

Class _____ Section _____

1. Graph the curve represented by the parametric equations $x = 1 + 3t$ and $y = t - 1$.

2. Eliminate the parameter and find the corresponding rectangular equation: $x = 1 + \cos\theta$, $y = 2 - \sin\theta$

3. Convert from rectangular to polar coordinates: $(-\sqrt{3}, -1)$ Give two representations.

4. Convert from polar to rectangular form: $r = 2\cos\theta$

5. Convert from polar to rectangular coordinates: $\left(4, \dfrac{5\pi}{6}\right)$

6. Identify the conic, then sketch the graph of the polar equation $r = \dfrac{4}{1 + \sin\theta}$.

7. Find the polar equation of the ellipse with vertices at $(1, 0)$, $(7, \pi)$ and focus at $(0, 0)$.

8. Classify each of the following as:

   cardioid, limaçon with inner loop, dimpled limaçon, or rose curve

   (State the number of petals.)

   (a) $r = 3 + 2\cos\theta$ (b) $r = 2\sin 3\theta$ (c) $r = 1 + \sin\theta$ (d) $r = 3\cos 2\theta$

9. Sketch the graph of $r = 5\sin 2\theta$.

10. Sketch the graph of $r = 4 + 4\sin\theta$.

Test Form E　　　　Name _____　Date _____

Chapter 11　　　　Class _____　Section _____

1. Eliminate the parameter and determine the corresponding rectangular equation:

   $x = 3 + \cos\theta, \ y = \sin\theta - 1$

2. Eliminate the parameter and determine the corresponding rectangular equation: $x = t^3, \ y = 1/t$

3. Graph the curve represented by the parametric equations $x = t - 4$ and $y = 2t^2$.

4. Plot the points whose polar coordinates are:

   (a) $\left(3, \dfrac{\pi}{2}\right)$　　　　　(b) $\left(-2, \dfrac{\pi}{4}\right)$　　　　　(c) $\left(3, -\dfrac{\pi}{6}\right)$

5. Convert from rectangular to polar form: $x^2 + y^2 - 4x + 6y = 0$

6. Name the conic represented by each of the following:

   (a) $r = \dfrac{10}{3 + 5\sin\theta}$　　(b) $r = \dfrac{5}{3 - 5\sin\theta}$　　(c) $r = \dfrac{10}{5 - 3\cos\theta}$　　(d) $r = \dfrac{2}{1 - \cos\theta}$

7. Sketch the graph of $r = 4\cos 2\theta$.

8. Find the polar equation for the parabola with vertex at $(3, \pi)$ and focus at $(0, 0)$.

9. Identify the kind(s) of symmetry in the graph of each of the following:

   (a) $r = 3 + 4\cos\theta$　　　　　　　(b) $r = \sin 2\theta$

10. Sketch the graph of $r = 1 - 2\sin\theta$.

Answers to CHAPTER 1 Tests

TEST FORM A

1. c	**2.** a	**3.** d	**4.** b	**5.** e
6. b	**7.** d	**8.** a	**9.** c	**10.** b
11. e	**12.** c	**13.** d	**14.** a	**15.** b
16. d	**17.** c	**18.** a	**19.** d	**20.** b

TEST FORM B

1. a	**2.** c	**3.** d	**4.** a	**5.** b
6. d	**7.** c	**8.** c	**9.** a	**10.** d
11. b	**12.** b	**13.** c	**14.** a	**15.** e
16. d	**17.** e	**18.** a	**19.** b	**20.** c

TEST FORM C

1. c	**2.** a	**3.** d	**4.** b	**5.** b
6. c	**7.** e	**8.** a	**9.** b	**10.** d
11. b	**12.** a	**13.** d	**14.** c	**15.** a
16. b	**17.** d	**18.** c	**19.** a	**20.** b

TEST FORM D

1.

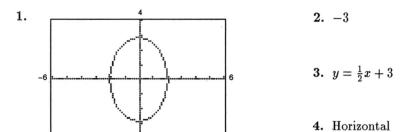

2. -3

3. $y = \frac{1}{2}x + 3$

4. Horizontal

5. $y = 2x - 5$

6. Yes

7. $2x + 1 + \Delta x$

8. -25

9. $(-\infty, 4]$

10. 225 ft^2

11.

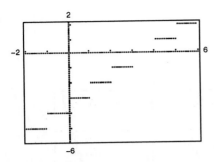

12. Neither

13. Horizontal shift 1 unit to the left
Vertical shift 7 units down

14.

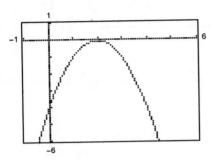

15. $x^2 + 3x - 3$

16. $x - 1$

17.

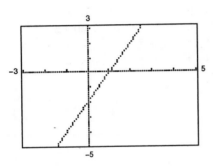

18. $(x + 5)^2,\ x \geq -5$

19. No

20. 8

TEST FORM E

1.

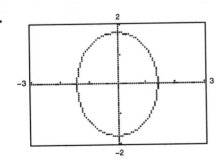

2. $\frac{3}{4}$

3. $y = 2x - 9$

4. $y = -\frac{1}{2}x - 2$

5. Yes

6. −3

7. 3

8. (−∞, ∞)

9. Relative minimum at (2, −10.7)
Relative maximum at (−2, 10.7)

10.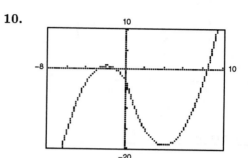

11. (−∞, ∞)

12. Odd

13. Decreasing on (−∞, 16]

14. $y = |x - 2| + 2$

15. 6

16.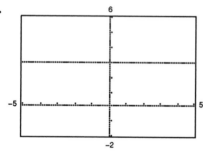

17. 0

18. $\dfrac{4}{x} - 1$

19. Yes

20. x

Answers to CHAPTER 2 Tests

TEST FORM A

1. a	**2.** b	**3.** b	**4.** a	**5.** c
6. d	**7.** a	**8.** b	**9.** d	**10.** c
11. c	**12.** c	**13.** a	**14.** b	**15.** d
16. a	**17.** d	**18.** a	**19.** b	**20.** c

TEST FORM B

1. d	**2.** d	**3.** a	**4.** a	**5.** b
6. a	**7.** a	**8.** c	**9.** b	**10.** c
11. a	**12.** d	**13.** b	**14.** a	**15.** a
16. a	**17.** b	**18.** a	**19.** b	**20.** a

TEST FORM C

1. c	**2.** a	**3.** c	**4.** a	**5.** d
6. b	**7.** b	**8.** d	**9.** a	**10.** a
11. b	**12.** d	**13.** c	**14.** b	**15.** c
16. d	**17.** d	**18.** c	**19.** c	**20.** d

TEST FORM D

1. $\dfrac{11}{6}$ **2.** $\dfrac{1}{4}(7 \pm \sqrt{145})$ **3.** $-7, \dfrac{2}{3}$ **4.** $\dfrac{1}{5}(1 \pm \sqrt{46})$

5. $\dfrac{gr^2}{4\pi^2}$ **6.** 0.7344 **7.** $2\left(x - \dfrac{3}{2}\right)^2 + \dfrac{9}{2}$ **8.** 2 **9.** $-1, 343$

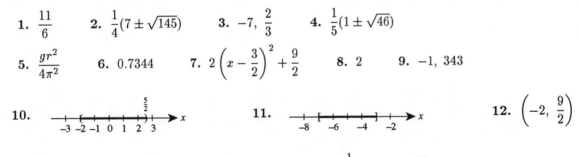

10. ⟶ x   **11.** ⟶ x   **12.** $\left(-2, \dfrac{9}{2}\right)$

13. $13, 14$ **14.** $10\dfrac{7}{9}\%$ **15.** No Solution   **16.** $\dfrac{1}{7}(-14 \pm 2\sqrt{21})$

17. $0, \pm 5$ **18.** $-1, 1.72$ **19.** $|x| \le 7$ **20.** $[-6, 6]$

TEST FORM E

1. -1 **2.** Conditional   **3.** $\dfrac{5}{12}$ **4.** $\dfrac{3V}{\pi r^2}$ **5.** 4.68% **6.** 7.5 quarts

7. $-\dfrac{3}{2}, 1$ **8.** $4 \pm \sqrt{14}$ **9.** $-7 \pm \sqrt{5}$ **10.** $-2.78, 1.48$ **11.** 104 feet

12. $\dfrac{1}{2}(2 \pm \sqrt{10})$ **13.** 0 **14.** $0, \pm 6$ **15.** 7 **16.** $\pm 1, \pm \dfrac{\sqrt{10}}{2}$ **17.** $\dfrac{1600}{81}$

18. $1 < x \le \dfrac{23}{2}$ **19.** $x < -\dfrac{8}{3}, \ x > \dfrac{10}{3}$ **20.** $[-2, 2]$

Answers to CHAPTER 3 Tests

TEST FORM A

1. d	**2.** b	**3.** b	**4.** a	**5.** a
6. b	**7.** c	**8.** c	**9.** b	**10.** a
11. d	**12.** b	**13.** a	**14.** c	**15.** a
16. b	**17.** a	**18.** c	**19.** d	**20.** a

TEST FORM B

1. b	**2.** d	**3.** b	**4.** c	**5.** c
6. b	**7.** d	**8.** a	**9.** c	**10.** b
11. a	**12.** d	**13.** b	**14.** c	**15.** b
16. a	**17.** a	**18.** c	**19.** d	**20.** e

TEST FORM C

1. c	**2.** a	**3.** c	**4.** b	**5.** c
6. d	**7.** a	**8.** a	**9.** b	**10.** c
11. d	**12.** c	**13.** a	**14.** b	**15.** d
16. a	**17.** d	**18.** b	**19.** d	**20.** b

TEST FORM D

1. $f(x) = -(x-3)^2 = 1$ **2.** $(-5, -4)$ **3.** $f(x) = -(x+1)^2 + 2$

4. Up to the left, down to the right.   **5.** $-4, -3, 0$ **6.** $2x^3 - 2x^2 + x + 3 - \dfrac{4}{3x+1}$

7. $x^3 + 2x^2 + 6x + 11 + \dfrac{23}{x-2}$ **8.** $f(x) = x^4 - 6x^3 - x^2 - 6x$

9. $f(x) = x^5 + 2$ **10.** $\pm\dfrac{1}{3}, \pm 1, \pm\dfrac{5}{3}, \pm 5$ **11.** $-1, \frac{1}{3}, 2$

12. 1 positive, 0 negative   **13.** $(x+2)(x-2)(x+2i)(x-2i)$

14. $-2 - 23i$ **15.** $\dfrac{1}{5}(1 \pm \sqrt{29}i)$ **16.** $1, 5, -3i$ **17.** -0.473

TEST FORM E

1.

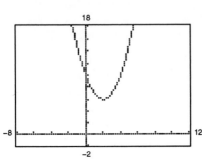

2. $f(x) = -\left(x - \dfrac{3}{2}\right)^2 + \dfrac{1}{4}$

3. $f(x) = x^2 - 6x$

4. Up to the left and right

5. $f(x) = x^4 - 2x^3 - x^2 + 2x$

6.

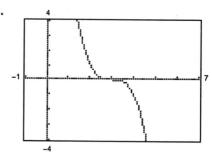

7. -64

8. $2x^2 - 6 + \dfrac{7x + 16}{x^2 + 3}$

9. $2,\ 3,\ -i$

10. $\pm\dfrac{1}{3},\ \pm\dfrac{2}{3},\ \pm1,\ \pm2$

11. $\dfrac{3}{2}$

12. Lower bound

13. $\pm2,\ \pm\sqrt{3}$

14. $f(x) = (x + \sqrt{10})(x - \sqrt{10})(x + \sqrt{10}\,i)(x - \sqrt{10}\,i)$

15. $2,\ 3,\ \pm i$

16. -1.213

17. $-\dfrac{1}{2} + \dfrac{5}{2}i$

Answers to CHAPTER 4 Tests

TEST FORM A

1. a	**2.** c	**3.** c	**4.** a	**5.** d
6. a	**7.** b	**8.** a	**9.** a	**10.** d
11. d	**12.** a			

TEST FORM B

1. c	**2.** b	**3.** c	**4.** a	**5.** b
6. a	**7.** b	**8.** a	**9.** c	**10.** b
11. d	**12.** d			

TEST FORM C

1. d	**2.** b	**3.** a	**4.** d	**5.** c
6. b	**7.** d	**8.** a	**9.** c	**10.** d
11. a	**12.** c			

TEST FORM D

1. $\left(0, -\dfrac{3}{5}\right)$, $x = 5$, $y = 0$ **2.** $x = 0$, $y = x - 2$ **3.**

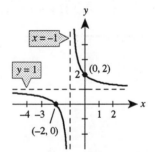

4. $\dfrac{3}{x-1} - \dfrac{1}{(x-1)^2} + \dfrac{9}{x+3}$ **5.** $-\dfrac{2}{x} + \dfrac{3x-1}{x^2+2}$ **6.** Circle

7. $y^2 + 28x = 0$ **8.** Center: $(0, 0)$, Vertices: $(\pm 3, 0)$, Foci: $(\pm\sqrt{13}, 0)$

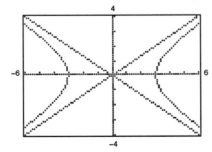

9. $25x^2 + 16y^2 - 160y = 0$ **10.** $(x + 2)^2 = 4(2)y$

TEST FORM E

1. $x = -1$, $x = 3$, $y = 0$ **2.** $x = 3$, $y = 3x + 7$

3.

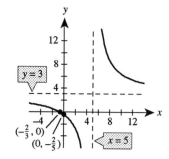

4. $\dfrac{3}{x-1} - \dfrac{1}{(x-1)^2} - \dfrac{3}{(x-1)^3}$ **5.** $\dfrac{4}{x+1} - \dfrac{1}{(x+1)^2} - \dfrac{1}{x-8}$ **6.** $y^2 = -4(5)x$

7. $\dfrac{x^2}{36} + \dfrac{y^2}{27} = 1$ **8.** $\dfrac{(y-5)^2}{36} - \dfrac{(x-2)^2}{64} = 1$ **9.** $(2, -6)$

10.

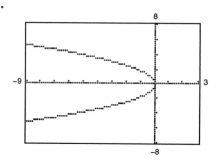

Answers to CHAPTER 5 Tests

TEST FORM A

1. a	**2.** d	**3.** a	**4.** b	**5.** b
6. c	**7.** c	**8.** d	**9.** a	**10.** a
11. b	**12.** d	**13.** a	**14.** b	**15.** d

TEST FORM B

1. b	**2.** c	**3.** a	**4.** d	**5.** d
6. d	**7.** a	**8.** c	**9.** c	**10.** a
11. c	**12.** b	**13.** b	**14.** c	**15.** b

TEST FORM C

1. d	**2.** a	**3.** c	**4.** d	**5.** b
6. c	**7.** a	**8.** c	**9.** d	**10.** d
11. c	**12.** b	**13.** a	**14.** a	**15.** a

TEST FORM D

1.

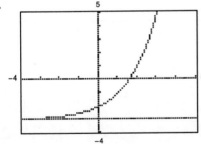

2. $2512.76   **3.** 194.3059

4. -1.6055 **5.** 1.9206   **6.** $\log \sqrt[5]{\dfrac{(x+1)^3(x-1)^2}{7}}$

7. $\log_3 243 = 5$ **8.** 214.2192   **9.** x

10.

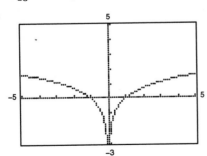

11. $(-\infty, -1), (1, \infty)$ **12.** 847

13. 2   **14.** -4.0977 **15.** 1.7411

TEST FORM E

1.

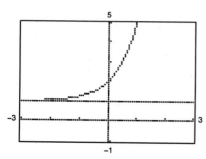

2. $\dfrac{3}{2}$ **3.** 21.5977

4. 1.7604   **5.** −1, 5   **6.** 1.09165

7.

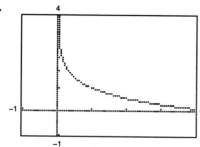

8. $(-\infty,\ -2),\ (2,\ \infty)$

9. $-1,\ \dfrac{5}{3}$ **10.** $K = \dfrac{1}{5}\ln\dfrac{12}{5}$

Answers to CHAPTER 6 Tests

TEST FORM A

1. b	**2.** a	**3.** b	**4.** c	**5.** d
6. c	**7.** c	**8.** c	**9.** b	**10.** b
11. a	**12.** c	**13.** d	**14.** a	**15.** d
16. b	**17.** b	**18.** a	**19.** d	**20.** b
21. c				

TEST FORM B

1. d	**2.** b	**3.** c	**4.** b	**5.** a
6. c	**7.** d	**8.** a	**9.** d	**10.** d
11. b	**12.** a	**13.** b	**14.** d	**15.** c
16. c	**17.** b	**18.** d	**19.** b	**20.** d

TEST FORM C

1. b	**2.** a	**3.** d	**4.** b	**5.** a
6. c	**7.** d	**8.** a	**9.** c	**10.** d
11. b	**12.** a	**13.** c	**14.** c	**15.** b

TEST FORM D

1. $297°$ **2.** $\dfrac{11\pi}{6}$ **3.** $128.5883°$ **4.** $6\pi \approx 18.85$ inches   **5.** $\dfrac{2\sqrt{21}}{21}$

6. $\dfrac{\sqrt{3}}{3}$ **7.** 0.7459 **8.** 6.5756 **9.** $-\dfrac{\sqrt{113}}{7}$ **10.** Period: $\dfrac{2\pi}{3}$, Amplitude: 7

11.

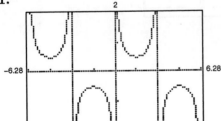

12.

13.

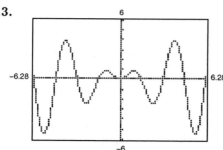

14. $\dfrac{10\sqrt{109}}{109}$ **15.** 52.5 feet

TEST FORM E

1. 225°   **2.** 81.7439°   **3.** 12°28′34″   **4.** 24.1 inches   **5.** $\dfrac{56}{3}$

6. $\dfrac{15\sqrt{3}}{2}$ **7.** 0.8693   **8.** $-\dfrac{\sqrt{77}}{9}$ **9.** 25°   **10.** $-\dfrac{\sqrt{113}}{7}$

11.

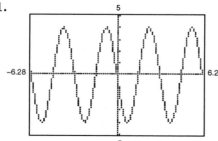

12. Period: 4π, Amplitude: 5   **13.** $\dfrac{\pi}{3}$

14.

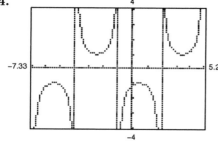

15.

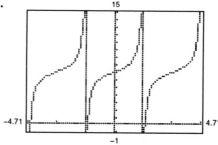

16.

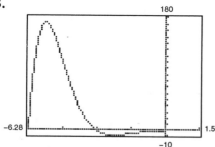

17. 153.1637° or 2.6732 radians   **18.** $\dfrac{3\sqrt{10}}{10}$ **19.** 2   **20.** 1072.5 feet

Answers to CHAPTER 7 Tests

TEST FORM A

1. d	**2.** b	**3.** d	**4.** a	**5.** c
6. b	**7.** a	**8.** b	**9.** b	**10.** a
11. b	**12.** d	**13.** a	**14.** a	**15.** b

TEST FORM B

1. c	**2.** c	**3.** a	**4.** c	**5.** b
6. d	**7.** c	**8.** a	**9.** d	**10.** b
11. c	**12.** b	**13.** a	**14.** a	**15.** b

TEST FORM C

1. d	**2.** a	**3.** c	**4.** a	**5.** b
6. b	**7.** d	**8.** b	**9.** d	**10.** b
11. d	**12.** b	**13.** b	**14.** c	**15.** b

TEST FORM D

1. $1 - \sin x$ **2.** $\dfrac{\pi}{2} < \theta < \dfrac{3\pi}{2}$ **3.** $\cos^2 x$ **4.** $\sec^4 x$ **5.** $\dfrac{2(1 + \sin \theta)}{\cos \theta}$

6. $\dfrac{\tan^2 x + 1}{\tan^2 x} = 1 + \dfrac{1}{\tan^2 x} = 1 + \cot^2 x = \csc^2 x$ **7.** $-\dfrac{\sqrt{6} + \sqrt{2}}{4}$ **8.** $\tan 12x$

9. $-\dfrac{3\sqrt{7}}{32}$ **10.** $\dfrac{\sqrt{14}}{7}$ **11.** $\dfrac{1 - \cos 8x}{8}$ **12.** $\dfrac{\cos 8x + \cos 16x}{8}$

13. $2 \cos x \sin 2y$ **14.** $\dfrac{\pi}{12}, \dfrac{5\pi}{12}, \dfrac{7\pi}{12}, \dfrac{11\pi}{12}, \dfrac{13\pi}{12}, \dfrac{17\pi}{12}, \dfrac{19\pi}{12}, \dfrac{23\pi}{12}$

15. $0, \dfrac{\pi}{6}, \dfrac{5\pi}{6}, \pi$ **16.** 2.68

TEST FORM E

1. 1   **2.** $\pi \le \theta < 2\pi$

3. $\sec x \csc^2 x - \csc^2 x = \csc^2 x(\sec x - 1)$

$$= \frac{1}{\sin^2 x}\left(\frac{1}{\cos x} - 1\right)$$

$$= \frac{1}{\sin^2 x}\left(\frac{1 - \cos x}{\cos x}\right)$$

$$= \frac{1}{1 - \cos^2 x}\left(\frac{1 - \cos x}{\cos x}\right)$$

$$= \frac{1}{(1 + \cos x)\cos x} = \frac{\sec x}{1 + \cos x}$$

4. $2\sin x \sec^2 x = 2\sin x\left(\dfrac{1}{\cos^2 x}\right) = 2\tan x \sec x$ **5.** $-\dfrac{\sqrt{33}}{4}$ **6.** $\dfrac{\sqrt{2} - \sqrt{6}}{4}$

7. $-\sqrt{3}$ **8.** $-\dfrac{5}{13}$ **9.** $-\dfrac{\sqrt{30}}{6}$ **10.** $\dfrac{3 - 4\cos 4x + \cos 8x}{3 + 4\cos 4x + \cos 8x}$ **11.** $\dfrac{3(\sin 3x - \sin 7x)}{2}$

12. $\sin(\pi + 2x)\sin(\pi - 2x) = \dfrac{1}{2}[\cos(\pi + 2x - \pi + 2x) - \cos(\pi + 2x + \pi - 2x)]$

$-\dfrac{1}{2}[\cos 4x - \cos 2\pi] = -\left(\dfrac{1 - \cos 4x}{2}\right) = -\sin^2 2x$

13. $0, \dfrac{\pi}{2}, \pi$ **14.** $\dfrac{\pi}{12}, \dfrac{5\pi}{12}, \dfrac{13\pi}{12}, \dfrac{17\pi}{12}$ **15.** $\dfrac{\pi}{3}$ **16.** 1.57

Answers to CHAPTER 8 Tests

TEST FORM A

1. b	**2.** a	**3.** c	**4.** d	**5.** b
6. d	**7.** a	**8.** d	**9.** a	**10.** d
11. b	**12.** d	**13.** c	**14.** b	**15.** d
16. a	**17.** a	**18.** b	**19.** d	**20.** c

TEST FORM B

1. b	**2.** b	**3.** d	**4.** d	**5.** a
6. c	**7.** b	**8.** a	**9.** b	**10.** d
11. b	**12.** a	**13.** d	**14.** b	**15.** a

TEST FORM C

1. a	**2.** b	**3.** a	**4.** d	**5.** a
6. b	**7.** c	**8.** c	**9.** d	**10.** b
11. a	**12.** c	**13.** b	**14.** c	**15.** d

TEST FORM D

1. $B = 150.62°$ **2.** $C = 51.09°$ or $16.91°$ **3.** 56.7 miles

4. 20,297.5 square units   **5.** 314.9 square units

6. $A = 27.5°, B = 5.1°, C = 147.4°$ **7.** $\left\langle -\dfrac{1}{2}, \dfrac{\sqrt{3}}{2} \right\rangle$ **8.** $43.15°$ **9.** $\dfrac{75}{2}\mathbf{i} + 19\mathbf{j}$

10. $\sqrt{7}(\cos 139.1° + i \sin 139.1°)$ **11.** $8\left(\cos\dfrac{\pi}{4} + i\sin\dfrac{\pi}{4}\right) = 4\sqrt{2} + 4\sqrt{2}i$

12. $-\dfrac{3\sqrt{3}}{2}+\dfrac{3}{2}i$

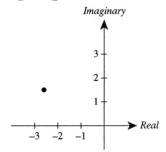

13. -4096 **14.** $2\left(\cos\dfrac{\pi}{9}+i\sin\dfrac{\pi}{9}\right), 2\left(\cos\dfrac{7\pi}{9}+i\sin\dfrac{7\pi}{9}\right), 2\left(\cos\dfrac{13\pi}{9}+i\sin\dfrac{13\pi}{9}\right)$

15. $-\sqrt{2}+\sqrt{2}i, \sqrt{2}-\sqrt{2}i$

TEST FORM E

1. $C=70°, a=5022.33, b=4333.77$ **2.** 89.8 square units   **3.** 16.54°

4. 700.6 feet   **5.** (a) 0 solutions   (b) 1 solution   (c) 0 solutions

6. $a=81.79$ **7.** $\|\mathbf{v}\|=5, \theta=126.9°$ **8.** $\langle-21.84, -15.87\rangle$

9. 94.71 pounds   **10.** $36.235(\cos 117.98°+i\sin 117.98°)$ **11.** $128(\cos 50°+i\sin 50°)$

12. $6-2i$

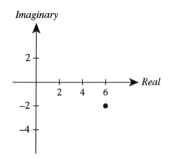

13. $-64\sqrt{3}+64i$ **14.** $2-2\sqrt{3}i, -4, 2+2\sqrt{3}i$ **15.** 1215.27 square units

Answers to CHAPTER 9 Tests

TEST FORM A

1. c	**2.** c	**3.** e	**4.** a	**5.** b
6. b	**7.** c	**8.** a	**9.** a	**10.** d
11. a	**12.** c	**13.** a	**14.** c	**15.** c
16. b				

TEST FORM B

1. b	**2.** c	**3.** c	**4.** d	**5.** b
6. a	**7.** b	**8.** c	**9.** c	**10.** a
11. b	**12.** a	**13.** c	**14.** b	**15.** b
16. c	**17.** a			

TEST FORM C

1. b	**2.** b	**3.** a	**4.** c	**5.** a
6. b	**7.** b	**8.** a	**9.** c	**10.** d
11. a	**12.** a	**13.** b	**14.** a	**15.** b
16. c	**17.** c			

TEST FORM D

1. Early 1987   **2.** $\left(-\frac{2}{5}, \frac{1}{2}\right)$ **3.** $(-1, 2), (1, 2)$ **4.** $(5, -3, 3)$

5. $\left(\frac{-3+6a}{7}, \frac{13-5a}{7}, a\right)$ **6.** Inconsistent system

7. $\left(2, -\frac{1}{5}\right)$ **8.** $y = -2x^2 + 7x - 5$

9. $\begin{bmatrix} 1 & 0 & 0 & \frac{5}{16} \\ 0 & 1 & 0 & \frac{3}{16} \\ 0 & 0 & 1 & -\frac{37}{16} \end{bmatrix}$ **10.** $\begin{bmatrix} 18 & 24 \\ 45 & 3 \end{bmatrix}$ **11.** $\begin{bmatrix} 39 & 10 & 27 \\ 18 & 9 & 34 \end{bmatrix}$

12. $\begin{bmatrix} \frac{1}{2} & -\frac{1}{2} & -\frac{1}{2} \\ \frac{1}{10} & \frac{3}{10} & \frac{1}{10} \\ -\frac{1}{5} & \frac{2}{5} & -\frac{1}{5} \end{bmatrix}$ **13.** $\left(\frac{37}{11}, -\frac{73}{11}, \frac{46}{11}\right)$ **14.** $(5, -1, 2)$

15.

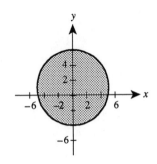

16.

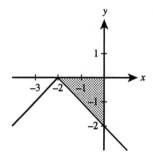

17. 51

TEST FORM E

1. $h = 4d - 16$ **2.** $(1, 1)$, $\left(5, \dfrac{1}{5}\right)$ **3.** $\left(\dfrac{2}{7}, 1\right)$ **4.** $\left(\dfrac{1 + 6a}{11}, \dfrac{25 + 7a}{11}, a\right)$

5. $(-1, 2, -2)$ **6.** Inconsistent system   **7.** 6   **8.** $y = 4x^2 - 5x + 2$

9. $\begin{bmatrix} 1 & 0 & 0 & \frac{9}{7} \\ 0 & 1 & 0 & -\frac{9}{7} \\ 0 & 0 & 0 & -\frac{1}{7} \end{bmatrix}$ **10.** $\begin{bmatrix} 19 & 19 & -2 \\ -31 & 1 & 4 \\ -8 & -11 & 16 \end{bmatrix}$ **11.** $AB = \begin{bmatrix} 8 & 12 & 4 \\ 1 & 6 & 26 \end{bmatrix}$

12. $A^{-1} = \begin{bmatrix} -\frac{1}{14} & \frac{11}{14} & \frac{1}{2} \\ \frac{2}{7} & -\frac{1}{7} & 0 \\ \frac{5}{14} & \frac{1}{14} & \frac{1}{2} \end{bmatrix}$ **13.** $\left(\dfrac{1}{2}, -\dfrac{3}{4}, 2\right)$ **14.** $\left(\dfrac{1}{3}, \dfrac{2}{3}, -1\right)$

15.

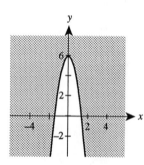

16.

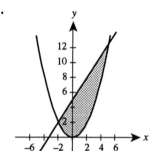

17. 17

Answers to **CHAPTER 10** Tests

TEST FORM A

1. b	**2.** a	**3.** b	**4.** d	**5.** c
6. c	**7.** c	**8.** c	**9.** d	**10.** b
11. b	**12.** d	**13.** d	**14.** d	**15.** b
16. b	**17.** b	**18.** a	**19.** d	**20.** b

TEST FORM B

1. b	**2.** a	**3.** d	**4.** a	**5.** d
6. c	**7.** a	**8.** c	**9.** d	**10.** a
11. a	**12.** c	**13.** d	**14.** b	**15.** d
16. a	**17.** b	**18.** c	**19.** b	**20.** d

TEST FORM C

1. a	**2.** b	**3.** d	**4.** a	**5.** c
6. b	**7.** a	**8.** d	**9.** c	**10.** a
11. b	**12.** a	**13.** d	**14.** d	**15.** c
16. a	**17.** c	**18.** b	**19.** c	**20.** c

TEST FORM D

1. $\dfrac{1}{2}, \dfrac{1}{6}, \dfrac{1}{12}, \dfrac{1}{20}, \dfrac{1}{30}$ **2.** 70   **3.** 29   **4.** $465\sqrt{2}$

5. 12, 22, 32   **6.** Yes, $r = -\dfrac{2}{3}$ **7.** 30

8. Let $n = 1$,   then $\dfrac{n(n+1)(2n+1)}{6} = \dfrac{(1)(2)(3)}{6} = 1 = 1^2$

For $n = k$, $S_k = 1^2 + 2^2 + 3^2 + \cdots + k^2 + (k+1)^2 = \dfrac{k(k+1)(2k+1)}{6}$

For $n = k+1$, $S_{k+1} = \dfrac{k(k+1)(2k+1)}{6} + (k+1)^2$

$$= (k+1)\left[\dfrac{k(2k+1) + 6(k+1)}{6}\right]$$

$$= \dfrac{(k+1)(12k^2 + 7k + 6)}{6}$$

$$= \dfrac{(k+1)(k+2)(2k+3)}{6}$$

$$= \dfrac{(k+1)[(k+1)+1][2(k+1)+1]}{6}$$

Thus the formula is valid.

9. $\dfrac{n(7+5n)}{2}$ **10.** 220   **11.** $-225,792$ **12.** 1260 ways

13. 27,405   **14.** $\dfrac{1}{15}$ **15.** $\dfrac{1}{16}$

TEST FORM E

1. $-\dfrac{1}{2},\ 0,\ \dfrac{1}{10},\ \dfrac{2}{17},\ \dfrac{3}{26}$ **2.** $\displaystyle\sum_{n=1}^{5}\dfrac{n}{(n+1)!}$ **3.** $\dfrac{14}{3}$ **4.** 3280

5. 9, 11, 13, 15   **6.** 274.7411   **7.** 453.320   **8.** $n(2n-5)$

9. S_1: $2^1 - 1 = 2 - 1 = 1$

S_k: $1 + 2 + 2^2 + 2^3 + \cdots + 2^{k-1} = 2^k - 1$

S_{k+1}: $1 + 2 + 2^2 + 2^3 + \cdots + 2^k = 2^{k+1} - 1$

Assuming S_k, we have:

$$(1 + 2 + 2^2 + 2^3 + \cdots + 2^{k+1}) + 2^{(k+1)-1} = (1 + 2 + \cdots) + 2^k$$
$$= (2^k - 1) + 2^k$$
$$= 2^{k+1} - 1$$

Hence, the formula is valid for all $n \geq 1$.

10. 990   **11.** $\dfrac{270}{4^5}$ **12.** 34,650   **13.** 720

14. $\dfrac{1}{16}$ **15.** $\dfrac{20}{21}$

Answers to CHAPTER 11 Tests

TEST FORM A

1. c   **2.** d   **3.** d   **4.** b   **5.** d

6. c   **7.** d   **8.** b   **9.** b   **10.** c

TEST FORM B

1. a   **2.** d   **3.** d   **4.** d   **5.** a

6. d   **7.** a   **8.** a   **9.** b   **10.** d

TEST FORM C

1. a   **2.** b   **3.** c   **4.** a   **5.** a

6. d   **7.** b   **8.** d   **9.** a   **10.** c

TEST FORM D

1. $y = \frac{1}{3}x - \frac{4}{3}$ **2.** $x^2 + y^2 - 2x - 4y + 4 = 0$ **3.** $\left(2, \frac{7\pi}{6}\right)$, $\left(-2, \frac{\pi}{6}\right)$

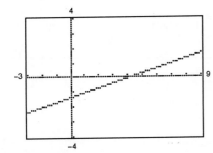

4. $x^2 + y^2 - 2x = 0$ **5.** $(-2\sqrt{3},\ 2)$ **6.** Parabola

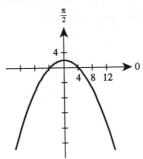

7. $r = \dfrac{7}{4 + 3\cos\theta}$ **8.** **(a)** Limaçon with one flattened loop
     (b) 3 petal rose curve
     (c) Cardioid
     (d) 4 petal rose curve

9.

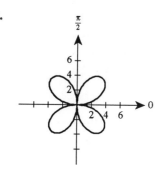

10. $r = 4 + 4\sin\theta$

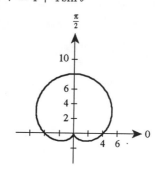

TEST FORM E

1. $x^2 + y^2 - 6x + 2y + 9 = 0$ **2.** $xy^3 = 1$

3.

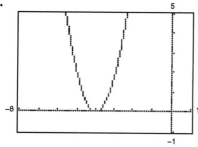

4.

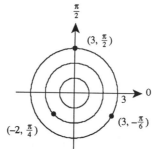

5. $r = 4\cos\theta - 6\sin\theta$

6. **(a)** Hyperbola
   (b) Hyperbola
   (c) Ellipse
   (d) Parabola

7.

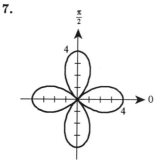

8. $r = \dfrac{6}{1 - \cos\theta}$

9. **(a)** Symmetrical to the polar axis.
   (b) Symmetrical to the line $\theta = \dfrac{\pi}{2}$, the polar axis, and the pole.

10.

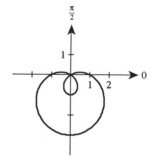